ADVANCES IN LIPID RESEARCH

Volume 15

Advances in Lipid Research

Volume 15

Edited by

Rodolfo Paoletti

Institute of Pharmacology
Milan, Italy

David Kritchevsky

The Wistar Institute
Philadelphia, Pennsylvania

 1977

ACADEMIC PRESS
New York   San Francisco   London
A Subsidiary of Harcourt Brace Jovanovich, Publishers

ACADEMIC PRESS, INC.
111 Fifth Avenue, New York, New York 10003

United Kingdom Edition published by
ACADEMIC PRESS, INC. (LONDON) LTD.
24/28 Oval Road, London NW1

LIBRARY OF CONGRESS CATALOG CARD NUMBER: 63–22330

ISBN 0–12–024915–4

PRINTED IN THE UNITED STATES OF AMERICA

CONTENTS

Long-Range Order in Biomembranes

Mahendra K. Jain and Harold B. White, III

The Pharmacodynamics and Toxicology of Steroids and Related Compounds

Fritz Bischoff and George Bryson

Fungal Lipids

Momtaz K. Wassef

The Biochemistry of Plant Sterols

William R. Nes

LIST OF CONTRIBUTORS

Numbers in parentheses indicate the pages on which the authors' contributions begin.

FRITZ BISCHOFF, *Santa Barbara Cottage Hospital Research Institute, Santa Barbara, California* (61)

GEORGE BRYSON, *Santa Barbara Cottage Hospital Research Institute, Santa Barbara, California* (61)

MAHENDRA K. JAIN, *School of Life and Health Sciences and Department of Chemistry, University of Delaware, Newark, Delaware* (1)

WILLIAM R. NES, *Department of Biological Sciences, Drexel University, Philadelphia, Pennsylvania* (233)

MOMTAZ K. WASSEF,* *Department of Plant Pathology, University of Kentucky, Lexington, Kentucky* (159)

HAROLD B. WHITE, III, *Division of Health Sciences and Department of Chemistry, University of Delaware, Newark, Delaware* (1)

* Present address: Department of Biochemistry, New York Medical College, Valhalla, New York 10595.

PREFACE

This volume of *Advances in Lipid Research* is devoted to rather extensive discussions of important subjects which are not often reviewed. The first chapter is devoted to the subject of long-range order in biomembranes. The authors propose and defend the thesis that the proteins and lipids of biological membranes are partitioned into functional and structural aggregates in the plane of the membrane. The second chapter reviews the pharmacology and toxicology of steroids and related compounds. This exhaustive review covers methodology, physiologic mechanisms, transport mechanisms, and effects on the central nervous system, among others. An interesting class of lipids, fungal lipids, is the subject of the third chapter. This review covers all aspects of lipid composition of all classes of fungi. It goes on to discuss the intracellular distribution and biosynthesis of the lipid components of fungi. The final contribution is a comprehensive treatise on the biochemistry of plant sterols, including structure, stereochemistry, biosynthesis, metabolism, and function. The evolutionary role of plant sterols is the subject of thoughtful speculation.

RODOLFO PAOLETTI
DAVID KRITCHEVSKY

Long-Range Order in Biomembranes

MAHENDRA K. JAIN AND HAROLD B. WHITE, III

*Division of Health Sciences and
Department of Chemistry,
University of Delaware, Newark, Delaware*

*A violent order is disorder; and a great disorder
is an order. These two things are one.*[1]

Wallace Stevens

I. Introduction

Recently, there has been an upsurge of interest in biological membranes. Cell membranes are being studied with respect to their anatomy or gross structures, their physiology or function, and the chemistry of their components. The central problem of membrane structure and its correlation with physiological and biochemical functions is to define the organization of constituent molecules. Thus the organization of membrane constituents in a semiinfinite continuous sheet can be described in terms of the covalent

[1] In "Connoisseur of Chaos" from *The Collected Peoms of Wallace Stevens.* Alfred A. Knopf, New York (1957), p. 215–216.

structure of the constituents, the organizational characteristics of lipid/water system as bilayer, and the molecular conformations that determine subtle phase characteristics of lipid bilayer. The possibility remains that the whole can be qualitatively different from the sum of its parts, and yet be dependent upon the organization of its parts for its unique properties. Indeed, we cannot but share the perspective articulated by Teilhard de Chardin (1959): "The farther and more deeply we penetrate into matter, by means of increasingly powerful methods, the more we are confounded by the interdependence of its parts. . . . It is impossible to cut into this network, to isolate a portion without it becoming frayed and unravelled at all its edges."

In the last 50 years, biomembranes have been extensively studied. The existence of bilayers in biomembranes is firmly established by a variety of physicochemical techniques. It has been shown that the subtleties of organizational and phase characteristics of the bilayer arise from the segmental motion and the transverse, rotational, and lateral mobilities of constituent lipids. These molecular features of lipids in the bilayer organization satisfactorily account for dielectric (capacitance, reflectance), viscoelastic (surface tension, resealability), partitioning, and passive permeability characteristics (Jain, 1972). It has been realized for quite some time now that a simple lipid bilayer structure cannot adequately account for the properties of biomembranes. Experimental evidence indicates that the membrane lipids not only create a barrier to the free entry and exit of molecules into and out of the cell, but lipids also provide a matrix *in/on* which biochemical reactions can take place (Fourcans and Jain, 1974); *through* which certain metabolites can pass selectively; and *with* which recognition, adhesion, aggregation and fusion of cells can be mediated. A molecular explanation of these varied processes would require a detailed description of the interactions among the membrane components.

Most, if not all, of the forces between membrane components are noncovalent, similar to those that hold the molecules of most organic solids and liquids together. The two-dimensional matrix, a lamellar lipid structure, seems to arise from the amphipathic nature of the phospholipid molecule. Since a typical biomembrane has a large variety of lipids and proteins, one may expect a certain degree of suborder or fine structure within its organization. Such aspects of membrane organization and their functional significance are the underlying theme of this review. From a review of the literature pertaining to biomembrane properties, it emerges that the current models of biomembrane structure need elaboration and further modification at least in one important respect. A wide array of experimental data appears to be consistent with a postulate that *the biomembrane continuum is broken up into a number of "plates" that are in relative motion with respect to each other. The ordered and rigid regions may be separated from each other by relatively fluid and disorganized regions. These regions are contiguous and in equilibrium.*

II. The Models of Biomembrane Organization

The plasma membrane has proved to be a durable, dynamic, and functionally complex structure that performs a wide range of physiologic tasks besides delineation of cellular boundaries. A rational explanation of most, if not all, of the above processes requires involvement of specific and selective sites that could result only from proteins present in biomembranes. The organization of proteins in a lipid bilayer lends itself to several possibilities and, therefore, to considerable speculation in the form of membrane models. So far about 50 such models have been proposed to describe membrane organization. Models of necessity oversimplify, and they also tend to over-emphasize certain features in order to stress their importance. It may be noted that the main role of models is not so much to explain and to predict—though ultimately these are the functions of science—as to polarize thinking, to establish dialectics, to pose sharp questions, and above all, lead to some radical, undreamed of unifying concept. It must be emphasized at the outset that most membrane models are not mutually exclusive. Indeed, they seem to emphasize different aspects of membrane organization. A short review of the various models that have been proposed to account for the functional and organizational features of biomembranes will be useful in elaborating the major theme of this review. Although a thorough historical review of membrane models is outside the scope of this chapter, a brief summary of some of the major features of membrane organization emphasized in these models is given in this section. The conceptual evolution of the various models can be reduced to three major categories as discussed in sequence: the bilayer hypothesis, the "iceberg" models, and the fluid-mosaic model.

A. The Bilayer Hypothesis

Classical studies of Overton at the turn of the last century showed rather convincingly that the permeability barrier of biomembranes is lipidlike. In the years to follow, the lipids from a variety of sources were purified and their structures were determined. Langmuir in the second and third decades of this century showed conclusively that most lipidic substances orient themselves at an air/water interface such that the polar groups are directed toward water and the hydrocarbon chains toward air, the less polar of the two phases. It has been taken as axiomatic ever since that similar forces govern the organization of lipid molecules in water: the molecules that cannot be compressed at the air/water interface are forced to form their own nonpolar phase. Such a tendency to form an oil/water interface by lipid molecules has been the basic hypothesis in membrane models in general, and in the bilayer-based models (Fig. 1) in particular.

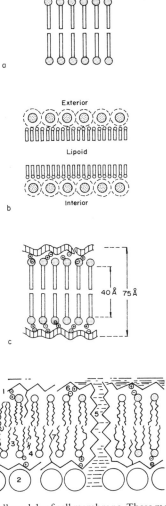

FIG. 1.   The "paucimolecular" models of cell membrane. These models essentially emphasize the molecular dimensions of biomembranes. Diagrams are adapted from Mazliak (1971) based on the work of the authors cited: (a) Gorter and Grendel (1925); (b) Danielli and Davson (1935); (c) Davson and Danielli (1943); (d) Stein and Danielli (1956).

The hypothesis that a living cell had a well-conducting interior, surrounded by a relatively impermeable, poorly ion-conducting region, had by 1921 been well supported by electrical measurements on red blood cells and several tissues. Fricke (1923, 1925) determined electrical capacity of red cell membranes as 0.81 μF/cm^2. Assuming that the membrane might be an oil with a dielectric constant of 3, the above value of capacity corresponds to a membrane thickness of 33 Å, thus indicating that the biomembrane may have molecular dimensions. These results and assumptions have been proved to be correct by subsequent experiments.

Based on their studies on pressure–area relationships for monolayers of lipid isolated from red blood cell membrane, Gorter and Grendel (1925; however, see Bar *et al.*, 1966) were probably the first to suggest the existence of bilayer structure in biomembranes (Fig. 1a). This theme was reinforced by Danielli and Davson (1935) as primarily associated with the physicochemical behavior of amphipaths in water. The bilayer is simply the most efficient and, therefore, the most probable way for lipid molecules to arrange themselves consistent with minimization of free energy. It has been argued that a bilayer arrangement of lipids would be thermodynamically stable under physiological conditions, and would also impart to the membranes the electrical and permeability properties that are observed in living cells. Direct experimental support for the radial (perpendicular to the plane of the membrane) arrangement of molecules in the bilayer came from birefringence measurements (Schmidt, 1936; Schmitt *et al.*, 1936). Inability of a simple bilayer structure to account for a variety of biomembrane characteristics, such as ionic permeability and low surface tension, was realized and appreciated fairly early. This meant that a simple bilayer hypothesis needed modification. Danielli and co-workers experimented with adding globular proteins, such as hemoglobin and ovalbumin, to solutions in contact with lipid/water interfaces; they found that the proteins adsorbed on the interfaces. A reduction in interfacial tension accompanied adsorption. This observation could explain the low interfacial tension of biological membranes. Further experiments with hemoglobin at water/lipid interface indicated that the free energy of adsorption was of the order of 100 kcal per mole, presumably arising from interaction between the nonpolar moieties of the protein and lipid molecule. This model could accommodate not only globular proteins, but also "unrolled" (sheet) structural conformations of proteins in close contact with the lipid layers. Thus, the cell membrane was visualized as "a sort of sandwich—two slices of lipid between two slices of flattened out protein—and probably with a garnish of globular protein over all." Some protein-lined pores were also postulated (see below). All this is consistent with the observation that membranes contain, besides lipids, varying proportions of proteins.

Significant support for the bilayer hypothesis was obtained by electron microscopic studies. These studies confirmed what was suspected from a variety of physiological studies, that the biomembrane is asymmetric and the bilayer structure is a universal mode of organization (unit membrane hypothesis) at least in plasma membranes (Robertson, 1960, 1964, 1967). This theme was further modified by various physicochemical studies that gave indications of the presence of additional features of bilayer organization (Fig. 2). On the basis of electron microscopic studies, Staehelin (1968)

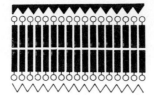

a

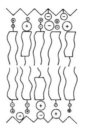

b

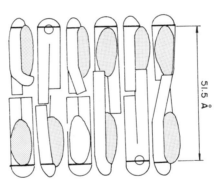

51.5 Å

c

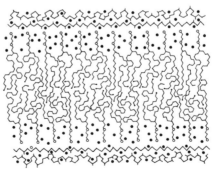

d

FIG. 2 (a–d).

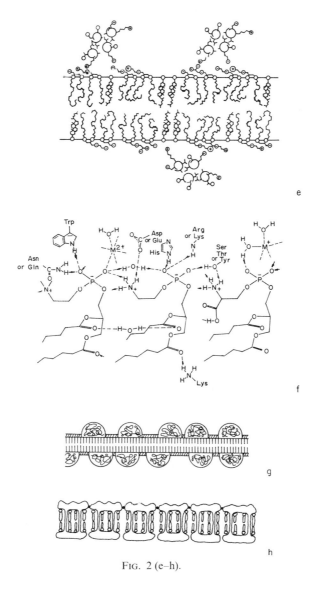

FIG. 2 (e–h).

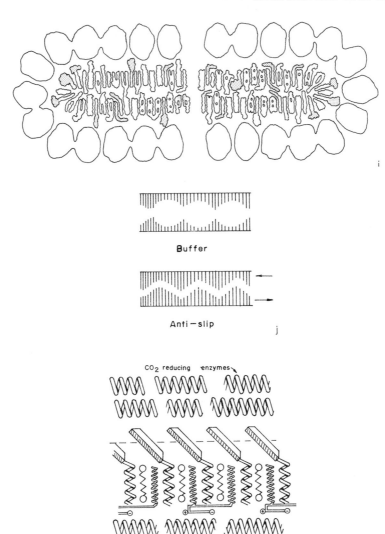

FIG. 2.   The lipid bilayer-based models that emphasize substructure within biomembranes. The aspects that have been emphasized include asymmetry (Robertson), specific intermolecular interaction (Finean, Vandenheuvel), conformation of polymethylene chains (Stoeckenius, Sundaralingam), presence of specific components (Calvin, Menke), segregation of lipids (Crawford and Sinclair). Diagrams are adapted from Mazliak (1971) based on the work of the authors cited: (a) Robertson (1964); (b) B. Boois and H. G. Burgenberg de Jong (1952, cited in Mazliak, 1971, p. 68); (c) Vandenheuvel (1965); (d) Stoeckenius (1963); (e) Haggis (1964); (f) Sundaralingam (1972); (g) Staehelin (1968); (h) Gross (1967); (i) Menke (1966); (j) Crawford and Sinclair (1972); (k) Calvin (1959).

suggested the presence of globular structures on the surface of the lipid bilayer. B. Boois and H. G. Bungenberg de Jong (1952, cited in Mazliak, 1971, p. 68) emphasized the presence of cholesterol in membranes in stoichiometric proportions. Calvin (1959) proposed the bilayer structure constituted of several overlapping and interdigitated components characteristic to the chloroplast membranes. In accordance with compositional and X-ray diffraction studies, Finean (1953) suggested the presence of several lipid species in the bilayer and a sheet of protein on the interface. The model proposed by Menke (1966) emphasized the presence of globular proteins on the bilayer constituted of diverse lipid components. On the basis of his studies with molecular models, Vandenheuvel (1965) inferred specific interactions between cholesterol and certain phospholipids (see also Finean, 1953; Engström and Finean, 1958; Hechter, 1966), and the model for bilayer organization proposed by him emphasized such aspects of lipid composition and molecular association. Similar studies have been carried out by O'Brien (1967). The cis-trans and gauche-trans conformations in the polymethylene chains of phospholipids were probably emphasized by Stoeckenius (1963) first, and also by Haggis (1964). Sundaralingam (1972), on the basis of his X-ray crystal structure studies of phosphoglycerol derivatives, emphasized the relative orientation and conformations of polar groups that could be involved in the metal binding and hydrogen binding with proteins at the interface of lipid bilayer. Crawford and Sinclair (1972) have emphasized the difference in the length of acyl chains in various species of phospholipids in the membrane. According to their model, differences in the lateral organization of the chains could allow either a "buffering" or an "interlocking" arrangement, which could lead to some special biological advantages by juxtaposition or by relative movement of the opposing bilayers, or by buffering against mechanical shock. Such arguments have also been made by Fergason and Brown (1967).

Some of the basic functions of a biomembrane are associated with its barrier properties, that is, for most solutes the diffusion rate is far less (by a factor of 10^6 to 10^9) than the "free" diffusion rate in the absence of a membrane. This is consistent with the bilayer hypothesis where the biomembrane behaves as a thick wall (about 50 Å) through which various molecules move at a rate predicted from their lipid solubility and size. However, there are some significant exceptions. Abnormally rapid and sometimes uphill (against the gradient) movement of certain solutes was observed across certain cell membranes. These phenomena could be lumped together in the following categories.

1. Generally, fast movement (permeability) of small molecules like urea could be accounted for by assuming the presence of polar pores of about 4 Å radius.

2. Fast movement of certain large polar molecules like sugars and amino acids could be accommodated by assuming the presence of selective carriers in the lipid bilayer.

3. The uphill (active) transport needed to be invoked to account for the existence and maintenance of ionic and metabolite gradients across the cell membrane.

4. Endocytosis (pinocytosis, phagocytosis) and exocytosis, which accounts for the movement of large proteins and bulk material into and out of the cell.

These departures from the behavior of simple lipid bilayer required the presence of "pores" or "active regions" or patches of discontinuity in the sandwich bilayer. Local variations in the arrangement of lipids might exert a significant effect on transport across the lipid bilayer or might even be involved in the formation of these regions of discontinuity. It could be calculated on the basis of several observations that not more than 2% of the membrane surface could be involved in all the above functions. A direct examination of the organization of the pores and patches required for the various specialized membrane function is, therefore, not possible by most experimental techniques. The situation is complicated by the observation that different membranes contain between 20% and 70% proteins by weight, and they are associated in some as yet undefined way with the lipids of the membrane, and together both form a stable-selective barrier at the cell periphery. Stein and Danielli (1956) introduced a few protein lined pores (Fig. 1) in an *ad hoc* fashion, without an explanation as to which proteins they involved or what made them stable. Similarly a continuous unfolded layer of protein would of necessity have many nonpolar residues exposed to water, an energetically unfavorable situation.

Several authors in the early 1960s reported the presence of elaborations (pits, dimples, and wrinkles) in high-resolution electron micrographs. This stimulated suggestions about their origin (Fig. 3). Kavanau (1965), Lucy and Glaubert (1964), Sjöstrand (1963, 1968), and Colacicco (1972) proposed in models of different degrees of sophistication that these substructures in the bilayer could arise from micellar arrangement of lipids and/or from globular proteins within the bilayer. Several other authors have tried to propose plausible models in which a mosaic of lipid and protein could exist (Winkler and Bungenberg de Jong, 1940; Ponder, 1951; Mitchison, 1953). The "patches," "pores," and carriers are particularly hard to visualize in such a micellar mosaic. A hydrophilic opening in an otherwise hydrophobic bilayer would normally be expected to enlarge because of the interfacial tension, to the point where the membrane would be destroyed. This is obviously not the case. Furthermore, a protein layer covering up the hydrophilic residues of lipid is not a generally acceptable situation. Probably

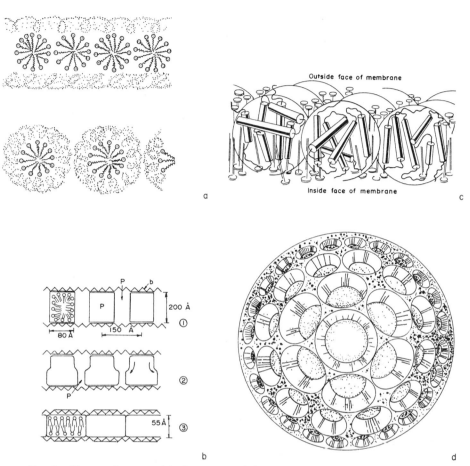

Fig. 3. The membrane models that suggested the presence of the micellar regions of discontinuity within a bilayer. Here the term micelle is taken to implicate organized lipid structures or phases other than a bilayer. Diagrams are adapted from Mazliak (1971) based on the work the authors cited: (a) Lucy and Glauert (1964); (b) Kavanau (1965); (c) Sjöstrand (1968); (d) Colacicco (1972).

the weakness of this category of models lies in their attempt to provide a generally applicable mode of insertion of proteins in lipid by breaking the bilayer continuity with micellar structures.

B. The Iceberg and Protein Crystal Models

Various physicochemical studies are consistent with the presence of a lipid bilayer in biomembranes (Oseroff *et al.*, 1973). However, more direct evidence suggests that the volume of the bilayers in the biomembranes is

20–40% greater than it ought to be if made up only of lipids (Dupont *et al.*, 1973; Blaurock, 1972). Such studies do not allow a quantitative assessment of the bilayer content of the membrane. By the middle of the last decade, it became obvious that the specialized functions of biomembranes arise from the proteins embedded in the lipid bilayer. A large number of models tried to visualize the orientation of proteins into lipid. These models, generally speaking, range from proteins dipped in the lipid matrix to lipid embedded in a protein matrix.[2]

Direct support for such assertions came from freeze-fracture electron microscopy. By this technique one can prepare specimens so that large areas of surface membrane can be visualized. Cells or membrane fragments can be frozen rapidly, either with or without chemical fixation, and then subjected to a fracturing step which splits individual membranes along a plane more or less down the middle of the membrane. As a result of this splitting, large regions of membranes *within* the lipid bilayer are exposed and these can be replicated by platinum–carbon shadowing. The strongest evidence for the existence of a bilayer in biomembranes comes from the susceptibility of the membranes to fracture across their midplanes at low temperature. Besides this, several new features of membrane structure were uncovered by this technique, the principal one being the discovery that globular units of ca 75 Å diameter are present within the bilayer region of the membrane (Branton, 1966a,b, 1969, 1971). The principal advantage of this technique over conventional shadowing and cell-spreading methods is that cell membranes need not be subjected to drying or other stabilizing procedures. Replicas prepared of freeze-etched material seem to be capable of resolving macromolecules in a 30–50 Å range. The technique also offers a unique opportunity to examine structural features in the interior of the membrane.

The models attempting to describe the orientation and localization of proteins into membranes are almost as diverse as the functions that membrane

---

[2] A membrane composed solely of proteins can be made artifically (Bahadur, 1966); however, such a membrane has not been observed in biological systems except perhaps for the protein coats of certain bacteriophages and viruses (Erickson, 1973). Orgel (1972) and Brack and Orgel (1975) suggested that the first coded proteins to evolve may have had an alternating sequence of hydrophobic and hydrophilic amino acid residues. Such simple proteins would have the capacity to form extended β-sheets with a hydrophobic face and a hydrophilic face. These sheets in turn could form protein bilayers. It is unlikely that such a membrane system, if it ever existed, could have persisted. The barrier function of membranes requires an essentially continuous impermeable surface. In a system with many different proteins interconnecting like pieces of a jigsaw puzzle, almost any mutation would disrupt the fit of adjacent proteins. The lipids in contemporary membranes have the advantage of forming a continuous sheet while providing a matrix that can accommodate a variety of proteins in varying stoichiometries. The evolution of specific interactions among membrane components is possible without the severe restrictions necessary for continuous protein membrane.

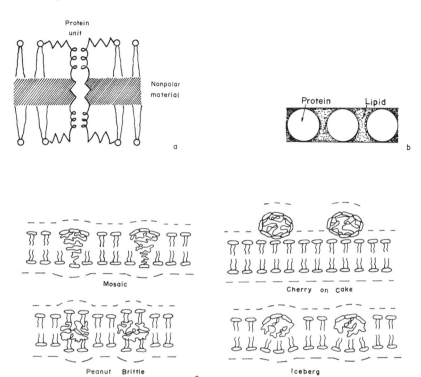

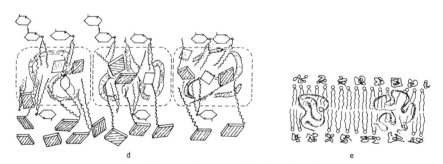

FIG. 4 (a–e).   See page 15 for figure legend.

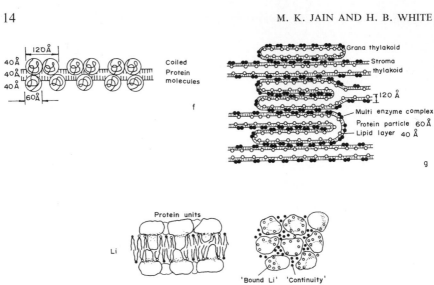

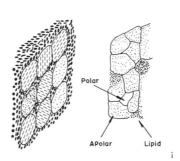

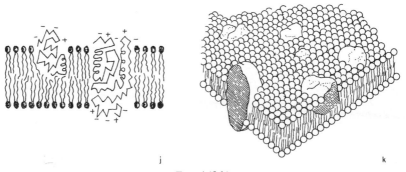

Fig. 4 (f–k).

proteins perform. Several authors have developed the theme that hydrophobic proteins are inserted into the hydrophobic region of the bilayer. The hydrophobic interactions stabilize the lipid–protein association, and the hydrophilic regions in the protein line the passage for polar solutes as first suggested by Stein and Danielli (1956) (Fig. 1). Similarly, other functional and catalytic proteins could be inserted into the bilayer to varying degrees. The "iceberg" models (Fig. 4), which conform to this general hypothesis, were proposed by Muhlethaler *et al.* (1965), Branton (1966a,b), Lenard and Singer (1966), Benson (1966), Weier and Benson (1966, 1967), P. Weibel and P. Zahler (cited in Finean, 1973), Dewey and Barr (1971), Wallach (1972), and Singer and Nicolson (1972). There is widespread agreement on general features, and the differences in proposed models are largely a matter of emphasis.

Several other membrane models tend to emphasize higher proportion, asymmetric distribution, specific interaction, and association of proteins. These organizational features are certainly called for on the basis of the biochemical functions of these membranes. Both fractionation and electron microscopic studies on mitochondrial membranes, for example, suggest the existence of substructure in membrane organization. Thus, in these "protein crystal" models (Fig. 5) it has been postulated that a set of proteins could form a subunit and the association of such subunits in a two-dimensional matrix would give rise to a two-dimensional membrane. The lipids could not only act to cement the subunits, but also aid in specific association of the components of the subunit. Such models invoking subunit lattice structure for membranes were proposed for mitochondrial (Green and Perdue, 1966; Green *et al.*, 1967; Green and Baum, 1970; Vanderkooi and Green, 1970; Lussan-Bothorel, 1969; Crane and Hall, 1972) and axonal and synaptosomal (Changeux and Thiery, 1968) membranes. Interestingly enough, a model for chloroplast membrane organization proposed by Frey-Wyssling (1957) and Frey-Wyssling and Steinmann (1953) contained not only the suggestion of asymmetry, but also the aspects of subunit organization in a biomembrane. Several other models for membrane structure in chloroplast

---

FIG. 4.   The "Iceberg" models, in general, have tried to visualize proteins of various forms and shape embedded in or on lipid bilayer. The various possible arrangements are probably best articulated in the models considered by Dewey and Barr. These models tend to suggest a more or less random organization of membrane components. Aspects of asymmetry and discontinuity are generally attributed to membrane proteins. Diagrams are adapted from Mazliak (1971) based on the work of the authors cited: (a) Lenard and Singer (1966): (b) Branton (1966a,b); (c) Dewey and Barr (1971); (d) Weier and Benson (1967); (e) Benson (1966); (f) Muhlethaler *et al.* (1965); (g) Muhlethaler *et al.* (1965); (h) P. Weibel and P. Zahler (cited in Finean, 1973); (i) Wallach (1972); (j) Singer (1972); (k) Singer and Nicolson (1972).

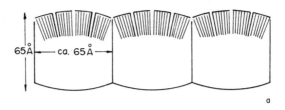

a

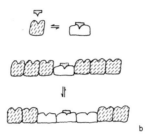

b

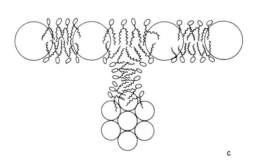

c

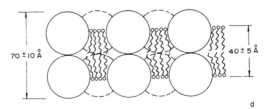

d

FIG. 5 (a–d).   See page 18 for figure legend.

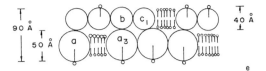

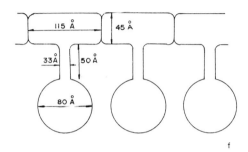

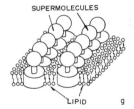

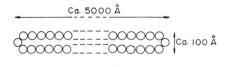

FIG. 5 (e–i).   See page 18 for figure legend.

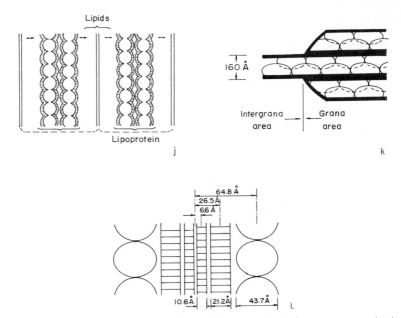

FIG. 5. The "protein crystal" models have tried to emphasize long-range organization of membrane components. In general, lipid–protein complexes are visualized to form the subunits that arrange themselves to form a two-dimensional lattice. Diagrams are adapted from Mazliak (1971) based on the work of the authors cited: (a) Frey-Wyssling (1957); (b) Changeux *et al.* (1967); (c) Lussan-Bothorel (1969); (d) Vanderkooi and Green (1970); (e) Crane and Hall (1972); (f) Green and Perdue (1966); (g) Green *et al.* (1967); (h) Green and Baum (1970); (i) Frey-Wyssling and Steinmann (1953); (j) Goedheer (1957); (k) Park and Pon (1961); (l) Kreutz (1963).

have also exploited the theme of subunit structure (Frey-Wyssling and Steinmann, 1953; Goedheer, 1957; Park and Pon, 1961; Kreutz, 1963).

These models appear to differ fundamentally from the idea that membranes feature a predominantly continuous lipid layer with which active proteins associate or into or through which they may penetrate. However, when the penetration amounts to 30% and the proteins carry with them a substantial amount of bound lipid, such lipoproteins might be considered to become equivalent to subunits cemented together by continuity lipid. They nevertheless form what amounts to a predominantly continuous phase of lipid, which serves to maintain the orientation of the active lipoproteins and to complete the barriers required to compartmentalize the cell.

The subunit organization in these membrane models allows for the possibility of cooperativity or allosteric interactions, that is, transfer of information over long distances, possibly over the whole cell membrane. This cooperative behavior provides a molecular basis for the control of many sites by a small number of effector molecules (hormones, transmitters, drugs). Although such a concept allows for a physical explanation of some complex membrane phenomenon (sigmoid dose-response curve, threshold, large Hill coefficient, higher order molecularity), a rational explanation for the stability of such large cooperative units has not been proposed. Other explanations not invoking long-range cooperativity among membrane bound proteins could also account for these phenomena.

From the experimental evidence, it seems certain that the cell membrane does consist of a lipid protein "mosaic," the lipids serving to isolate the cell from its environment and the lipid bilayer acting as a two-dimensional matrix for the macromolecules. The proteins embedded in this matrix serve to reinforce the lipid bilayer, to insulate it from external physical and chemical stresses, to promote the selective interchange of substances with the environment on which the cellular life depends, to act as receptors for external stimuli, and to provide polar pathways through the thickness of the membrane. None of these mosaic models provide any insight as to how membrane proteins perform the functions that they are supposed to. Extrapolation from the behavior of water-soluble proteins has not necessarily yielded any additional insight. A particularly extreme view of the role of proteins with special reference to the energy transduction function of the mitochondrial membrane has been articulated by Green and Ji (1972). "The programming of the protein for catalysis has three main ingredients—the molecular strategy for the conversion of thermal energy to the strain energy of the protein, the achievement of a conformation appropriate to a reaction before its occurrence, and finally, the changing pattern of reactive groups in the catalytic cavity required for the different stages in the catalytic process. Conformation, thus, is not merely a barometer of chemical change. It is in effect the molecular carrot for the catalytic rabbit."

Since the membrane functions are diverse, one would expect that the nature and localization of the molecules that mediate these functions would also be diverse. Typically, a cell membrane may have more than 100 different proteins (Guidotti, 1972). To understand the mechanism of their action, one needs much more information on the structure of the individual proteins. This has not been possible except in a few cases. Attempts to isolate membrane proteins were carried out with the idea that these proteins would have a high affinity for lipids and also be insoluble in aqueous media. Unfortunately, most proteins are able to bind lipids and may also be insoluble in water, especially after denaturation. Thus, the attempts to isolate and characterize such proteins based on these criteria were largely unsuccessful since there was no way to determine whether the preparation represented denatured or proteolyzed contaminants rather than proteins of a special type. Moreover, generally speaking, it has not been possible to put even the semipurified membrane proteins back into a lipid matrix to generate specific functions, although limited success has been achieved in several laboratories (Fourcans and Jain, 1974). Such observations seem to imply that the properties of purified proteins could be different from their properties in their natural environment unless extreme precautions are taken during their isolation. Such experimental difficulties leave the question of lipid/protein interaction to considerable speculations. Indeed, our ideas as to how lipids and proteins are held together in an essentially two-dimensional matrix are still unsettled, and this state of uncertainty will remain until we learn more about membrane proteins and how they might be arranged. Similarly, it has been convenient to divide membrane proteins into two groups: *extrinsic* proteins remaining largely on the aqueous side of the membrane attached by electrostatic forces which can be disrupted by dilute salt solutions, and *intrinsic* proteins making substantial contact with the hydrocarbon region of the lipid bilayer which can only be disrupted by use of ionic detergents. In practice, however, this distinction is difficult to apply (e.g., see Langdon, 1974; Nelson *et al.*, 1974; also see below).

Any spatial models proposed for membranes should make provision for both polar and nonpolar interactions, and a variety of models do so. The data of Branton (1969) and Coleman *et al.* (1970) suggest that the extent of interruption of the lipid bilayer in the erythrocyte membrane by proteins is no more than 30%. Taking these suggestions together, it would seem that the most satisfactory explanation would be a centrally located lipid bilayer with protein penetrating into or though it so as to occupy up to 30% of the total area. This theme has been emphasized in models by Wallach (1972) and P. Weibel and P. Zahler (cited in Finean, 1973). In the first model the biomembrane is visualized as being assembled from various subunits so as to form a tangentially mobile patchwork, penetrated to varying depths by both protein and lipid. In the model by Weibel and Zahler (cited in Finean, 1973), mushroom-shaped or dumbbell-shaped protein moieties are arranged with their narrower shafts or stalks penetrating into or through a lipid bilayer and their more bulbous heads located outside the lipid to form predominantly nonlipid layers. There would be considerable variation in the extent of penetration of individual protein molecules into the lipid layer, and the configuration of the exposed protein may also vary. These features distinguish the "continuity lipid" from the directly protein-bound lipid. These features are also invoked in the fluid-mosaic model (Section II,C).

The clustering of lipid molecules around predominantly nonpolar protein stalks and their simultaneous binding to the polar undersides of the protein heads would tend to make a clean separation of protein and lipid difficult both in aqueous media and in organic solvents and would also encourage conformational changes in the protein when isolated in either polar or non-polar media. The difficulties encountered in interpreting the action of solvents on membranes would certainly be understandable in these circumstances. So, too, would be the problems of reconstituting a membrane from separated lipid and protein components. Reaggregation through predominantly polar or nonpolar forces might be readily effected and this would probably form a layered structure with membrane-like morphology, but the restoration of the specific penetrations of protein moieties into the interior of the lipid would be much less certain, and many of the membrane functions may depend on these deeper interactions. Some detergents may break only the continuity lipid. Functionally, significant reconstitution might then be possible simply by removal of detergent by dialysis (see Fourcans and Jain, 1974, for a review and earlier references).

A model of this kind also has interesting implications in relation to membrane biogenesis and membrane fusion. It might be assumed that some of the membrane proteins have specific requirements for lipid which become directly associated with them. They may acquire this lipid immediately after synthesis in order to preserve a critical configuration or they may at a later stage select lipid molecules from an existing pool in order to acquire a functionally critical configuration. In situations where the continuity lipid is similar in two membranes, fusion may be readily effected, perhaps aided by the incorporation into these regions of further elements that tend either to introduce a slight instability or to make the two systems more compatible.

C. THE FLUID-MOSAIC MODEL:
   A NEW LIFE TO THE BILAYER CONCEPT

Wallach and Zahler (1966) and Lenard and Singer (1966) visualized membrane proteins as globular and folded up so as to be amphipathic, as are membrane lipid molecules. The hydrophobic end would be embedded in the interior of the lipid bilayer, while the hydrophilic end would project out into the aqueous medium (like an "iceberg" in a "sea" of lipid). Similarly, one could conceive of protein molecules spanning the bilayer. These amphipathic proteins need not have higher proportions of hydrophobic amino acids; only the way the amino acid residues are arranged or distributed would be different for membrane-bound compared to soluble proteins. These aspects are consistent with the structural studies on membrane proteins like cytochrome b_5 and glycophorin, which have stretches of hydrophilic and hydrophobic residues (Marchesi, 1975; Tomita and Marchesi, 1975), and from the Fourier electron microscopy of *Halobacterium* membrane (Henderson and Unwin, 1975). Also consistent with this is the observed chemical and functional asymmetry of biomembranes, which suggests that the outside and inside of the membrane must do quite different things (Bretscher, 1972, 1973; Segrest *et al.*, 1973; Steck, 1974). This follows from a postulate implicit in iceberg models; that is, the membrane proteins would not be free to pass from one side of the membrane to the other. Such a process, for both lipid and protein, would involve "submerging" the hydrophilic end among the hydrophobic lipid chains—a thermodynamically unlikely process. This suggests that some proteins that are asymmetrically oriented must be placed there during biosynthesis.

Proteins inserted into and stuck onto a lipid bilayer turn out to be a fairly versatile concept for biomembrane structure. Direct support for this concept is derived from freeze-fracture electron microscopy. Thus one can observe quantities of protein particles protruding beyond the midline of the lipid bilayer. Every membrane that has been looked at this way has shown the presence of similar particles, although their number, size, and topological distribution vary in different membranes. Such aspects of organization of proteins has been exploited most in the fluid-mosaic model (Singer and Nicolson, 1972; Singer, 1974). This model has been particularly successful in encompassing the salient features of most models that preceded it, and to some extent, it has integrated the wealth of the old and the new experimental results that became available in the last decade. To a certain degree it emphasizes the balance between the structural organization and the fluid disorder of membrane lipids and proteins. One of the distinguishing features of this model is the postulate that some membrane proteins, in order to perform their functions, must be free to rotate within their lipid matrix, as well as to move (float) in the plane of the membrane. Such mobility would be impossible for an unfolded continuous layer of protein over all the membrane. Indeed, on the basis of the experimental data that became available in the last decade, one may distinguish five types of molecular movements or motions in the membrane:

a. Gauche–trans Transition. The energy of gauche conformation is approximately 0.5 kcal/mole above that of the trans conformation, and the energy barrier between the trans and gauche conformation is about 3.6 kcal/mole (Hagele and Pechald, 1970). The jump frequency for trans–gauche transition would be about 10^9 to 10^{10} sec^{-1} as compared to 3 to 6 × 10^{12} sec^{-1} for C—C bond oscillation frequency.

b. Segmental Motion: Flexing of the Fatty Acid Chains and Their Oscillations about an Axis Perpendicular to the Plane of the Bilayer. The time constant for such motions is expected to be less than a nanosecond and the resultant disorder increases as one moves toward the center of the bilayer from the interface (McFarland and McConnell, 1971; Metcalfe *et al.*, 1971; Schreier-Muccillo *et al.*, 1973; Seelig and Niederberger, 1974; Godichi and Landsburger, 1974; Sears, 1975). Similar conclusions are arrived at from the

Table I
RATES OF TRANSBILAYER MOVEMENT ("FLIP-FLOP")

Membrane system	Species studied	Half-time flip-flop (°C)	Reference
Phospholipid vesicles	Lecithin	~11 Days	Rothman and Davidowicz (1975)
Phospholipid vesicles	Cholesterol	~6 Days	Poznansky and Lange (1976)
Phospholipid vesicles	Lecithin	>4 Days	L. W. Johnson *et al.* (1975)
Glycerol dialeate planar bilayer	Oleylacid phosphate	>15 Hours	Sherwood and Montal (1975)
Influenza virus	Cholesterol	~13 Days	Lenard and Rothman (1976)

calculations based on C—C bond rotations along the chain (Rothman, 1973). Such a change in disorder towards the center of the bilayer creates packing problems. The increased volume toward the center of the bilayer can be accommodated either by a bend in the fatty acid chains (McFarland and McConnell, 1971) or by a decreased packing density in the glycerol backbone region, perhaps with the extra space being taken up by water (Montal and Muller, 1972; see also Benz *et al.*, 1975; Griffith *et al.*, 1974).

c. Transverse Motion: Flipping of Molecules from One Face of the Bilayer to the Other. Such a flip-flop is relatively slow (Table I), half-times being in the range of days (Kornberg and McConnell, 1971; McNamee and McConnell, 1973; Lenard and Rothman, 1976). Flip-flop in biomembranes appears to be rather fast. This could be due to some yet undiscovered protein "flippase" that catalyzes flip-flop (Bretscher, 1975).

d. Rotational Motion: Rotation of Molecules about Their Axes Perpendicular to the Plane of the Bilayer. Values of such rotational displacement times are in the microsecond to nanosecond range (Table II).

e. Lateral Diffusional Motion: Lateral Passage of Components Past One Another in the Plane of the Membrane. The lateral diffusion constant has been calculated to be in the range of 10^{-8} to 10^{-12} cm^2 sec^{-1} for a variety of systems (Table III). The significance of lateral diffusion has been discussed in detail elsewhere (Edidin, 1974) and is presented below in the context of this review. It may, however, be noted that the diffusion constant for the passive permeability of solutes like water and methanol across bilayer and biomembrane is also about 10^{-9} cm^2 sec^{-1}. The significance of this similarity remains to be established. It may be pertinent to point out here that the direction of diffusion in permeability measurements is across the plane of the bilayer, whereas the lateral diffusion occurs in the plane of the bilayer.

Optical visualization of membrane antigens tagged with labeled (fluorescent or electron dense) antibodies show that their arrangement is not orderly,

Table II

VALUES OF ROTATIONAL DISPLACEMENT TIMES

System	Component	MW	Rotational displacement times (Reference)
Mitochondrial	Cytochrome oxidase membrane (25°)	≥70,000	≤100 μsec (Junge, 1972)
ROS[a] (frog)	Rhodopsin (20°)	≈40,000	3.0 ± 15 μsec (Cone, 1972; Brown, 1972)
Lobster nerve	Spin-labeled steroid (25°)	~500	10–100 nsec (Hubbell and McConnell, 1971)
Electroplax	Fluorescent label on acetylcholine receptor	>100,000	>0.7 μsec (Wahl et al., 1971)
Sonicated liposomes	Phospholipid (above T_c)	~700	~0.5 μsec (Chan et al., 1971)
Sonicated liposomes		~700	0.14 nsec (Levine et al., 1972a)
Liposomes	Fatty acid (21.5°) spin label	~200	2.5 nsec (Schindler and Seelig, 1973)
n-Alkanes	In bulk phase	~500	0.01 nsec (Levine et al., 1974)
Erythrocyte	Fluorescent label	~90,000	~1 msec (Cherry et al., 1976)
Halobacterium	Bacteriorhodopsin	~60,000	Very slow (Henderson and Unwin, 1975)

[a] Retinal rod outer segment.

but random. Similarly Frye and Edidin (1970) observed thorough mixing of human and mouse antigens in heterokaryons after virus-induced fusion in about 40 minutes at 37°C. Control experiments suggest that the process is not energy dependent, nor the result of synthesis and insertion of new protein molecules, but rather a matter of simple diffusion of the existing molecules within the membrane. Enough evidence has accumulated suggesting that the binding of an antigen to its specific antibody on the surface of lymphocytes can cross-link the receptors in the membrane and drag them to one pole of the cell. Indeed, a large number of observations suggest that the lateral motion of components within the plane of biomembrane may play a significant role in a variety of membrane-mediated biological (see Singer, 1974, for a review) and biochemical processes (Strittmatter *et al.*, 1972; Rogers and Strittmatter, 1975). There are obvious biological advantages in having a membrane in which its components can diffuse laterally. It may facilitate interaction of membrane proteins with their lipophilic ligands (substrates, hormones, transmitters and other modulators); it provides a simple means of distributing the components to regions of the membrane remote from where they are inserted; it facilitates cell locomotion and membrane fusion; it allows dividing membrane components to distribute evenly during cell division; it regulates the function of various receptors.

The biomembrane according to the fluid-mosaic model is visualized as a two-dimensional liquid "mosaic" in which the components float, and, owing to a large degree of rotational and lateral mobility, these components are randomly distributed within the matrix. This model does not necessarily rule out, under particular conditions, localized regions in certain membranes that may have restricted fluidity or mobility. As reviewed elsewhere (Fourcans and Jain, 1974) a large variety of enzymes and transport systems show an absolute requirement for specific lipids. Similar specificity of intermolecular interaction among various membrane components has also been implicated for hormone-activated adenylcyclase, respiratory and photosynthetic, electron transport chains, and various receptor–effector systems. Such a specificity is probably best manifested in reconstitution studies, where a specific order of addition of various components is so critical for optimal reactivation. Thus, some lipids may be tightly bound to specific proteins and thereby regulate or modulate proteins, tertiary or subunit structure, and allosteric behavior.

A specificity of interaction (not necessarily an absolute requirement for a specific lipid) would imply that the lipid bound to these proteins may be immobilized. In the case of cytochrome oxidase, for example, it has been shown that as much as 40% of the lipid added to reactivate the purified protein may be "immobilized" compared to the other 60% (Jost *et al.*, 1973a,b). Similarly less than about two-thirds of the lipid appears to be

Table III

Lateral Diffusion Constants in Various Membrane Systems[a]

Membrane	Diffusing species	Method	Temperature (°C)	D (cm^2 sec^{-1})	Reference
Bilayer (DPC)	Pyrene	Fluorescence	50°	1.4×10^{-7}	Galla and Sackmann (1974)
Bilayer (DPC + Chol)	Pyrene	Fluorescence	50°	0.64×10^{-7}	Galla and Sackmann (1974)
Bilayer (DPC + Chol)	Phospholipid	ESR	20°–50°	$0.1–10 \times 10^{-8}$	Lee et al. (1973), Scandella et al. (1972), Devaux and McConnell (1972)
Monolayer and bilayer (DPC)	Androstan	ESR	50°	3×10^{-8}	Trauble and Sackmann (1972)
Bilayer (egg lecithin)	Phospholipid	NMR	20°	5×10^{-9}	Lee et al. (1973)
Bilayer (DPC)	Phospholipid	ESR	25°	1.8×10^{-8}	Devaux and McConnell (1972)
Bilayer (DPC)	Fatty acid	ESR	20°–40°	3×10^{-8}	Stier and Sackmann (1973)
Bilayer (egg lecithin)	Fatty acid	ESR	20°–40°	14×10^{-8}	Stier and Sackmann (1973)
Bilayer (DME)	—	ESR	59°	2.8×10^{-8}	Galla and Sackmann (1975a)
Bilayer (DPA)	—	Fluorescence	60°	1.7×10^{-7}	Galla and Sackmann (1975a)
Monolayers	Cholesterol	Radio tracer		$10^{-6\,b}$	Stroeve and Miller (1975)
				$10^{-7\,c}$	

System	Component	Method	Temperature	Value	Reference
Sarcoplasmic reticulum	Phospholipid	ESR	40°	10×10^{-8}	Scandella et al. (1972)
Sarcoplasmic reticulum	Phospholipid	NMR	31°	4×10^{-9}	Lee et al. (1973)
Electroplax	Phospholipid	NMR	33°	$\geq 10^{-9}$	Lee et al. (1973)
Liver microsome	Fatty acid	ESR	20°–40°	$9.5\text{–}13.7 \times 10^{-8}$	Stier and Sackmann (1973)
Sciatic nerve	Phospholipid	NMR	31°C	5×10^{-9}	Lee et al. (1973)
Escherichia coli	Phospholipid	NMR	31°C	1.8×10^{-8}	Davis (1972)
Red cell	Protein (?)	Fluorescent label	20°–23°	$<3 \times 10^{-12}$	Peters et al. (1974)
Heterokaryons	Antigen	Fluorescent label	40°	$2\text{–}5 \times 10^{-10}$	Frye and Edidin (1970)
Retinal rod outer segment (frog)	Rhodopsin	Absorption	37°	5×10^{-9}	Poo and Cone (1973, 1974)
Fibroblast	Protein	Fluorescent label	23°	2.6×10^{-10}	Edidin et al. (1976)
Salmonella typhimurium	Protein?	Ferritin label	25°	3×10^{-3}	Muhlradt et al. (1974)
Cultured muscle fiber	Protein?	Fluorescent label	40°	$1\text{–}2 \times 10^{-9}$	Edidin and Fambrough (1973)
3T3 Mouse fibroblast	Protein?	Gold particle	37°	2×10^{-10}; 2×10^{-11}	Albrecht-Buhler (1973)
Bilayers (egg lecithin)	Benzene[d]	Radiotracer	20°	2×10^{-6}	Rigaud et al. (1973)
Red cell	Water[d]	NMR	20°	$\sim 10^{-9}$	Finch and Schneider (1975)
Red cell	Methanol[d]	Permeability	20°	5.1×10^{-8}	Solomon (1974)

[a] Abbreviations used: Chol, cholesterol; DPC, dipalmitoyllecithin; DME, dimyristoylethanolamine; DPA, dipalmitoylphosphatidic acid; ESR, electron. spin resonance; NMR, nuclear magnetic resonance.

[b] At 40 Å^2/cholesterol molecule.

[c] At 38 Å^2/cholesterol molecule.

[d] These values relate to diffusion of solute across the membrane.

27

fluid in several membranes (Machtiger and Fox, 1973), including rod outer segment membrane (Pontus and Delmelle, 1975), sarcoplasmic reticulum (Robinson *et al.*, 1972; McConnell *et al.*, 1972), and *E. coli* membrane (Trauble and Overath, 1973). Results leading to the same conclusion have been obtained for reconstituted rhodopsin (Hong and Hubbell, 1972), cytochrome reductase (Stier and Sackmann, 1973), Na + K-ATPase (Grisham and Barnett, 1973), and Ca^{2+} pump (Warren *et al.*, 1975). However, such restrictions are considered exceptions rather than rule in terms of the fluid-mosaic model.

Membranes may also consist of a large number of protein molecules in tight contact with one another, producing a relatively rigid sort of structure as in *Halobacterium halobium* (Blaurock and Stoekenius, 1971), plaques, "super icebergs" like synaptosomes (Sytkowski *et al.*, 1973), or gap junctions (Goodenough and Stoeckenius, 1972; Gilula, 1974). Such ordered structures are special in that they consist of a single protein (or very few species of protein molecules) which form a large two-dimensional regular lattice by virtue of specific oriented protein–protein interactions in the plane of the membrane (see also Poo and Cone, 1973; Hammerling and Eggers, 1970). Such large aggregates would have very restricted mobility. In the case of the *Halobacterium* purple membrane, this lack of mobility is reflected in the very ordered Fourier-transform electron micrographs obtained from these membranes. Fourier-transform methods have been applied to the diffraction patterns from the electron micrographs, yielding a three-dimensional structure of the retinol-binding protein in this membrane at 7 Å (Henderson and Unwin, 1975). Selective and nonrandom localization of membrane proteins (or a lack of) based on morphologic specializations (in folds, microvilli, asymmetric distribution) would also be expected, for example in membranes of intestinal (Fujita *et al.*, 1973), kidney (Stevenson, 1973), liver (Evans, 1970), and other epithelial cells (Sheffield and Emmelot, 1972). Yet another restriction to the motion of membrane proteins is based on their being anchored by "peripheral," cytoplasmic, or externally added binding proteins or other specifically interacting molecules (Ukena and Berlin, 1972; Edelman *et al.*, 1973). Although these various restrictions to the motion of membrane proteins can be accommodated in the fluid-mosaic model, an explanation is yet to be advanced for such subtle restrictions to the movement, distribution, and density of membrane proteins.

III. Limitations of Fluid-Mosaic Model

Although other possibilities are not ruled out, one of the basic assumptions implicit in the fluid-mosaic model is that the membrane components are more or less randomly distributed in the plane of the membrane. There is considerable evidence that many (if not most) molecules are distributed nonrandomly in membranes and that most of the lipid molecules may experience a much more constrained environment than implied by the fluid mosaic model. It is very likely that some clustering of lipid species may occur within the bilayer. Indeed, pulse-labeled radioautographic studies of exponentially growing *Bacillus megaterium* cells using labeled palmitic acid show a highly nonuniform distribution of radioactive phospholipids (Morrison and Morowitz, 1970). The method devised by Nicolson and Singer (1971) to study the location of antigenic and other receptor activities on the surface of red cells is based on the fact that when red cells are dropped on a hypotonic medium some of the cells lyse and flatten into pancakelike structures. These can be collected on collodion-coated electron microscope grids and then treated with different ferritin-conjugated labeling reagents (antibodies or lectins), which bind to the appropriate sites on the exposed membrane. The distribution of the ferritin label is detected on the basis of its iron core with a standard transmission electron microscope. Since large areas of membrane surface can be examined, it is much easier to determine patterns of receptors than would be possible by a reconstruction based on multiple electron micrographs of serially examined thin sections. This technique depends upon the capacity of cells to lyse and form flattened regions of membrane that are thin enough to be examined without embedding and sectioning. Since the labeling of receptor sites on the cell surfaces takes place after the cells have been spread on hypotonic medium and then partially dried on coated grids, the question can be raised whether rearrangements might take place in the membrane during one of these steps. To the best of our knowledge, this possibility has not been excluded.

Most, if not all, of the evidence supporting "fluidity" or rotational and translational mobility of lipid in the bilayer is derived from the use of external probes (Table II). Examples of such techniques are ESR spectroscopy of spin-labeled probe molecules, optical spectroscopy of chromophore-labeled probe molecules, and fluorescence in microscopy of antibody-labeled membrane. This evidence suggests that it is reasonable to consider the nature of inter- and intramolecular motion. The evidence, however, is somewhat indirect in the sense that they require the incorporation of an extrinsic probe molecule into the host membrane as an "impurity," and this may perturb the local environment in the host to varying extents depending on the physicochemical nature of the probe and its environment in the membrane. Such probes, therefore, "see" some approximation to the natural membrane; the less perturbation the probe provides, the better the approximation. The probes may be localized selectively in an atypical environment of higher "fluidity" or they may perturb the organization of at least the neighboring membrane components. Also, based on these considerations, the probe, whether a spin label or fluorescent antibody, may not be uniformly distributed over the membrane (Butler *et al.*, 1974) even though it may appear to cover the whole cell under light microscope.

Keith *et al.* (1973) and Bieri *et al.* (1974) have raised serious reservations about the use of data derived from these probes. Indeed, physicochemical studies have provided definite evidence that, even in the presence of 1 mole percent of the probe, the lipid organization in the bilayer is significantly perturbed and "fluidized" (Jain *et al.*, 1975). Similarly, monolayer studies of spin-labeled fatty acids have shown that the nitroxide group has a tendency to orient at the air/water interface (Tinoco *et al.*, 1972; Cadenhead and Muller-Landau, 1973). Even more significantly, natural-abundance ^{13}C–NMR studies on various isolated and intact biomembranes show broad-line spectra indicative of a rather immobilized state of lipids (Metcalfe *et al.*, 1971; Darke *et al.*, 1972; Levine *et al.*, 1972a,b; Williams *et al.*, 1973). These studies suggest that at least 80% of the lipid in biomembranes has rotational correlation times that are larger by at least a factor of 100 (maybe 1000) than the highest values obtained from spin labels and fluorescent probes. The correlation times, which express the reorientational motion of the rotor axis and the rotation about the axis, have been estimated to be $\sim 10^{-6.5}$ and 10^{-10} seconds, respectively (Chan *et al.*, 1971). Similarly, the entropy change calculated from the order parameter (Hubbell and McConnell, 1971) measured by the use of spin labels in bilayers is consistently smaller than the calorimetrically measured entropy changes by a factor of 2 or 3. This systematic deviation suggests that the environment of the spin label is considerably more fluid than the bilayers matrix as a whole.

The lateral diffusion constant (D) for both lipids and proteins in bio-membranes, bilayer, and monolayers has been found to be in the range 10^{-13} to 10^{-8} cm^2 sec^{-1} (Table II). Theoretical calculations based on the theory of time-dependent magnetic interactions and the assumption that the position of a phospholipid in a direction perpendicular to the bilayer surface is constant, yield a value of $D = 2 \times 10^{-8}$ cm^2 sec^{-1} for the phospholipid molecule (Brulet and McConnell, 1975). Both the experimental and theoretical computations are based on the assumption that the effective viscosity of the bilayer is in the range 0.5–10.0 poise. The value of D in bilayers is found to be only slightly dependent upon the lipid composition and temperature. This would imply that the environment, in which the probes used in these measurements are localized, at best represents only limited and maybe atypical regions in the membrane. This would again indicate that spin label does, at least to some extent, make its own liquid domain. Similarly, Abercrombie *et al.* (1970) have proposed that lateral movements in living cell are caused by a rapid flow of the membrane from the leading ruffled edge of cells back to some "sink" in the central area. At the "sink" the membrane material is disassembled, and it is reassembled at the leading edge of the cell. Thus a more likely explanation of mixing in the membrane could be in terms of the circulation of membrane components, perhaps involving microfilaments.

The lateral-diffusion coefficient and the partition coefficient of di-*t*-butyl nitroxide (DTBN) in sonicated aqueous dipalmitolyllecithin vesicles has been studied by ESR spectroscopy at various temperatures (Shimshick *et al.*, 1973; Dix *et al.*, 1974). Although the partition coefficient changed dramatically as a function of temperature, the lateral-diffusion coefficient is affected only slightly. This is consistent with the view that although temperatures below the transition temperature (T_c) "freeze out" DTBN, the environment experienced by residual DTBN in the bilayer remains essentially the same below and above T_c. This would suggest that DTBN is distributed through a larger proportion of hydrocarbon interior above T_c, but below it DTBN is concentrated either at the center of the bilayer (near the terminal methyl group) or it is localized only in certain region(s) in the plane of the bilayer. The fraction of bilayer volume occupied by DTBN would thus increase with increasing temperature and would show an abrupt change around T_c, where the long-range order is altered drastically. It is particularly important to note that the value of the lateral diffusion constant does not change below T_c even though a large portion of lipid is in gel or "solid" form (see below), thus implying that the lateral diffusion occurs through fluid regions which may lie between the solid phase. Movement through such "netlike" structures or "canals" is expected to be much more tortuous.

A significant proportion of evidence suggesting rotational and translational mobility of intramembranous macromolecules in different conditions is derived from the observations on the movement of fluorescent labeled lectins and antibodies, and by the localization of ferritin conjugated antibodies in electron micrographs (Nicolson, 1974). In cells that occur in the unassociated state, the distribution of the surface macromolecules has been found to be either random (diffuse or netlike) distribution giving a spotted or ringlike appearance, or "polar," giving a crescent or caplike appearance over one pole of the cell under light microscope. Thus, short-range order beyond the sensitivity of various techniques may still exist over a several hundred nanometer range. In fact, there is evidence suggesting that the various antigens visualized by electron microscopy of fluorescent lectins or antibodies occur in small isolated or interconnected regions (Stackpole *et al.*, 1971; DiPauli and Bradiczka, 1974). Such a segregation of membrane components could "canalize lateral diffusion of surface antigens" (Petit and Edidin, 1974; Pinto Da Silva, 1972).

Indeed, in nucleated cells, three distinct types of redistributions have been characterized: (a) *patch formation*, which is the passive clustering of cross-linked macromolecules into aggregates; (b) *cap formation*, the polar segregation of the cross-linked molecules from other membrane components, probably dependent on cytoplasmic processes; and (c) *pinocytosis* of the complexes, which in some cases may lead to extensive loss of membrane proteins. These redistributions can be induced and modulated by a variety of agents: antibodies, hormones, lectins, energy poisons, certain specific drugs, and membrane-expanding agents. The nature of the membrane mosaicism is not clear yet, but could exist at either a structural or a molecular level. Edidin (1974) has reviewed evidence suggesting clustering of intramembranous particles under a variety of physiologically relevant conditions (pH, temperature, trypsin treatment, and addition of specific ligands) for a variety of membranes. This includes capping or clustering induced by lectins and antibodies against surface antigens. There is a growing body of evidence that the mobility of antigens and lectin receptors in certain cells may be modulated by cytoplasmic structures and may be related to the functional state of the cell. In such studies of lateral diffusion, it is generally assumed that the interaction of antibodies with surface antigens induces little or no significant change in the membrane organization. It is known that antigen–antibody interaction on membranes causes both specific and general change in membrane permeability, thus implying a change in organization. However, a more direct relationship is implicated by an immediate effect of lectins and cytochalasin B on mediated transport in lymphocytes (Peters and Hausen, 1971) and erythrocytes (Bloch, 1973), respectively. Similarly, a reversible glycerol-induced intramembranous particle clustering has been demonstrated in lymphoid (McIntyre et al., 1973) and Entamoeba histolytica cells (Pinto Da Silva and Martinez-Palomo, 1974). These observations imply that subtle changes in the environment do affect the distribution of particles in membrane.

Much of the recent literature in the lectin receptor field contains conclusions based on the assumption that movement of lectin receptors in transformed mammalian cells is severely impeded when membrane lipids are in the "solid" state (Nicolson, 1973; Chen and Hubbell, 1973; Jan and Revel, 1974). In most of these cases, lowered temperature affects diffusion to a far greater extent than would be predicted from the diffusion equation: $Q_{10} \sim 3$. This is caused by a phase change of some or all membrane lipids. In one well-documented study, however, the diffusion of certain cell surface antigens appears to proceed readily below a temperature where lectin receptor mobility may be impeded (Petit and Edidin, 1974). Yet another enigma is the restriction of cell surface receptor mobility characteristic of normal mammalian cells, but not of their oncogenic transformed counterparts, when membrane lipids are in the fluid state (Rosenblith et al., 1973; Inbar et al., 1973a,b; Shinitzky and Inbar, 1974; Silbert, 1970). Redistribution of surface components has been described where it is independent of membrane lipid fluidity (Karnovsky et al., 1972) or even when membrane proteins are immobilized by cross-linking (Larsen, 1975).

The relationship of the lipid phase to the distribution of membrane proteins as implicated above has several biological consequences (M. H. Johnson *et al.*, 1975). The biochemical consequences of the effect of lipid phase are probably best illustrated by the modulation of catalytic and transport functions by membrane fluidity (for a review, see Fourcans and Jain, 1974). The idea that the lipid composition of plasma membrane is strongly influenced by the growth temperature has received significant support recently (Cronan and Vagelos, 1972). More than a decade ago (Johnston and Roots, 1964), it was suggested that cells must maintain lipids near the critical point of phase transition in order to achieve an appropriate degree of expansibility and solid:liquid ratio. They argued further that varying the degree of fatty acid unsaturation could provide an effective way to preserve this particular state. Indeed, data made available in the last few years not only confirm these suggestions, but also suggest that isolated lipid domains are required for functional membrane assembly.

Escherichia coli and other bacteria vary the fatty acid composition of membrane lipids as a function of the growth temperature (Marr and Ingraham, 1967), presumably to maintain constant membrane viscosity (Sinensky, 1974). As cells are grown at increasingly higher temperatures, there is an increasing tendency to incorporate longer and more saturated fatty acids into phospholipids (Sinensky, 1971), and these phospholipids exhibit progressively higher gel to liquid crystalline phase-transition temperatures. The liposomes made from these lipids with higher fatty acids also show a decreased permeability to nonelectrolytes at a given temperature (Haest *et al.*, 1969). The newly synthesized lipids in *E. coli* seem to randomize rapidly at higher temperatures (Overath *et al.*, 1970). However, at lower temperatures the newly synthesized lipid seems to form a distinct phase, which coexists with the old lipid (Tsukagoshi and Fox, 1973).

It has been noted that the various lipid-activated enzymes and transport systems undergo a sudden change in the activation energy (slope of Arrhenius plot) at a temperature characteristic of the phase-transition temperature of the lipid. However, it has been observed that not all the lipid-activated enzymes and transport systems that undergo such a change in activation energy in a given organism do so coincident with the phase transition in lipid (Esfahani *et al.*, 1971; Mavis and Vagelos, 1972; see, however, Esfahani *et al.*, 1972). Moreover, the change in activation energy for some processes is rather sharp, while for others such a change occurs over a wide temperature range (Fourcans and Jain, 1974). Such observations, therefore, suggest that the various functions may be localized in distinct lipidic environment in a membrane (Morrisett *et al.*, 1975; Wisnieski *et al.*, 1974). Such data strongly suggest that lipids may segregate into domains of different fluidity and composition. Wisenieski *et al.* (1974) observed four transitions in *E. coli* membranes for partitioning of spin label. These have been attributed to two independent lateral phase separations of lipids in the inner and outer halves of the bilayer, which presumably requires an asymmetric lipid distribution.

It is particularly important to note that the decrease in apparent activation energy above the phase transition temperature may not necessarily result from a change in the turnover (as would be expected from the considerations of membrane fluidity), but from a change in "affinity" as measured by the Michaelis–Menten constant (Sullivan *et al.*, 1974), thus implying a conformational change at the active site.

In summary, the data on both the distribution and function of membrane proteins indicate that the environment in which various membrane proteins are localized in the same membrane is not necessarily identical. Indeed, clustering of membrane proteins and association of proteins with specific lipidic environment is much more frequent than is implicated by the fluid mosaic model. Moreover, such clustering and associations may have yet unappreciated functional significance. Since the clustering and associations are based on weak interactions, none of the techniques available thus far are capable of providing unambiguous evidence for their existence. Moreover, the use of molecular probes in membranes, generally speaking, would tend to disrupt the weak interactions leading to the ordering of components in biomembranes.

IV. Long-Range Organization in Membranes

From the preceding discussion one cannot escape the conclusion that some sort of long-range order in biomembrane may have functional significance. The molecular basis for such an order is probably best appreciated in terms of specificity of intermolecular interaction among membrane components. The nature, extent, and magnitude of such ordering could be estimated from the studies on a variety of phenomenon discussed below.

A. Specific Interactions among Membrane Lipids

Yet another objection to the "fluid-mosaic" model arises from the observed constancy of the difference in the lipid composition of different membranes present in the same cell, especially since there is an interchange and exchange of lipids between various membranes. It seems unlikely that the variation in the lipid composition of different membranes can be explained by dissimilarities in the biosynthetic or degradative capacity of a given membrane for a given type of lipid. However, this difference in composition could arise if proteins and lipids of a given species of membrane showed specificity of intermolecular interaction. A similar explanation would account for the observed asymmetric distribution of several membrane components at the two interfaces (Branton, 1969; Bretscher, 1973).

The evidence summarized in the preceding section leads to the hypothesis that the various components in biomembranes are not randomly distributed. However, the basic assumption implicit in the fluid-mosaic model is that there is little or no specificity of lateral intermolecular interactions among membrane components especially lipids. Owing to a lack of specificity of intermolecular interaction, the membrane components can assume a more-or-less random or homogeneous distribution in the plane of the membrane. In the past decade, a considerable amount of work has been done to understand the noncovalent interactions among various membrane components. The chemical heterogeneity of both lipids and proteins, and participation of lipids at different levels of membrane function, already indicate that it is improbable that any single molecular arrangement accounts for such a multiplicity of functions. There is indeed considerable evidence suggesting that the various membrane components may show varying degrees of specificity in their interactions that may give rise to a difference in the organization in the plane of the membrane. Some of that evidence is summarized below:

1. A variety of lipids show selective mixing in neat phase, whereas other lipids do not cocrystallize. For example, low-angle X-ray diffraction evidence has been presented to suggest that in a mixture in neat phase of monoglucodiglyceride (MGD), diglucodiglyceride (DGD), lecithin, and chlorophyll present in the proportion in which they are present in thylakoid membrane, only DGD interacts selectively with chlorophyll (Kreutz, 1970). The other lipids form a separate matrix. A similar tendency for selective mixing of lipids in sonicated liposomes has been noted (Litman, 1973; Tocanne *et al.*, 1974). Thus in the case of phosphatidylinositol and phosphatidylcholine, ideal mixing is observed in the whole range of concentration (a linear correlation between the initial and the incorporated mole fraction). In phosphatidylethanolamine and phosphatidylcholine liposomes, however, ideal incorporation is observed below 0.2 mole fraction of phosphatidylethanolamine, and a slightly negative deviation from ideality at higher mole fraction. Mole fractions of phosphatidylethanolamine above 0.7 yield unstable preparations that precipitate on standing. The instability of pure and mixed phosphatidylethanolamine vesicles may be a reflection of the formation of a hexagonal phase that is incompatible with the lamellar structure and/or curvature of the sonicated vesicle wall.

2. Extensive experimental evidence has accumulated suggesting a specific interaction between lecithin and cholesterol (for reviews, see Jain, 1975;

Papahadjopoulos, 1974; Rothman, 1973). The structural features of both lipid and cholesterol determine specificity of such interaction.

Such observations suggest that at least a part of lipid molecules may be effectively immobilized in biomembranes. It may be that such local lipid phases affect both the distribution and the function of membrane proteins. The functional significance of bound lipid may be derived from the hypothesis that this lipid may stabilize a catalytically active configuration. Exactly how much of the total lipid content of a membrane will be immobilized in this way remains to be established. A nonuniformity in the binding of lipids in biomembranes can, however, be demonstrated by detergent and solvent extraction (Van Deenen, 1969; Kirkpatrick *et al.*, 1974) and phospholipase treatment (Jain, 1973). It has been known for quite some time that different lipids in a given membrane can be extracted to different extents by a given lipid solvent. Thus red blood cell membrane lipids have been divided into two categories: (1) "loosely" bound lipids that can be extracted by diethyl ether, which is mostly cholesterol and about 50% of the phosphatidylethanolamine and phosphatidylserine; and (2) "strongly bound lipids," which can be extracted only by 3:1 ethanol + ether, consisting of almost all the sphingomyelin and phosphatidylcholine and about 50% of the phosphatidylethanolamine + phosphatidylserine. In red cell, more than 60% of the total lipid appears to be strongly bound. Moreover, these results indicate that similar phospholipid molecules may display different degrees of stability of their binding into the membrane.

Specific intermolecular interaction of certain lipids with proteins or other lipids in membranes may lead to the formation of islands or patches with concentrations different from the average concentration of a given lipid. These patches would show rotational and diffusional mobilities considerably lower than the single unassociated components in the membrane. At present there appears to be evidence accumulating in support of heterogeneity of organization of the biomembrane that presumably arises from specificity of intermolecular interaction of its components. We wish to propose here an alternative model that is not only capable of accommodating all the observations incorporated in the fluid-mosaic model, but also will account for a variety of yet unexplained membrane phenomena. This new model differs from the fluid-mosaic model in several significant ways.

B. COOPERATIVITY AND LONG-RANGE ORGANIZATION OF MEMBRANE COMPONENTS

Spatial interactions generated by a variety of extrinsic and intrinsic factors influence the patterns within an assemblage. Membranes are no exception. Probably one of the most significant concepts in membrane study that has evolved in the last decade is the realization *that the chemical composition and molecular organization of membranes can and do change with changing conditions.* Sometimes this fact has been stated in the form that membranes are dynamic (not static) structures. A set of physicochemical explanations for such changeability remains to be established. One aspect of the dynamics of membrane organization is emphasized by the observations suggesting lateral motion of membrane components. Other observations that bear on the implications of molecular motions and specific interactions form the basis of the rest of this review.

All the biomembranes examined so far contain different lipid classes, and each of these classes has not one, but a variety of, discrete fatty acids associated with it (Ansell *et al.*, 1973). Lecithin, for example, is actually not a compound, but rather a group of compounds, all of which contain the polar phosphatidylcholine group but different fatty-acid chains. Although a stable membrane could be formed from one class of lipids, and probably a functional membrane could contain several classes of lipids with only one fatty acid residue, the significance of such large variability can be appreciated only in terms of interorganelle, intertissue, and interspecies differences, undoubtedly reflecting differences in function, physiology, and environment. The fatty acid composition of membrane phospholipids differs markedly from one tissue to another within the same organism and also from one organelle to other within the same cell. But the fatty acid composition turns out to be remarkably similar in a particular type of tissue or organelle, regardless of species. In contrast, the fatty acid composition of glycerides, which serve mainly as a nutritional reserve, shows noticeable differences from one species to another but much similarity in different tissues from the same species. Thus, the correct lipid composition is presumably necessary for optimal functioning of the membrane.

A rationale for this variability can be found in terms of organizational constraints and specificity of intermolecular interaction between various membrane components. It has been known for quite some time that bacteria grown at a lower temperature or the organisms adapted to a colder climate have membrane lipids containing more unsaturated and shorter-chain fatty acids. This adaptation seems to counteract changes in rates of physiological and biochemical functions, such as permeability and transport, that a change in temperature may bring about (for a review, see Fourcans and Jain, 1974). Some clues to the significance of these variations in membrane fatty acids have come from studies on model membranes. Generally speaking, the temperature range of the gel-to-liquid crystalline phase transition of these membrane lipids encompasses the growth temperature of the organism, so that lipids in both gel and liquid crystalline phases are present.

An aqueous dispersion of phospholipid containing only one molecular species shows a characteristic heating and cooling profile with a transition that depends upon the nature of the polar group and the fatty acyl chain length. For dipalmitoylphosphatidylcholine, a sharp transition occurs at 41.6°C and can be detected by a variety of methods. Experiments with phospholipids that differ only in the nature of their fatty acid chains have established that the transition temperature is dependent on chain length, degree of unsaturation, and branching. This cooperative endothermic transition is best explained in terms of a change in the organization of the poly-methylene chains. Below the transition temperature the lipid exists in a *gel* phase characterized by an all-trans orientation of the chains. Above the transition temperature the lipid chains exist in *liquid crystalline* phase, characterized by a mixed gauche–trans conformation of the chains. This later arrangement confers a certain disorder and mobility, the methyl end of the chain having greatest motion. As expected, such a disorder can be introduced internally by shortening the length of the acyl chain, by the presence of trans or cis double bonds or branching in the acyl chains, or by the incorporation of an agent in between the chain such as cholesterol. Such disordering would be reflected in a lowering of the phase-transition temperature.

Coexistence of ordered and disordered states can be best demonstrated by a typical heat capacity-temperature curve (Ladbrook and Chapman, 1969; Oldfield and Chapman, 1972; Oldfield, 1973). These curves show transitions that range from broad, often indistinct, changes in cell plasma membrane, to the sharp, cooperative transitions characteristic of pure phospholipid dispersions in water. Such transitions correspond to a progressive clustering of phospholipid molecules into domains of solid-phase components with the eventual solidification of the entire membrane at lower temperature. Pure lipids, particularly saturated ones, give relatively sharp transitions that extend only a few degrees corresponding to a highly cooperative transition. This is the case even with a mixture containing lipids of different chain length. These mixtures apparently cocrystallize below the phase-transition temperature to give a series of solid solutions (Phillips *et al.*, 1970, 1972; Chapman *et al.*, 1974). When the difference of chain length between lecithins is increased to four methylene groups, monotectic behavior without cocrystallization becomes apparent. It has been suggested that several transition temperatures can be defined in mixed lipid bilayers in which certain classes of lipid molecules coaggregate and solidify when cooled, leaving other lipids in fluid state. Thus, while the lattice arrangement can accommodate small differences in chain length so that cocrystallization occurs, with greater differences in chain length, as the system is cooled, migration of lipid molecules within a given bilayer occurs to give regions corresponding to the two separate components.

The evidence for coherently packed domains in a bilayer—that is, for coexistence of several phases or "lateral phase separation" in mixed lipid bilayers—has been obtained by a variety of techniques including freeze-fracture electron microscopy (Shimshick *et al.*, 1973; Verkleij *et al.*, 1972, 1974; Ververgaert *et al.*, 1972, 1973a,b; Klecman and McConnell, 1974; Grant *et al.*, 1974; Kleeman and McConnell, 1974; Shimshick and McConnell, 1973a,b), differential scanning calorimetry (Chapman *et al.*, 1974; Stein *et al.*, 1969; McElhaney, 1974; Melchior *et al.*, 1970; Stein *et al.*, 1969; Ladbrook *et al.*, 1968; Ladbrook and Chapman, 1969; Muhlradt *et al.*, 1974), reflectivity measurements (Pagano *et al.*, 1973), X-ray diffraction studies (Gulik-Krzywicki *et al.*, 1967; Levine, 1973), and selected reflection dark-field electron microscopy (Hui and Parsons, 1974, 1975; Hui *et al.*, 1974). All these studies suggest that the mixed lipid bilayers may consist of domains in the gel phase that are typically up to several micrometers in diameter; that is, the cooperative unit may contain up to several hundred molecules.

Little information about the extent of coherently packed domains in a bilayer has been obtained from X-ray diffraction because of the large diameter of the X-ray beam. Elastic-scattering experiments involving X-ray and neutron diffraction cannot, in general, distinguish between the ensemble-average of a frozen statistically disordered structure and a dynamical structure whose time-average is identical to the ensemble-average of the frozen structure (Hoseman and Bagchi, 1962). If the areas of continuously striated surface seen in freeze-fracture electron micrographs are regarded as domains, the domains would measure from a fraction of micrometer to several micrometers across, depending on the material, the cooling rate, and the quenching temperature of the membrane (Grant *et al.*, 1974; Ververgaert *et al.*, 1973a,b; Haest *et al.*, 1974). These domains have been visualized directly under physiological conditions by dark-field electron microscopy (Hui and Parsons, 1975). The domains of dipalmitoyllecithin bilayers measured by this method are typically several micrometers wide below phase-transition temperature. No domain structure was observed above T_c. In bilayers of an equimolar mixture of dipalmitoyl- and dilauroyllecithin, the domains are typically 300 nm wide at temperatures between the two transitions. Similarly, in mixtures of dipalmitoyllecithin plus cholesterol the domains had ribbonlike structures, the size of which varied with the composition.

Coexistence of separate phases would give rise to broad-phase transition characteristics of low cooperativity as observed for *Acholesplasma laidlawii* B and *Escherichia coli* membranes (Stein *et al.*, 1969; McElhaney, 1974; Melchior *et al.*, 1970). Thus coexistence of several phases (monotectic behavior) has been noted in pure dipalmitoylcholine (Hui and Parsons, 1974; Muhlradt *et al.*, 1974), lecithin plus cholesterol (Trauble and Sackmann, 1972; Darke *et al.*, 1972; DeKruyff *et al.*, 1973; Verkleij *et al.*, 1974), and sarcoplasmic reticulum membrane (Scandella *et al.*, 1972). Lateral phase separation in mixed monolayers of phosphatidylcholines of different chain lengths has also been observed at the phase transition (Taylor *et al.*, 1973).

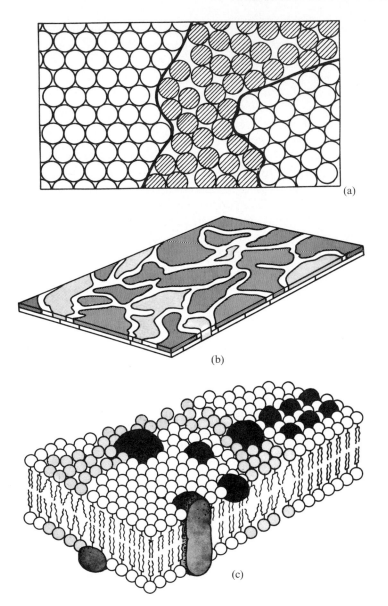

(a)

(b)

(c)

All these observations strongly suggest that at physiological temperatures mixed lipids in a bilayer may exist in domains and these domains differ significantly in their composition and organizational characteristics.

V. The "Plate Model" of Membrane Structure

Many features of membrane phenomena can be explained by viewing the membrane assemblage as a spatial and temporal mosaic of small-scale aggregated systems, recognizing that the individual component plates, islands, or patches are not necessarily closed. They could be part of an integrated patchwork with individual plates constantly exchanging materials directly or indirectly. The basic hypothesis that we wish to propose here is that *the biomembrane continuum is broken up into a number of relatively rigid plates or patches that are in relative motion with respect to each other*. In general, a patch is taken to mean a bounded, connected discontinuity in a homogeneous reference background that may consist of either single or multiple components. No restrictions *a priori* are imposed with regard to its size, its period of persistence, its invasibility or species composition, or its topographical location. Modeling of the structure of such systems essentially rests upon the processes underlying the structure, that is, on the development of spatial heterogeneity. The ordered and rigid regions may be separated from each other by relatively fluid and disordered regions. The separation of ordered and relatively disordered regions is lateral in two dimensions and could occur in two monolayer halves of the bilayer. These regions are contiguous and in equilibrium. A model based on this hypothesis is schematically indicated in Fig. 6. A superficial analogy to this may be found in the celebrated plate-tectonics model for continental drift.

FIG. 6. Structural framework of typical biomembrane in various degrees of schematization. (a) Organized lipid molecules (white circles) may form discrete plates that are separated from each other by regions of relatively disorganized lipids (hatched circles). The composition and the resulting system properties of such regions may be quite different.

(b) The organized and disorganized regions are viewed as plates, each having characteristic system properties specified by its components. Some plates may extend through the bilayer. The size, shape, and lifetime of plates and the mobility, exchange rate, and residence times of components within these plates has not been defined. However, these parameters are expected to vary significantly from plate to plate and from membrane to membrane. The size of the plates may, for example, be up to several thousand molecular diameters.

(c) Various molecules (within the bilayer of biomembrane) interact hydrophobically and are distributed asymmetrically. Moreover, there is also a distinct long-range organization (over several hundred molecular diameters) of both lipids and proteins. Thus bilayers with distinct organizational features and composition may coexists within the plane of a biomembrane. These organizational changes may arise from distinct molecular conformations and specificity (or lack of it) of intermolecular interactions among components.

The problem of correlating membrane function to its structure can be looked upon in terms of not only the structure of the components mediating the function, but also the system properties of the membrane that will be determined by the relative populations of components in various plates, the size of plates, the lifetime of the plates, rate of movement of the plates, possibility of long-range cooperativity within plates, cooperative modulation by interaction of plates, residence time of components within a plate, rate of exchange of components between the plate and the fluid region. It is implicit that the intrinsic mobility of components (gauche–trans, segmental, transverse, rotational, and lateral) would depend upon their localization in the fluid region or on a given patch.

A. DISTINCTIVE FEATURES OF THE MODEL

The distinctive features of the model proposed herein arise from the (postulated) specificity of intermolecular interaction among membrane components. On one extreme, such interactions would give rise to a long-range order resulting in a two-dimensional ordered matrix. On the other extreme, a complete lack of such interactions would result in a homogeneous and random distribution of the components (as articulated in the fluid-mosaic model). The transition temperature marks the disappearance of long-range order, although correlation among near neighbors may persist above the transition. The relative distribution of components for most biomembranes may fall somewhere in between; that is, the components interacing specifically with each other would be organized as "plates"; and those that cannot interact would give rise to disorganized regions. Thus a metastable condition may be produced in which a nonequilibrium disorder is "frozen" in an otherwise organized bilayer. The plates may differ significantly in relative composition, amount, organization, localization, and distribution in the plane of the membrane.

The separation of ordered regions (plates) from the disordered regions (fluid) is a natural consequence of specific intermolecular interaction and lattice deformation. The formation of a disordered zone in the plane of a bilayer can be visualized as a crystallization of solids from an impure solution. Only molecules that fit into a crystal lattice would be part of the organized structure. Others may form a separate lattice or remain in a disorganized region. The molecules in disorganized regions are less ordered in the plane of the membrane and have greater segmental, rotational, and lateral mobilities. The molecules in the ordered as well as in the disordered regions are, however, anisotropically oriented. Thus the arrangement of components in plates may be in a two-dimensional close-packed lattice with identical or equivalent units, whereas in the disordered state the units may be more or less randomly organized. However, even in the organized state several types of defect structures are encountered. These include point defects or vacancies, dislocations or subgrain boundaries (Bonart *et al.*, 1963; Smith, 1964; Sworakowski, 1973; Williams, 1975). On the other extreme, clustering of molecules has been detected in various liquids near their freezing points (Horne, 1969) and in liquid crystals (De Vries, 1970). Indeed, computer simulation of a model for an orientation distribution pattern of units in a two-dimensional lattice can generate nonrandom patterns under conditions of thermal fluctuations (Maruyama and Oosawa, 1975). The functional significance of defect structures in the context of membrane structure and function remains to be established (however, see below). Such defect regions would be preferred sites for the incorporation of impurities, and these regions could act as "channels" along which diffusion is greatly enhanced (Nabarro, 1967). In fact, two lateral diffusion coefficients, one $\sim 10^{-11}$ cm^2 sec^{-1} and other $\sim 10^{-5}$ cm^2 sec^{-1}, have been detected in naphthalene crystals (Sherwood and White, 1967). The higher diffusion coefficient is attributed to crystal defects.

Formation of disorganized regions in the plane of a bilayer can occur for a variety of reasons. The driving force for such deformations could be due to either a lack of specificity of intermolecular interaction to the state of stress (compressive and/or tensile forces—for example, those arising from conformational changes), or to accommodate deformations of surface topography. Thus a *biomembrane can be visualized as a disturbed crystalline phase* (*rather than amorphous liquidlike phase*) *in which progressive loss of perfect translational periodicity has occurred.*

B. Functional Significance of Plate Formation

The concept of long-range order refers to the regular states of condensed matter. Periodic organization of particles in biomembranes has been demonstrated by a variety of techniques. Of particular interest are the observations that in certain membranes (synaptic membranes, gap and septate junctions between cells, endoplasmic reticulum, mitochondrial membrane, certain axon membranes) a periodic organization is revealed by high-resolution electron microscopy (Robertson, 1963; Nilson, 1964; Revel and Karnovsky, 1967; Gemne, 1969; Green, 1972). Indeed, long-range order in biomembranes has been invoked to suggest the possibility of long-range cooperativity to account for certain membrane phenomena, such as excitability (Wyman, 1969). These situations may represent only one end of the spectrum of possibilities. On the other extreme one can envision certain areas or folds in the same membrane where the lipid bilayer would be essentially free of any proteins. Such arrangements could accompany the morphological changes in the cell, which may require areas of large and small radii of curvature. The coexistence of several phases could also account for the high viscosity of cell membranes estimated from mechanical deformation of whole cells (Rand, 1968; Weiss and Clement, 1968; Hiramoto, 1970). However, this high viscosity is non-Newtonian, that is, the membrane changes as the forces acting on it vary. In terms of the plate model, this thixotropic behavior is a consequence of shifting equilibria between the phases that coexist. These viscoelastic properties, therefore, should strongly depend upon the rate of change of shear as well as on the shearing force, as is indeed the case (Curtis, 1961).

The relationship of cell movement to cell surface events has also suggested segregation of certain membrane sites. In studying this problem, a number of factors can be distinguished: local movement of cell surface receptors (diffusion and patch formation), global movements of these receptors (capping), local morphological changes (microvillus formation, blebbing, and ruffling), global morphological changes altering cell shape, and translocation of the whole cell. As pointed out earlier in support of the fluid-mosaic model, it has been shown that the distribution of glycoprotein receptors for lectins such as concanavalin A (Con A) and specific surface antigens as visualized by fluorescent antibodies is random in most cell types. However, nonrandom distribution of specific lectin binding sites or antigens can be induced in a variety of cells (for reviews, see Edidin, 1974; Singer, 1974). Such changes are strongly temperature and pH dependent, are inhibited by energy poisons like azide, and appear to be due to structural or metabolic changes in the surface membrane (Inbar et al., 1971, 1973a,b; Shinitzky and Inbar, 1974). The selective segregation and disappearance of specific surface determinants induced by specific agents (antibody, lectin, etc.) imply that at least some membrane components can move relative to one another. In certain cases this could arise from the phase properties of lipids. In fact, studies on E. coli suggest that the beginning of a phase-separation of membrane lipids lies in the temperature range in which the particle distribution changes from netlike to one of nearly complete particle aggregation (Kleeman and McConnell, 1974). In the course of the phase separation, the particles are initially excluded from the growing solid patches and collected into aggregates. The patterns of distribution of particles in the membrane seem to have functional significance. Above the temperature at which the phase separation begins, the particles are randomly distributed over the entire membrane. Similar behavior has been observed in *Tetrahymena* (Speth and Wunderlich, 1973; Wunderlich et al., 1975), liposomes treated with rhodopsin (Chen and Hubbell, 1973), mouse spermatozoa (Stackpole and Devorkin, 1974), and *Bacillus stearothermophilus* (Esser and Souza, 1974).

The molecular basis for increased mobility of the cell surface is still obscure. A direct effect on the viscosity of membranes as manifested in the gross lipid composition can be essentially ruled out. In terms of the plate model, trypsin- or virus-induced transformation or antibody-induced cap formation and pinocytosis could accompany a change in relative distribution of plate population and composition, thus changing the microenvironment of the receptor sites. Redistribution of plate population could, of course, alter other membrane characteristics, such as permeability and mediated transport properties. Such a redistribution of plates could also be brought about by other membrane components (Edelman *et al.*, 1973; Berlin *et al.*, 1974; Taylor *et al.*, 1971; Wessels *et al.*, 1971), or by cytoplasmic effectors of intramembrane mobility (Edelman *et al.*, 1973; Berlin *et al.*, 1974; Taylor *et al.*, 1971; Wessels *et al.*, 1971), or by a change in membrane surface electrostatic profile (Stackpole *et al.*, 1972). In any event the effective local membrane viscosity will be determined by relative distribution of lipid in plates and in disorganized regions.

In intact biomembranes, the interpretation of the effect of temperature (and other perturbations such as change in pH, drugs, electrical potential, and ionic concentration) is very complex. Such changes could induce (a) aggregation or segregation of membrane components, (b) liquid crystalline to gel phase (or reverse) transition, (c) conformational changes in membrane components, and (d) clustering of lipids and proteins into distinct phases.

The complexity of the states of various membrane components is presumably related to a wide variety of functions that the biomembrane is required to perform. The presence of different phases in a membrane would lead to high lateral compressibility, leading in turn to a control on conformation of membrane proteins. The disordered regions present at the boundaries between different phases could segregate certain components in a more fluid environment or could act as nucleation sites for growth and repair of the membrane. Aggregated proteins would also have advantages of specific interaction, high collision rates, and fast movements in two dimensions. All these factors are expected to have molecular and physiological significance, especially in functions related to transport, permeability, fusion, and aggregation. An indication for these can be obtained from the following observations.

1. In liposomes prepared from synthetic lecithin, under the conditions of lateral phase separation there is an enhanced permeability of ions (Vanderkooi and Martonosi, 1971). This increase in permeability depends on both the properties of the permeating compounds and the length of the hydrocarbon chains. It could also be due to the passage of ions at the boundaries of liquid and solid domains (Block *et al.*, 1975). Indeed a maximum permeability for ions has been observed when gel and liquid crystalline are present in equal amounts, i.e., at the transition temperature (Papahadjopoulos *et al.*, 1973). Similarly, a pronounced increase in ionophore-induced permeability around the phase transition temperature of lipid has been

observed in liposomes (Wu and McConnell, 1973) and black lipid membranes (Krasne *et al.*, 1971; Stark *et al.*, 1972). Similar results have been reported recently by Marsh *et al.* (1976) on the permeability of a spin-labeled choline derivative.

2. The permeability of egg-lecithin liposomes for water as a function of the mole fraction of cholesterol shows a biphasic response (Jain *et al.*, 1973). The permeability for water increases to a maximum as cholesterol is added to a mole fraction of about 0.1; with more cholesterol the permeability falls, and at a mole fraction of about 0.3 is back to the level observed in the absence of cholesterol; beyond this point there is a further steep reduction in permeability. If the permeability for water is greater at the phase boundaries, then at low cholesterol concentrations one would expect increased permeability if the lecithin and cholesterol (2:1) phase is separated from the lecithin phase. The cholesterol content at the permeability maximum may reflect the relative sizes and the permeabilities of the two phases.

3. A variety of drugs are known to increase the fluidity of the bilayer and/or cause phase separation (Seeman, 1972; Jain *et al.*, 1975). These drugs may, therefore, affect a variety of membrane functions that depend upon the pattern of distribution of proteins on membrane surface, such as susceptibility of untransformed cells to agglutination by lectins (Poste *et al.*, 1975a; Lustig *et al.*, 1975; Ferguson *et al.*, 1975) and membrane fusion (Kosower *et al.*, 1975; Van der Bosch and McConnell, 1975; Papahadjopoulos *et al.*, 1974). Similarly, a number of proteins have been shown to induce phase transition (Papahadjopoulos *et al.*, 1975).

4. Phase separation or plate formation in the plane of the membrane could be an important factor in the rapid alteration of membrane protein conformation (see p. 33)

5. Enzymic hydrolysis of pure lecithin is rapid only near its transition temperature. Both below and above this transition the hydrolysis occurs at a much lower rate (Op den Kamp *et al.*, 1974, 1975). Studies with pure and mixed liposomes suggest that the action of the phospholipase A_2 is strongly enhanced by irregularities in lipid packing in the bilayer when both gel and liquid crystalline phases coexist. Activation of phospholipase A- and C-mediated hydrolysis of lecithin liposomes by *n*-alkanols (Jain and Cordes, 1973a,b) can also be rationalized in terms of increased irregularity resulting from an increased number of plates. The *n*-alkanol-induced increase in the phase boundary is also reflected in an increase in water permeability of doped liposomes (Jain *et al.*, 1973).

6. The orientation of polar groups at the lipid/water interface in the bilayer leads to an electrostatic field that will extend into the surrounding water. This field may be perturbed either by changing the electrical potential (White, 1970a,b) or ionic concentration (see below). The effect of electrical potential on the bilayer organization is not very well understood; however, the effects

are expected to be similar to those induced by ions. The effect of the electrical double layer on thermal-phase transition is seen in studies of pH dependence (Trauble and Eibl, 1974). Increasing ionization causes a decrease in transition temperature. The reason is simply that the electrostatic free energy of the bilayer in the liquid crystalline phase is smaller than in the gel phase, so that an increase in surface charge will favor the liquid crystalline phase.

7. The interactions of metal ions with the lipid bilayer have been shown to have important effects on the packing of the lipid molecules in the bilayer. They strongly suggest that divalent ions are adsorbed onto specific sites on the membranes, whereas the alkali metal ions probably are not. The divalent ions have been shown to increase the phase-transition temperature not only for the acidic phospholipids (Trauble and Eibl, 1974), but also for dipalmitoyl-lecithin, a zwitterionic phospholipid (Fig. 7). These data demonstrate not

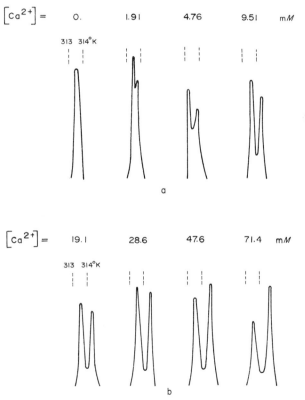

FIG. 7. Heat change vs. temperature profiles (by differential scanning calorimeter) of dipalmitoyllecithin liposomes (65 mM) doped with various concentrations of CaCl^2. The buffer also contained 100 mM KCl and 10 mM Tris Cl$^-$ at pH 7.4. These results show that Ca^{2+} induced a phase separation within bilayer. The new phase apparently consists of a complex of Ca^{2+} with phosphatidylcholine.

only that Ca^{2+} interacts at specific sites, but that the new higher melting phase coexists with the original phase. Indeed, Ca^{2+}-induced separation in mixed lipid bilayers, in which at least one component is acidic, has been demonstrated in several laboratories (see p. 49).

8. Regions of highly ordered but inhomogeneous arrangements, such as domains or plates in bilayer, could be prime movers for processes involving membrane fusion. This is implied in the studies where membrane fusion is induced by agents that cause the formation of smaller plates (e.g., see Jain and Wu, 1977). Existence of domains as prelude to fusion has also been demonstrated in heliozoan axopods (Bardele, 1976). A discussion of the functional significance of such "frozen" membrane domains is also presented by this paper.

C. SOME CONSEQUENCES AND PREDICTIONS

The behavior of a phase containing "clusters" of structurally distinct polymorphs (the plates) would be quite characteristic. In analogy to the behavior of glass (Goodman, 1975), on progressive lowering of the temperature, such a mix would not behave like the melt of a solid. Instead, the mixed-cluster associations may result in a persistent, continuous, bonded network, leaving many of the boundaries of the clusters nonbonded and with the material between them still "liquidlike," even though the system as a whole would behave now like "locked up solid." Such a system would, therefore, have a "memory"; that is, its behavior would be determined by its history. This model suggests some interesting consequences and predictions:

1. A mixed-plate matrix would predict that different components have different mobilities. The existence of material with different mobilities should be amenable to direct verification. For example, the movement of gold particles on the surface of 3T3 mouse fibroblasts can be characterized by two diffusion coefficients: a slow motion with $D \simeq 2 \times 10^{-11}$ cm^2 sec^{-1}, and a faster motion with $D \simeq 2 \times 10^{-10}$ cm^2 sec^{-1} (Albrecht-Buhler, 1973).

2. The mixed-plate model suggests that the edges of the cluster should have properties distinct from those of component phases. These irregularities could modify insertion, distribution, mobility, orientation, and conformation of components and solute permeability characteristics of the bilayer (see below). NMR (Salsbury and Chapman, 1968) and X-ray diffraction studies (Engelman, 1971) suggest the presence of disordered regions that coexist with otherwise ordered regions in the gel state of bilayers and *Acholeplasma* membrane.

3. A mixed-plate matrix may be more stable to compressions, stresses, and strains than either of the pure solid or liquid phases. For a membrane to form an irregular closed surface, it cannot have a perfect two-dimensional

lattice. A perfectly solid membrane would tend to be planar, and a homogeneous liquid membrane would tend to be spherical. A living cell not only has distinctly nonspherical shape, but it also undergoes morphological changes in its life cycle. The forces arising from incorporation or removal of new components and morphological processes can be best accommodated in a mixed-plate matrix.

4. It has been pointed out by Linden *et al.* (1973) that, over the temperature range for which gel and liquid crystalline phases coexist, the system will exhibit large fluctuations. In a single pure phase, fluctuations in any thermodynamic property about its mean value will be very small. In a two-phase equilibrium, the fluctuations will be large, because the property can range between the two extreme values appropriate to the separate phases. It can be shown that the isothermal compressibility is related to fluctuations of density in the system (Hill, 1956; Williams, 1975). Thus for a first-order transition (e.g., gel to liquid crystalline), the smaller the cooperative unit, the broader the temperature range over which both phases coexist. However, the smaller the cooperative unit, the smaller will be the fluctuations.

5. Membrane volume expansion studies (dilatometry) should show breaks in thermal expansion curves for biomembranes. The effect of pressure on these curves may also provide some information about compressibility of a mixed-cluster matrix. Measurements on partition coefficients as a function of temperature would also provide similar information. For example, Lee *et al.* (1974) have calculated that about 50% of the lipid may be present in clusters in dioleoyllecithin bilayer at 2°C, that is 24°C above its phase-transition temperature.

6. Several drugs that modify membrane phase-transition characteristics would also influence localization of receptors (Lustig *et al.*, 1975; Ferguson *et al.*, 1975), which in turn may influence agglutinability, aggregation, and mitogenesis.

7. Microviscosity experienced by the various components in the same membrane could be different.

8. Phase separations may be induced by a variety of chemical agents, such as Ca^{2+} ions (Rand and Sengupta, 1972; Ito *et al.*, 1975; Ohnishi and Ito, 1974; Ito and Ohnishi, 1974); (Fig. 7), polylysine (Galla and Sackmann, 1975a,b; Papahadjopoulos *et al.*, 1974, 1975), and drugs such as ketamine and 1-aminoadamantane derivatives (Jain and Wu, unpublished). In principle, a similar phase change may be induced by changes in the membrane potential.

9. Within each plate the molecules are relatively constrained, and only the short-range perturbations would affect the local mobilities (kinks, thermal vibrations, vacancies, dislocations, or substituted fixed crystals). In addition to the short-range and point defects centered around fixed lattice sites, some

entirely different long-range disturbances leading to the two-dimensional fluid structure are also possible. These disturbances are expected to be quite mobile, and the external stress required to move a dislocation would be quite small. Clusters of disordered molecules could arise as a result of condensation of "defect" structures under various conditions of stress and temperature. These conditions could, for example, arise from changes in interfacial tension, membrane potential, surface-charge profile, ionic concentration, and topographical deformation.

VI. Epilogue

According to Jean-Paul Sartre, "Everything we see and experience impels us to say, this can't last! And yet change is not even conceivable, except in the form of a cataclysm." In spite of such fears, all disciplines of knowledge have assimilated new ideas from time to time. There has not yet been a dearth of new ideas in membrane biology, and quite a few of these have been articulated in membrane models. It must, however, be emphasized that the models are to be used, but not to be believed. The structural and organizational concepts encountered in these models are:

1. Organization in two dimensions (lipid bilayer) as a general theme

2. Membrane components held together mostly by weak noncovalent forces

3. Specific intermolecular interactions among membrane components giving rise to selective ordering and segregation of components

4. Functional and morphological asymmetry of interfaces

5. Slow exchange of components from one interface to the other

6. Possible diffusional mobility of components (not necessarily for all components) in the plane of the membrane

7. Flexing of polymethylene chains and their oscillation about an axis perpendicular to the plane of the membrane (segmental motion), which increases toward the center of the membrane

8. Possible rotation of components about the axis perpendicular to the bilayer

9. Regions of discontinuity and mismatch in the plane of the membrane due to phase separation and coexistence of various lipid phases

10. Short-range order and cooperativity within the membrane that may be modulated by temperature, small molecules, ions, and membrane potential

From the available evidence there is little doubt of the existence of substructure within membranes. Similarly, various types of molecular motions within bilayers have strong experimental support. However, both the extent and magnitude of the substructure and molecular motions within biomembranes remains to be established. We propose that the protein and lipid components of biological membranes are partitioned into functional and structural aggregates in the plane of the membrane. This plate model for biomembranes bears superficial resemblance to the crustal plates of the earth's surface and is in contrast to the fluid-mosaic model of membranes, in which lipids and proteins are more or less randomly distributed. The state of the molecules in these plate domains, as described by such terms as mobility, fluidity, and organization, is relative and is described arbitrarily in the context of a two-dimensional phase. However, the organizational variability within the plane of the biomembrane and relatively restricted mobilities of most biomembrane components is emphasized as a working model. The phenomenological and molecular basis of differential organization within the plane of the biomembrane is provided by a hypothesis invoking specificity (or lack of it) of intermolecular interaction among various membrane components. A quantitative description of certain aspects of this model, such as molecular motions and molecular organization, is possible, at least in principle, on the basis of energetics of these interactions and the geometrical features of the component molecules. Similarly, it may be possible with available techniques to determine within an order of magnitude, the various parameters characterizing different domains. The "plate domain" model, therefore, offers explanations for a wide range of properties of biomembranes and can also be used to predict interesting new possibilities. It is, however, only a descriptive approach and obviously requires detailed development before it could be used in any but the crudest manner.

The coexistence of plates of differing composition within the plane of the biomembrane could play a part in component distribution under a variety of physiological and pharmacological conditions. Recent studies have suggested the possibility that the cytoplasmic processes (microtubules and microfilaments) may regulate the motion and distribution of certain membrane proteins. There is intense research activity directed toward understanding the tethering of membrane proteins by the cytoplasmic matrix. Although there are distinct biological advantages to the lateral motion of membrane components, there are situations where a mechanism for controlling the distribution and mobility of membrane components within the membrane milieu is essential. This balance between freedom and control is provided in our model by segregation/aggregation modulated by the phase change and separation of lipids. The functional significance of phase segregation and aggregation of membrane components is far-reaching. It may provide a phenomenological basis for various membrane processes and regulatory mechanisms, including the role of Ca^{2+}, excitability phenomenon, mode of action of certain drugs and hormones, cell adhesion, surface antigenicity, and neoplastic transformation.

Acknowledgments

We wish to express our sincere thanks to Dr. Robert Bittman (CUNY) and Drs. Karl and Lynda Koehler (University of North Carolina) for suggestions and critical reading.

References

Abercrombie, M. J., Heaysman, E. M., and Pegrum, S. M. (1970). *Exp. Cell Res.* **62**, 389–398.

Albrecht-Buhler, G. (1973). *Exp. Cell Res.* **78**, 67–70.

Ansell, G. B., Hawthorne, J. N., and Dawson, R. M. C. (1973). "Form and Function of Phospholipids." Elsevier, Amsterdam.

Bahadur, K. (1966). "Synthesis of Jeewanu the Protocell." Ram Narain Lal, Beni and Sons, Prasad, Allahabad, India.

Bar, R. S., Deamer, D. W., and Cornwell, D. G. (1966). *Science* **153**, 1010–1012.

Bardele, C. F. (1976). *Z. Naturforsch.* **31C**, 190–194.

Benson, A. A. (1966). *J. Am. Oil Chem. Soc.* **43**, 265–270.

Benz, R., Fröhlich, O., Läuger, P., and Montal, M. (1975). *Biochim. Biophys. Acta* **394**, 323–334.

Berlin, R. D., Oliver, J. M., Ukena, T. E., and Lin, H. H. (1974). *Nature (London)* **247**, 45–46.

Bieri, V. G., Wallach D. F. H., and Lin P. S. (1974). *Proc. Natl. Acad. Sci. U.S.A.* **71**, 4797–4801.

Blaurock, A. E. (1972). *Chem. Phys. Lipids* **8**, 285–289.

Blaurock, A. E., and Stoekenius, W. (1971). *Nature (London), New Biol.* **233**, 152–155.

Bloch, R. (1973). *Biochemistry* **12**, 4799–4801.

Block, M. C., Van Der Neut-Kok, E. C. M., Van Deenen, L. L. M., and DeGier, J. (1975). *Biochim. Biophys. Acta* **406**, 187–196.

Bonart, R., Hoseman, R., and McCullough, R. L. (1963). *Polymer* **4**, 199–211.

Brack, A., and Orgel, L. E. (1975). *Nature (London)* **256**, 383–387.

Branton, D. (1966a). *Proc. Natl. Acad. Sci. U.S.A.* **55**, 1048–1056.

Branton, D. (1966b). *Exp. Cell Res.* **45**, 703–707.

Branton, D. (1969). *Annu. Rev. Plant Physiol.* **20**, 209–238.

Branton, D. (1971). *Phil. Trans. R. Soc. London, Ser. B* **261**, 133–138.

Bretscher, M. S. (1972). *Nature (London), New Biol.* **236**, 11–12.

Bretscher, M. S. (1973). *Science* **181**, 622–629.

Bretscher, M. S. (1975). *In* "Perspectives in Membrane Biology" (S. Estrada-O. and C. Gitler, eds.), pp. 3–24. Academic Press, New York.

Brown, P. K. (1972). *Nature (London), New Biol.* **236**, 39–43.

Brulet, P., and McConnell, H. M. (1975). *Proc. Natl. Acad. Sci. U.S.A.* **72**, 1451–1455.

Butler, K. W., Tattrie, N. H., and Smith, I. C. P. (1974). *Biochim. Biophys. Acta* **363**, 351–360.

Cadenhead, D. A., and Muller-Landau, F. (1973). *Biochim. Biophys. Acta* **307**, 279–286.

Calvin, M. (1959). *Rev. Mod. Phys.* **31**, 147–156.

Chan, S. J., Seiter, C. H. A., and Feigeusen, G. W. (1971). *Biochem. Biophys. Res. Commun.* **46**, 1488–1492.

Changeux, J. P., and Thiery, J. (1968). *In* "Regulatory Functions of Biological Membranes" (J. Jarnefelt, ed.), pp. 116–138. Elsevier, Amsterdam.

Changeux, J. P., Thiery, J., Tung, Y., and Kittel, C. (1967). *Proc. Natl. Acad. Sci. U.S.A.* **57**, 335–341.

Chapman, D., Urbina, J., and Keough, K. M. (1974). *J. Biol Chem.* **149**, 2512–2521.

Chen, Y. S., and Hubbell, W. L. (1973). *Exp. Eye Res.* **17**, 517–532.

Cherry, R. J., Burkli, A., Busslinger, M., Schneider, G., and Parish, G. R. (1976). *Nature* **263**, 389–392.

Colacicco, G. (1972). *Ann. N.Y. Acad. Sci.* **195**, 224–261.

Coleman, R., Finean, J. B., Knutton, S., and Limbrick, A. R. (1970). *Biochim. Biophys. Acta* **219**, 81–92.

Cone, R. A. (1972). *Nature (London), New Biol.* **236**, 39–43.

Crane, F. L., and Hall, J. D. (1972). *Ann. N.Y. Acad. Sci.* **195**, 24–34.

Crawford, M. A., and Sinclair, A. J. (1972). "Lipids, Malnutrition and the Developing Brain," pp. 267–292. Elsevier, Amsterdam.

Cronan, J. E., Jr., and Vagelos, P. R. (1972). *Biochim. Biophys. Acta* **265**, 25–60.

Curtis, A. S. G. (1961). *Exp. Cell Res., Suppl.* **8**, 107–122.

Danielli, J. F., and Davson, H. (1935). *J. Cell. Comp. Physiol.* **5**, 495–508.

Danielli, J. F., and Harvey, E. N. (1935). *J. Cell. Comp. Physiol.* **5**, 483–494.

Darke, A., Finer, E. G., Flook, A. G., and Phillips, M. C. (1972). *J. Mol. Biol.* **63**, 265–279.

Davis, D. G. (1972). *Biochem. Biophys. Res. Commun.* **49**, 1492–1497.

Davson, H., and Danielli, J. F. (1943). "The Permeability of Natural Membranes." Cambridge Univ. Press, London and New York.

Deamer, D. W., and Branton, D. (1967). *Science* **158**, 655–657.

DeKruyff, B., Demel, R. A., Slotboom, A. J., Van Deenen, L. L. M., and Rosenthal, A. F. (1973). *Biochim. Biophys. Acta* **307**, 1–19.

Devaux, P., and McConnell, H. M. (1972). *J. Am. Chem. Soc.* **94**, 4475–4481.

DeVries, A. (1970). *Mol. Cryst. Liq. Cryst.* **10**, 219–236.

Dewey, M. M., and Barr, L. (1971). *Curr. Topics Membr. Transp.* **1**, 1–33.

DiPauli, G., and Bradiczka, D. (1974). *Biochim. Biophys. Acta* **352**, 252–259.

Dix, J. A., Diamond, J. M., and Kivelson, D. (1974). *Proc. Natl. Acad. Sci. U.S.A.* **71**, 474–478.

Dupont, Y., Harrison, S. C., and Hasselbach, W. (1973). *Nature (London)* **244**, 655–658.

Edelman, G. M., Yahara, I., and Wang, J. L. (1973). *Proc. Natl. Acad. Sci. U.S.A.* **70**, 1442–1446.

Edidin, M. (1974). *Annu. Rev. Biophys. Bioeng.* **3**, 179–201.

Edidin, M., and Fambrough, D. (1973). *J. Cell Biol.* **57**, 27–53.

Edidin, M., Zagyansky, Y., and Lardner, T. J. (1976). *Science* **191**, 466–468.

Engelman, D. M. (1971). *J. Mol. Biol.* **58**, 153–165.

Engström, A., and Finean, J. B. (1958). "Biological Ultrastructure," pp. 190–248. Academic Press, New York.

Erickson, R. O. (1973). *Science* **181**, 705–716.

Esfahani, M., Limbrick, A. R., Knutton, S., Oka, T., and Wakil, S. J. (1971). *Proc. Natl. Acad. Sci. U.S.A.* **68**, 3180–3184.

Esfahani, M., Crowfoot, P. D., and Wakil, S. J. (1972). *J. Biol. Chem.* **247**, 7251–7256.

Esser, A. F., and Souza, K. A. (1974). *Proc. Natl. Acad. Sci. U.S.A.* **71**, 4111–4115.

Evans, W. D. (1970). *Biochem. J.* **116**, 833–842.

Farber, T. E. (1958). *Proc. R. Soc. Lond., Ser. A* **248**, 460.

Fergason, J. L., and Brown, G. H. (1967). *J. Am. Oil Chem. Soc.* **45**, 120–127.

Ferguson, R. M., Schmidtke, J. R., and Simmons, R. L. (1975). *Nature (London)* **256**, 744–745.

Finch, E. D., and Schneider, A. S. (1975). *Biochim. Biophys. Acta* **406**, 146–154.

Finean, J. B. (1953). *Exp. Cell Res.* **5**, 202–215.

Finean, J. B. (1961). *Int. Rev. Cytol.* **12**, 303–336.

Finean, J. B. (1973). *In* "Form and Function of Phospholipids" (G. B. Ansell, J. N. Hawthorne, and R. M. C. Dawson, eds.), BBA Library, Vol. 3, pp. 171–203. Elsevier, Amsterdam.

Fourcans, B., and Jain, M. K. (1974). *Adv. Lipid Res.* **12**, 147–226.

Frey-Wyssling, A. (1957). "Macromolecules in Cell Structure," p. 59. Harvard Univ. Press, Cambridge, Massachusetts.

Frey-Wyssling, A., and Steinmann, E. (1953). *Vierteljahrsschr. Naturforsch. Ges. Zuerich* **98**, 20–29.

Fricke, H. (1923). *Phys. Rev.* **21**, 708–709.

Fricke, H. (1925). *J. Gen. Physiol.* **9**, 137–152.

Frye, L. D., and Edidin, M. (1970). *J. Cell Sci.* **7**, 319–335.

Fujita, M., Kawai, K., Shigetaka, A., and Nakao, M. (1973). *Biochim. Biophys. Acta* **307**, 141–151.

Galla, H. J., and Sackmann, E. (1974). *Biochim. Biophys. Acta* **339**, 103–115.

Galla, H. J., and Sackmann, E. (1975a). *Biochim. Biophys. Acta* **401**, 509–529.

Galla, H. J., and Sackmann, E. (1975b). *J. Am. Chem. Soc.* **97**, 4114–4120.

Gemne, G. (1969). *In* "Symmetry and Function of Biological Systems at the Macromolecular Level" (A. Engström and B. Stradberg, eds.), pp. 305–309. Wiley (Interscience), New York.

Gilula, N. B. (1974). *In* "Cell Communication" (R. P. Cox, ed.), pp. 1–29. Wiley, New York.

Glauert, A. M., and Thornley, M. J. (1969). *Annu. Rev. Microbiol.* **23**, 159–198.

Godichi, P. E., and Landsburger, F. R. (1974). *Biochemistry* **13**, 362–368.

Goedheer, J. C. (1957). Proefschrift. Drukkerij Gebr. Janssen, Nijmegen, Netherlands.

Goodenough, D. A., and Stoeckenius, W. (1972). *J. Cell Biol.* **54**, 646–656.

Goodman, C. H. L. (1975). *Nature (London)* **257**, 370–372.

Gorter, E., and Grendel, F. (1925). *J. Exp. Med.* **41**, 439–443.

Grant, C. W. M., Wu, S. H., and McConnell, H. M. (1974). *Biochim. Biophys. Acta* **363**, 151–158.

Green, D. E. (1972). *Ann. N.Y. Acad. Sci.* **195**, 150–172.

Green, D. E., and Baum, H. (1970). "Energy and Mitochondrion." Academic Press, New York.

Green, D. E., and Ji, S. (1972). *Proc. Natl. Acad. Sci. U.S.A.* **69**, 726–729.

Green, D. E., and Perdue, J. F. (1966). *Proc. Natl. Acad. Sci. U.S.A.* **55**, 1295–1302.

Green, D. E., Allman, D. W., Bachmann, E., Baum, H., Kopaczyk, K., Korman, E. F., Lipton, S., MacLennan, D. H., McConnell, D. G., Perdue, J. F., Rieske, J. S., and Tzagoloff, A. (1967). *Arch. Biochem. Biophys.* **119**, 312–335.

Griffith, O. H., Dehlinger, P. J., and Van, S. P. (1974). *J. Membr. Biol.* **15**, 159–192.

Grisham, C. M., and Barnett, R. E. (1973). *Biochemistry* **12**, 2635–2637.

Gross, L. (1967). *J. Theor. Biol.* **15**, 298–306.

Guidotti, G. (1972). *Annu. Rev. Biochem.* **41**, 731–776.

Gulik-Krzywicki, T., Rivas, E., and Luzzati, V. J. (1967). *J. Mol. Biol.* **27**, 303–322.

Haest, C. W. M., DeGier, J., and Van Deenen, L. L. M. (1969). *Chem. Phys. Lipids* **3**, 413–417.

Haest, C. W. M., DeGier, J., van Es, G. A., Verkleij, A. J., and Van Deenen, L. L. M. (1972). *Biochim. Biophys. Acta* **288**, 43–53.

Haest, C. W. M., Verkleij, A. J., DeGier, J., Scheek, R., Ververgaert, P. H. J., and Van Deenen, L. L. M. (1974). *Biochim. Biophys. Acta* **356**, 17–26.

Hagele, P. C., and Pechald, W. (1970). *Kolloid Z. Z. Polym.* **241**, 977–990.

Haggis, G. H. (1964). "Introduction to Molecular Biology," 1st Ed. Wiley, New York.

Hammerling, V., and Eggers, H. J. (1970). *Eur. J. Biochem.* **17**, 95–99.

Hammerling, V., Aoki, T., deHarven, E., Boyce, E. A., and Old, L. J. (1968). *J. Exp. Med.* **128**, 1461–1473.

Hechter, O. (1966). *Science* **153**, 324–325 (Report).

Henderson, R., and Unwin, P. N. T. (1975). *Nature (London)* **257**, 28–32.

Hill, T. L. (1956). "Statistical Mechanics." McGraw-Hill, New York.

Hiramoto, Y. (1970). *Biorheology* **6**, 201–234.

Hong, K., and Hubbell, W. L. (1972). *Proc. Natl. Acad. Sci. U.S.A.* **69**, 2617–2621.

Horne, R. A. (1969). *Adv. High Pressure Res.* **2**, 169–223.

Hoseman, R., and Bagchi, D. N. (1962). "Direct Analysis of Diffraction by Matter." North-Holland Publ., Amsterdam.

Hubbell, W. L., and McConnell, H. M. (1971). *J. Am. Chem. Soc.* **93**, 314–326.

Hui, S. W., and Parsons, D. F. (1974). *Science* **184**, 77–78.

Hui, S. W., and Parsons, D. F. (1975). *Science* **190**, 383–384.

Hui, S. W., Parsons, D. F., and Cowden, M. (1974). *Proc. Natl. Acad. Sci. U.S.A.* **71**, 5068–5072.

Inbar, M., Ben-Bassat, H., and Sachs, L. (1971). *Proc. Natl. Acad. Sci. U.S.A.* **68**, 2748–2751.
Inbar, M., Ben-Bassat, H., and Sachs, L. (1973a). *Int. J. Cancer* **12**, 93–99.
Inbar, M., Ben-Bassat, H., and Sachs, L. (1973b). *Proc. Natl. Acad. Sci. U.S.A.* **70**, 2577–2581.
Ito, T., and Ohnishi, S. (1974). *Biochim. Biophys. Acta* **352**, 29–37.
Ito, T., Ohnishi, S., Ishinaga, M., and Kito, M. (1975). *Biochemistry* **14**, 3064–3069.
Jain, M. K. (1972). "The Bimolecular Lipid Membrane: A System," 470 pp. Van Nostrand-Reinhold, New York.
Jain, M. K. (1973). *Curr. Top. Membr. Transp.* **4**, 175–254.
Jain, M. K. (1975). *Curr. Top. Membr. Transp.* **6**, 1–57.
Jain, M. K., and Cordes, E. H. (1973a). *J. Membr. Biol.* **14**, 101–118.
Jain, M. K., and Cordes, E. H. (1973b). *J. Membr. Biol.* **14**, 119–134.
Jain, M. K., and Wu, N. M. (1977). *J. Membr. Biol.* **33**, 1–45.
Jain, M. K., Toussaint, D. G., and Cordes, E. H. (1973). *J. Membr. Biol.* **14**, 1–16.
Jain, M. K., Wu, N. M., and Wray, L. V. (1975). *Nature (London)* **255**, 494–496.
Jan, L., and Revel, J. P. (1974). *J. Cell Biol.* **62**, 257–273.
Johnson, L. W., Hughes, M. E., and Zilversmit, D. B. (1975). *Biochim. Biophys. Acta* **375**, 176–185.
Johnson, M. H., Eager, D., Harris, A. M., and Grave, H. M. (1975). *Nature (London)* **257**, 321–322.
Johnston, P. V., and Roots, B. I. (1964). *Comp. Biochem. Physiol.* **11**, 303–309.
Jost, P., Griffith, O. H., Capaldi, R. A., and Vanderkooi, G. (1973a). *Proc. Natl. Acad. Sci. U.S.A.* **70**, 480–487.
Jost, P., Capaldi, R. A., Vanderkooi, G., and Griffith, O. H. (1973b). *J. Supramol. Struct.* **1**, 269–280.
Jost, P., Griffith, O. H., Capaldi, R. A., and Vanderkooi, G. (1973c). *Biochim. Biophys. Acta* **311**, 141–152.
Junge, W. (1972). *FEBS Lett.* **25**, 109–112.
Karnovsky, M. J., Unanue, E. R., and Levinthal, M. (1972). *J. Exp. Med.* **136**, 907–930.
Kavanau, J. L. (1965). "Structure and Function in Biological Membranes," Vol. 1. Holden-Day, San Francisco, California.
Keith, A. D., Sharnoff, M., and Cohn, G. E. (1973). *Biochim. Biophys. Acta* **300**, 379–419.
Kirkpatrick, F. H., Gordesky, S. E., and Marinetti, G. V. (1974). *Biochim. Biophys. Acta* **345**, 154–161.
Kittel, C. (1968). "Introduction to Solid State Physics." Wiley, New York.
Kleeman, W., and McConnell, H. M. (1974). *Biochim. Biophys. Acta* **345**, 220–230.
Kornberg, R., and McConnell, H. M. (1971). *Biochemistry* **10**, 1111–1120.
Kosower, N. S., Kosower, E. M., and Wegman, P. (1975). *Biochim. Biophys. Acta* **401**, 530–534.
Kraft, R. W. (1966). *J. Met.* **18**, 192–198.
Krasne, S., Eisenman, G., and Szabo, G. (1971). *Science* **174**, 412–414.
Kreutz, W. (1963). *Z. Naturforsch. B* **18**, 1098–1104.
Kreutz, W. (1970). *Adv. Bot. Res.* **3**, 54–90.
Ladbrook, B. D., and Chapman, D. (1969). *Chem. Phys. Lipids* **3**, 304–367.
Ladbrook, B. D., Jenkinson, T. J., Kamat, V. B., and Chapman, D. (1968). *Biochim. Biophys. Acta* **164**, 101–109.
Langdon, R. G. (1974). *Biochim. Biophys. Acta* **342**, 213–228.
Larsen, B. (1975). *Nature (London)* **258**, 344–345.
Lee, A. G., Birdsall, N. J. M., and Metcalfe, J. C. (1973). *Biochemistry* **12**, 1650–1659.
Lee, A. G., Birdsall, N. J. M., Metcalfe, J. C., Toon, P. A., and Warren, G. B. (1974). *Biochemistry* **13**, 3699–3705.
Lenard, J., and Rothman, J. S. (1976). *Proc. Natl. Acad. Sci. U.S.A.* **73**, 391–395.

Lenard, J., and Singer, S. J. (1966). *Proc. Natl. Acad. Sci. U.S.A.* **56**, 1828–1835.

Levine, Y. K. (1973). *Prog. Surf. Sci.* **3**, 279–352.

Levine, Y. K., Birdsall, N. J. M., Feeney, J., Lee, A. G., and Metcalfe, J. C. (1972a). *Biochemistry* **11**, 1416–1421.

Levine, Y. K., Partington, P., Roberts, G. C. K., Birdsall, N. J. M., Lee A. G., and Metcalfe, J. C. (1972b). *FEBS Lett.* **23**, 203–208.

Levine, Y. K., Birdsall, N. J. M., Lee, A. G., Metcalfe, J. C., Partington, P., and Roberts, G. C. K. (1974). *J. Chem. Phys.* **60**, 2890–2899.

Linden, C. D., Wright, K. L., McConnell, H. M., and Fox, C. F. (1973). *Proc. Natl. Acad. Sci. U.S.A.* **70**, 2271–2275.

Litman, B. J. (1973). *Biochemistry* **12**, 2545–2554.

Lucy, J. A. (1964). *J. Theor. Biol.* **7**, 360–373.

Lucy, J. A., and Glaubert, A. M. (1964). *J. Mol Biol.* **8**, 727–748.

Lussan-Bothorel, C. (1969). *C.R. Acad. Sci., Ser. D* **269**, 792–794.

Lustig, S., Pluznik, D. H., and Kosower, N. S., and Kosower, E. M. (1975). *Biochim. Biophys. Acta* **401**, 458–467.

Machtiger, N. A., and Fox, C. F. (1973). *Annu. Rev. Biochem.* **42**, 575–600.

Marchesi, V. T. (1975). *In* "Biochemistry of Cell Walls and Membranes" (C. F. Fox, ed.), pp. 123–154. Butterworth, London.

Marr, A. G., and Ingraham, J. L. (1967). *J. Bacteriol.* **84**, 1260–1267.

Marsh, D., Watts, A., and Knowles, P. F. (1976). *Biochemistry* **15**, 3570–3578.

Maruyama, M., and Oosawa, F. (1975). *J. Theor. Biol.* **49**, 249–262.

Mavis, R. D., and Vagelos, P. R. (1972). *J. Biol. Chem.* **247**, 652–659.

Mazliak, P. (1971). "Les Membranes Protopasmiques." Doin, Paris.

McConnell, H. M., Wright, R. C., and McFarland, B. G. (1972). *Biochem. Biophys. Res. Commun.* **47**, 273–281.

McElhaney, R. N. (1974). *J. Mol. Biol.* **84**, 145–157.

McFarland, B. G., and McConnell, H. M. (1971). *Proc. Natl. Acad. Sci. U.S.A.* **68**, 1274–1278.

McIntyre, J. A., Karnovsky, M. J., and Gilula, N. B. (1973). *Nature (London), New Biol.* **245**, 148–149.

McNamee, M. G., and McConnell, H. M. (1973). *Biochemistry* **12**, 2951–2958.

Melchior, D. L., Morowitz, H. J., Sturtevant, J. M., and Tsong, T. Y. (1970). *Biochim. Biophys. Acta* **219**, 114–122.

Menke, W. (1966). *In* "Biochemistry of Chloroplasts" (T. W. Goodwin, ed.), pp. 3–18. Academic Press, New York.

Metcalfe, J. C., Birdsall, N. J. M., Feeney, J., Lee, A. G., Levine, Y. K., and Partington, P. (1971). *Nature (London)* **233**, 199–201.

Mitchison, J. M. (1953). *J. Exp. Biol.* **30**, 397–433.

Montal, M., and Muller, P. (1972). *Proc. Natl. Acad. Sci. U.S.A.* **69**, 3561–3566.

Morrisett, J. D., Pownall, H. J., Plumlee, R. T., Smith, L. C., Zehner, Z. E., Esfahani, M., and Wakil, S. J. (1975). *J. Biol. Chem.* **250**, 6969–6976.

Morrison, D. G., and Morowitz, H. J. (1970). *J. Mol. Biol.* **49**, 441–459.

Muhlethaler, K., Moor, H., and Szarkowsky, J. W. (1965). *Planta* **67**, 305–323.

Muhlradt, P. F., Menzel, J., Golecki, J. R., and Speth, V. (1974). *Eur. J. Biochem.* **43**, 533–539.

Nabarro, F. R. N. (1967). "Theory of Crystal Dislocations." Oxford Univ. Press (Clarendon), London and New York.

Nelson, T. C., Wasserman, L. A., and Schemberger, D. H. (1974). *Biochem. Biophys. Res. Commun.* **58**, 1087–1091.

Newkirk, J. B., and Wermick, J. H., eds. (1962). "Direct Observations of Imperfections in Crystals." Wiley (Interscience), New York.

Nicolson, G. L. (1973). *Nature (London), New Biol.* **243**, 218–220.

Nicolson, G. L. (1974). *Int. Rev. Cytol.* **39**, 89–190.

Nicolson, G. L., and Singer, S. J. (1971). *Proc. Natl. Acad. Sci. U.S.A.* **68**, 942–948.

Nilson, S. E. G. (1964). *Nature (London)* **202**, 509–510.

O'Brien, J. S. (1967). *J. Theor. Biol.* **15**, 307–324.

Ohnishi, S., and Ito, T. (1974). *Biochemistry* **13**, 881–887.

Oldfield, E. (1973). *Science* **180**, 982–983.

Oldfield, E., and Chapman, D. (1972). *FEBS Lett.* **23**, 285–297.

Oliver, J. M., Ukena, T. E., and Berlin, R. D. (1974). *Proc. Natl. Acad. Sci. U.S.A.* **71**, 394–398.

Op den Kamp, J. A. F., DeGier, J., and Van Deenen, L. L. M. (1974). *Biochim. Biophys. Acta* **345**, 253–256.

Op den Kamp, J. A. F., Kauerz, M. T., and Van Deenen, L. L. M. (1975). *Biochim. Biophys. Acta* **406**, 169–177.

Orgel, L. E. (1972). *Isr. J. Chem.* **10**, 287–292.

Oseroff, A. R., Robbins, P. W., and Burger, M. (1973). *Annu. Rev. Biochem.* **42**, 647–682.

Overath, P., Schraier, H. V., and Stoffel, W. (1970). *Proc. Natl. Acad. Sci. U.S.A.* **67**, 606–612.

Pagano, R. E., Cherry, R. J., and Chapman, D. (1973). *Science* **181**, 557–559.

Papahadjopoulos, D. (1974). *J. Theor. Biol.* **43**, 329–337.

Papahadjopoulos, D., Jacobson, K., Nir, S., and Isac, T. (1973). *Biochim. Biophys. Acta* **311**, 330–348.

Papahadjopoulos, D., Poste, G., Schaeffer, B. F., and Vail, W. J. (1974). *Biochim. Biophys. Acta* **352**, 10–28.

Papahadjopoulos, D., Moscarello, M., Eylar, E. H., and Isac, T. (1975). *Biochim. Biophys. Acta* **401**, 317–335.

Park, R. B., and Pfeifhofer, A. O. (1969). *J. Cell Sci.* **5**, 299–303.

Park, R. B., and Pon, N. G. (1961). *J. Mol. Biol.* **3**, 1–10.

Peters, J. H., and Hausen, P. (1971). *Eur. J. Biochem.* **19**, 502–508, 509–513.

Peters, R., Peters, J. H., Tews, K. H., and Bahr, W. (1974). *Biochim. Biophys. Acta* **367**, 282–294.

Petit, V. A., and Edidin, M. (1974). *Science* **184**, 1183–1185.

Phillips, M. C. (1972). *Prog. Surf. Membr. Sci.* **5**, 139–221.

Phillips, M. C., Ladbrook, B. D., and Chapman, D. (1970). *Biochim. Biophys. Acta* **196**, 35–44.

Phillips, M. C., Hauser, H., and Paltauf, F. (1972). *Chem. Phys. Lipids* **8**, 127–133.

Pinto Da Silva, P. (1972). *J. Cell Biol.* **53**, 777–787.

Pinto Da Silva, P., and Martinez-Palomo, A. (1974). *Nature (London)* **249**, 170–171.

Ponder, E. (1951). *J. Exp. Biol.* **28**, 567–575.

Pontus, M., and Delmelle, M. (1975). *Biochim. Biophys. Acta* **401**, 221–230.

Poo, M., and Cone, R. A. (1973). *Exp. Eye Res.* **17**, 503–510.

Poo, M., and Cone, R. A. (1974). *Nature (London)* **247**, 438–441.

Poste, G., Papahadjopoulos, D., Jacobson, K., and Vail, W. J. (1975a). *Nature (London)* **253**, 552–554.

Poste G., Papahadjopoulos, D., and Nicolson, G. L. (1975b). *Proc. Natl. Acad. Sci. U.S.A.* **72**, 4430–4434.

Poznansky, M., and Lange, Y. (1976). *Nature (London)* **259**, 420–421.

Radda, G. K., and Vanderkooi, J. (1972). *Biochim. Biophys Acta* **265**, 509–549.

Rand, R. P. (1968). *J. Gen. Physiol.* **52**, Part 2, 173–178.

Rand, R. P., and Sengupta, S. (1972). *Biochim. Biophys. Acta* **255**, 484–492.

Revel, J. P., and Karnovsky, M. J. (1967). *J. Cell Biol.* **33**, C7–C12.

Rigaud, L., Gary-Bobo, C. M., and Lange, Y. (1972). *Biochim. Biophys. Acta* **266**, 72–84.

Robertson, J. D. (1960). *Prog. Biophys. Biophys. Chem.* **10**, 343–418.

Robertson, J. D. (1963). *J. Cell Biol.* **19**, 201–221.

Robertson, J. D. (1964). *Symp. Soc. Study Dev. Growth* **22**, 1–82.

Robertson, J. D. (1967). *Protoplasma* **63**, 218–245.

Robinson, J. D., Birdsall, N. J. M., Lee, A. G., and Metcalfe J. C. (1972). *Biochemistry* **11**, 2903–2909.

Rogers, M. J., and Strittmatter, P. (1975). *J. Biol. Chem.* **250**, 5713–5718.

Rosenblith, J. S., Ukena, T. E., Yin, H. H., Berlin, R. D., and Karnovsky, M. J. (1973). *Proc. Natl. Acad. Sci. U.S.A.* **70**, 1625–1629.

Rothman, J. E. (1973). *J. Theor. Biol.* **38**, 1–16.

Rothman, J. E., and Davidowicz, E. A. (1975). *Biochemistry* **14**, 2809–2816.

Sackmann, E., Trauble, H., Galla, H. J., and Overath, P. (1973). *Biochemistry* **12**, 5360–5369.

Salsbury, N. J., and Chapman, D. (1968). *Biochim. Biophys. Acta* **163**, 314–324.

Scandella, C. J., Devaux, P., and McConnell, H. M. (1972). *Proc. Natl. Acad. Sci. U.S.A.* **69**, 2056–2060

Schindler, H., and Seelig, J. (1973). *J. Chem. Phys.* **59**, 1841–1850.

Schmidt, W. O. (1936). *Cold Spring Harbor Symp. Quant. Biol.* **4**, 7.

Schmitt, F. O., Bear, R. S., and Ponder, E. (1936). *J. Cell. Comp. Physiol.* **9**, 89.

Schreier-Muccillo, S., Marsh, D., Dugas, H., Schneider, H., and Smith, I. C. P. (1973). *Chem. Phys. Lipids* **10**, 11–27.

Sears, B. (1975). *J. Membr. Biol.* **20**, 59–73.

Seelig, J., and Niederberger, W. (1974). *Biochemistry* **13**, 1585–1588.

Seelig, J., and Seelig, A. (1974). *Biochem. Biophys. Res. Commun.* **57**, 406–411.

Seeman, P. (1972). *Pharmacol. Rev.* **24**, 583–655.

Segrest, J. P., Kahane, I., Jackson, R. L., and Marchesi, V. T. (1973). *Arch. Biochem. Biophys.* **155**, 167–178.

Sheffield, J. B., and Emmelot, P. (1972). *Exp. Cell Res.* **71**, 97–105.

Sherwood, D., and Montal, M. (1975). *Biophys. J.* **15**, 417–434.

Sherwood, J. N., and White, D. J. (1967). *Philos. Mag.* **16**, 975–980.

Shimshick, E. J., and McConnell, H. M. (1973a). *Biochem. Biophys. Res. Commun.* **53**, 446–451.

Shimshick, E. J., and McConnell, H. M. (1973b). *Biochemistry* **12**, 2351–2360.

Shimshick, E. J., Kleemann, W., Hubbell, W. L., and McConnell, H. M. (1973). *J. Supramol. Struct.* **1**, 285–294.

Shinitzky, M., and Inbar, M. (1974). *J. Mol. Biol.* **85**, 603–615.

Silbert, D. F. (1970). *Biochemistry* **9**, 3631–3640.

Sinensky, M. (1971). *J. Bacteriol.* **106**, 449–455.

Sinensky, M. (1974). *Proc. Natl. Acad. Sci. U.S.A.* **71**, 522–525.

Singer, S. J. (1972). *Ann. N.Y. Acad. Sci.* **195**, 16–23.

Singer, S. J. (1974). *Annu. Rev. Biochem.* **43**, 805–833.

Singer, S. J., and Nicolson, G. L. (1972). *Science* **175**, 720–731.

Sjöstrand, F. S. (1963). *J. Ultrastruct. Res.* **9**, 304–361, 561–580.

Sjöstrand, F. S. (1967). *Protoplasma* **63**, 248–261.

Sjöstrand, F. S. (1968). "Regulatory Functions of Biological Membranes" (J. Jarnefelt, ed.), BBA Library, Vol. 11, pp. 1–20. Elsevier, Amsterdam.

Sleytr, U. B., and Glauert, A. M. (1975). *J. Ultrastruct. Res.* **50**, 103–116.

Smith, C. S. (1964). *Rev. Mod. Phys.* **36**, 524–532.

Solomon, A. K. (1974). *Biochim. Biophys. Acta* **373**, 145–149.

Speth, V., and Wunderlich, F. (1973). *Biochim. Biophys. Acta* **291**, 621–628.

Stackpole, C. W., and Devorkin, D. (1974). *J. Ultrastruct. Res.* **49**, 167–187.

Stackpole, C. W., Aoki, T., Boyce, E. A., Old, L. J., Lumley-Frank, J., and deHarven, E. (1971). *Science* **172**, 472–474.

Stackpole, C. W., DeMilio, L. T., Hamerling, V., Jacobson, J. B., and Lardis, M. P. (1972). *Proc. Natl. Acad. Sci. U.S.A.* **71**, 932–936.

Staehelin, L. A. (1968). *J. Ultrastruct. Res.* **22**, 326–347.

Stark, V., Benz, R., Pohl, G. W., and Janko, K. (1972). *Biochim. Biophys. Acta* **266**, 603–613.

Steck, T. L. (1974). *J. Cell Biol.* **62**, 1–19.

Stein, J. M., Tourtellotte, M. E., Reinert, J. C., McElhaney, R. N., and Rader, R. L. (1969). *Proc. Natl. Acad. Sci. U.S.A.* **63**, 104–109.

Stein, W. D., and Danielli, J. F. (1956). *Discuss. Faraday Soc.* **21**, 238–251.

Stevenson, F. K. (1973). *Biochim. Biophys. Acta* **311**, 409–416.

Stier, A., and Sackmann, E. (1973). *Biochim. Biophys. Acta* **311**, 400–408.

Stoeckenius, W. (1963). *In* "The Interpretation of Ultrastructure" (J. C. Harris, ed.), pp. 349–367. Academic Press, New York.

Strittmatter, P., Rogers, M. J., and Spatz, L. (1972). *J. Biol. Chem.* **247**, 7188–7194.

Stroeve, P., and Miller, I. (1975). *Biochim. Biophys. Acta* **401**, 157–167.

Sullivan, K., Jain, M. K., and Koch, A. L. (1974). *Biochim. Biophys. Acta* **352**, 287–297.

Sundaralingam, M. (1972). *Ann. N.Y. Acad. Sci.* **195**, 324–355.

Sworakowski, J. (1973). *Mol. Cryst. Liq. Cryst.* **19**, 259–268.

Sytkowski, A. J., Vogel, Z., and Nirenberg, M. W. (1973). *Proc. Natl. Acad. Sci. U.S.A.* **70**, 270–274.

Taylor, J. A. G., Mingins, J., Pethica, B. A., Tan, B. Y. J., and Jackson, C. M. (1973). *Biochim. Biophys. Acta* **323**, 157–160.

Taylor, R. B., Duffers, W. P. H., Raff, M. C., and DePetris, S. (1971). *Nature (London), New Biol.* **233**, 225–229.

Teilhard de Chardin, P. (1959). "The Phenomenon of Man." Harper, New York.

Tinoco, J., Ghosh, D., and Keith, A. D. (1972). *Biochim. Biophys. Acta* **274**, 279–285.

Tocanne, J. F., Ververgaert, P. H. J. T., Verkleij, A. J., and Van Deenen, L. L. M. (1974). *Chem. Phys. Lipids* **12**, 220–231.

Tomita, M., and Marchesi, V. T. (1975). *Proc. Natl. Acad. Sci. U.S.A.* **72**, 2964–2968.

Trauble, H., and Eibl, H. (1974). *Proc. Natl. Acad. Sci. U.S.A.* **71**, 214–219.

Trauble, H., and Overath, P. (1973). *Biochim. Biophys. Acta* **307**, 491–512.

Trauble, H., and Sackmann, E. (1972). *J. Am. Chem. Soc.* **94**, 4499–4510.

Tsukagoshi, N., and Fox, C. F. (1973). *Biochemistry* **12**, 2822–2829.

Ukena, T. E., and Berlin, R. D. (1972). *J. Exp. Med.* **136**, 1–7.

Van Deenen, L. L. M. (1969). *In* "The Molecular Basis of Membrane Function" (D. C. Tosteson, ed.), pp. 47–60. Prentice-Hall, Englewood Cliffs, New Jersey.

Vandenheuvel, F. A. (1965). *Ann. N.Y. Acad. Sci.* **122**, 57–76.

Van der Bosch, J., and McConnell, H. M. (1975). *Proc. Natl. Acad. Sci. U.S.A.* **72**, 4409–4413.

Vanderkooi, G., and Green, D. E. (1970). *Proc. Natl. Acad. Sci. U.S.A.* **66**, 615–621.

Vanderkooi, J., and Martonosi, A. (1971). *Arch. Biochim. Biophys.* **147**, 632–642.

Verkleij, A. J., Ververgaert, P. H. J., Van Deenen, L. L. M., and Elbers, P. F. (1972), *Biochim. Biophys. Acta* **288**, 326–332.

Verkleij, A. J., Ververgaert, P. H. J., DeKruyff, B., and Van Deenen, L. L. M. (1974). *Biochim. Biophys. Acta* **373**, 495–501.

Ververgaert, P. H. J., Elbers, P. F., Luitingh, A. J., and Van den Berg, H. J. (1972). *Cytobiology* **6**, 86–96.

Ververgaert, P. H. J., Verkleij, A. J., Elbers, P. E., and Van Deenen, L. L. M. (1973a). *Biochim. Biophys. Acta* **311**, 320–329.

Ververgaert, P. H. J. T., Verkleij, A. J., Verhoeven, J. J., and Elbers, P. F. (1973b). *Biochim. Biophys. Acta* **311**, 651–654.

Wahl, P., Kasai, M., and Changeux, J. P. (1971). *Eur. J. Biochem.* **18**, 332–338.

Wallach, D. F. H. (1972). "The Plasma Membrane: Dynamic Perspectives, Genetics and Pathology," p. 87. Springer-Verlag, Berlin and New York.

Wallach, D. F. H., and Zahler, P. (1966). *Proc. Natl. Acad. Sci. U.S.A.* **56**, 1552–1559.

Warren, G. B., Housley, M. D., Metcalfe, J. C., and Birdsall, N. J. M. (1975). *Nature (London)* **255**, 684–687.
Weier, T. E., and Benson, A. A. (1966). *In* "Biochemistry of Chloroplasts" (T. W. Goodwin, ed.), pp. 91–113. Academic Press, New York.
Weier, T. E., and Benson, A. A. (1967). *Am. J. Bot.* **54**, 389–402.
Weiss, L., and Clement, K. (1968). *Exp. Cell. Res.* **58**, 379–387.
Wessels, N. K., Spooner, B. S., Ash, J. F., Bradley, M. O., Ludvena, M. A., Taylor, E. L., Wrenn, J. T., and Yamada, K. M. (1971). *Science* **171**, 135–143.
White, S. H. (1970a). *Biochim. Biophys. Acta* **196**, 354–357.
White, S. H. (1970b). *Biophys. J.* **10**, 1127–1148.
Williams, E., Hamilton, J. A., Jain, M. K., Allerhand, A., Cordes, E. H., and Ochs, S. (1973). *Science* **181**, 869–871.
Williams, R. J. P. (1975). *Biochim. Biophys. Acta* **416**, 237–286.
Winkler, K. C., and Bungenberg de Jong, H. G. (1940). *Arch. Neerl. Physiol.* **25**, 431–466, 467.
Wisnieski, B. J., Parkes, J. G., Huang, Y. O., and Fox, C. F. (1974). *Proc. Natl. Acad. Sci. U.S.A.* **71**, 4381–4385.
Wu, S. H., and McConnell, H. M. (1973). *Biochem. Biophys. Res. Commun.* **55**, 484–491.
Wunderlich, F., Ronai, A., Speth, V., Seelig, J., and Blume, A. (1975). *Biochemistry* **14**, 3730–3736.
Wyman, J. (1969). *In* "Symmetry and Function of Biological Systems at the Macromolecular Level" (A. Engstrom and B. Strandberg, eds.), pp. 267–282. Wiley (Interscience), New York.

The Pharmacodynamics and Toxicology
of Steroids and Related Compounds

Fritz Bischoff and George Bryson

Santa Barbara Cottage Hospital Research Institute, Santa Barbara, California

I. Introduction 62
II. Methodology of Measurement 63
    A. Fluorometry 63
    B. Radioimmunoassay and Related Methods 63
    C. Gas–Liquid Chromatography and Mass Fragmentographic Analysis 66
III. Theories of Physiologic Mechanisms 67
    A. The Oxo–Hydroxy Hormone Pairs 67
    B. The Estrogens 68
    C. The Corticosteroids 68
    D. The Androgens 69
    E. Progesterone 69
    F. Stereochemistry 70
    G. Steroid–Receptor Interactions 71
IV. Enzyme Systems 72
    A. Structurally Modified Hormone Preparations 72
    B. Serum Esterase 73
    C. Fate of Methoxy Steroids 74
    D. 17-Hydroxydehydrogenases 75
    E. The Hydroxylases 77
    F. Steroid Hormone Syntheses 78
    G. The Oxidation of Cholesterol 80
V. Transport Mechanisms 81
    A. Interstitial Fluid, Lymph, and Cerebrospinal Fluid 81
    B. Plasma 82
    C. Red Blood Cells 86
    D. Receptor Site Binding Proteins 87
    E. Cholesterol 90
    F. Pharmacodynamics 92
VI. Safety Testing for Carcinogenic Hazards 96
    A. The Rare Tumor Type 96
    B. Malignant Tumors in Rodents 97
    C. The Immune Defense Mechanism against Carcinogenesis 99
    D. Cholesterol Oxidation Products 100
    E. Estrogens in Primates 102
    F. Chloroderivatives 102
VII. Drug Side Effects 103
    A. Reserpine 103
    B. Estrogen Therapy 107

I. Introduction

The steroid hormones are cyclopenta[α]phenanthrene derivatives. Attention was first focused on secondary alcohols of biologic origin, such as cholesterol in animals and digitoxigenin in plants. Because of the OH grouping, these were properly designated as sterols—solid alcohols—and subsequently shown to have the carbon-ring linkage of cyclopenta[α]phenanthrene.

In this review the material is grouped around categories comprising the naturally occurring gonadal and adrenal steroid hormones of the higher animals and the biologically active plant steroids. It was inevitable that organic chemists and pharmacologists would develop structurally related compounds as therapeutic tools in order to enhance desirable or minimize undesirable pharmacologic effects of the natural products.

In order to understand the pharmacodynamics of a synthetic steroid, it is necessary to know the physiologic mechanisms at the molecular level of the natural steroid that serves as the type model. Since hormones by definition function at a target site removed from the site of origin, transport mechanisms for and their different affinities for natural or synthetic steroids contribute to the physiologic response. The origin of the natural steroid and the fate of it and its synthetic analogs are governed by endogenous enzyme systems. Finally, the role of the steroid at the receptor site, whether it be physical, resulting from secondary valence effects, or by chemical reactivity, is considered.

Synthetics or natural products that do not have the exact steroid carbon-ring skeleton are included in this review if they produce physiologic effects akin to those of natural steroids by virtue of required spatial configurations and similar active functional groups.

The nature and abundance of the literature on steroids necessitates exemplary rather than exhaustive approaches in developing a summary overview.

II. Methodology of Measurement

Measurement of steroids in early research relied largely upon the biologic assay, which remains today a final arbiter when different methodological approaches yield different reported values. Thus the solubility of 0.6×10^{-6} mole per liter for estradiol-17β at 25°C in physiologic buffer solution (Eik-Nes *et al.*, 1954), as obtained by colorimetric analysis, is one-tenth of the bioassay value (Bischoff and Katherman, 1948). The order of the latter value was subsequently confirmed by oil–aqueous estradiol-17β distributions (Bischoff *et al.*, 1954). However, sensitivity of the bioassay is usually too low for measuring hormone levels from individual specimens of blood and other physiologic fluids. With the pooling of samples, the amount of within-subject variation (sex, weight, age, stress, diet, etc.) as well as inter- and intra-assay variations often warrant increased numbers per group in order to observe statistically significant responses. The bioassay, under most conditions encountered in the laboratory, is not amenable to handling large numbers of biologic samples.

A. FLUOROMETRY

Fluorometric methods are rapid and can handle large numbers of samples. With an Aminco Bowman spectrophotofluorometer, the sensitivity for estradiol is 10 ng/ml, and for equilenin it is 1 ng/ml. This is the same range as sensitivities for the catecholamines. Epinephrine and estradiol have maximum activation and fluorescent wavelengths of 285 nm and 325–330 nm, respectively, though in different solvent systems. After conversion of the catecholamines to hydroxyindole derivatives, a shift occurs in maximum wavelengths in the fluorescence procedure (Udenfriend, 1959). As measured with a fluorometric adaptation of a colorimetric method for assaying estrogen conjugates, a sensitivity of 0.5 ng for estriol-16-glucosiduronate has been reported (Lee and Hähnel, 1971). A fluorometric method for 11-hydroxycorticosteroids depends on the production of a fluorophor by treatment with alcoholic sulfuric acid. Excitation and fluorescent wavelengths are 470 nm and 530 nm, respectively. Sensitivity is in the 10 ng/ml range (Koch *et al.*, 1973). Prealkalinization and increased fluorescent development time (60 minutes) gave a method having increased specificity and sensitivity (5 ng/ml) for cortisol (Mejer and Blanchard, 1973).

B. RADIOIMMUNOASSAY AND RELATED METHODS

With the development of radiolabeling procedures, rapid techniques for evaluating a large range of biologic levels of sex and adrenal steroid hormones as well as other substances have been made available. The procedures being in the height of fashion, the ensuing literature has given rise to new terms, each referring to something slightly different. Three excellent sources for elucidation of and information about these procedures are: Diczfalusy (1970), Skelley *et al.* (1973), and Hawker (1973).

The original terms "saturation analysis" or "displacement analysis" specified that a limited quantity of antibody is added to an excess of two forms of the same antigen (labeled and unlabeled), the assay depending on the competition between two forms of the antigen for binding sites on the antibody. "Radioligand binding analysis" involves a protein or a nonprotein chelating agent, in which the ligand (that which is bound—usually the smaller molecule) is used as a radioactive tracer.

1. Competitive Protein Binding

"Competitive protein-binding analysis" is defined as that form of saturation analysis in which one reacting molecule is a protein with high affinity and high specificity for the other—which is a ligand. The term "radioimmunoassay" defines the protein as an antibody, whereas in "radioenzymic assay" the protein is an enzyme. Many of the competitive protein-binding assays utilize normal circulating plasma proteins or tissue receptor proteins. Disadvantages of the competitive binding proteins are their relative instability and limited range of affinity and the need for removal of any competing analogs or other binding protein before assay. The competitive protein-binding method of Murphy (1967) has given good correlation with fluorescent assay of cortisol (Mejer and Blanchard, 1973).

2. Radioimmunoassay

There is a difference between an antigen and an immunogen: antigens are capable of binding to a specific antibody; immunogens provoke an immune response. Proteins with molecular weights less than 5000, peptides, and nonprotein hormones such as steroids, although possessing antigenic properties, must be coupled to a large protein molecule in order to be immunogenic. The smaller molecule conjugated with the carrier protein is called the haptan (Hawker, 1973). The higher-affinity constants and the nature of the specific reactor antibody in the radioimmunoassay offsets the time and cost of developing the specific antiserum.

With respect to practical steroid hormone determination, radioimmunoassay procedures are based on the principle that at low concentrations of antibodies to an excess of antigenic hormone, all sites of the antibody are occupied by an antigen—either labeled or unlabeled. Unknown concentrations of an aliquot of the unlabeled hormone can be determined by utilizing the competition of reversible binding between the unlabeled and a radiolabeled tracer hormone for the binding sites of the antibody. The assay requires that an unlabeled standard hormone and the hormone whose concentration is being determined replace radiolabeled hormone from the labeled antigen–antibody immune complex to the same degree. It is not required that either the standard or "unknown" hormone behave in the identical manner as the radiolabeled tracer at the binding site.

After incubation of the antibody with the radiolabeled hormone and the addition of unlabeled standard or "unknown," the antigen–antibody complexes are separated from the free antigenic hormones on a column containing dextran-coated charcoal, and various samples of the bound complex are subjected to scintillation counting. The amount of radioactivity present in a sample gives an inverse relationship to the amount of the unknown hormone.

In "solid-phase antibody radioimmunoassay" an antibody protein is rendered insoluble by covalent cross-linking of the protein, by covalent binding, or physical adsorption of the protein to an insoluble carrier prior to the immune reaction of physical adsorption. In the "immunoradiometric assay," the antibody is radiolabeled instead of the antigen. This change has the advantages of: low blank values, easier labeling of antibodies than of many low-molecular-weight antigens, accommodation of larger amounts of unlabeled antigen, and longer storage periods for the tagged antibody. Although the basis of radioimmunoassay is immunologic rather than biologic, the advantages of radioimmunoassay over competitive protein binding include elimination of deproteinization of the sample and increased sensitivity and specificity; sensitivity for steroids is in general in the picograms per milliliter range.

3. Double Antibody Technique

A separate, second antibody formed from antiserum prepared from injection of the antibody–antigen complex into another species is used in this test to combine with the antigen–antibody complex. The second antibody–antibody–antigen complex produces such a large molecule that it can be precipitated, leaving the labeled and unlabeled antigens in solution, where they can be measured directly by scintillation counting.

4. Double Isotope Derivative Method

Using double isotope derivative methods, the steroids in the unknown are tagged by the formation of derivatives with a tagged agent. Also a differently tagged internal standard is added initially and serves to establish recovery during the process of purification. This may involve chromatography or other complex procedures. A classic method for the measurement of estrone and estradiol-17β in peripheral human blood and other biologic fluids using [^{35}S] pipsyl chloride (Baird, 1968; Baird and Guevara, 1969) is a reference standard for other methods. The phenolic extracts of blood are allowed to react with [^{35}S] p-iodobenzene sulfonyl chloride. [^{3}H]estrone or estradiol-17β is added for recovery determinations. Separation and purification of the unknown steroids to be detected from other steroids or substances having similar chemical properties entail a considerable loss. To compensate for this loss, which is necessary to obtain absolute specificity, the tagged standard is used.

5. *Tissue Receptor Assay*

Radioreceptor assays use tissue receptors (cellular-binding proteins) as specific reactors. Adrenocortical receptors for ACTH, uterine cytosol receptors for estrogen, interstitial testicular cell fractions for luteinizing hormone and human growth hormone as well as receptors for cyclic AMP have been developed. Such assays attain enhanced specificity on a biologic rather than on an immunologic basis (Skelley *et al.*, 1973).

6. *Sources of Error*

Measures such as accuracy checks, blanks, internal standards, and rigid methodological reproducibility are essential in reducing errors. Certain errors may unwittingly be introduced where methods developed clinically for one species are used experimentally to investigate other parameters or another species. Cross-reactivity for compounds other than the test substance may be at a very low ratio. However, where the test unknown is at a concentration considerably lower than that of the cross-reactive substance, cross-reactivity may occur at a high enough magnitude to invalidate the result. Polarities of different solvent systems may affect the partitioning of fractions being separated on columns. Adsorption on plastic utensils and creepage on glassware contribute to the loss of a specific hormone being tested. Sampling technique, especially that for plasma, can be susceptible to local concentrations of hormone, arteriovenous differences, and fluctuations in concentration resulting from circadian rhythms.

C. GAS–LIQUID CHROMATOGRAPHY AND MASS FRAGMENTOGRAPHIC ANALYSIS

Gas–liquid chromatographic methods are coming into prominence in the study of steroids, biogenic amines, and other biological materials because they allow separation with a high resolving power from small samples of materials yielding sensitivity in the nanogram and subnanogram range. Moreover, they allow separation of compounds often structurally or metabolically related in the same sample. The mass spectrometer achieves a high specificity when allocating prepurified effluents of the gas–liquid chromatographic system. An electron-capture detector or the mass spectrometer serves this purpose. Using the latter device with one single ion detection, or two or multiple ion detections, fragment ions are monitored during the gas–liquid chromatographic elution. Thus estrone, the two estradiol isomers, and the four estriol isomers can be completely resolved as the trimethylsilyl derivatives, 40 ng each. Internal standards of perdeuterated trimethylsilyl ethers of the substances to be determined in the "unknown" sample are used for quantitative analysis, as well as a nonbiological isomer of the test compound (Maume *et al.*, 1973).

III. Theories of Physiologic Mechanisms

A. The Oxo-Hydroxy Steroid Hormone Pairs

Clues to physiologic effects based on characteristic structural manifestations were directed to the pairs of steroids sharing a common oxo or hydroxy oxygen at the 3 position but differing by two hydrogen atoms in a hydroxide–oxo shift at another position: estradiol-17β versus estrone for the estrogens; testosterone versus 4-androstene-3,17-dione for the androgens; 4-pregnen-20α-ol-3-one versus progesterone for the progestins; and cortisol versus cortisone for the corticosteroids. The phenolic hydroxy groups of estrogens are shared at the 3 position. With the 3 pairs of nonphenolic steroid hormones, oxo groups are shared at the 3 position.

1. *Biologic Activity*

Estradiol, testosterone, and cortisol all show enhanced biologic activity in assay tests over their corresponding keto derivatives. However, 4-pregnen-20α-ol-3-one has less activity than progesterone. 4-Pregnen-20α-ol-3-one and the 20β derivative are less active than progesterone (Zander *et al.*, 1958) with the Clauberg test (the uterine effect on subcutaneous injection into an immature rabbit primed with estrogen). With direct injection into a ligated segment of the uterine horn of ovariectomized adult mice, the 20β-ol derivative is twice as active as progesterone, the 20α-ol derivative less active (Hooker and Forbes, 1949). Androsterone (3α-hydroxy-5α-androstan-17-one), a metabolite of testosterone, has one-fourth the biologic activity of androstane-3α, 17β-diol (Butenandt *et al.*, 1935). Since each of the four pairs of major steroid hormones are interconvertible by enzyme systems, the member of each pair with enhanced bioassay activity was considered as the one involved in physiologic activity per se, the other serving as a readily available reservoir. This concept is oversimplistic as dihydrotestosterone, formed from testosterone, has a high degree of biologic activity of its own. Whereas, estradiol remains intact in promoting physiologic activity, testosterone is converted to dihydrotestosterone and 3β-androstanediol at accessory male sex glands, brain, and skin (Wilson and Walker, 1969) testosterone-target sites. In the ventral prostate of the rat, dihydrotestosterone stimulates epithelial cell multiplication and the diol stimulates protein secretory activity (Wilson and Gloyna, 1970). Testosterone maintains the integrity of the epithelial cells of the ventral prostate. In human skin as well as the prostate in a number of species, local dihydrotestosterone formation correlates with growth response (Wilson and Lasnitzki, 1971). Estrone, androstenedione, and cortisone possibly are devoid of biologic activity, being converted *in vivo* to the active derivative in the bioassay.

2. *Spatial Configurations*

The spacing of the two hydroxy groups in estradiol critically determines physiologic activity. Diethylstilbestrol, which has the same spacing of hydroxy groups, is estrogenic but not a steroid. Administered to experimental animals, androstan-17β-ol (Sydnor, 1958) and the hydrocarbon 5α-androstane (Segaloff, cited in Dorfman, 1961) are androgenic as well as the perhydrophenanthrene derivative R02-7239 (2-acetyl-7-oxo-1,2,3,4,4α,5,6,7,9,10,10α-dodecahydrophenanthrene) (Dorfman, 1960), which is not a steroid. The assumption that these examples prove that the 3 and 17 oxygen substitutions are not essential for androgenic activity is dubious. The reviewers suggest that *in vivo* enzymic hydroxylation at the positions of the steroid or hydrophenanthrene nucleus crucial for androgenic activity is possible. Although the perhydrophenanthrene compound was tested in castrated-adrenalectomized rats, other tissue-sites with hydroxylation activity could account for such an oxygenation. By analogy, the hydroxylation of the carcinogenic hydrocarbons indicate that this would be the lung, liver, and other tissues (see Section IV,E,1). All the four major hormone classes have an oxygen or carbonyl group or both attached at the 17 position.

B. The Estrogens

The mechanism of the physiologic effects induced by the estrogens has been attributed to the alteration of enzyme systems to increase the energy available to the cell for endergonic synthetic reactions (Hagerman and Villee, 1961).

C. The Corticosteroids

No single mechanism such as is attributed to the estrogens has been ascribed to the corticosteroids. The adrenal steroid hormones have been divided into two groups, the glucocorticoids and the mineralocorticoids. The former influence enzyme systems including gluconeogenesis in the liver, protein synthesis in the muscle and the liver, and cell permeability. As identified by specific antibody precipitation, rat liver tryptophan-oxygenase synthesis was increased 4- to 5-fold by hydrocortisone (Schimke, 1974). Although the mitochondria appeared to be a focus for activity (White *et al.*, 1961), no primary physical or chemical phenomenon had been elucidated. The mineralocorticoids are concerned with electrolyte balance. The two types of corticosteroids share both the metabolic and electrolyte-regulating properties in various degrees and are not mutually exclusive.

D. THE ANDROGENS

In contrast to the estrogens, which influence enzyme activity, the androgens appear to invoke synthesis of specific enzymes resulting in the growth of tissues (Dorfman, 1961). In male pigs, administration of testosterone propionate decreased the high level of plasma arylesterase activity produced by castration but had no effect on the enzyme activity *in vitro*. This indicates that the male sex hormones inhibit the synthesis of this enzyme (Augustinsson and Olsson, 1961). In rats estradiol had a biphasic effect upon plasma arylesterase activity, which was dependent upon the time span of administration (Augustinsson and Henricson, 1970). Phenyl acetate, not an aromatic steroid ester, was the substrate in these experiments. Dihydrotestosterons is not formed in human testes or muscle (Kelch *et al.*, 1971), but at local sites related to androgen-dependent activity.

E. PROGESTERONE

A specific physiologic role for progesterone is not readily summarized. Menthol with menthone or menthone alone demonstrate the same effects that progesterone has in stimulating galactose metabolism in human congenital galactosemia. On the basis of the structural differences between progesterone and menthone, a ring ketone of a monocyclic terpene, the mechanism elevating the metabolic response is not readily apparent (Topper, 1961). The differences of the effects of estrogens and progesterone upon the rabbit myometrium under *in vivo* or *in vitro* conditions raise the question whether they or their metabolites are directly involved (Csapo, 1961). An intrauterine contraceptive progesterone system, which releases 50 μg of progesterone per day over a year, interferes with fertilization by way of endometrial cells, ova, and sperm. Since the menstrual cycle is not affected, the action is restricted to the surface cells of the endometrium (Zaffaroni, 1974). The multiple complicating effects of systemic involvement including biochemical

interactions in transport following parenteral or oral administration are eliminated. Medroxyprogesterone acetate (17α-acetoxy-6α-methylprogesterone)
and cyproterone (6-chloro-6-dehydro-17α-hydroxyl-1,2α-methyleneproges-
terone) are both antiandrogens with a common 17α-hydroxyprogesterone
nucleus. Nevertheless, they apparently function by different mechanisms. In
rats, medroxyprogesterone acetate increases the catabolism of testosterone
in the liver by increasing reductase activity and cyproterone decreases the
uptake of testosterone by the prostate (Albin *et al.*, 1973). In human males,
cyproterone raises plasma testosterone levels (Rausch-Stroomann *et al.*,
1970). These differences point to various possible mechanisms of action for
naturally occurring analogs.

F. Stereochemistry

The stereochemistry of the steroids involves the asymmetric carbon atom,
the cis-trans relationships of the four fused rings, and the axial and equatorial
relationship of side groups to the steroid plane as a whole. Moreover,
radicals influence adjacent radicals on linked carbons.

Extended series of steroids with substituted alkyl or electronegative groups,
resulting in structural or electronic alterations in the natural steroid hormone
molecules, have been synthesized. The comparative biologic activity of these
compounds indicated the steric requirements for steroid hormone reactivity
at the intracellular level (for review, see Ringold, 1961). The β side (top) of
the steroid hormone molecules is the one at which the angular methyl
groups at C-10 and C-13, or at C-13 alone, project.

The studies with group substitutions in the testosterone and dihydrotestosterone molecules indicated that the α side (bottom) is required to
react with the cellular or enzyme surfaces to evoke an adrogenic response.
This also holds for aldosterone (Fried, 1961). In contrast, similar studies with
the estrogens, progestins, and glucocorticoids indicated that the β surface
interacts at the receptor site. The data for the estrogens are not extensive.
According to these studies, the phenolic group at the C-3 position is essential
for estrogenic activity. The ketone group in the unsaturated ring A and the
oxygen linkage at C-17 or C-20 are required for the progestational activity
of progesterone and its derivative or for the 17α-substituted testosterones.
Three 19-nor compounds, one with a Δ^5, 3β-OH grouping and two deoxy
derivatives at C-3 or C-20, also demonstrated progestational activity. In
view of the bioassay procedure for these three compounds, required structural changes may ensue by enzymic activity during their metabolic route.
With the glucocorticoids, even gross substitutions at the α side of the molecule do not interfere with the receptor site occupancy at the β side with its
axial groupings at C-11, C-18, and C-19 as essential components. The binding

forces for oxygen at C-3 would be less for the androgens than for the glucocorticoids and the progestins.

G. Steroid–Receptor Interactions

Receptor models, borrowed from enzyme theory and applied to pharmacology, may be further extended in application to steroid–receptor interaction. The mechanism of drug action at the receptor site involving a steroid hormone would relate to the mechanism of the steroid itself. It should not be assumed that all *in vivo* chemical reactions involving steroids are enzymic (see Section IV,G,2) or that all steroid enzymic reactions are intracellular (see Section IV,B). The instability of steroids under *in vitro* conditions with concentrations in the biologic range demonstrates nonenzymic reactions.

A steroid may react noncovalently with a receptor protein to initiate an enzymic reaction. Another chemically related or nonrelated compound adsorbed on the receptor site may inactivate the receptor site for biologic function only until the compound is replaced or degraded. The original theory of occupancy (Clark, 1926), which did not envisage this situation, was modified (Ariëns, 1954) to account for it. Estradiol-17β and estrone benzoates were 50–25 times as effective on a weight basis as the free steroids, both injected subcutaneously in sesame oil, for the activation of lordosis in ovariectomized guinea pigs (Feder and Silver, 1974). The dose difference may be attributed to a longer action span for the esters producing lower and continuous levels by slower release from the depot and esterase hydrolysis. The results suggested not only a triggering mechanism at the receptor site, but the requirement of the prolonged presence of estrogen.

The rate theory envisions receptor site activity as the number of encounters at the receptor site in any given time and does not require a stable occupancy (Paton and Payne, 1968). The effect of nonsteroid estrogen antagonists is not so much a competition for cytoplasmic estrogen receptors producing a complex that is a poor stimulation for growth, but relates to failure in stimulating replenishment of the receptor (Clark *et al.*, 1974).

The high concentration gradient of a steroid with relatively low affinity for the receptor may be competing with a high-affinity steroid in low concentration. Competition of transport proteins of low or high affinity in plasma for the same steroid (Bryson, 1971) would also apply to fixed receptor sites. The four condensed-ring system of the steroids is more inflexible than that of the protein chains, and it is in the process of adsorption of the steroid to an enzyme receptor that the flexibility of the protein in conforming to the steroid may be one of the requirements that triggers the enzyme reaction. A model of this kind illustrates the induced-fit theory of receptor site activation (Koshland, 1964), which has been extended (Belleau, 1964) to account for conformational perturbation of the receptor protein through chemical mechanisms such as hydrophobic forces.

The cellular receptor proteins for steroid hormones are of three types: in the cytosol fraction when the cells have not been subjected to hormone exposure, and in the nuclear fraction when the cell has been exposed, one extractable, the other insoluble. The receptors vary quantitatively, e.g., in the estrous cycle and between the endometrium and myometrium in early pregnancy. The same cells may contain different receptors for the same hormone types, varying in affinities and specificity (Baulieu, 1975). When testosterone enters the human prostate it is reduced to 5α-dihydrotestosterone, which binds to the nuclei and ribonucleoprotein-containing endoplasmic reticulum sites. Testosterone is retained in the cells but the dihydrotestosterone which induces growth and differentiation of the prostate is in equilibrium with the extracellular transport mechanisms (Grant *et al.*, 1975). The binding of dihydrotestosterone, estradiol, and aldosterone by their respective classical target organs, the prostate, uterus, and kidney has its counterpart in the brain. Estradiol concentrates primarily in the cell nuclei of the preoptic region and hypothalamus, with lesser amounts in the amygdaloid region (Stumpf *et al.*, 1971). Testosterone and dihydrotestosterone are found in similar brain regions as estradiol but not strongly bound to the cell nuclei (see McEwen *et al.*, 1971). Progesterone and aldosterone appear more uniformly distributed in brain regions. Corticosterone-binding macromoles in adrenalectomized rats are found in the cytosol and nuclear fractions of the hippocampus. Corticosteroids can suppress cell function in the thymus and lead to the death of hormone-sensitive lymphocytes.

In tissue culture of rat muscle cells, testosterone but not estradiol-17β,5β-pregnanediol, 5α-dihydrotestosterone, or androstenedione demonstrated a direct interaction as measured by a labeling index of the cell nucleus using [^{3}H]thymidine (Powers and Florini, 1975).

IV. Enzyme Systems

A. Structurally Modified Hormone Preparations

In many steroid hormone or structurally related pharmaceuticals, OH groups have either been esterified, alkylated, or otherwise modified.

1. *Ester Preparations*

β-Estradiol-3-benzoate, the 17-propionate, dipropionate, 17-undecanoate, 17-valerate, and 17-cypionate (cyclopentanepropionate) are examples. Diethylstilbestrol ester pharmaceuticals include the dipalmitate, diphosphate, disulfate, and dipropionate. Transdiethylstilbestrol is considerably more biologically active than the cis form and is the isomer of choice in pharmaceutical preparations. Estrone esters include the acetate, sulfate, and sulfate piperazine salt; estriol esters, the 16,17-bis sodium hemisuccinate. With cortisone or deoxycorticosterone, the C_{21} acetates are used. Progesterone is devoid of an OH group. In medroxyprogesterone acetate, an OH has been introduced at the 17 position and esterified without destroying the progestational effect. Testosterone ester pharmaceuticals include the acetate, cypionate, heptoate, isobutyrate, ketolaurate, nicotinate, and propionate.

2. *Ether Preparations*

A derivative related to estriol but with a 16β instead of an α-OH group and an additional 16-methyl group is used clinically as the 3-methoxy derivative. Other methyl ethers are derived from pregnenolone and diethylstilbestrol. A cyclopentyl enol ether of 17α-methyltestosterone retains its androgenic properties. The maltosides of steroid hormones and related compounds would be ethereal sugar derivatives. Water solubility of the steroid hormone or related compound is increased by etherizing it with a sugar molecule (Plattner and Uffer, 1944).

B. Serum Esterase

The effect of esterification or etherization would depend on whether the derivative reached the receptor site intact. Determination of receptor conformation by measuring uptake of the steroid derivative requires target tissue free from enzymes that could release the parent steroid hormone or related compound. Whether both or either of the two hydroxyl groups of estradiol must be intact to function at a receptor is not known (Reynolds and Bryson, 1974). Steroid esters introduced orally or parenterally encounter the blood enzyme systems on transportation to the target site. Proteolytic enzymes may have esterase activity (Kaufman *et al.*, 1948), and a distinction between blood lipases and esterases is untenable (Seligman *et al.*, 1949). Hydrolysis of steroid hormone esters should be considered even though cholesterol esters are rather immune to the action of serum esterases (Sperry, 1935). The enzymic hydrolysis of steroid hormone esters was originally demonstrated for estradiol benzoate, estradiol dipropionate, and estrone acetate in human and/or rabbit, bull, rat, and chicken serum (Bischoff *et al.*, 1949). In human and rabbit sera, estrone sodium sulfate and estrone palmitate were resistant to enzyme hydrolysis (Bischoff *et al.*, 1951a). An hepatic aryl sulfatase in the liver and other tissues hydrolyzes the natural estrogen sulfates, which, nevertheless, have a low metabolic clearance and a long half-life (Ruder *et al.*, 1972). A partially purified esterase from human red cells, not associated with the membrane, hydrolyzed estrone acetate, and 3α- and 17β-acetoxy steroids (Oertel *et al.*, 1975). On incubation of estradiol with human serum no esterification occurred. This is analogous to the reaction of cholesterol added to serum. However, the free endogenous cholesterol of serum is esterified on incubation (Sperry, 1935).

C. Fate of Methoxy Steroids

Information on enzyme systems that would deetherize steroid alkoxy compounds is sparse. Since enzyme systems are reversible, the *O*-methyltransferase system which is one of the routes in the metabolism of catecholamines was studied for specificity. 2-Hydroxy-17β estradiol is methylated at the 2-hydroxy position by an *O*-methyltransferase of rat liver, but estrone, estradiol-17β, and estriol are not (Breuer *et al.*, 1962). In humans the metabolic pathways for estrone are hydroxylation at the 16, 2, or 6 positions. An *O*-methyltransferase converts the 2-hydroxyestrone to the methyl ether. Demethylation of 2-methoxyestrone occurs, but the reverse reaction is favored (Fotherby, 1974). In rats, 2-methoxyestrone and 2-hydroxyestrone 3-methyl ether are metabolic products conjugated as glucuronides (Bartke *et al.*, 1971; Watanabe, 1971). The absence of *O*-methylation in other metabolic routes for estrone indicates a specificity of this enzyme for catechols. A comparison of the action of three placental enzymes (an estrogen-dependent transhydrogenase and a DPN and TPN dehydrogenase) shows that the estradiol-17β-3-monomethyl ether has 32% the activity of estradiol-17β with the former and 145% and 144%, respectively, with the two latter enzymes. The stability of the ether group under these conditions is not known. However, the ether leakage decreases or abolishes the activity in the transhydrogenase reaction but definitely increases it with the two dehydrogenases. Thus the 3-methoxy group enhances steroid metabolism and is therefore biologically active. In contrast, the free OH group is essential or much more efficient in the physiologic activity of the hormone in which the hormone itself is not changed (Hagerman and Villee, 1959).

The splitting of the ether linkage of mestranol to form ethynylestradiol was indicated when ethynylestradiol was found in plasma after oral administration of mestranol (Warren and Fotherby, 1973). Other studies (Wijmenga and von der Molen, 1969; Bird and Clark, 1973) confirm this deetherization. The major metabolite in urine of both the 3-methyl ether (mestranol) and the cyclopentyl ether of ethynylestradiol appears to be ethynylestradiol itself, suggesting that splitting of the ether linkage occurs rapidly (Reed *et al.*, 1972). About 35% of mestranol appears to be demethylated to ethynylestradiol in rats as compared to 60% in mice (Kappus *et al.*, 1972).

D. 17-Hydroxydehydrogenases

The conversion of estrone to a product possessing increased biologic activity by incubation with rabbit or mouse uterus, heart, lung, spleen, kidney (Heller, 1940) and rabbit or human red cells (Bischoff *et al.*, 1951b) led to the extensive research on the 17-hydroxydehydrogenases. The enzymic nature of the red cell conversion was established (Bischoff *et al.*, 1952), and estradiol-17β was isolated as the reaction product (Gray and Bischoff, 1955). The above observations with red cells were confirmed: (1) serum is devoid of this enzyme activity; (2) either intact or hemolyzed red cells may be used; and (3) glucose restores the activity of washed cells. Glucose 6-phosphate may be substituted for glucose (Repke and Markwardt, 1954a,b). The augmentation of the enzymic conversion by substituting glucose 6-phosphate for glucose was not observed for 11 diverse mammalian tissues (Bischoff *et al.*, 1957). TPN accelerated the action of glucose but not of glucose 6-phosphate with or without glucose 6-phosphate dehydrogenase. A species difference was established for cow, sheep, and goat red cells, which convert estrone to estradiol-17α instead of the previously described 17β system for man, mouse, rat, and rabbit (Portius and Repke, 1960). The D(T)PN-linked 17β-estradiol dehydrogenase of human placenta is stereo-specific for the 17β-hydroxy group and requires the aromatic A ring. Diethyl-stilbestrol is a weak inhibitor (Karavolas and Engel, 1971). Two abbreviations for the same nucleotide appear in the literature, viz., NAD^+ and DPN^+ for nicotinamide adenine dinucleotide, also called diphosphopyridine nucleotide; $NADP^+$ and TPN^+ for nicotinamide adenine dinucleotide phosphate, also called triphosphophyridine nucleotide. In this review the abbreviations of the experimenter are used.

With the red cell incubation technique previously used with estrone (Bischoff *et al.*, 1951b, 1952), testosterone retained its Δ^4, 3-keto grouping but developed a keto group (presumably at the 17 position), the reverse process taking place with androstenedione and dehydroandrosterone. The establishment of a 17α-hydroxy steroid dehydrogenase, which interconverts androstenedione and epitestosterone (Linder, 1965) and a 17β-hydroxy steroid dehydrogenase which interconverts testosterone and androstenedione (Linder, 1961) followed.

In Table I a comparison is made between the ability of various human tissues to convert estrone to 17β-estradiol as measured by the increase in biologic activity utilizing the weight increase of the immature rat uterus for bioassay. The "estronase index" is the percentage increase in biologic activity resulting when 1 gm of tissue acts during 2 hours upon 200 μg of estrone at 38°C (Bischoff *et al.*, 1953). In the bioassay, estradiol-17β has 20 times the biologic activity of estrone. There are patterns of variation in

Table I
HUMAN ESTRONASE INDEX[a]

Low 0–8	Medium 9–29	High 30–115
	Normal	
Adrenal	Breast, female	Chorionic membrane
Gastric muscle	Duodenum, glandular	Ileum, terminal
Lymph node, hilar lung	Ileum	Lung
Meninges membrane	Myometrium, secretory	Mucosa, glandular
Myometrium	Ovary	Placenta
Prostate	Red blood cells	Testes
Seminal fluid	Skin	
Spleen	Thyroid	
Submucosa		
Tunica albuginea, testes		
	Pathologic	
Adrenal adenoma	Colon, adenocarcinoma	Colon, sigmoid adenocarcinoma
Bladder carcinoma	Esophagus, adenocarcinoma	Bronchogenic carcinoma
Bronchogenic carcinoma	Kidney, adenocarcinoma	Duodenum, adenocarcinoma
Colon, carcinoma	Neurilemmoma	Endometrium, fibrosis
Endometrium, adenocarcinoma	Ovarian cyst, serous	Meningioma
Glioblastoma multiform	Ovary, aplastic carcinoma	Tonsils, hyperplastic
Hydrocele fluid	Stomach, adenocarcinoma	
Hydrocele membrane	Synovial sarcoma	
Ileum, lymphosarcoma	Teratoembryonal carcinoma	
Mammary carcinoma (4)	Thyroid, colloid adenoma	
Ovary, adenocarcinoma	Thyroid, adenocarcinoma	
Prostate, nodular	Uterus, adenomyosis	
Rectum, adenocarcinoma		
Skin, fibrosarcoma		

[a] From Bischoff *et al.* (1953) and Bischoff (1956).

the distribution of estronase (estradiol-17β-hydroxy dehydrogenase) activity in tissues of man and rodents that are not species specific. In mice, rats, rabbits, and humans the estronase levels are all high in the testes and lung and very low (if at all) in the striated muscle (Bischoff *et al.*, 1953, 1957; Bischoff, 1969). The highest estronase value obtained, 300, is for a human hydatidiform mole (exceeded tabular values).

For human testes, 7% estradiol was identified and 47% estrone recovered on incubation of estrone (Ryan and Engel, 1953). Countercurrent distribution and photofluorometry were used to separate, characterize, and estimate the estrone and estradiol after incubation in this study. With the human ileum, placenta, liver, adrenal, breast, endometrium, and myometrium, the enzyme equilibrium favors the formation of estrone. Normal skin and malignant breast tissues incubated with testosterone converted more testosterone to androstenedione than did other tissues studied (Wotiz *et al.*, 1954).

E. THE HYDROXYLASES

1. *Aryl Hydrocarbon Hydroxylase*

The polycylic hydrocarbons that are carcinogenic in laboratory animals (and possibly in humans) are hydroxylated by microsomal enzyme systems that have been found in the liver, lung, placenta, leukocytes, and some other tissues (for references, see Abramson and Hutton, 1975). This is apparently a defense mechanism and begins with the formation of epoxides. The specificity of these hydroxylases, whether they exclude or include steroids and at what sites, is of considerable importance.

2. *Cholesterol 24-Hydroxylase*

Cholesterol 24-hydroperoxide may be formed by autoxidation. It decomposes thermally to form 3β-hydroxycholest-5-en-24-one. Enzymic reduction would be required to produce the stereospecific cerebrosterol (cholest-5-ene-3β,24-diol). The biologic formation of this diol is brought about by a highly specific sterol-24 hydroxylase, which has been isolated from bovine cerebral cortex. Molecular oxygen is required. NADPH$_2$ increases hydroxylation 6-fold (Dhar *et al.*, 1973). Cerebrosterol has been isolated from human cerebral cortex, subcortical white matter, midbrain, pons, and cerebellum; from equine whole brain; from bovine cerebral cortex; and from rabbit whole brain. In studies with rats (Lin and Smith, 1974) the concentrations of the diol in the brain roughly doubled from youth to maturity. Although present in nuclear, mitochondrial, microsomal, and soluble fractions, the concentrations of cholest-5-ene-3β,24-diol were highest in fractions of myelin and nerve endings, accounting for 75% of the total content in the brain. Whereas the diol is formed from cholesterol by oxidation, another brain metabolite, 5α-cholestan-3β-ol, is formed by reduction. The enzymic conversion of cholesterol to the diol has been demonstrated in bovine and rat cerebral cortex.

3. *11β-Hydroxylase*

A soluble steroid 11β-hydroxylase from bovine adrenal cortex hydroxylates both 11-deoxycortisol and 11-deoxycorticosterone at the same enzyme sites (Sharma *et al.*, 1962). An 11β-hydroxylase in the mitochondrial structures of the adrenal gland hydroxylates progesterone, androstenedione

17β-hydroxyprogesterone, 11-deoxycorticosterol, and 11-deoxycorticoste-
rone (Sweat and Bryson, 1961). Androst-4-ene-3,17-dione, dehydroepiandrosterone, dehydroepiandrosterone sulfate, and testosterone inhibited
the conversion of 11-deoxycorticosterone to corticosterone; 11β-hydroxy-
androst-4-ene-3,17-dione did not (Sharma *et al.*, 1963). The 11β-hydroxylase
of adrenal cortex mitochondria, which converts deoxycorticosterone to
corticosterone, appears to be a mixed-function oxidase. NADPH plays a
dual role as a reducing agent and in the formation of the active oxygen.
Only the latter reaction is directly involved with the steroid (Sih, 1969).
In the biosynthesis of aldosterone, 18- and 21-hydroxylation probably take
place before 11-hydroxylation (Fragachan *et al.*, 1969). 11β-Hydroxylase
deficiency is linked to the hypertensive form of congenital adrenal hyperplasia in humans because no 11-oxygenated C_{21} or C_{19} steroids were found
in either their blood or urine (Eberlein and Bongiovanni, 1956). Inhibition
of 11β-hydroxylation in the adrenal cortex of dogs by Metopirone (2-methyl-
1,2-di-3-pyridyl-1-propanone) produced similar symptoms (Adlin and
Channick, 1966).

4. *Other Hydroxylases*

7α-Hydroxylases have been shown to hydroxylate a number of C_{19} steroids, such as testosterone and dehydroepiandrosterone, in rat testes and
liver. Androstenedione is the preferential substrate in the testes. The enzymes
were isolated in the microsomal fractions (Inano and Tamaoki, 1971). A
21-hydroxylase, isolated from sheep adrenals, hydroxylated 17-hydroxypro-
gesterone in the absence of cytochrome P-450 (Matthijssen and Mandel,
1967).

Functional specificity for zones of the mammalian adrenal cortex indicate
that an 18-oxygenase occurs in the glomerulosa, a 17-hydroxylase in the
fasciculata-reticularis, and a 3β-dehydrogenase and 11- and 21-hydroxylases
in all of the zones (Stachenko and Giroud, 1959).

F. Steroid Hormone Syntheses

The testes, ovaries, and adrenals may be regarded developmentally as
bisexual glands with common steroid synthetic routes that vary in intensity
at various steps of the route. According to one probably oversimplistic
scheme, cholesterol is oxidized to pregnenolone and in turn to progesterone
(Samuels *et al.*, 1951) and 17α-hydroxyprogesterone (Slaunwhite and Samuels,
1956). Adrenal zones able to 17-hydroxylate pregnenolone bypass the
progesterone step. In the testes the metabolic route would lessen in intensity
after the formation of testosterone and androstenedione, in the corpus luteum
after the formation of progesterone. In the ovary more of the androgens

would be converted to estradiol. In the adrenals 17α-hydroxyprogesterone is hydroxylated at the 11 and 21 positions to form cortisol (Plager and Samuels, 1954); in the testes, ovarian follicles, and adrenals the 2-carbon side chain of 17α-hydroxyprogesterone is cleaved to form testosterone and androstenedione. The 2-carbon side chain of the progesterone derivatives is not cleaved if C_{21} is hydroxylated or the 20-keto group has been reduced (Lynn and Brown, 1958). Androgens can be aromatized to form estrogens in the placenta: in humans, estriol from dehydroepiandrosterone. [3-^{14}C]-Testosterone incubated with human ovarian slices was metabolized to 4-androstene-3,17-dione and [3-^{14}C]estradiol-17β (Baggett *et al.*, 1956). Other body sites are able to perform this same reaction, as was demonstrated in castrated–adrenalectomized human females (West *et al.*, 1956).

In keeping with the normal scrotal temperature, the testicular enzyme which cleaves cholesterol at the side chain has its maximum activity at 33°C (Wisner and Gomes, 1975).

Other Aromatization Sites

In the human male, 80–100% of estrone and estradiol production is accounted for by conversions of plasma precursors, such as androstenedione and testosterone. The route of estrogen production in males also applies to postmenopausal women. The complete elaboration of nonovarian estrogen does not appear to be accounted for by the testis or adrenal cortex (MacDonald *et al.*, 1971). There is evidence that in rodents and humans the adrenal cortex synthesizes androgens and estrogens. The production of extragenital estrogens by the hyperplastic adrenal cortical tissue that develops after gonadectomy in the dba and C_3H strains of mice has been assumed to explain the gradual recovery of the uterus, vagina, and breast from the castrate state (Woolley, 1943) and the development of mammary carcinomas. Adrenal cortical tumors in human males may produce impotence, atrophy of the genitalia, and mammary hypertrophy with lactation. The presence of raised estrogen levels (Broster, 1946) in urine, with decreases after surgical removal of such a tumor and return after recurrence of the tumor, indicate the potential of estrogen secretion by the adrenal cortex. Aromatization occurs in the CNS (see Section IX,B,1,a).

The isolation of estradiol-17β from the phenolic fraction of the lipid extract of human testes does not prove its synthesis by the testes. This was accomplished by incubating radiolabeled acetate, testosterone, cholesterol, senecioate, β-hydroxyisovalerate, β-hydroxy-β-methylglutarate, and mevalonate with fortified human testicular homogenates; mevalonate was the most efficient precursor for synthesis both of cholesterol and estradiol-17β. The cholesterol was more heavily tagged than the estradiol, indicating that it was the intermediary for the synthesis of the latter (Rabinowitz, 1959).

Stallion testes contain considerably more estradiol-17β than sow ovaries on a milligram per kilogram basis (Beall, 1940). The other sites of steroid aromatization in males and females are yet to be identified.

A sequence of interplay between the primate placenta and the fetal adrenal is required for estrogen synthesis. The fetal adrenal removes the side chain of the C_{21} steroids elaborated by the placenta to produce C_{19} derivatives or produces them without placental precursors. Aromatization, however, is restricted to the placenta (Siiteri and MacDonald, 1966).

G. THE OXIDATION OF CHOLESTEROL

The primary oxidation of cholesterol may be considered as proceeding by four diverse routes: autoxidation, radiation-induced oxidation, oxygen donor acceptance, and various enzyme reactions.

1. *Autoxidation of Cholesterol*

By autoxidation of crystalline cholesterol held at 70°C in air and in the dark for two 4-week periods, 3β-hydroxycholest-5-ene-7β-hydroperoxide and 6β-hydroperoxycholest-4-en-3-one were formed along with a low yield of the epimer of the first compound (Teng *et al.*, 1973). Cholest-5-ene-3β,7-diol, 3β-hydroxycholest-5-en-7-one, cholesta-3,5-dien-7-one, and 5α-cholestane-3β,5,6β-triol are stable reaction products formed by autoxidation of cholesterol under the mildest conditions (Bergström and Wintersteiner, 1941; Mosbach *et al.*, 1952) simulating conceivable biologic environments. They are derived from the hydroperoxides initially formed which suffer thermal decomposition. Likewise the stable products, oxidized at the cholesterol side chain, presumably are accounted for by a similar mechanism in which the cholesterol 20α-, 24-, 25-, and 26-hydroperoxides are initially formed (van Lier and Kan, 1972) and decompose.

2. *Nonenzymic Oxidation*

It should not be assumed that all *in vivo* steroid chemical reactions are enzyme dependent or that the isolation of a reaction product of a steroid incubated in biologic material constitues proof of an enzyme system. The ease with which cholesterol undergoes autoxidation at body temperatures and the instability of reaction products require that rigid criteria be instituted to determine whether a similar *in vivo* conversion is indeed enzymic. Neither the formation of the α and β 7-hydroperoxides of cholesterol nor their decomposition products, α and β 7-hydroxides, are necessarily enzymic when formed in the liver or other body tissues (Smith and Teng, 1974). Nonenzymic reactions in aqueous protein solutions were observed for isomerization of 3β-hydroxy-5α-cholest-6-ene-5-hydroperoxide to cholesterol 7α-hydroperoxide, the epimerization of the latter compound, and thermal decomposition of these hydroperoxides (Teng and Smith, 1973).

3. *Oxidation Products of Cholesterol Involving Radiation*

In solution, excited-state molecular oxygen forms 3β-hydroxy-5α-cholest-6-ene-5-hydroperoxide and the 4-ene-6-hydroperoxides from cholesterol. This is a photosensitized system. By radical oxidation of cholesterol in solution the 7-hydroperoxides are produced (Smith *et al.*, 1973).

V. Transport Mechanisms

The site of liberation of a therapeutic steroid, whether introduced by the oro-gastrointestinal or parenteral routes, is in most instances remote from the target site. One of the functions of the body fluids comprising the interstitial fluid, lymph, cerebrospinal fluid, and blood is that of transportation not only of steroids, but also of protein hormones and nutrients.

The expression "protein-binding" denotes noncovalent binding in this review. The concept of a protein–steroid hormone covalent linkage is no longer tenable. The French expression "liaison" to describe the affinity between a steroid hormone and a protein is better semantics. To the uninitiated, binding unfortunately appears to connote the covalent chemical bond. Liaison connotes a more or less transient arrangement.

A. INTERSTITIAL FLUID, LYMPH, AND CEREBROSPINAL FLUID

The liberated steroid first encounters the interstitial fluid. There are practically no data based on direct experimentation of the physiochemical status of the steroid in interstitial fluid because of the difficulty of obtaining sufficient amounts of the fluid. On the assumption that interstitial fluid is derived from the noncellular phase of blood by ultrafiltration or dialysis through the capillary endothelium, lymph should be an accumulation of it (Schmidt and Greenberg, 1935). The protein content of lymph is generally less than that of blood plasma and varies widely at different body areas, probably because of variation in capillary pore size. Deductions on the transport mechanism of steroids in interstitial fluid rest on what is known of the individual constituents of plasma that find their way into the interstitial fluid. Such deductions may, however, be hazardous. A steroid suspension, a solution of a steroid in a natural oily vehicle, a steroid pellet, or a plastic capsule containing a steroid invokes a foreign body reaction (Bischoff and Bryson, 1964) at the implant site (see Section V,F).

The sheet flow of interstitial fluid may replace capillary function as a transport mechanism in the glomerular bed of the kidney, in the alveoli of the lung, and in the liver (Sobin *et al.*, 1970). Evidence from chemical carcinogenesis indicates that such a local transport may also occur at the subcutaneous site (Bischoff and Bryson, 1974a).

The low normal protein concentration range in human ventricular cerebrospinal fluid (CSF), about 10 mg per 100 ml, as compared to 6500–8200 mg per 100 ml of plasma, indicates that once the steroids have arrived in the CSF, the CSF proteins would have little effect in regulating the transfer of a steroid across the cell membrane at the central target sites. The presence of steroid hormones in the CSF has been observed and measured in humans for cortisone and hydrocortisone (Baron and Abelson, 1954) and for progesterone during pregnancy (Lurie and Weiss, 1967). In rhesus monkeys estradiol-17β and metabolites were identified (Anand Kumar and Thomas, 1968). In rhesus monkeys injected intravenously with tritiated testosterone, progesterone, 17α-hydroxyprogesterone, norethynodrel (17α-ethynyl-17-hydroxy-5(10)-estren-3-one) or mestranol (17α-ethynylestradiol 3-methyl ether), the plasma and CSF levels were determined after 1 hour. For testosterone and progesterone, there was considerably less activity per unit volume CSF as compared to the plasma, with ratios of 0.03 and 0.4, respectively. For the other steroids the ratios were reversed, ranging from 1.5 to 7.0 (David and Anand Kumar, 1974). Although weakly progestational, 17α-hydroxyprogesterone may have biologic significance in the feedback of gonadotropins.

B. PLASMA

Under physiologic and pharmacologic ranges, the concentrations of steroid hormones as well as biogenic amines in human blood plasma do not exceed their aqueous solubilities. However, only a fraction of these hormones may be in true aqueous solution because of noncovalent binding with specific plasma proteins. A protein with a high orientation potential but present in low concentration may be competing with another protein with low orientation potential but present in high concentration. The two proteins and water will be competing for distribution of the steroid in transport (Bryson, 1971). Equilibrium for the steroid between the protein constituent and water is reached rapidly in plasma; the transfer rate from plasma to the formed elements of blood, crossing the cell wall, at physiologic and pharmacologic concentrations has not been extensively studied. With saline or serum and red cells, equilibrium was reached in less than 10 minutes at 37°C for estradiol (Bischoff and Katherman, 1948); also with albumin and serum for estriol, but not with saline (Bischoff *et al.*, 1951c).

The existence of an "estroprotein" (Szego, 1953) reported to be enzymically conjugated by the liver and theorized as the "estroprotein" circulating in the Cohn III-O fraction of plasma was not confirmed (Bischoff, 1969). Among the reaction products of radiolabeled estrone incubated with liver brei, estrone, 2-hydroxyestrone, their glucosiduronates, and a glucuronic acid derivative of 2-methoxyestrone were identified (Horwitz *et al.*, 1962; Brooks *et al.*, 1963). Conjugates of sulfates and a phosphate were indicated. An unknown metabolite was isolated. The presence of the glucosiduronate and glucuronic acid derivative at the albumin peak on electrophoresis is accounted for by the powerful noncovalent binding attraction for this class of compounds to albumin, not to covalent interaction by liver enzymes.

The 2-hydroxylation of estradiol-17β and estrone by microsomal enzymes precedes an apparently covalent reaction with proteins (Hecker and Marks, 1965) to a small degree if low levels of estrogen are present. Definite proof for the formation of a covalent bond awaits isolation of compounds in which the steroid decomposition product is attached to a functional group of amino acids after hydrolysis of the protein moiety. In these experiments unchanged estradiol and estrone did not form this type of protein complex. With 2-hydroxylated ethynylestradiol, the corresponding bound proteins are formed at triple the concentration at the same dose level (Kappus *et al.*, 1973) and being foreign proteins are antigenic. Such antigens could presumably exert profound effects on endogenous estrogen physiologic activity, and since the 2-hydroxyestradiols are catechols, even influence catecholamine activity (see Section IX,C,1).

1. *Temperature Sensitivity to Binding by Plasma Proteins*

The unbound cortisol in human plasma is about 1% of the total at 4°C (Daughaday, 1958) and rises to between 5 and 10% at 37°C (Bush, 1957). On overloading human plasma or human pregnancy plasma with cortisol, the amount bound is very sensitive to temperature, that bound at 38°C being less than 50% of that bound at 4°C for normal plasma (de Moor *et al.*, 1962). The time required for radiolabeled cortisol to replace endogenous corticosteroid bound to corticosteroid-binding globulin (CBG) in human serum was complete in 1 minute at 37.5°C, but incomplete in 1 hour at 4°C (Doe *et al.*, 1964; Murphy, 1964). The marked increase in the disassociation of cortisol from its CBG complex above 37°C may make available higher cortisol concentrations during acute fever or locally in areas of inflammation (Mills, 1961).

With human serum albumin (HSA), comparisons at 5° and 25°C showed little difference in binding for estrone, estradiol, progesterone, or testosterone, but a marked reduction for cortisol at the higher temperature (Slaunwhite *et al.*, 1963). The progesterone-binding α_1-acid glycoprotein (AAG), like CBG, has a marked reduction in binding capacity for progesterone with rising temperature (Westphal and Carnighan, 1964). The binding affinity of AAG for testosterone is about 20 times that of HSA at 40°C and 5 times at 37°C (Kerkay and Westphal, 1968).

Much early work with CBG was not performed at 38°C and therefore is not relevant for interpretation of mammalian binding and transport mechanisms at normal body temperatures.

2. Plasma Albumin

a. Free Steroid. Albumin plays a major role in transporting progesterone and under certain conditions estradiol. It is probably involved with estrone and androstenedione transport. After administration of estrone to humans most of the biologic activity was carried by the albumin fraction (Antoniades *et al.*, 1957).

b. Conjugates. Estradiol and estrone as they reach plasma are intraconvertible by the red cell 17β-hydroxy steroid dehydrogenase (see Section IV,D), but the equilibrium favors estrone. Both are rapidly esterified as sulfates (Ruder *et al.*, 1972). Estradiol and estrone sulfates appear to account for half the estrogens in human plasma (Ruder *et al.*, 1972); the latter is the main estrogen in plasma. A 2.6% albumin solution equilibrated with red cells gave the same order of distribution coefficient for estrone sulfate as did rabbit serum (Bischoff and Katherman, 1949). A similar experiment with human red cells and human protein fractions (albumin, Cohn IV-1 and IV-4), relegated approximately 90% of the orientation to albumin (Bischoff *et al.*, 1958a). More recent work estimates 98% estrone sulfate in plasma bound to albumin (Rosenthal *et al.*, 1972). Since the metabolic clearance rate of estrone sulfate is about one-tenth that of estradiol or estrone (Longcope *et al.*, 1968), the binding to albumin would indicate more powerful forces or protective mechanisms than those involved with the binding of estradiol to sex steroid-binding globulin (SBG). The binding of the glucosiduronates of estriol and estrone to human serum albumin was slightly higher than that bound to human plasma diluted 1 to 5, indicating that these conjugates are mostly transported by the albumin (Sandberg *et al.*, 1966). Although plasma albumin is generally accepted as the plasma protein with the greatest binding potential for the steroid hormone conjugates, some reservation should remain for some of the conjugates because many experiments were not performed at 38°C or even at the normal blood pH range. Following the injection of tritiated dehydroepiandrosterone into humans, the sulfates which formed were found in the albumin fraction and the corresponding glucosiduronates in the α_1-globulin fraction (Oertel *et al.*, 1969). The urinary conjugated metabolites of cortisol are not bound to CBG (Sandberg and Slaunwhite, 1959); the affinity of corticosterone sulfate is half that of corticosterone for CBG (Lebeau and Baulieu, 1970).

3. *SBG, Sex Steroid-Binding β-Globulin*

SBG plays the major role in blood transport of testosterone (Guériguian and Pearlman, 1967), 5α-dihydrotestosterone (Kato and Horton, 1968), and estradiol (Tavernetti *et al.*, 1967). At release sites and under certain clinical conditions with higher steroid concentrations, AAG is also involved with testosterone and albumin with estradiol. The degree to which this occurs in plasma will not be known with certainty until the association constants have been determined at 37°C. The 17β-hydroxy group appears to be essential for the tight binding of sex steroids to SBG (Mercier-Bodard and Baulieu, 1968); a substitution at C-17 both for methyl and ethynyl groups, double bonds at C-1 or C-6, and the absence of a methyl at C-19 lessen the binding forces. Androstene-3,17-dione (Moshang *et al.*, 1970) is not bound to SBG to any great extent. Estrone, which is devoid of a 17-hydroxyl group, was as effective as estradiol-17α in competing for tagged estradiol-17β in human pregnancy plasma; hexestrol and diethylstilbestrol did not compete in the 0.25–4 ng range (Soloff *et al.*, 1971). It may be physiologically significant that SBG, as a major sex hormone plasma transport agent, applies to testosterone, estradiol, and 17β-hydroxy-5α-androstanes (Mercier-Bodard *et al.*, 1970), but not to androstenedione and estrone. Androstenedione is bound more extensively to albumin than is testosterone (Eik-Nes *et al.*, 1954). The plasma levels of SBG rise during pregnancy as with CBG (Murphy, 1968).

4. *CBG, Corticosteroid-Binding Globulin (Transcortin)*

Both in normal and pregnancy plasma, approximately 8% of cortisol is free, 80% is bound to CBG and the remainder by albumin (Rosenthal *et al.*, 1969). Corticosterone, 11-deoxycorticosterone, and 17α-hydroxyprogesterone are also bound (Seal and Doe, 1966). This affinity was not noted for some synthetic glucocorticoids: triamcinolone (Δ^1-16α-hydroxy-9α-fluorohydrocortisone) and dexamethasone (16α-methyl-9α-fluoro-Δ^1-hydrocortisone) (Kolanowski and Pizarro, 1969).

In human pregnancy serum, CBG binds about half the circulating progesterone, and albumin a proportionate amount. Since normal serum contains less CBG, albumin would bind more (Westphal, 1966). AAG binds only about 1%. The plasma level of CBG rises in humans during pregnancy or after administration of estrogen, which in effect is what happens during pregnancy. The rise of 17-OH corticosteroids during pregnancy does not lead to hypercorticism because CBG reduces their availability at the target sites (Sandberg and Slaunwhite, 1959). Administration of diethylstilbestrol to males increased plasma transcortin (CBG) above the level in pregnancy (Doe *et al.*, 1960), and also SBG levels (Forest *et al.*, 1968).

5. AAG, α_1-Acid Glycoprotein

AAG occurs in relatively high concentration in human plasma, about 750 mg/liter (Westphal, 1971), and apparently plays an intermediate transport exchange role between CBG, SBG, or albumin and the nonprotein-associated states of the respective steroids with which it may be involved.

C. RED BLOOD CELLS

Early studies (Kemp and Bjergaard, 1932; Albrieux, 1941a,b) indicated that blood estrogens were divided between serum and red cells both in nonpregnancy and pregnancy blood. Because of the great difference in physiologic effects between the estrogens as measured by bioassay techniques, the results could only be regarded qualitatively. *In vitro* distribution coefficients between rabbit red cells and serum for estrone (35 μg/ml serum), estradiol (0.3–80 μg/ml serum) and estriol (25 μg/ml serum) as well as an analysis of the distribution in human pregnancy blood of endogenous estriol and the sum of estrone and estradiol, gave quantitative information as to the distribution of individual estrogens between serum and red cells (Bischoff and Katherman, 1948; Bischoff and Pilhorn, 1948; Bischoff *et al.*, 1951c; Bischoff and Stauffer, 1957). The transport of hormones, nutrients, metabolites, drugs, and toxins by red cells is in general a physical phenomenon involving diffusion rates and equilibria between constituents within and without the cell on the basis of noncovalent attractions. Enzymic conversions, however, also maintain the balance in certain instances, notably those between estradiol-17β and estrone and between testosterone or epitestosterone and 4-androstene-3,17-dione.

The uptake of sodium estrone sulfate by human red cells at 38°C, pH 7.2 to 7.4, μ 0.155 was demonstrated by equilibration of the cells with human 3.4% albumin, 1.0% Cohn fractions IV-1 or 0.85% Cohn fraction IV-4, each containing the steroid sulfate. The steroid concentration ratios, cells: protein, were 0.30, 5.1, and 6.5, respectively (Bischoff *et al.*, 1958a).

In vitro equilibration with androgens, corticosteroids, or progesterone in two phase systems comprising red blood cells and plasma or constituents have demonstrated the potentiality of red blood cells as a transport agent for these steroid hormones (Sandberg *et al.*, 1957). However, data on blood red cells for the actual concentrations of the hormones, their conjugates, or their precursors, whether adsorbed on the cell surface or within the cell, are meager, nonexistent, or controversial. A low-affinity high-capacity fraction and the 17β-hydroxy dehydrogenase indicated limited capacity for androgen-binding by red blood cells (Brinkman *et al.*, 1970a). For the glucocorticoids, no significant binding (Brinkman *et al.*, 1970b; Schaumburg and

Crone, 1971) as contrasted with significant amounts (Peterson *et al.*, 1955; Bush, 1957; Migeon, 1957; Kornel *et al.*, 1970) indicate that further work is necessary to reconcile these divergent results. For progesterone, red blood cell binding *in vivo* is low, probably not involving a specific receptor site (Devenuto *et al.*, 1969).

A glucocorticoid receptor site has been demonstrated for lymphocytes originating in the thymus (Munck and Brinck-Johnsen, 1968). Two structural specific binding requirements, with or without hormonal activity, indicated cortisol responsible for the former. Exclusive corticosteroid receptor site occupancy by the β face of the hormone is challenged.

Penetration of the Red Cell Plasma Membrane

The plasma membrane of the red cell has been pictured as two lipid layers between which are interspersed randomly distributed lipid molecules (Danielli and Davson, 1935). The exteriors of these lipid layers are covered by adsorbed proteins which have lipids interspersed (Schmitt *et al.*, 1938). A basic question is whether circulating estrogens transported by the red cells are adsorbed on the surface of the cell or penetrate into the intracellular fluid. A study with radioactive estrone (Wall and Migeon, 1959) gave inconclusive results. Distribution of estradiol-17β between intract red cells or reconditioned ghosts and ghost-free hemolyzates of red cells or solutions of crystalline hemoglobin was proportionate to the hemoglobin concentration after a correction for water solubility was made (Bischoff and Bryson, 1960). The enzyme, estronase, followed the hemoglobin in experiments with hemolyzed red cells or reconditioned ghosts. Since estrone is converted to estradiol by the red cell estronase (Bischoff *et al.*, 1951b), penetration of these steroids through the red cell wall into the interior would be required for this reaction. In the experiment with radioactive estrone, cited above, the ghost volume shrank to one-sixth the original volume of the red cells. Since ghosts prepared in this way carry a considerable amount of hemoglobin which binds noncovalently with estrone and since binding of the ghosts exclusive of hemoglobin would have to be reduced by one-sixth, the evidence is not incompatible with penetration into the cell interior.

D. RECEPTOR SITE BINDING PROTEINS

By means of tritiated estrogens in hormone-deprived animals it has been demonstrated that the uterus, vagina, adenohypophysis, and to a lesser degree the mammary gland contain receptor-binding sites with a high degree of specificity. Estradiol but not estrone is strongly bound. Tissues such as liver and muscle are not so characterized. At the receptor-binding sites the estradiol is not dehydrogenated to estrone nor conjugated and penetrates to the nucleus of the cell, where it is bound to a specific protein (Jensen and Jacobson, 1962). The estradiol on penetrating the cell membrane is adsorbed on an extranuclear protein, rendering the latter susceptible to disassociation and penetration into the nucleus. On the basis of this two-step mechanism, nuclear concentration of estradiol-17β is used as a criterion for target tissues. In the rat, in addition to those sites already mentioned, the oviduct, brain, interstitial cells of the testes, lamina propria cells of the seminal vesicles and granulosa cells of the ovary (Stumpf *et al.*, 1971) were held as likely target tissues for estradiol-17β.

The weakly estrogenic ethamoxytriphetol, 1-[p-(2-diethylaminoethoxy)phenyl]-2-(p-methoxyphenyl)-1-phenylethanol, increases lipids and some enzyme activity in the uterus (Harris *et al.*, 1968). It does not affect the weight of the uterus or pituitary but acts at their receptor sites as a blocking agent to estradiol 17β.

1. *Human Mammary Gland Receptors for Estrogen*

Specific high-affinity estrogen receptors were not identified in the normal human mammary gland (Feherty *et al.*, 1971). However [^{3}H]estradiol was taken up by it (Puca and Bresciani, 1969). Endogenous mammary gland estrogen is mostly concentrated in the cell nuclei. The uptake is reduced by diethylstilbestrol and estradiol (Puca and Bresciani, 1969). Whereas insignificant specific binding of estradiol was found in 15 of 16 normal human breast samples taken from cancer patients, 23 out of 29 carcinomas from postmenopausal women contained cytoplasmic receptors (Wittliff *et al.*, 1972). In benign human breast tumors, 2 of 26 samples demonstrated receptor-bound estradiol-17β (Johansson *et al.*, 1970). The synthesis of estradiol-17β from 7α-[^{3}H]testosterone was unequivocally demonstrated by incubation of human breast carcinoma tissue slices. The reconstructed sequence *in vivo* would be dehydroepiandrosterone sulfate from the adrenal, dehydroepiandrosterone, and testosterone, followed by either estradiol-17β or 5α-androstanediol and 5α-dihydrotestosterone.

With a hormone-responsive female mammary adenocarcinoma of the rat, small doses of estradiol-17β increased the growth of both the cancer and normal breast tissue. The effect was indirect by way of pituitary mammotropin (prolactin) stimulation since it did not occur after hypophysectomy. Large doses of estradiol-17β inhibited the growth of the mammary cancer; the prolactin plasma levels decreased, indicating an inhibitory effect on prolactin release. Exogenous prolactin, even after hypophysectomy, stimulated cancer growth (Kim *et al.*, 1963).

Treatment. In the palliative treatment of metastatic female breast cancer (*Natl. Cancer Inst.*, 1971), the choice, combination, and sequence of endocrinologic procedures (ovariectomy, adrenalectomy, hypophysectomy, administration of androgens, estrogens, corticosteroids) depends in part on pre- or postmenopausal tumor detection (see Section VI,E) and steroid receptor site occupancy. By testing mammary tissues of patients for estrogen receptor sites as described above, only those demonstrating receptor sites are selected for estrogen therapy. It is virtually impossible to rationalize the physiologic basis for the hormone treatment and the use of diethyl-stilbestrol for the treatment. Since the receptor site test is made with estradiol-17β, it should not be assumed that diethylstilbestrol would respond in like manner in all cases.

Early work with rodents showed that caloric restriction per se without deficiency of essential nutrients retards tumor growth and exogenous protein is required for maximum tumor growth (Bischoff and Long, 1938). The retardation of tumor growth by hypophysectomy (Bischoff *et al.*, 1934) mirrors the overall effect of caloric restriction and protein starvation; hormone-dependent tumors would in addition be subject to the role of the pituitary in supplying the necessary hormones for maximum tumor growth or survival. In female rats and mice, high fat diets increased the incidence of spontaneous tumors (Carroll and Khor, 1971); in rats, high-protein diets have increased the incidence of spontaneous anterior lobe pituitary tumors (Ross *et al.*, 1970) and of induced hepatomas (Homburger *et al.*, 1965). Temporary retardation in human mammary carcinoma growth by the various drastic manipulative procedures outlined above could very likely be the result of caloric restriction. Superimposed radiation therapy would obviously come into the same category because of radiation sickness.

2. Androgens

In autoradiographic studies with Sprague–Dawley rats injected subcutaneously with [1,2-^{3}H]testosterone, nuclear concentration of androgen was demonstrated in the epithelial cells of the coagulation gland, epididymis, prostate, seminal vesicles, and neurons in the brain (Stumpf *et al.*, 1971). In the hypertrophied human prostate, labeled testosterone and 5α-dihydrotestosterone are concentrated at specific sites and testosterone is converted to 5α-dihydrotestosterone (Becker *et al.*, 1972).

3. Glucocorticoids

The search for glucocorticoid receptors in the liver involved in gluconeogenesis is complicated by the synthesis of plasma glucocorticoid binding proteins. In rat liver, protein G apparently meets the requirement of a glucocorticoid receptor (Koblinsky *et al.*, 1972). Lymphocytes also have the three-step process for nuclear binding of glucocorticoids, a concept embodying cell membrane penetration as well as cytoplasmic and nuclear binding (Schaumburg and Crone, 1971). Working with tissue culture epithelial cells of bovine mammary tissue (Tucker *et al.*, 1971) incubated with 1.6×10^{-11} mole of [^{3}H]cortisol, the steroid was isolated in both the cytoplasmic and nuclear fractions. In the cytoplasm, bound cortisol was replaceable by other glucocorticoids, progesterone, aldosterone, and 17α-hydroxyprogesterone. In contrast, only glucocorticoids but not testosterone, estradiol-17β, cortisone, and 20α-hydroxyprogesterone replaced the cortisol at nuclear binding sites.

4. *Mineralocorticoids*

As demonstrated for aldosterone, the mineralocorticoid par excellence, the sequence of events in the rat kidney parallels those for the other classes of steroid at their respective receptor sites. Other epithelial secretory tissues involved with sodium ion transport include the duodenal mucosa (Swaneck *et al.*, 1969).

5. *Progesterone*

In the pregnant rat, the uptake of a 3-fold concentration of [^{3}H]progesterone by the mammary gland over that of plasma has been demonstrated (Lawson and Pearlmann, 1964; Laumas and Farooq, 1966). However, it was not higher than that taken up by adipose tissue. After [^{3}H]progesterone injection into rats, no significant nuclear concentration was found in uterine cells (Stumpf *et al.*, 1971). Evidence for estrogen–progesterone interaction at target receptor sites is still scant. A nuclear receptor for progesterone was isolated after incubation of diethylstilbestrol-treated chick oviduct tissue at 37°C but not at 0°C (O'Malley *et al.*, 1971). The nuclear binding sites for all steroids are temperature sensitive. Allocation studies done at temperatures significantly below 37°C are subject to possible equilibrium shifts.

E. Cholesterol

1. *Synthesis*

The smooth endoplasmic reticulum in specific intestinal and liver cells is the likely site of mammalian cholesterol synthesis for transport (Meddleton and Isselbacher, 1969). Intestinal absorption of exogenous cholesterol from the diet augments the cholesterol pool. By utilizing tagged acetate in tissue culture, it has been demonstrated that many cell lines are able to synthesize cholesterol (see Rothblat, 1969).

Enzymic biosynthesis of cholesterol begins with acetate (Bloch, 1965), continuing to mevalonic acid, which by phosphorylation, decarboxylation, and dephosphorylation leads to isopentenyl and dimethylallyl pyrophosphates. By a series of condensations, squalene is formed. This in turn is cyclized to lanosterol (Schneider *et al.*, 1957) and finally demethylated to form cholesterol.

2. *Transport*

In mammalian blood, cholesterol is found in the particulate chylomicrons, red cells, and white cells and in the plasma lipoprotein fraction. The solubility of cholesterol in water (Ekwall and Mandell, 1961; Bourges *et al.*, 1967) and in 3% albumin (Bischoff and Katherman, 1948) is less than 0.001%. This is in contrast to the steroid hormones for which albumin plays a primary or secondary role as a transport agent. In human plasma cholesterol esters are in excess of free cholesterol; in red cells about 80% of the cholesterol is free.

Chylomicrons and Lipoproteins. Chylomicrons are formed in the mucosa of the gut following fat dietary intake. Determination of the chemical composition of chylomicrons entails analytical difficulties. A rough approximation is 80% triglycerides, 7% phospholipids, 5% cholesterol esters, 3% cholesterol, and 2% protein (Dole and Hamlin, 1962). For the arbitrary divisions of plasma lipoprotein into very low density (VLD), low density (LD), and high density (HD), the phospholipid content is about 25% and the free cholesterol between 5 and 10%. The largest differences are for the glyceride contents that range from 55% for VLD to 6% for HD and for the protein which is only 10% for VLD and 50% for HD (see Scanu, 1965). The noncovalent-bound protein, in common with the other noncovalently bound constituents, serves a special protective function. In this model, chylomicrons with their protein-phospholipid layer would be included.

3. *Membranes*

Phospholipids without or with cholesterol or triglycerides form membrane-like components when dispersed in aqueous media, and are spatially arranged so as to minimize exposure of the hydrocarbon radicals and attract proteins by noncovalent binding. An artificial bilayer of this kind with absorbed protein has demonstrated electrical properties similar to the nerve cell membrane (Mueller and Rudin, 1969). Cholesterol is found in the plasma membrane of cells and the intracellular membranes of the mitochondria and endoplasmic reticulum. In contrast triglycerides are not found to any degree in mammalian membranes.

4. In Vivo Cholesterol Crystal Deposition in Human Pathology

Cholesterol crystals are found in gallstones in the plate form (Bogren and Larsson, 1963) and in varying degrees in the atheroma, pneumonitis, silicosis, and cutaneous cysts (see Bryson and Bischoff, 1967; Bischoff, 1969). At the subcutaneous site in mice, in saline, or in human clear or lipemic sera, cholesterol needles are converted to plates in the presence of added vegetable oil triglyceride, triolein, or serum triglyceride (Bischoff, 1963; Bischoff and Bryson, 1964; Stauffer et al., 1975). This does not occur with human sera equilibrated with cholesterol needles without addition of triglycerides. Phospholipids isolated from human plasma delayed but did not prevent the conversion of cholesterol needles to plates from cholesterol needle-saturated triglycerides in saline.

In a pathologic breakdown of lipoprotein in the transport mechanism phospholipids are removed. Liberated triglyceride globules would function in converting cholesterol needles to plates or deposit cholesterol plates from a cholesterol-saturated triglyceride suspension (Bischoff, 1969). The free cholesterol:triglyceride ratios in VLD, LD, and HD lipoproteins (Scanu, 1965) and chylomicrons (Dole and Hamlin, 1962) indicate that the free cholesterol content greatly exceeds its solubility at 38°C for the respective triglycerides of these lipoproteins and is in the range of saturation (supersaturated for the plate form) for the chylomicron triglycerides. In tissue culture of L cells, cholesterol added to the medium produced intracellular crystals (Bailey, 1961). With cultured mouse lymphocytes, the amount of cholesterol taken up by the cells was related to both the phospholipid and protein content (Rothblat and Kritchevsky, 1967). The solubility relations in the deposition of cholesterol ester crystals along with cholesterol plates in the atheroma are not clear because the separation of the plasma apoprotein from the lipid droplets in the fibrous lesions remains conjectural (E. B. Smith, 1974). The prevalence of atherosclerotic patches at the aortic arch may relate to the local turbulence of the blood in promoting denaturation of the lipoproteins. The increased local pressure would facilitate penetration of the liberated triglycerides and steroids into the wall of the aoretic arch.

F. PHARMACODYNAMICS

With the steroid hormones and some gonadotropins, divided dosage compared to a single injection of the same total amount produces augmentation of the physiologic effect. Three injections of estradiol-17β for 3 days compared with 1 injection per day for 3 days produced a 72% augmentation of uterine weight in the immature rat with a total dose of 0.15 μg (Bischoff and Pilhorn,

1947). The effect did not reach that of chorionic gonadotropin. However, the addition of sodium lauryl sulfate, which delays resorption, produced further augmentation. The augmentation effect of divided dosage or its equivalent delayed resorption, as by injection of insulin crystals, is observed with insulin-induced hypoglycemia (Bischoff and Jemtegaard, 1937; Bischoff and Bakhtiar, 1957). Divided doses of pituitary or human chorionic gonadotropin demonstrated the augmentation phenomenon with seminal vesicle and testicular weight gain in immature rats (Bischoff, 1936).

The use of esterified steroids produces an augmentation effect by a combination of delayed resorption and gradual hydrolysis by esterases. Testosterone propionate is 1/20 as soluble as testosterone in isotonic saline at 38°C (Bischoff *et al.*, 1954). With estradiol the presence of two OH groups leads to three possible esters with any acid, viz., at the 3, at the 17, or at both positions. This raises the question of whether either or both free OH groups are required for biologic activity and whether the required esterase is present at the local injection site. The esterase distribution and specificity has not been worked out for the brain (Reynolds and Bryson, 1974). Some esters given subcutaneously or intraperitoneally are probably hydrolyzed by the blood esterase (Bischoff *et al.*, 1951a). However, sodium estrone sulfate and estrone palmitate are quite resistant.

When steroids are deposited parenterally as crystals, in cholesterol or other pellets, or in plastic containers (silicone), the foreign body reaction ensues. The variation in this reaction is species and strain specific (Bischoff and Bryson, 1964). Under these conditions the permeability of the capillary wall is greatly increased initially and the larger protein molecules and formed elements will surround the foreign body. Small particles and the surfaces of large particles elicit different tissue responses. Very small particles may be removed by phagocytes. Finely pulverized substances become engulfed by a granuloma. Larger solid surfaces become encircled by a fibrous network leading to the formation of a fibrous capsule (Dobberstein, 1960). Cohesion of some particles is another variable that is dependent upon particle size.

With the application of the implant to an experimental model at the subcutaneous, intrathoracic, or intraperitoneal sites, the gradual release of the steroid is competing with encapsulation by the fibrous capsule following the foreign body reaction. At the myocardium of dogs the fibrous capsule developed around a transplanted silicone rubber capsule containing isoproterenol and triiodothyronine in a week, abolishing the pacemaker effect (Folkman and Long, 1964). By contrast in sheep implanted intramuscularly with a silicone capsule containing melengestrol acetate, cessation of ovulation was achieved over 2 years (Dziuk and Cook, 1966). Response to a foreign body is compared at the intraperitoneal and brain sites in the mouse (Fig. 1). With implants of tin cylinders 4 mm in diameter, the typical fibrous

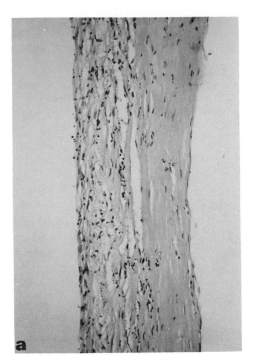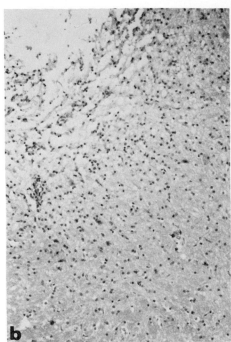

FIG. 1. Comparison of the tissue response to a foreign body (tin) at the intraperitoneal (a) and cerebral (b) sites in Marsh mice. (a) Intraperitoneal hyalinized capsule at tin implantation site 7 months later in a female mouse. × 160. (b) Thin zone of cerebral gliosis showing vacuoles characteristic of edema at margin of tin implantation site 6 months later in a male mouse. × 160 (Bischoff and Bryson, unpublished observation).

capsule was formed at the intraperitoneal site; the only reaction to the tin in the brain in areas remote from mesenchymal cells was gliosis. Tin was chosen because it is highly inert and would not, like plastics, introduce chemical factors, such as monomers, plasticizers, etc.

The rapid liberation of a high dose of estradiol-17β does not evoke the antihormone effect produced when rapidly released and slowly liberated preparations of a pituitary gonadotropin are administered simultaneously (Bischoff, 1940).

With the current sophistication regarding receptor site development, occupancy, and replacement, the older observations cited above have practical application to experimental design but unfortunately are frequently overlooked so that much research has little relevancy.

The following examples illustrate the uncertainty of the biologic effects of steroid esterification applied to an experimental design in which esterase

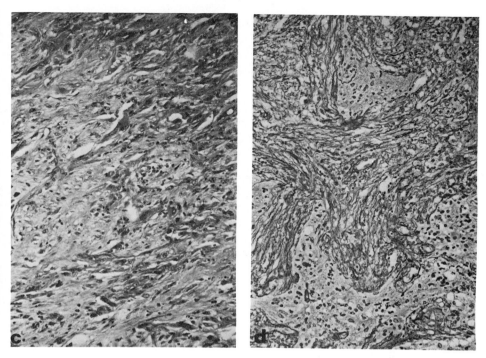

Fig. 1 (*continued*). Use of two staining techniques to demonstrate adjacent mesenchymal and glial neoplastic development in a human. (c) Mixed cerebral glioblastoma and fibrosarcoma with characteristic marmoreal pattern in a 72-year-old woman. Hematoxylin and eosin stain; ×400. (d) Mixed glioblastoma and fibrosarcoma as in (c) showing reticulum-free areas of glioma interrupted by sheets of fibrosarcoma with abundant reticulum. Gomori stain; ×400. (Courtesy of Dr. D. R. Dickson.)

activity is unknown. The acetylation of cyproterone increases antiandrogenic and introduces progestational activity (Neumann *et al.*, 1970a). *In vitro* infusion of human hyperplastic prostate with cyproterone inhibits cellular uptake of androgens and reduces 5α-reductase activity; the acetate has the reverse effect (Giorgi *et al.*, 1973). Castration in male and female rats decreased the adrenal secretion of corticosterone and increased the secretion of 5α-dihydrocorticosterone and 3β-,5α-tetrahydrocorticosterone. Subcutaneous testosterone cypionate administration reversed the effects of orchidectomy, and estradiol-17β cypionate reversed those of ovariectomy. On the assumption that cypionates are hydrolyzed by the transport or adrenal esterases, the 5α-reductase adrenal activity would be under the control of the respective steroids of gonadal origin (Colby and Kitay, 1972). The hepatic A-ring reduction of the corticosteroids (corticosterone in the rat, cortisol in the hamster) appears to be stimulated by estradiol and inhibited by testosterone in the rat, but stimulated by testosterone in the hamster. Hypophysectomy abolished these effects (Colby *et al.*, 1973). The steroids were administered subcutaneously as the cypionates. The effect of hypophysectomy on the esterase activity in these experiments was not controlled.

VI. Safety Testing for Carcinogenic Hazards

A. THE RARE TUMOR TYPE

When an increased incidence suddenly occurs with a rare tumor type, the link between a suspected etiologic agent becomes more readily apparent than when the tumor type is prosaic. Examples on the human scene are the positive correlation of mesothelioma with inahled asbestos dust, angiosarcoma of the liver with exposure to vinyl chloride, and adenocarcinoma of the vagina in young women with mothers who had received diethylstilbestrol during their pregnancy.

Willis (1948) considered the mesothelioma extremely rare although the asbestos-induced mesothelioma had already been recognized (Wedler, 1943). With angiosarcoma of the liver, the 21 deaths per year previously estimated for the whole United States (*Chem. Eng. News*, 1974a) compare with the 16 confirmed and suspected cases associated with exposure to vinyl chloride (*Chem. Eng. News*, 1974b). In contrast the 13 lung (expected 7.9) and 5 brain (expected 1.2) cancers in 161 deceased white males who worked in two plants, one of which produced vinyl cloride, the other polyvinyl chloride (*Chem. Eng. News*, 1974c), are not significantly above normal.

After many decades of estrogen therapy in human females, a carcinogenic response at the breast is still controversial (Bryson and Bischoff, 1969). Unusually large populations are required to demonstrate statistically significant increases. In a hypothetical situation where 70 cases of cancer of the breast occur in 1000 women who had estrogen therapy as compared with 50 cases in 1000 matched normal controls, the difference would not be significant ($p > 0.05$), even though the numerical increase is 40%. To comprise such a population would require the elimination of those with fibrocystic disease, menstrual disorders, and obesity among other disorders. The epidemiologic rigor required to classify such pathology in appropriately matched statistical populations would be staggering. It was not only the rarity of adenocarcinoma of the vagina in the population as a whole, but its occurrence at an early age (Herbst and Scully, 1970), that prompted the statistical studies leading to the correlation of adenocarcinoma of the vagina with transplacental effects of stilbestrol (see Section VIII,C,1,a).

B. Malignant Tumors in Rodents

Because of real or assumed differences between human and rodent malignancies involving spread through adjacent lymph nodes and metastases via the blood (Leonard, 1974), the malignancy of rodent tumors is frequently challenged (Benirsche, 1974). Although the histologic picture of the rodent tumor is not different from that of a corresponding human cancer, the evidence is deemed incomplete.

1. *Invasion and Metastases*

There are numerous well-documented rodent neoplasms that are steroid hormone related and ultimately spread to other body parts. Thus the mammary tumors of mice that infiltrate adjacent tissues, metastasize, recur after incomplete removal and are transplantable (Shimkin, 1945) obviously show no difference in their behavior from that of human breast cancers. Also, with mouse tumors of the blood-forming and blood-destroying tissues (round-cell sarcomas), there are generalized conditions in which mediastinal, intraperitoneal, and subcutaneous lymph nodes all become hypertrophied and release tumor cells into adjacent normal tissues and organs; gross involvement and metastatic nodules appear frequently in the kidneys, liver, and lungs. These same organs are also invaded by cells (lymphocytoma) originating in the lymphatic system. Cancers of myeloid-cell origin invade the muscle and other nonblood-forming tissues (see "Biology of the Laboratory Mouse," 1941). The estrone-dependent rat adrenal cortex carcinoma metastasizes to the lung and liver (Noble, 1967). The interstitial cell mouse tumors of the testes metastasize (Hooker and Pfeiffer, 1942). In mice, uterine tumors of the cervix of decidua cell origin induced by testosterone metastasized to the lung (Van Nie *et al.*, 1961).

Implantation of stainless steel or polymethylmethacrylate disks intragluteally in rats produced the usual "solid-state" sarcomas, which metastasized to the lung and mesenteric glands (Stinson, 1964). This is in contrast to the usual course of development at the subcutaneous site. Here, the primary tumor occasionally spreads to regional lymph nodes, rarely metastasizing to the lung; however, after serial transplantation or recurrence of incompletely removed original tumor tissue, lung metastases occurred for 50 and 10–20% of the original tumors, respectively (Nothdurft, 1961).

Transplantability with a demonstration of proliferation and invasion is one of the criteria for establishing malignancy of a tumor. The transplant is in a sense an artificially induced metastasis. The establishment of mammary tumors in mice as cancerous depended in part on behavior after transplantation (Shimkin, 1945).

Experimental oncologists do not invariably let the test animal die of cancer as humans die. The animal is usually sacrificed before the tumor has become necrotic, and it is in prime condition for optimal histologic studies. It is the histologic studies with the criteria of mitosis, pleomorphism, invasiveness, etc., which, as with humans, decide malignancy. Doubtless, if animals were followed through more frequently to the cachectic stage, more metastases would be found and there would be more trouble with the "antivivisectionists." It should be apparent that such a practice is quite unnecessary, as the success of "safety testing" affirms.

2. Species and Strain Differences

A number of implications or categorical statements made at the Meeting on Pharmacological Models to Assess Toxicity and Side Effects of Fertility Regulating Agents, WHO, Geneva, Sept. 17–20, 1973 should be clarified. Rodent safety testing for carcinogenicity has recently enjoyed enhanced credibility: with safety testing for vinyl cloride in rodents, angiosarcoma of the liver was induced in mice and rats. The same tumor type has appeared in humans exposed to this monomer (Bischoff and Bryson, 1974b). This is only one of a series of examples.

The requirement that dogs be used for chronic toxicity tests for antifertility agents has been questioned (Tuchmann-Duplessis, 1974) because they have a high sensitivity to progestins and a high incidence of spontaneous mammary tumors. Since women have a high incidence of spontaneous mammary carcinoma and fibrocystic disease, dogs can be conceived of as ideally suited as a test animal because of this common denominator. As previously discussed, a high spontaneous incidence requires a higher experimental incidence to achieve statistical significance. In spite of this disadvantage, the choice is better than one in which the test animal is completely resistant. The recommendation to test with as many species as is practical is well taken because it will help minimize the extremes of response due to species-strain differences.

The overview (Drill, 1974) that female mice of high mammary cancer strains or males or females of low cancer strains do not respond to exogenous estrogens with increased mammary carcinoma development does not apply in all instances. In the dba strain, 24.2% of nonbreeding females, 65.6% of breeding females, 54.5% of estrogen-dosed nonbreeding females, and 28.6% of estrogen-dosed males developed mammary tumors. In the R3 strain, corresponding incidences were 52, 73.6, 74.8, and 87.5% (Shimkin, 1945). These differences (nonbreeding vs breeding females, nonbreeding females vs nonbreeding estrogen-dosed females, and males vs estrogen-dosed males) are highly significant, $p < 0.01$. These examples represent mouse strains for which estrogen has a profound effect in augmenting spontaneous mammary cancer; estrogen raises this cancer rate in nonbreeding females and males to the approximate extent it occurs regularly in breeding females

(Shimkin, 1945). In the R4, 17, and CBA (low) strains, estrogen administration has produced mammary cancers in males.

Evidence to date indicates that estrogens may be unable to promote mammary cancer in mice without the presence of a mammary tumor virus. It is on this basis that the genetic variation of high and low mammary cancer strains interacts with the effect of estrogen on mammary cancer as mediated by viruses (for review, see Bischoff, 1969). However, in four virus-free strains, estrogens did produce mammary tumors (Boot and Mühlbock, 1956). Castrated C_3H male mice with and without mouse mammary tumor virus (Gass *et al.*, 1974) receiving 250 ppm diethylstilbestrol in the diet demonstrated the synergistic effect (virus and estrogen): 36/50 adenocarcinomas after 18 months and 9/30 in another series after 12 months. In this study the virus alone produced no tumors in groups of 50 and 30, respectively. In one of the two series which were originally virus-free, the authors suggested there was some virus cross contamination because 1/50 of the controls and 5/50 of the estrogen-treatment group developed mammary tumors during the 18-month period. This did not occur during the 12 month period. The reviewers agree with the authors that the virus was unable to induce carcinoma without the estrogen. Whereas 1/50 versus 5/50 is not significant, and a 12-month period was not sufficiently long, a repetition of the experiment on a larger scale, with careful isolation of the virus-free and virus-bearing groups would be required to determine whether estrogen was tumorigenic without the virus.

In the rat, a mammary tumor virus has not been found when prolonged administration of exogenous estrogens has significantly increased the low spontaneous incidence of mammary adenocarcinomas. These cancers are hormone dependent and are probably mediated by release of pituitary mammotropic hormones (for review, see Bischoff, 1969). Evidence to date is lacking for viral involvement for human oncology of the breast.

C. The Immune Defense Mechanism against Carcinogenesis

In rodents the immune defense mechanism that restricts a locally developing malignancy from spreading to other body sites is generally more efficient than that of humans. Whereas mammary carcinomas in mice do metastasize to the lung (Shimkin, 1945), spontaneous or carcinogen-induced mammary carcinomas in rats usually do not unless the immune reaction is suppressed by splenectomy and/or thymectomy. By this surgical procedure the production of mammary carcinomas which metastasized extensively was achieved by feeding methylcholanthrene to young female rats (Kim, 1970). In rats mammary carcinomas that were induced by estrogens were hormone dependent for maintenance of continued growth (see Bischoff, 1969).

The critics of rodent carcinogenicity have overlooked an aspect of the immune defense reaction that is more effective in humans than in rodents, at least at the subcutaneous site, *viz.*, solid-state carcinogenesis. At this site in humans the induction of foreign-body-induced neoplasms has a very low incidence (see Bischoff, 1972). With rodents, the defense mechanism is ineffective against the original induction of local cancers and their growth, but it is effective in preventing the spread of these cancers by metastatic invasion. Apparently the avascular fibrous capsule around the foreign body implant makes the host's immune defense mechanism less accessible, so that activation would occur only after the fibrous capsule had been destroyed by the invading neoplasm. Experiments with BALB/c mice (Bates and Prehn, 1965), implanting fibrosarcomas within and without the fibrous capsule, neither proved nor disproved the concept of the altered immune defense mechanism imposed by the fibrous capsule.

D. CHOLESTEROL OXIDATION PRODUCTS

1. *Cholesterol α-Oxide*

Injected as a suspension in an aqueous isotonic vehicle, cholesterol α-oxide (cholestan-5α,6α-epoxy-3β-ol) is locally carcinogenic in rats and mice at the subcutaneous site and at the intratesticular site in mice (for review, see Bischoff, 1969). Human skin when exposed to ultraviolet light *in vitro* develops cholesterol α-oxide (Black and Lo, 1971; Lo and Black, 1972), as does the skin of hairless mice when exposed *in vivo* (Black and Douglas, 1972). Chronic suberythemic levels of ultraviolet light on the skin of hairless albino mice produced increases of cholesterol α-oxide which reached a maximum at 10 weeks. After this period, squamous cell carcinomas appeared, reaching an incidence of 90% at 24 months. No such tumors appeared in concurrent controls. A total of 135 mice in these experiments were divided into two irradiated series and two control series; one of each series served for determination of the cholesterol α-oxide content of the skin by means of gas–liquid radiochromatography (Black and Douglas, 1972). The 16 μg per mouse of cholesterol α-oxide formed in the skin preceding the appearance of squamous cell carcinomas contrasts greatly with the 10 or 20 mg of α-oxide introduced subcutaneously or intratesticularly into Marsh mice to produce local sarcomas (Bischoff and Bryson, 1969). In the latter experiments the active dose concentration relationship at the subcutaneous site was determined at time intervals by analyses of cholesterol α-oxide deposits which formed at the injection site (Bischoff and Bryson, 1974a). In groups of 4 to 8 males, recovery of α-oxide after injection was 67% at 14 days, 56% at 31 days, 51.5% at 91 days, 43.5% at 200 days, 31.5% at 330 days, and 12.0% at 420 days. In 8 female mice, 21% of the α-oxide was recovered at

547 days. The release or metabolism of the oxide at the subcutaneous injection site ranged from 7 to 22 μg per mouse per day and is of the same order as the α-oxide formed by irradiation. This supports a hypothesis for the mechanisms of radiation-induced carcinogens at the skin. Since the subcutaneous reaction to the α-oxide is fibroplasia and cellular fibrosis, the ultimate local sarcoma follows logically in contrast to carcinoma at the skin. It should be noted, however, that after intratesticular injection of the α-oxide in Marsh mice, two undifferentiated carcinomas in mesenteric lymph nodes were observed in addition to the local sarcomas (Bryson and Bischoff, 1963); after subcutaneous injection, a carcinoma of the pancreas was observed (Bischoff *et al.*, 1958b). Whereas such small incidences are not statistically significant when compared with O in the controls, possible carcinogenic activity of the α-oxide remote from the injection site is suggested. Moreover, the metastatic spread in the lymph nodes is of interest in demonstrating that carcinomas in rodents do metastasize (see Section VI,B).

2. *6β-Hydroxy-4-cholesten-3-one*

6β-Hydroxy-4-cholesten-3-one was carcinogenic in three strains of mice when injected subcutaneously in an oily vehicle; 6β-hydroperoxy-4-cholesten-3-one was also carcinogenic when administered in an oily vehicle, but not as an aqueous suspension (Bischoff, 1969). A test was therefore made for the 6β-hydroxy compound injected in an aqueous vehicle with female Marsh mice (20 mg/mouse) at the subcutaneous site (Bischoff and Bryson, 1970). During a 16-month test period, 14/33 local pleomorphic or fibrosarcomas developed versus 0/33 for controls. Confirming earlier experiments, 6α-hydroperoxy-4-cholesten-3-one injected in an aqueous vehicle produced a low yield of local sarcomas: 2/30 versus 0/33 for the controls. As with cholesterol α-oxide, the hydroxy compound developed local cysts, which retained some of the compound and accumulated cholesterol and other lipids. Analyses of pooled cyst contents 16 months after dosage averaged 3.9% for the hydroxy compound, 2.0% for cholesterol, and 2.5% for fat. The 6β-hydroxy compound was determined by absorption spectrophotometry utilizing the absorption maximum at 238 nm. In contrast to the 6β-hydroxy compound, the hydroperoxy compound had disappeared from the injection site during the 16-month observation period. The hydroxy compound like cholesterol α-oxide functions as a carcinogen in its own right, whereas a derivative of the peroxy compound formed at the injection site may serve as the carcinogen.

3. *β-Cholestanol*

Twenty milligrams of β-cholestanol per mouse, injected subcutaneously as a 10% slurry in isotonic saline, produced no local cancers in 37 Marsh females over an 18-month period (Bischoff *et al.*, 1973). This reduction product of cholesterol, like cholesterol α-oxide and 6β-hydroxy-4-cholesten-3-one, was found as encapsulated material at the end of the experimental period. However, more than half of the original dose of β-cholestanol had disappeared. The cyst contents were assayed for cholesterol (Stauffer and Bischoff, 1966) and contained from 1 to 10%. Insoluble deposits of calcium salts were found, as they were at the injection site of cholesterol α-oxide. The local deposition of cholesterol and calcium in forms not promoting solid-state carcinogenesis are not involved in the carcinogenic process linked with oxidation products of cholesterol, such as cholesterol α-oxide and 6β-hydroxy-4-cholesten-3-one. The deposits are, however, of interest in the etiology of atherosclerosis.

E. Estrogens in Primates

In a study with 10 rhesus monkeys (Pfeiffer and Allen, 1948) large doses of estrogens were not carcinogenic. With squirrel monkeys, 6 of 10 implanted subcutaneously with diethylstilbestrol developed sarcomas of the uterine wall and peritoneal mesothelial surfaces (McCluer and Graham, 1973). This estrogen has also produced fibromyoma in guinea pigs (Lipschutz, 1950). One of six mature female rhesus monkeys given 1 mg of Enovid (norethynodrel and mestranol) daily by mouth developed a metastasizing duct carcinoma of the breast. More extended series are in progress (Kirschstein et al., 1972).

Etiology of Human Breast Cancer

The positive correlation of postmenopausal breast cancer with diseases involving adrenal function suggested a causal relationship. By contrast premenopausal breast cancer would be related to ovarian function, which is markedly reduced after the menopause (De Waard et al., 1960). As compared with normal controls, the urinary output of tetrahydrocorticosterone was lower for the premenopausal and higher for the postmenopausal cancer group, indicating a shift of potentiation from the ovaries to the adrenals (Kodama et al., 1975). An interaction between corticosteroids and androgens, but not estrogen, during tumor regression gains support from animal experimentation.

F. Chloroderivatives

In a 4-year study, beginning at the age of 6–12 months, 100 female beagles served as controls; groups of 20 received, respectively, 0.01, 0.10, and 0.25 mg/kg/day megestrol acetate or 0.25 mg/kg/day of chlormadinone acetate, both drugs orally. The two higher doses of these progestational and antifertility agents produced mammary hyperplasia. The higher dose of megestrol acetate and chlormadinone acetate produced 5 and 4 benign mixed mammary tumors, respectively. The one mammary adenocarcinoma occurred in a chlormadinone-dosed dog. It metastasized early and may not have been dose related since it was not preceded by nodular hyperplasia (Nelson *et al.*, 1973).

In mice fed technical polychlorinated biphenyls in a stock diet (Oriental NMF) over a 32-week period, one of three different products produced hepatocellular carcinoma in 5 of 12 male dd mice at a level of 550 ppm in the diet. No cancers were produced at the lower level of 250 or 100 ppm or at the 500 ppm level for the two other products studied (Ito *et al.*, 1973a). The α-isomer of benzene hexachloride also produced a high incidence (17/20) of hepatocellular carcinoma on diets containing 550 ppm and fed 24 weeks (Ito *et al.*, 1973b).

In addition to vinyl cloride, bis(chloromethyl)ether has been considered as a human carcinogen associated with four deaths from cancer of the lung; other chloro derivatives are under study (*Chem. Eng. News*, 1973). In a survey between 1956 and 1970 comprising 25,000 workers in the Yerevan region in Russia, those who produced chloroprene had a 3% incidence of skin cancer. In contrast, the incidence was 0.12% for those who never worked in heavy industries, with intermediate incidences for those who had worked with the compound, with other chemicals, or in nonchemical industries. For lung cancer, corresponding incidences were 1.1% and 0.064% (A.P., 1975).

VII. Drug Side Effects

A. RESERPINE

Reserpine is 3,4,5-trimethoxybenzoyl methyl reserpate. Reserpic acid like estradiol has a phenolic OH group on a benzene ring and another OH on an aliphatic ring which is separated by polycyclic ring systems. In reserpine these two OH groups are methylated. Reserpine has therefore in this study been considered to be a steroid-related compound, although the ring adjacent to the benzene ring is a pyrrole.

Certain physiologic effects of reserpine are akin to those of prolactin interacting with estrogen stimulation.

1. *Laboratory Animals*

a. Ovarian Effects. Twenty-four micrograms of reserpine given daily to mice in their food produced an increase in ovarian weight from 5 to 18 mg (Lacassagne *et al.*, 1958). In a study with 41 white rats given 0.2 mg/kg reserprine intraperitoneally for 31 days, the interval between estrus increased from 4.5 to 15.1 days (Däring and Günther, 1959). This confirmed earlier work (Dal Monte and D'Amico, 1956).

b. *Mammary Gland Effects.* Reserpine caused an increase in the development of ducts and alveoli of the mammary gland of rats, which was suppressed by the simultaneous administration of estrogen (Grönroos *et al.*, 1959). The administration of reserpine to 140-gm virgin rats produced a condition analogous to lactation. Augmented with 0.5 mg of estradiol benzoate, the condition exhibited development associated with pregnancy (Mayer *et al.*, 1958). The observed 48% decrease of pituitary lactogen content in prenursing rats after administration of reserpine indicates that reserpine stimulates release of the hormone, either by suppressing an inhibitory center or by direct action on the adenohypophysis (Moon and Turner, 1959).

c. *Hepatic Nodules.* Reserpine given at 1 μg per gram of body weight once a week to SMA/MS mice reduced the incidence of hepatic nodules produced by feeding 2,7-diacetamidofluorene. In experiments utilizing 8 males and 16 females per group, the difference for the nodule count between groups with or without reserpine was significant: $p < 0.05$ for males and < 0.01 for females. Only one actual cancer was produced in the males. For the incidence of 10/13 versus 5/14 cancers (reserpine) for the females based on survivors, $p > 0.05$ (Kozuka, 1970). The experiment therefore does not prove that reserpine reduces the incidence of cancer of the liver produced by the carcinogen, but only the hepatic nodule. The reserpine-dosed mice slept during the day of dosage and therefore consumed less carcinogen. Gastric carcinomas were not produced either by the carcinogen or in combination with reserpine.

d. *Implantation and Gestation.* In adult rats the delayed implantation of blastocytes by reserpine injected from the second through the sixth day after mating was reversed by concomitant administration of cortisone, estradiol cyclopentylpropionate, or human chorionic gonadotropin. Adrenalectomy did not abolish the effect of reserpine. Treatment with reserpine from the sixth through the thirteenth day of pregnancy resulted in a high incidence of abortion and/or resorption of the embryo. This effect was also reversed by cortisone or by the estrogen. The administration of adrenocorticotrophic hormone produced the results of reserpine described above. Estrogen but not cortisone abolished the adrenocorticotrophic effect. The total dose levels of hormones and the drug are not readily ascertained from the data given (Chatterjee and Harper, 1970). The experiments confirm earlier work that reserpine breaks up the estrogen-progesterone stimulation required for implantation and maintenance of pregnancy by interference with the gonadotropin secretions.

e. Carcinogenesis. In studies with mammary tumors induced in immature female rats by intravenous injection of 5 mg of 7,12-dimethylbenzanthracene (DMBA), 100 μg of reserpine given intravenously before the DMBA decreased tumor incidence by 20%, decreased mean number of tumors per rat by 70%, and increased mean latency period by 98 days. The growth and development of DMBA-induced mammary tumors was increased when 10 μg of reserpine were administered after onset of the tumors. This effect of reserpine was abolished by ovariectomy (Welsch, 1970).

Earlier studies indicated that reserpine accelerated liver carcinogenesis induced by *p*-dimethylaminobenzene (DAB) in the rat, but retarded this type of carcinogenesis induced by diethylnitrosamine (Lacassagne *et al.*, 1970). Simultaneous administration of deoxycorticosterone or hydrocortisone with reserpine produced an inhibitory action on liver carcinogenesis induced by DAB. Although reserpine accelerates this type of carcinogenesis by itself, it had a synergistic effect with deoxycorticosterone. Hydrocortisone and reserpine, each promoting DAB-induced liver cancer by itself, inactivate this effect when working simultaneously. The adrenal atrophy that developed in the DAB-fed animals which received the corticosteroids was abolished with the simultaneous administration of reserpine (Lacassagne and Hurst, 1963).

2. The Human Scene

a. Carcinoma of the Breast. Independent statistical studies in Boston, England, and Finland indicated an association between carcinoma of the breast in women and the use of reserpine. In the first study (Boston Collaborative Drug Surveillance Program, 1974) carcinoma of the breast is matched with medical and with surgical controls, comprising three statistical group samples. Eleven of 150 newly diagnosed cases of breast cancer indicated that reserpine-containing drugs had been used prior to admission. Medical and surgical controls matched for age, decade, and hospital of source, each showed 13 of 600 cases to be reserpine users. Among the three groups the use of other antihypertensive drugs showed similar incidences: 4.7, 4.8, and 4.3%. The point estimate of 3.5 risk ratio for breast cancer between reserpine users and nonusers, pooling both medical and surgical controls, appeared highly significant ($p = 0.007$).

In the English study, patients with carcinoma of the breast are compared with patients with other types of cancer, eliminating those which the American study indicated might have a possible association with the use of reserpine. In 708 cases of breast cancer compared with 1430 controls which had other types of cancer, the association between breast cancer and the use of rauwolfia drugs was significant ($p = 0.05$) (Armstrong *et al.*, 1974).

In the Finnish studies, 438 pairs were matched for newly diagnosed carcinoma of the breast with controls admitted for elective surgery of a benign
condition both the same year and within five years of their respective ages.
Sixty-eight reserpine users appeared in the cancer series and 23 in the controls
($p < 0.01$) (Heinonen *et al.*, 1974). The results of the three studies have been
challenged (Immwich, 1974) because of the way controls were selected,
resulting in inhomogeneity between groups.

   b. Carcinoma of the Prostate. Forty-nine prostatic cancer patients who
had received treatment with reserpine were matched with 49 controls who
also had prostatic cancer but had not received reserpine. Age, blood pressure,
acid phosphatase, metastases, activity, pain, and hemoglobin were considered
in matching. There was no significant difference in survival. There was no
evidence that reserpine exacerbates carcinoma of the prostate either by increasing serum prolactin or by other mechanisms (Newball and Byar, 1973).

3. Carcinogenic Mechanisms of Reserpine

Reserpine often produces gynecomastia in human males (Williams, 1968)
and raises serum prolactin levels in rats (Welsch and Meites, 1968). The
relation between these two physiologic effects is considered in the etiology
of the reserpine-linked human female carcinoma of the breast (Meites and
Nicoll, 1966). On the basis of earlier work it was postulated that prolactin
would not be carcinogenic in women but would in rats because it is so strongly
luteotropic in rats in contrast to women. Only during pregnancy and lactation do women have higher prolactin blood levels. At other times the level
approaches that of the human male (Frantz *et al.*, 1972). In humans lactation
is not associated with breast cancer risk, and pregnancy may have a protective action (MacMahon *et al.*, 1973). Reserpine is only one of the drugs
associated with gynecomastia (Williams, 1968). Among these, the natural
estrogens, testosterone, spironolactone, and the digitalis glucosides have in
common a pentaphenanthrene nucleus. Diethylstilbestrol, which is estrogenic, does not. Neither the tranquilizers hydroxyzine and meprobamate
nor phenothiazine are pentaphenanthrenes. A side effect of phenothiazine
administration may be toxic hepatitis. It is evident that the etiologic relations
of these drugs to gynecomastia are not the same. The toxic effect to the liver
may decrease the metabolic destruction of the normal estrogens, achieving
the same estrogen levels as augmentation by exogenous estrogenic sources.
The release of prolactin by affecting hypothalamic or midbrain function
certainly pertains to another class of drugs. A direct tumorigenic effect of
reserpine at the human mammary target site cannot therefore be ruled out,
particularly since the evidence for prolactin as a human carcinogenic agent
is not forthcoming.

B. ESTROGEN THERAPY

1. *Heart Disease in Males*

Since premature coronary heart disease is associated with high cholesterol levels, the putative lipid-lipoprotein influencing effects of conjugated equine–estrogen mixture, clofibrate, *d*-thyroxine, niacin, and a lactose placebo were assessed by comparing morbidity and mortality risk factors in the patient-treatment groups. The rationale for studying the estrogen, which was done at levels of 2.5 or 5 mg/day, was based in part on the statistic that postmenopausal females are more prone to have heart attacks than those in lower age groups. Since premenopausal women produce more estrogen than postmenopausal women (see Section IV,F), a protective influence of estrogen was indicated and hence tried on males.

The study initiated in 1966 at 53 United States clinical centers included 8341 males 30 to 64 years of age who had recovered from one or more episodes of myocardial infarction. Since the 5 mg/day mixed conjugated equine–estrogen regimen was associated with more cardiovascular problems than the placebo, the group with this level of estrogen was discontinued in 1970; the group on a 2.5 mg/day regimen was later discontinued in 1973 because a slightly higher death rate was observed for those using it as compared with the placebo controls; also pulmonary blood clots and deaths from pulmonary cancer ($p > 0.05$) appeared disproportionately high. In 1971, the *d*-thyroxine regimen was also terminated because of a trend toward an adverse mortality rate. Those who were living at the time the drug regimens were terminated are included in the long-term longitudinal study (Coronary Drug Project Research Group, 1973). In these studies the mixed conjugated estrogens from a natural source involve confounded chemical entities. Sodium estrone sulfate is one of the principal estrogens in these preparations.

Earlier deaths by heart disease were also correlated with administration of 5 mg of diethylstilbestrol daily in a 7-year study of 2300 patients with carcinoma of the prostate, half of which received a placebo, the other half the estrogen (Bailar, 1967).

2. *In Females*

The protective effect of estrogens against cancer in the human female was suggested by a number of observations. Estradiol-17β inhibits polycyclic hydrocarbon enzymic hydroxylation to carcinogens in the mouse (Nebert *et al.*, 1970; Selkirk *et al.*, 1971) and protects against polycyclic hydrocarbon cytotoxicity in tissue culture (Schwartz, 1973). Estrogens administered to hysterectomized women postoperatively produced a favorable decline in the overall cancer mortality rate (Burch and Byrd, 1971). In 120 women with osteoporosis who received estrogen therapy, the incidence of cancer was nil as compared with the 5 to 6 expected (Mustacchi and Gordon, 1958).

Endometrial carcinoma in women with amenorrhea untreated with hormone therapy had not been reported below the seventh decade of life. However, five endometrial carcinomas have been associated with estrogen therapy in women with gonadal dysgenesis, including two in a series of 24 women who had been treated with diethylstilbestrol (Cutler et al., 1972). The study again points to the importance of the emergence of the rare tumor type (three of the endometrial carcinomas were adenosquamous). The chromosomal disorders mediating gonadal dysgenesis leave open the possibility of inheritable predisposition to malignancy. Sustained liberation of estrogen by granulosa and thecal cell tumors (see Bischoff, 1969) has been correlated with a 5–10% incidence of endometrial carcinoma. Exogenous estrogens (Smith et al., 1975), more specifically conjugated estrogens such as sodium estrone sulfate (Ziel and Finkle, 1975), have been associated with endometrial carcinoma. Although women with endometrial cancer show an accelerated rate of conversion of androstenedione to estrone in certain tissues (Schindler et al., 1972; Siiteri et al., 1974), it remains to be demonstrated that the estrogen blood levels are elevated, a possible requirement for pathologic endometrial stimulation. In the United States there was a stable incidence of endometrial cancer during the three decades before 1970. Increases exceeding 10% per year have been subsequently noted in some ares (Weiss et al., 1976). This may be related to the use of estrogens. In a study of retirement-community residents which developed endometrial carcinoma compared with controls, evidence of estrogen use was obtained from medical and pharmacy records and from interviews. The risk ratio for the use of an estrogen was ascertained to be 8.0 (Mack et al., 1976).

C. Contraceptives

1. The Pill

Among the estrogens found in oral contraceptive preparations are ethynylestradiol, its 3-methyl ether (mestranol), and diethylstilbestrol; among the synthetic progestins are compounds related to 19-nortestosterone and 17α-hydroxyprogesterone. Since the nortestosterone-related progestins follow a metabolic route producing some estrogens, they also have an antiovulatory effect (Leonard, 1974). Oral contraceptives approved by the U.S. Food and Drug Administration consist of norethindrone or its derivatives, alone or with either ethynylestradiol or mestranol (see Berliner, 1974).

Oral contraceptives may be classified into four groups. The "combined pill" contains both estrogen and progestin, inhibits ovulation and is taken on the 5th day of the menstrual cycle and for 20 to 21 days thereafter. Two different pills are used in the "sequential contraceptive" regulation. A pill containing only the estrogen is given daily for 15 to 16 days, followed by the combined estrogen–progestin containing pill, given daily for 5 to 6 days. The "minipill" contains only a progestin, is taken daily, and affects the lining of the uterus and cervical mucus. The "morning-after pill," for emergency use, is taken after intercourse.

a. Carcinogenic Hazards. Diethylstilbestrol, which is used as a morning-after pill, has had a low-grade transplacental tumorigenic effect in offspring whose mothers took it during pregnancy (see Section VIII,C,1,a). When pregnancy ensues in spite of this "morning-after pill," the mother is thus confronted with the alternative of an abortion (UPI, 1973). The significance of an apparent higher incidence of cervical carcinoma *in situ* among those using oral contraceptives as compared with those using a diaphragm (Melamed *et al.*, 1969) has been challenged on the basis of inadequate control factors (WHO, 1971). Studies in the United Kingdom and the United States do not show that women at the child-bearing age on the pill have an increased incidence of breast cancer (Vessey *et al.*, 1972; Sartwell *et al.*, 1973; Boston Collaborative Drug Surveillance Program, 1973a). There was some indication that fibrocystic disease was actually decreased. In studying 452 women with breast cancer and 446 with benign breast disease, each matched with two controls, oral contraceptives apparently accelerated the rate of growth of predeveloping breast cancers but were not linked with tumor induction. The incidence of the benign breast disease over the period studied was decreased (Fasal and Paffenbarger, 1975).

b. Venous Thrombosis and Pulmonary Embolism. Studies on the relation of thromboembolic disease to the use of oral contraceptives have been approached in various ways and in different geographic locations:

1. Deaths attributed to thromboembolism during 1966 in married women, 20–44 years of age (Inman and Vessey, 1968)

2. Thromboembolic disease observed for admissions (Vessey and Doll, 1969) in 19 hospitals in the London area, 1964–1967; in 48 hospitals in the eastern United States, 1963–1967 (Sartwell *et al.*, 1969); and in Swedish hospitals, 1964–1968 (Böttiger and Westerholm, 1971)

3. Interviews with family doctors in England, 1961–1966 (Royal College General Practioners, 1967)

4. A surveillance program in Boston, 1973 (Boston Collaborative Drug Surveillance Program, 1973a)

Pooling the results of the earlier studies (WHO, 1971), it was concluded that the risk of developing vein thrombosis or pulmonary embolism in so-called healthy women taking the pill was five times that of controls. An American study (Solash, 1974) confirmed the British studies with the effects of estrogen–progestin oral contraceptives and showed changes in plasma coagulation levels in women taking the pill, accredited to the estrogen but not the progestin. As a result of the British studies (Inman *et al.*, 1970), the content of the pill was decreased to 50 μg or less of estrogen for general use in the United Kingdom (Bradford-Hill, 1974).

In contrast to these conclusions, studies with 7000 human females who had taken mestranol or ethynylestradiol demonstrated no dose relationship to thromboembolic disease (Drill and Calhoun, 1972). With 30 μg of ethynyl-estradiol, 1.8 cases per 1000 women per year developed phlebitis (Bye and Elstein, 1973). In these studies, dose levels of estrogen ranging from 50 to 100 μg did not enhance the normal incidence of thromboembolic disease. In another study the use of "the pill" was apparently correlated with an increased incidence of stroke and was contraindicated for women with high blood pressure, migraine headaches, or excess cigarette smoking habits (Heyman, 1975).

   c. Hepatotoxicity. A number of testosterone derivatives with an alkyl group at the 17α position may adversely affect icterogenic activity. These include 17-methyltestosterone, norethandrolone (17α-ethyl-19-nortestoster-one), methylestrenolone (17α-methyl-19-nortestosterone), methandienone (1-dehydro-17α-methyltestosterone), and norethisterone (19-nor-17α-ethy-nyltestosterone). Ethynylestradiol also shares this property (see R. L. Smith, 1974). Cholestatic jaundice associated with some oral contraceptives is more prevalent in some geographic locations, as in Chile and Sweden Orellana-Alcalde and Dominguez, 1966; Westerholm, 1967, 1970). The jaundice sub-sides soon after the drug is discontinued. The incidence of jaundice was 1/4000 per year. Postmenopausal women using estrogens and younger women on the pill had twice the incidence of gallbladder disease of those not taking estrogens (Boston Collaborative Drug Surveillance Program, 1973a, 1974).

   d. Other Complications. Hypertension following the use of "the pill" occurs in 3 out of 100,000 women on it. The blood pressure usually returns to normal 4 months after discontinuing "the pill." Estrogen theoretically would stimulate the kidney to accelerate aldosterone production resulting in salt retention. This in turn would liberate angiotensin which restricts the blood vessels. The sequence of events explains the development of malignant hypertension in some cases (Laragh, 1973).

   e. Pill for Males. A male birth control regimen under study with two pills per day, each containing 20 μg of ethynylestradiol and 10 mg of methyl-testosterone, decreased the sperm count for 9 to 15 weeks without diminishing libido. The sperm count began to rise 15 weeks after cessation of treatment, returning to normal in 9 to 10 months (Briggs and Briggs, 1974). This dose of estrogen appears adequate to suppress the secretion of follicle-stimulating hormone (FSH) by the pituitary of normal adult human males (Kulin and Reiter, 1972). Oral contraceptives inhibit spermatogenesis by the same mechanism which inhibits ovulation by suppressing the mid-cycle gonadotropin release from the pituitary.

f. Other Approaches. In an effort to regulate fertility by manipulating ovum transport, basic studies on the mechanism of steroid hormone action appeared more promising than searching for agents which affect adrenergic responses (Croxatto, 1976).

2. Steroid-Injectable Contraceptives

An aqueous suspension of medroxyprogesterone acetate (6α-methyl-17α-hydroxyprogesterone) has been under study as a contraceptive, and 500,000 women in over 80 countries are estimated to be using it for this purpose. In a Los Angeles, California study on about 500 women, begun in 1965, no unwanted pregnancy or breast cancer had developed (Lilliston, 1974). The suspension is usually injected every 3 months intramuscularly. On cessation of the injection routine, fertility returned within 3 to 9 months to most past users, though infertility has been observed for a year. Menstrual irregularity, absence of menstruation for months, or continued spotting follows the use of this drug as a contraceptive. Formal Federal approval of the depot injection for contraceptive purposes, scheduled for October 1974, met with opposition (A.P., 1974b), although it appeared valuable for the mentally retarded, or those who found other contraceptive devices unacceptable. One of the main objections to the use of the progestin was the production of mammary carcinomas in beagles, some carcinomas having metastatic potentialities (Upjohn, 1974). Estrogens and progestins are not required to stimulate tubuloalveolar growth in the human female breast (Hammerstein, 1971). In the dog, the progestins induce lobuloalveolar growth in the mammary gland (Folley, 1955) and there is a positive feedback of prolactin by progestin administration (Neumann *et al.*, 1974). Medroxyprogesterone acetate produces mammary cancer in susceptible dogs (beagles), as do the estrogens in susceptible rodents with mammary gland hypertrophy preceding tumorigenesis. In contrast, megestrol acetate, another progestin, produced only benign mammary tumors (see Section VI,F). The difference between the two progestins in triggering carcinogenesis is not explained by species differences alone. The continued use of the beagle in cancer safety testing thus gains support (see Section VI,B,2).

An aqueous suspension of medroxyprogesterone acetate is used in the palliative treatment of inoperable, recurrent, and metastatic endometrial carcinoma. The binding site capacity for progesterone in human carcinoma of the endometrium varied from nil to that of the hyperplastic or proliferative endometrium (Haukkamaa *et al.*, 1971).

D. Marijuana

Tetrahydrocannabinol, the psychoactive ingredient of marijuana, is also linked to gynecomastia (see Section VII,A,3). A small percentage of males, and probably of females, develop hypertrophied breasts following heavy smoking of marijuana. The same effect was produced in male rats with tetrahydrocannabinol (Harmon and Aliapoulios, 1974). In this study 16 human male marijuana smokers between 18 and 30 years of age showed gynecomastia. Although decreased plasma testosterone has been associated with chronic marijuana use (Kolodny et al., 1974), another study failed to demonstrate such decreases with high dosage of the drug (Mendelson et al., 1974). Normal episodic, temporal variation in blood sampling and the suppression of plasma testosterone by narcotic analgesics and by alcohol were cited as uncontrolled variables in the former study. Cannabinol is 3-amyl-1-hydroxy-6,6,9-trimethyl-6H-dibenzo[b,d]pyran. The space relationship of the two six-membered carbon rings to those of pentaphenanthrene should be noted. Smoke condensates, collected by a smoking machine, contained more three-ring polynuclear hydrocarbons for marijuana as compared with standard tobacco. Among these were the rodent carcinogens indeno[1,2,3-cd]pyrene and dibenzopyrene, practically absent in the tobacco fraction (Novotny et al., 1975). However, tetrahydrocannabinol administered to chimpanzees, hamsters, rabbits, rats, or mice has revealed no consistent pattern indicating teratogenesis (Fleischman et al., 1975).

E. Stilbestrol in Food Products

Livestock feeding with augmentation of diethylstilbestrol to increase the weight before slaughter has been subjected to a number of federal regulations. Certification procedures required by cattle growers for food were readopted and in effect in 1972, dropped in 1973 because of a Federal Department of Agriculture ban on the use of diethylstilbestrol in feed. The U.S. Court of Appeals overturned the ban on January 24, 1974. Effective March 17, 1975 feeders were required to state that their livestock had not received diethylstilbestrol 14 days prior to slaughter or have the meat subjected to analysis to show freedom from diethylstilbestrol residues (USDA Explains New DES Ruling, 1975). During 1974, the Department of Agriculture found 7 of 3050 liver samples of cattle to contain diethylstilbestrol (Los Angeles Times, 1974).

A gas chromatographic technique for determining 2 to 10 ppb of diethylstilbestrol and its monoglucuronide in animal tissues demonstrated residues in steer liver and kidney after feeding 10 mg diethylstilbestrol daily for 7–10 days (Coffin, 1973).

VIII. Transplacental Effects

A. The Human Placental Microcosmos

In primates, including human females, the placenta takes over ovarian function after the first 6 weeks of pregnancy and maintains pregnancy by the production of estrogens, progestins, and a chorionic gonadotropin. Mice, rats, and rabbits have functional ovaries during pregnancy. The guinea pig is an exception among rodents (Heap and Deanesly, 1966). The human male and the human female produce nongonadal estrogen.

The placental, intestinal, and blood–brain barriers function largely through a lipid–protein membrane that favors the passage of lipophilic substances. Sex steroid hormones cross the placental barrier as shown by the feminizing and masculinizing effects upon the fetus by the appropriate steroid. Administered $[4\text{-}^{14}C]$ progesterone finds its way into the fetus, as do prednisone and prednisolone (Tuchmann-Duplessis, 1974). In contrast to the free estrogens, transplacental transport of the hydrophilic steroid esters is retarded. The aryl sulfates and the 3-sulfates of the 3β-hydroxy-Δ^5-steroids are transferred across the placental barrier more readily than the glucosiduronates (Diczfalusy, 1974). The transfer of labeled estrogen glucosiduronates from the fetus to the maternal pool was very slow as compared with the steroid sulfates (Goebelsmann *et al.*, 1968).

Placental aromatization begins with dehydroepiandrosterone sulfate, which after crossing the placental barrier is enzymically hydrolyzed. By means of enzymic oxidation, ring A dehydrogenation, and 17β-hydrogenation, androstenedione, estrone, and estradiol-17β are formed within the placenta. Estrogens are hydroxylated at the 16 position and esterification to acid sulfates occurs somewhere in the fetal complex (Tuchmann-Duplessis, 1974). In the reverse process, free steroids arise by hydrolysis of their sulfates and are transferred across the placental wall. Hydrolysis is, however, not necessary for transfer of sulfates (Benagiano *et al.*, 1971) or the glucosiduronates (Zucconi *et al.*, 1967).

A mechanism protects the fetus from hydrophilic metabolites not crossing the placental barrier. Since the original lipophilic steroid drug can cross the placental barrier and is not conjugated by the fetal liver, it reverts to the maternal pool when the concentration of the drug in this pool falls because the maternal liver has the ability to detoxify it. After birth, however, the baby's liver is able to form glucuronides, which concentrate, sometimes with toxic effects, because of their slow clearance rate (Tuchmann-Duplessis, 1974). The clearance of fetal cortisol largely dependent upon the fetal cortisol binding capacity will regulate the release of maternal ACTH which governs the elaboration of estrogens in the last trimester of humans (Oakey, 1975).

B. Clinical Statistical Studies

In general the relation of birth defects to transplacental hormone or drug penetration from the maternal pool becomes apparent after the accumulation of isolated case reports, extended by a search for other patients who had been exposed to similar therapeutic regimens. Multiple unique combinations of anomalies, rather than a rare type as with the epidemologic carcinogens, first focus attention. Associated with the failure of the estrogen–progestogen birth control type pill to circumvent pregnancy are vertebral, anal, cardiac, tracheal, esophageal, renal, and limb defects in the offspring (Nora and Nora, 1974).

1. Estrogens

A boy was born with missing hands and other birth defects following the use of the ovulation-inducing drug, Clomid, by his mother (A.P., 1974a). Clomid has the diphenylethylene nucleus of diethylstilbestrol; it is also a substituted vinyl chloride. Vinyl chloride is a chemical carcinogen both in man and rodents (Bischoff and Bryson, 1974b). In three instances the progeny of mothers who had imbibed high does of 4,4'-(diethylideneethylene)diphenol (dienoestrol) to induce abortion had malformations (von Uhlig, 1959). This compound is also structurally related to diethylstilbestrol. The treatment of the mother exclusively with diethylstilbestrol has been associated with masculinization in four offspring (Bongiovanni et al., 1959). The mothers were not suffering from a virilizing syndrome, and the offspring excreted 17-ketosteroids within normal limits. The report includes two cases as observed by others.

The pooling of birth defect case reports associated with a common treatment in the above instances does not have significance until data from randomly selected populations with and without the treatment have been gathered in order to compare the incidences of the defect.

2. Progestins

An orally active progestogen, 19-nor-17α-ethynyltestosterone (norethindrone) can be masculinizing in rats, monkeys, and humans (Wilkins, 1959). Of the daughters of 385 mothers who had received this drug, 18% demonstrated masculinization as compared with no such effect in 108 daughters whose mothers had received 17α-hydroxy-6α-methylprogesterone (medroxyprogesterone) (Pincus, 1965). A combination of norethindrone and the estrogen 17α-ethynylestradiol 3-methyl ether (mestranol) in large doses taken during pregnancy was associated with an antiandrogenic effect as indicated by normal female genitalia (Gardner et al., 1970) but with an XY chromosome pattern and testes. The association of an etiologic relation to the oral contraceptive in this case is challenged (Neumann et al., 1970b).

3. *Congenital Limb Defects*

In a matched study, 108 women who had given birth to children with congenital limb reduction defects were compared with controls who had given birth to so-called normal children (Janerich *et al.*, 1974). Fifteen mothers in the first group had been exposed to hormones during pregnancy, whereas only 4 in the controls had a similar experience. Of the 15 mothers, 6 had become pregnant despite birth control pills and 9 had received steroid hormones as supportive measures or as a test for pregnancy during the pregnancy. The 11 defective offspring of mothers who had received hormones orally were all males, an association that indicates that the ingested progestins may have a sex-specific effect upon the developing fetus. The weakness of this report is in not identifying the various steroids which had been used by patients in the study. Since the hormones and the concentrations used varied from patient to patient, one of the statistical parameters is uncontrolled. The failure of birth control pills to prevent conception is about 1%. It was concluded that further surveys are necessary before recommendation can be made to women who become pregnant while taking "the pill." Whereas reliable alternative pregnancy tests are in use, the "*in vivo*" pregnancy tests based on failure to produce menstruation following administration of the steroid hormone should be abandoned. The demonstration of the absence of pregnancy before instituting a regimen of oral contraceptives is another safeguard (Nora and Nora, 1974).

C. LATENT TRANSPLACENTAL EFFECTS OF NONSTEROIDAL ESTROGENS

1. *Human Offspring*

Diethylstilbestrol administered orally during pregnancy may exert a transplacental effect on both the male and female offspring 6 to 22 years later. The drug was widely prescribed from 1945 to 1971 to prevent miscarriages, often routinely to pregnant women whose past experience was difficulty in maintaining pregnancy to full term.

a. Effect on Female. The unusual observation of 7 cases of adenocarcinoma of the vagina, a rare tumor, in adolescent girls (Herbst and Scully, 1970) during a 4-year period led to a retrospective controlled epidemologic study. This was suggested by a practicing gynecologist after the mother of a patient with vaginal adenocarcinoma recalled that she had taken diethylstilbestrol during her pregnancy. In 7 of 8 cases of vaginal adenocarcinoma *in utero*, diethylstilbestrol exposure was substantiated (Herbst *et al.*, 1971). A registry organized by these authors has documented over 100 cases of vaginal or cervical adenocarcinoma linked to transplacental diethylstilbestrol up to October, 1973 (*Cancer Res.* 1973). In California 23 such cases have come to light up to July, 1973 (Hodges, 1973). Over 90% of the females with documented exposure to diethylstilbestrol or dienestrol, 4,4'-(diethylidene-ethylene)diphenol, *in utero* had adenosis of the vagina. Two of 188 patients subjected to excisional biopsy for the adenotic lesions had small foci of clear-cell adenocarcinoma (Sherman *et al.*, 1974). In the Los Angeles area about 25,000 females 3 to 25 years old were exposed during their fetal life (Townsend, 1973). In Britain, the Committee on Safety of Medicines (1973) found no cases of adenocarcinoma of the vagina linked to estrogen therapy during their mothers' pregnancy. At the Mayo Clinic no cases of cervical or vaginal adenocarcinoma had been observed among 23,816 girls born there between 1943 and 1959; of these 1568 mothers had taken estrogens during their pregnancy. At an earlier period beginning with 1939, 4 of the mothers of 6 patients with mesonephric adenocarcinoma of the cervix had taken estrogens (Noller *et al.*, 1972). Dienestrol, 4,4'-(diethylideneethylene)diphenol, a nonsteroid estrogen structurally related to diethylstilbestrol, was used in one case. Hexestrol (dihydrodiethylstilbestrol) was also used (Herbst *et al.*, 1972). In the follow-up Mayo Clinic study (Lanier *et al.*, 1973) of children who had been subjected to estrogens *in utero*, 26% of the mothers had also taken progestogens. Since none of the female offspring in this study developed vaginal or cervical carcinomas, this additional factor has to be considered in studies where they did. A maximum of 50,000 live-born females born in the United States between 1960 and 1970 are thought to have been exposed to diethylstilbestrol *in utero*, a lower range of 10,000 to 16,000 being more likely. In 12 hospitals, the use of diethylstilbestrol during pregnancy ranged from 1.5% to 0.8% of the pregnancies (Boston Collaborative Drug Surveillance Program, 1973b). The importance of the time of administration of the estrogen during pregnancy is indicated in an isolated case study with sibling progeny. Administration beginning at 6 weeks for one and 8 weeks for the other was contrasted with development of vaginal mesonephroma with adenosis in the former daughter and benign papillomatosis in the latter (Nissen and Goldstein, 1973).

Adenosis of the vagina was recognized as a prelude to adenocarcinoma of the vagina in the rare cases that arose in females who had not been subjected to estrogen therapy (Plaut and Dreyfuss, 1946; Hertig and Gore, 1960). Twelve patients with adenomatous and cribriform hyperplasia of gland and reserve cells of the uterine cervix, forming polypoid and nodular excrescenses, all had received progestins. Eleven had taken an estrogen in addition (Candy and Abell, 1968). The incidence of anomalous morphologic dyscrasias of the cervix or vagina, including benign polyps, in daughters exposed to estrogens during fetal life is roughly 30%, the ratio of cervical to vaginal cancers is 24/50, and the risk of these cancers is in the order of 0.1% (Ulfelder, 1973). Nearly all the cases of malignancy develop after onset of menstruation;

females over 13 who have been exposed should have routine examinations. Percentagewise the cancer risk to date appears to be comparatively low, but the final figure will not be available until all the offspring have reached adult life. Of the 66 cases of adenocarcinoma of the cervix or vagina for which pertinent history was obtained, 8 had not been subjected to estrogen therapy (Herbst *et al.*, 1972).

Since diethylstilbestrol does not have the binding affinity for SBG in plasma that estradiol-17β does, the protective role of this transport protein does not apply for diethylstilbestrol and may account for the adverse transplacental effect of diethylstilbestrol.

b. Effect on Male. Estrogen–progestin therapy has been used to prevent the pregnancy complications of diabetic women. On the basis of a number of physical and psychological ratings, 20 sons aged 16 and 20 sons aged 6, both of diabetic mothers who had received hormone treatment during the boy's fetal life, were compared with sons of nondiabetic and diabetic mothers who had not received the hormone treatment (Yalom *et al.*, 1973). The experimental group included two boys with hypospadias. The estrogens were diethylstilbestrol for the 16-year-olds and estradiol valerate for the 6-year-olds. The progestin which each mother had received in addition was identified as hydroxyprogesterone for the 6-year-olds. The 16-year-olds exposed to the hormone therapy *in utero* were rated lower on some variables applicable to masculinity, assertiveness, and athletic ability. The 6-year-olds were lower on aggressivity and athletic ability. The study unfortunately is confounded by the use of two different estrogens and progestins and by the small number of sons from nontreated diabetic mothers, 3 in the 6-year-old series and 8 in the 16-year-old series. Moreover, pregnancy without steroid therapy in diabetes does not occur, terminates prematurely, or terminates successfully depending upon the degree of diabetic involvement. The problem of an adequate control, to separate the *in utero* effects of diabetes itself from those of exogenous hormone treatment, appears insurmountable.

This raises the question of what happened to the sons of nondiabetic mothers who were subjected to diethylstilbestrol *in utero*. At the University of Chicago's Lying-In Hospital, during 1951–1952, 840 pregnant women were treated with diethylstilbestrol. A control group was given a placebo. Twenty-five years later 10% of 134 male offspring exposed to diethylstilbestrol *in utero* demonstrated cysts in the testes. One-third of the exposed males examined had low sperm counts indicative of sterility, a finding not observed in the controls (NIH, 1976).

2. *Uterine–Vaginal Neoplasms in Rodents*

The occurrence of mouse uterine–vaginal neoplasms after prolonged estrogen treatment has been reviewed (Bischoff, 1969). The association of corresponding human neoplasms with transplacental estrogens as described in this section has been attributed to nonsteroidal estrogens. In experiments with $C_3H♀ \times PM♂$ and $PM♀ \times C_3H♂$ hybrid mice, 9 of 18 mice which had received estradiol benzoate and 4 of 6 mice which had received estradiol benzoate plus testosterone propionate developed uterine–cervical carcinomas or invasive epithelial lesions. None of 11 mice which received diethylstilbestrol but had a shorter life-span developed these tumors (Pan and Gardner, 1948). Lesions of the vaginal epithelium which were hyperplastic and in some cases resembled epidermoid carcinomas were observed in BALB/c Crgl mice which had received neonatal administration of estradiol or testosterone in daily doses of 25 and 5 μg the first 5 days of life (Kimura and Nandi, 1967). The experiments were terminated at the age of 15–17 months. Similar lesions of the vagina and cervix were observed between 10 and 14 months of age in other strains of mice which had received 5 μg of estradiol per day the first 5 days of life (Takasugi and Bern, 1964). BALB mice, ovariectomized at 100–120 days of age, demonstrated a reduced incidence of vaginal hyperplastic lesions as compared with intact mice, both of which had received estradiol or testosterone postnatally (Kimura and Nandi, 1967). Mice of the BALB/c and C_3Hf strains were injected neonatally or subjected to long-term feeding regimens with diethylstilbestrol or Enovid, a commercial antifertility drug containing the progestational agent norethynodrel [17α-ethynyl-17-hydroxy-5(10)-estren-3-one] and an estrogen, mestranol (17α-ethynylestradiol 3-methyl ether) (Dunn and Green, 1963; Dunn, 1969). The experiments were so poorly controlled and confounded with so many variables that the observations for carcinomas of the uterine cervix are not amenable to statistical analysis. In summation, it should not be assumed that the carcinogenic effect of estrogens on humans at the vagina and cervix is a phenomenon restricted to their nonsteroidal analogs. Although there are no unequivocal experiments with prenatally administered estrogens in experimental animals, the results from safety testing with neonatally dosed rodents should have served as a warning for the human embryos which were subjected to estrogens.

3. Carcinogenic Mechanisms

The carcinogenicity of diethylstilbestrol in the offspring but not in the mother may be accounted for by the difference of susceptibility to a carcinogen between the infant and the adult, and the dual theory of carcinogenesis (see Bischoff, 1969). Diethylstilbestrol would be the "initiator" and the upsurge of hormone activity during puberty the "promoter." It is assumed that the original genetic defect triggered by diethylstilbestrol lies dormant until mitosis is stimulated at puberty (Folkman, 1971). Another explanation would be the breakdown at puberty of the defense mechanism against unrestricted growth, originally initiated by diethylstilbestrol. This would also explain the long latent period. According to the summation theory of carcinogenesis (Nakahara, 1961) diethylstilbestrol would initiate only one of the intramolecular irreversible alterations required, the upsurge of other estrogens at puberty stimulating other discontinuous alterations of the duplicant macromolecules ultimately leading to carcinogenesis.

4. *Geographic Distribution*

The absence of vaginal adenocarcinomas in young women in specific regions of the world, such as Connecticut, U.S.A.; Frankfurt, Germany; Basel, Switzerland; and Denmark during periods ranging from 1943 to 1968 (Ulfelder *et al.*, 1971; Carstens and Clemmesen, 1972; Christine, 1971) implies either that exogenous transplacental estrogens were not prescribed during pregnancy, that the reported statistical data were for series which were too small, or that some other unknown etiologic factor is linked to these cancers. A similar situation exists with regard to asbestos-induced lung or mesothelial neoplasms in man. There was no increase for those exposed to asbestos over the normal population during the period 1952–1957 in Dresden, Germany, but there was a marked increase during 1958–1964 (Jacob and Anspach, 1965). Differences in survival rate due to other diseases were offered as an explanation.

IX. Effects on the CNS

A. Regulatory and Feedback Mechanisms

The problem of feedback mechanisms can be appreciated by a consideration of the implantation paradox (see Gorski, 1971). Effects of intrahypothalamic estrogen depots can be ambiguous if the median eminence is involved and if the hypophysial portal vessels distribute the steroid to the entire anterior pituitary lobe. Also, the inefficient distribution of direct intrapituitary hormone implants and compensatory metabolism of unaffected regions can mask an effect, confounding dose-response comparisons (Bogdanove, 1963). Testosterone propionate inhibition of testicular weight is mediated by acting at the median eminence, not necessarily upon the pituitary (Smith and Davidson, 1967). The label of tritiated estradiol implanted into the median eminence was detected in the pituitary (Palka *et al.*, 1966). Whereas increased pituitary weight followed intrahypothalamic or intrahypophysial estrogen implantation, only median eminence implants facilitated luteinizing hormone release, indicating a dual action but with neural control of release. Such dual actions apply generally to adrenocortical and ovarian steroids (Davidson, 1971). Many of the implantation studies are confounded by the use of steroid esters and by the lack of control for different neural and glandular local tissue responses to foreign bodies (crystals). The influence of ventricular circulation and the possibility of active transport by ependymal cells must be taken into consideration when effects remote from the implant area are observed.

1. Androgens

After the intraperitoneal administration of [^{3}H]testosterone in castrated adult rats of both sexes, the levels of radioactivity for the hypothalamus, pituitary, preoptic region, and septum were markedly higher than that for blood. A comparison of the effect of male and female castration of adult and male neonatal rats demonstrated recovery of the radioactivity as testosterone of up to 75% in the former and 25% in the latter (McEwen et al., 1971). Low-capacity, high-affinity binding sites in the brain are indicated because the uptake of [^{3}H]testosterone in the amygdala, septum, and preoptic region is limited by the endogenous testosterone; nontagged testosterone, cyproterone, which is antiandrogenic, and estradiol-17β decrease the uptake of [^{3}H]testosterone in the hypothalamus, olfactory bulbs, pituitary, preoptic region, and septum. The restoration of sexual behavior in castrated male rats by testosterone propionate implants at the medial preoptic region of the hypothalamus indicates independence of androgen-sensitive peripheral mechanisms (Davidson, 1966). The use of the propionate complicates an understanding of the mechanism of the receptor site occupancy (see Section V,F). The electrical activity of the preoptic region (Pfaff and Pfaffman, 1969) and the release of gonadotropin (Lisk, 1967) from it are also testosterone sensitive.

In the brain the 5α-reductase apparently functions irreversibly. ^{3}H-Labeled testosterone is converted to 5α-dihydrotestosterone in the anterior and posterior hypothalamus and other areas of the brain (Whalen and Rezek, 1972). However, on incubation of dihydrotestosterone with brain tissue, testosterone was not identified: 5α-androstane-3α,17β-diol and 5α-androstanedione were, indicating reversible dehydrogenase activity at the 3 and 17 oxygen-substituted groups. The 5α-reductase is present in the basal hypothalamus (Karavolas and Herf, 1971). As with testosterone, progesterone is converted to a 5α-dihydro derivative in the anterior pituitary and hypothalamus. These derivatives are biologically more potent in inhibiting gonadotropin release from the anterior pituitary (see Lloyd and Karavolas, 1975).

2. Estrogens

Evidence for specific target sites for estrogens in the brain include the concentration of tagged estradiol at specific central neuronal systems (Michael, 1965; Stumpf, 1968), the blocking effect of this phenomenon by compounds which also inhibit estradiol uptake by the vagina or uterus (Eisenfeld and Axelrod, 1967), and the induction of lordosis by direct implantation of estrogens in specific brain areas (Harris and Michael, 1964). The induction of lordosis as a measure of central mediation was compared with the development of vaginal cornified epithelial cells as a peripheral manifestation. The comparison was quantified by correlating dose level of a particular estrogen with a 50% incidence of response. Progesterone was administered 24, 48, or 72 hours after the estrogens. Results for the optical isomers of 17β-estradiol benzoate, between 17β- and 17α-estradiol benzoate, between mesohexestrol and mesobutestrol and other stereo or structurally related compounds showed a good degree of correlation (Meyerson, 1971).

The thyroid hormone is required for the synthesis of the estrogen receptors in the hypothalamus and anterior pituitary in the rat and so regulates the gonadotropin secretion (Hagino *et al.*, 1975).

As measured by lever-pressing for heat reinforcement, estradiol benzoate administration increased responding in intact and gonadectomized male and female rats. Estrogen treatment depressed pre- and posttest rectal temperatures of ovariectomized females and elevated them in intact males. Castration alone had no consistent thermoregulatory effect on either sex (Wilkinson *et al.*, 1976).

a. Hypothalamic Effects. Estrogen-sensitive areas in the hypothalamus have been shown to control sexual behavior and pituitary gonadotropic function. Single unit activity in the rabbit brain has demonstrated estrogen-sensitive cells in six different hypothalamic regions. After intravenous injection of estrone sulfate, anterior and dorsomedial hypothalamic cells changed their firing rate as a correlate of hyperarousal and olfactory stimulation (Faure and Vincent, 1971). Regional differences in hypothalamic unit activity independent of the animal's behavioral state were observed on comparison of ovariectomized with intact rabbits. Ovulation-inducing vaginal stimulation, but not estrogen injection, in intact rabbits increased the activity of premammillary hypothalamic cells.

The effects of physiological or pharmacological concentrations of estradiol-17β on body weight-gain rate were compared in adult male and female Sprague–Dawley rats having undergone ventromedial hypothalamic (VMH) lesioning, gonadectomy, VMH lesioning combined with gonadectomy, or control procedures. VMH lesioning produced an effect on weight-gain rate greater than that of castration in either sex. The anorexic action of estradiol was enhanced by ovariectomy and/or VMH lesioning suggestive that changes in food intake are mediated by other estrogen-sensitive areas than the VMH nucleus (Reynolds and Bryson, 1974).

A significant concentration of estrone was chromatographically detectable in rat posterior hypothalamus following the intrajugular administration of estradiol (Whalen and Luttge, 1970). Consideration of whether the estrone peak represented local *in vivo* conversion or selective uptake following conversion in the liver led to the study of selective neuronal effects as measured by uptake and retention of radiolabeled estrone or estradiol in rat-brain regions. Anterior–posterior gradients were observed for both steroids. With estradiol, anterior structures maintained the highest radioactivity levels and posterior structures the least. With estrone, an opposite gradient was observed, the highest levels occurring in the most posterior basal brain sample (cerebral peduncle). No sex differences were observed.

b. *Ovulation Cycles.* By recording multiple unit activity during the complete estrous cycle, three activity components were observed in the rat brain: diurnal fluctuations in intrinsic rhythm, endogenous estrogen–progesterone influences in the estrous cycle, and a diurnal variation induced by exogenous steroids. These may be integrated to induce spontaneous ovulation (Kawakami *et al.*, 1971). Although the stimulus for ovulation is generated daily, its effectiveness is limited by whether excitability of the medial basal hypothalamus is high enough to process the daily spontaneous stimulus. Ovarian estrogen secretion must begin between the first and second days of diestrus for excitability of the medial preoptic area and arcuate nucleus to be sufficient for ovulation. The estrogen-facilitated release of gonadotropic hormone is followed by maturation of follicles and secretion of estrogen and progesterone. The high-estrogen : low-progesterone ratio activates neural excitability in the medial preoptic area and arcuate nucleus, preparing a pathway between them during the proestrous critical period. The intrinsic daily stimulus at this time interacts with the neural excitation and the brain starts the release of luteinizing releasing factor into the pituitary portal vessels. On the day before proestrus, low estrogen levels in the morning or high progesterone levels in the afternoon can depress excitability of the basal hypothalamus and delay ovulation. Hormonal environment on this day is thus essential for follicular maturation as well as activation in the brain of the final common pathway controlling the release of ovulatory hormones.

Multiple unit recording in freely moving or gallamine triethiodide-immobilized cats showed changes in the discharge of neurons located in the lateral hypothalamus which predominantly behaved opposite (inhibition) from those of the ventromedial hypothalamus and reticular formation during anestrus (Beyer, 1971). During estrogen-induced estrus, vaginal probing resulted in acceleration of discharge in the reticular formation and ventromedial hypothalamus. Differences in the degree of convergence to mesencephalic and hypothalamic neuronal pools under anestrous and estrous conditions suggest that afferent conduction to the brain stem can be modified by estrogen. The neuronal changes observed with this species might reflect the activation by estrogen of a mesencephalic reticular reflex arc involved in ovulation.

3. Corticosteroids

Increased brain excitability as measured by electroshock seizure threshold following cortisol treatment in adult rats was used to investigate critical developmental periods of hormone susceptibility in the maturing rat (Vernadakis and Woodbury, 1971). Cortisol (10 mg/kg) significantly decreased the threshold of various seizure patterns when subcutaneously administered at 8–11 days of age, but not when given earlier. Cortisol may also facilitate transmission or conduction in the spinal cord. The increase in cerebroside content of spinal cord in rats 16 days of age following cortisol treatment points to a possible metabolic acceleration of myelination. The development of the cerebroside-containing myelin sheath enhances neuronal conduction. Influences on inhibitory neurotransmitter substances and lowered membrane potentials in glia cells may also be related to cortisol. In experiments with parenteral administration of cortisol, it should not be assumed that cortisol rather than a metabolite regulates receptor site activity. In the rat corticosterone is the principal corticosteroid.

Other changes in electrical activity of the brain following cortisol administration include increased evoked potentials in the anterior hypothalamus and midbrain reticular formation in cats and rats, and in the septum and ventromedial hypothalamus in rabbits (see Feldman, 1971). Cells predominantly responding to sensory stimuli by increased firing rate were inhibited in the anterior and facilitated in the posterior hypothalamus after cortisol injections in cats. Such differences were observed in the anterior, but not the posterior, hypothalamus of rats (Feldman, 1971). In cats and rats, spontaneous firing was increased in the anterior and posterior hypothalamus after cortisol treatment. The opposing electrophysiological effects of cortisol between anterior and posterior hypothalamus point to a role for glucocorticoids in the hypothalamic regulation of adrenocortical secretion. Abolition of a cortisol-increased firing rate in hypothalamic islands suggests that the hormone effects are also exerted at extrahypothalamic levels. The increased firing rate of units in the intact structures observed with cortisol related to the general excitatory effect of glucocorticoids on the brain.

The effect of locally administered or intravenously injected dexamethasone 21-phosphate (a soluble and potent ACTH suppressor) on the firing rate of single units in rats was used to identify steroid-sensitive neurons implicated in the control of ACTH secretion. Most of these neurons were inhibited although some were facilitated regardless of the route of administration (Steiner, 1971). Prior intravenous administration of the drug occluded its effects by microelectrophoretic delivery, indicating a saturation mechanism. Steroid-sensitive units are scattered over large areas of the hypothalamus rather than localized in "centers." They are distributed in a pattern roughly corresponding to midline structures in the periventricular gray matter. The functional significance of this proximity to cerebral ventricles is a matter of speculation. Dexamethasone also inhibited neurons in the septum, but was without effect on those in the cortex, dorsal hippocampus, and thalamus. Locally delivered Tetracosactide (a synthetic ACTH) activated neurons sensitive to steroids, dopamine, and acetylcholine. Although a comparable number of steroid-sensitive neurons were found under two types of anesthesia (urethane or a combination of urethane and chloralose), possible interaction of dexamethasone with chloralose–urethane in treated rats may selectively supress activity in cells more sensitive to corticosteroids, especially those relating to nonstress pituitary–adrenal function (Critchlow, 1971).

  a. Circadian Rhythms. The presence of a 24-hour rhythmic component in integrated multiple unit activity in all major regions of the rat brain (Colombo *et al.*, 1974) may be another confounding variable in the above studies. Patterns of ACTH-cortisol secretion in humans show that this 24-hour cycle is relatively resistant to changes and can be readily separated from sleep-wakefulness cycles that are highly correlative under stable activity-cycle conditions (Weitzman and Hellman, 1974). Time of sampling can also have marked effects on measures such as total urinary 17-hydroxycortico-steroids—of value as a correlate of personality variables and a possible prognosis in cancer (see Curtis, 1974). Shifts in mean level and variability from serial measurements made over a few weeks and at different parts of the total time-span are observed to average out to a pattern of relative constancy with daily measurement followed for 4 years in a healthy male subject (Curtis, 1974). However, prolonged hypokinesis (bedrest) produces a subsequent rise in plasma ACTH suggestive of decreasing cortisol levels, an effect that may influence homeostatic mechanisms over extended periods of weightlessness and inactivity as in projected space flights (Leach *et al.*, 1974).

  The circadian rhythmic fluctuation of corticosterone levels in rat plasma and adrenals, determined by fluorometry, were used as a nonstress background against which acute responses to stress could be observed (Critchlow, 1971). Immobilization or ether stress applied during the trough or peak periods of the rhythm produced changes in corticosterone levels superimposed on different levels of diurnal variation. Little or no interaction between stress and nonstress mechanisms of ACTH secretion was implied. Maximal activation of the pituitary–adrenal system occurred only in relation to stress imposed during the diurnal peak. The nonstress component observed during the diurnal peak represented a considerable contribution (50%) to circulating corticosterone levels. Two independent hypothalamic ACTH control systems are indicated by the following observations. The nonstress system but not the stress system was suppressed by dexamethasone 21-phosphate or corticosterone injected subcutaneously, by intracranial implantation of agar pellets containing 1–2.5 μg of dexamethasone in the ventromedial diencephalon or rostral midbrain, and by decreased pituitary–adrenal function following the isolation of the median basal hypothalamus. The stress system appears to be relatively insensitive to glucocorticoid feedback. The nonstress system, with its extrahypothalamic connections and circadian rhythmicity, is preferentially sensitive to suppression by physiological levels of circulating corticosterone. The observed depression of corticosterone levels following stress, commonly interpreted as evidence for interference with stress responses, may represent suppression of the nonstress system.

b. Fluid Balance. At the caudate nucleus, the levels of an angiotensin-forming proteolytic enzyme in the brain, which is independent of kidney and plasma renin, are increased by progesterone and decreased by aldosterone administration. These are the hormones that influence tissue excitability and electrolyte balance (Ganten *et al.*, 1971) and participate directly in the CNS in regulating water intake and fluid balance.

4. Progestins

The action of progesterone has been inferred by studies showing an effect following exogenous administration or some peak in endogenous efflux. This is at best circumstantial evidence. The high amounts of progestational agents, relative to estrogen concentrations, necessary to produce an effect indicate possible dissipation along a pathway toward some metabolite. Identification by radiolabeling and by serial and simultaneous measurement of related radiolabeled hormones may elucidate different neuroendocrinologic levels of metabolic involvement.

a. Temperature-Raising Effect. The mechanism of the temperature-raising effect of progesterone, synthetic progestins, and some naturally occurring steroids of the pregnane and androstane series in man, and by inference in the cow, African dwarf goat, rat, and monkey, but not in the pig, has not been elucidated (Rothchild, 1969). The temperature-raising effect is apparently not heat-producing and not related to progesterone-induced increased respiration or anesthesia (Merryman, 1954).

b. Hypnotic Effect. The hypnotic effect of progesterone (Gyermek *et al.*, 1967) is regarded as centrally mediated by progesterone metabolites of the 5β-pregnane type which would be products of reductive metabolism. Such an enzyme system may be deficient in swine. Norethynodrel, norethisterone, and lynestrenol have minor or no anesthetic action (Meyerson, 1967). They have 17-ethynyl and 17-hydroxy groups and are thus less closely related chemically to pregnanolone than is progesterone. On overdosing with deoxycorticosterone, surgical anesthesia of the dog, mouse, and rat is produced. This steroid is more closely related structurally to progesterone than the above three progestins. The ethynyl group in some progestins also abolishes the respiratory effect of progesterone (Lyons, 1969).

   c. *Anticonvulsant Effect.* The anticonvulsant effects of progesterone as measured by electric shock threshold is influenced by sex, castration, type of progestin, estrogen progesterone ratios, and estrous cycle timing (Stitt and Kinnard, 1968). Progesterone and related compounds appear to lessen the effects of signals in the reticular formation and hypothalamus from producing changes in the electrical activity of the cortex. Since the reticular formation is involved with both consciousness and convulsive activity, a role for progesterone is indicated (Magoun, 1958; Penfield and Jasper, 1954). Research in general is in agreement that levels of circulating progesterone influence activity of both the reticular formation and hypothalamus.

B. Brain-Differentiating Effects

1. *Physiological*

   In androgen-sterilized rats, the estradiol-binding capacity of the anterior and middle, but not posterior, hypothalamus and of nonneural target tissues was decreased significantly (Flerko, 1971). This suggests inhibition of the development of estrogen receptors in the target tissues. The absence of estrogen-sensitive hypothalamic neurons may explain the loss of neurohormonal feedback, cyclic gonadotropin release, and ovulation in androgen-sterilized rats. This hypothalamic sterilization resulting in permanent anovulation is dependent on hormone dose levels, time, and duration of administration and can be inhibited by barbiturates, antiandrogen (cyproterone acetate), or antibiotics (actinomycin D or puromycin) (see Arai, 1971). The inhibition of DNA-dependent RNA and protein synthesis by those antibiotics suggests that hypothalamic sterilization may depend on these intracellular biochemical processes. Neonatal testosterone propionate treatment decreased RNA synthesis rate and produced new uncharacteristic species of RNA. When the protective action of barbiturate or antiandrogen failed to counteract the effect of testosterone propionate, a condition was observed similar to the delayed anovulation syndrome of Gorski (1968), which occurs in female rats exposed to subphysiological levels of androgen or low doses of estrogen during the neonatal competent period. Large doses of estrogen or androgen during the first 30 days of life in female rats produce persistent vaginal diestrus (PD) with atrophic ovaries showing no follicular growth or copora lutea, a characteristic of weanling or hypophysectomized rats. The constant-estrous syndrome in rats is produced by permanent damage to the hypothalamus following neonatal administration of androgen or estrogen (Barraclough, 1966). The potential for hypothalamic receptor synthesis existing at birth is apparently affected, with reduction of estrogen receptors and hence LH release. Smaller doses of estrogen (10 μg/day) produce persistent-estrous rats which, unlike PD rats, can be induced to ovulate by electrochemical stimulation of the preoptic hypothalamic area (a neural substrate governing release of LH). The higher neonatal dose levels of steroid hormones thus involve a wider disturbance of the pituitary gonado-tropic regulatory centers, including the anterior hypothalamic control of follicle-stimulating hormone release (Arai, 1971).

a. Aromatization. The aromatization of testosterone in the brain does not necessarily account for neonatal androgenization, which does occur in rodents but not in the rabbit (Campbell, 1965) or rhesus monkey (Treloar *et al.*, 1972). Since dihydrotestosterone resists aromatization and is effective in suppressing gonadotropin release (Swerdloff *et al.*, 1972), a direct andro-genic receptor site role for some specific activities of the brain is indicated.

The *in vivo* and *in vitro* formation of aromatic estrogen-like substances from dehydroepiandrosterone occurs in the baboon brain (Knapstein *et al.*, 1968). Observations on the conversion of [^{3}H]4-androstene-3,17-dione to estrone on incubation with human fetal or adult rat hypothalamus (Naftolin *et al.*, 1972) have been extended to rabbits, monkeys, and fetal and neonatal rats; also with limbic tissues (see Reddy *et al.*, 1974). This conversion supports a hypothesis of brain sex differentiation by androgens as mediated through local aromatization to estrogens. The role of testosterone but not dihydro-testosterone in masculinizing specific cells of the neonatal brain of the rat by abolishing cyclic release of gonadotropin apparently depends upon aromatization: small amounts of estradiol benzoate have the same effect and antiestrogens inhibit the action of testosterone propionate (Korenbrot *et al.*, 1975). Differences in repressing ovarian cyclicity and sexual receptivity in adult rats following ovariectomy together with estrogen and progesterone administration were effected by subcutaneous, neonatal administration of estradiol-17β benzoate or 11β-methoxy-17-ethynyl-1,3,5(10)-estratriene-3, 17β-diol (RU 2858), but not by estradiol-17β. The failure of estradiol-17β to defeminize is explained on the basis of its noncovalent binding by the neonatal plasma estradiol-binding protein. Such binding is minimal for RU 2858. The former would, therefore, not reach the brain to the extent of the latter (Doughty *et al.*, 1975). The repressive action of the benzoate would depend upon its survival in resisting hydrolysis in the neonatal rat because of insufficient blood esterase activity (see Section V,F) and minimal binding to the plasma proteins. The α ethynyl group in RU 2858 would block receptor site occupancy by the α side of the steroid, suggesting that the mechanism underlying defeminization involves some cross reactivity of competing steroids.

2. Behavioral

In rodents after gonadectomy, sexual mating behavior ceases immediately in the female but persists in the male, e.g., ejaculatory patterns in the castrated male rat persist for 5 months. Various dualistic mechanisms, such as "arousal" and "consummatory" (Beach, 1958) have been proposed for the latency phenomenon in males. Since a single environmental episode may produce relatively long-lasting behavioral patterns, as with noise or anesthesia, experienced males may continue sexual behavior after castration (Davidson, 1966).

In the ovariectomized rabbit, testosterone, androstenedione, 19-hydroxyandrostenedione, and dehydroepiandrosterone gave a positive lordotic response, 5α-dihydrotestosterone, androsterone, and 4-chlorotestosterone a negative response. Since the first group of androgens is capable of endogenous aromatization, the latter resistant (Beyer, 1971), aromatization appears as a requirement for lordosis. However, in female cats and rabbits, testosterone administration fostered receptivity without affecting the uterus or vagina at the morphologic level (Whalen and Hardy, 1970). The continuous aggressive behavior of ovariectomized hamsters is increased by estradiol benzoate administration and abolished by progesterone, but only when preceded by the estrogen (Kislak and Beach, 1955).

The effects of subcutaneously administered estradiol benzoate were compared in ovariectomized, intact, and neonatally androgenized female (0.1–100 μg/kg) and male (0.1 and 1.0 mg/kg) rats (Komisaruk, 1971). The intensity of the lordosis response to cervical stimulation by hand testing and the vaginal smear correlated highly with the dose level of estrogen in the females. Both levels of estrogen treatment produced strong lordotic responding by rectal stimulation in both sexes with none observed in the controls. After surgical opening of the fused vaginal orifice, neonatally androgenized but otherwise untreated adult females showed lordosis which was increased following estrogen administration. Lordosis was a functional and estrogen-sensitive neural reflex in males, ovariectomized, "masculinized," or intact diestrous females even under conditions of insufficient estrogen to induce sexual receptivity but with adequate sensory stimulation. The immobilizing effects of cervical stimulation also may indicate a role for the lateral and ventral hypothalamus in the control of locomotion. Patterns of excitation and inhibition mediated by these estrogen-sensitive structures may account for the running and stopping movements characteristic of rats during estrus. The above 40–46-hour interval between estradiol benzoate administration and peak of receptivity relate to dose and time responses which differ by about 2-fold from those (Whalen, 1971) for unesterified estradiol in combination with progesterone (see Section V,F).

C. CLINICAL IMPLICATIONS

1. *Steroid-Neurotransmitter Interactions*

In rat hypothalamus the conversion of estradiol and estrone to catechol estrogens, which compete with O-methylation of catecholamines by inhibiting catechol-O-methyltransferase (see Fishman and Norton, 1975), suggests a biochemical link in the functioning of steroid hormones and biogenic amines. The catechol steroids, 2-hydroxyestradiol-17β or 2-hydroxyestrone, have one-tenth the affinity of the parent estrogens for the cytosol estrogen receptor sites of rat pituitary and hypothalamus (Davies *et al.*, 1975). The effects of steroids on monoamine oxidase (MAO), another enzyme governing the metabolic inactivation of catecholamines (Kopin, 1964), can influence adrenergic functioning in the CNS. Adrenergic activity varies inversely with MAO levels. Endogenous and exogenous estrogens influence MAO activity in rats (Kobayashi *et al.*, 1966) and women (Klaiber *et al.*, 1971). MAO activity is elevated in castrated rats and depressed by estradiol benzoate administration. Plasma MAO activity is significantly lower in menstruating compared with amenorrheic women (low blood and urinary estrogen). Administration of estrogens to amenorrheic women significantly decreased plasma MAO activity. The Rod and Frame Test of Perception of Verticality showed perceptual activation by women during the first half of the menstrual cycle followed by inhibition during the second half (Klaiber *et al.*, 1974). Low levels of plasma MAO activity induced by the MAO inhibitor isocarboxazid (Marplan), 10 mg/day, in normal men produced a similar perceptual activation as compared to increasing inhibition for the placebo group in the Rod and Frame Test.

   a. Depression (Estrogen). In depressed patients impaired central adrenergic functioning has been postulated as an underlying biochemical basis (Schildkraut, 1965). Significant differences in improvement on the Hamilton Rating Scale following estrogen therapy (Premarin) correlated with lowered plasma MAO activity in a double-blind study (Klaiber *et al.*, 1974). These changes in depressed women and MAO activity in premenopausal females suggest that depressive symptoms cycle with menstrual cycles as a function of plasma MAO activity and presumably central adrenergic states. The sensitivity of MAO activity and catecholaminergic function to gonadal steroid hormones is further indicated by the cyclicity of mood during the human menstrual cycle (Benedek and Rubenstein, 1942), the prevalence of premenstrual suicides (Mandell and Mandell, 1967), and premenstrual accidents (Dalton, 1972). The effectiveness of conjugated estrogen in depressed female patients suggests that impairments in adrenergic function may be amenable to hormone therapy (Klaiber *et al.*, 1974). The increased susceptibility of women to endogenous depression (see Weil-Malherbe and Szara, 1971) and the well-known postpartum depression bring to mind that human females are unique among the mammals in that they do not cannibalize their placenta, rich in steroids.

b. *Minimal Brain Dysfunction in Children* (*Androgen*). Impaired central adrenergic activity has also been postulated as underlying so-called minimal brain dysfunction syndrome or hyperkinesis in children (Wender, 1971). The paradoxical quieting response in these children following amphetamine administration, which is not observed after puberty, directed attention to possible deficits in limbic catecholamines. These deficits, associated with the activity of positive and negative reinforcement systems, are ameliorated at the onset of sexual maturation with increased androgen levels, which in turn decrease MAO activity. Increased adrenal 17-ketosteroids having androgenic activity in both sexes as well as pubertal estrogens would also contribute to a MAO-lowering effect. The resulting increase in adrenergic activity can potentiate the activity of the reinforcement systems associated with reticular activating system function. The observation that castration elevated brain MAO activity in male rats whereas testosterone administration lowered MAO activity in castrated rats (see Klaiber and Broverman, 1967) and the following behavioral study support the above hypothesis. The effects of androgens on operant behavior reinforced by electrical stimulation in the rat brain showed in the dorsomedial caudate nucleus an all-or-none relationship between rate of response and testosterone level (Olds, 1958). Castrated rats failed to respond even to high levels of electrical stimulation. Testosterone administration restored previous levels of sensitivity.

c. *Corticosteroids.* The *in vivo* blockage of glucocorticoids by Metopirone in rats is followed by significantly increased MAO activity in the hypophysis, hypothalamus, and the rest of the brain but not in the pineal gland. Catechol-*O*-methyltransferase (COMT) was increased in the hypophysis (56%) but not in the brain proper (Parvez and Parvez, 1973). The results suggest that glucocorticoids in the circulation of normal animals inhibit MAO and COMT activity, possibly by interference with enzyme induction at the level of RNA transcription from DNA. Metopirone and hydrocortisone both directly inhibit MAO and COMT activity *in vitro*. However, with the blockade of 11β-hydroxylation of glucocorticoidogenesis by Metopirone, the predominating action is the increased activity of MAO and COMT found *in vivo*. Complete ablation of the adrenal cortex resulted in a 167% increase in MAO activity in the hypophysis and 11% in the hypothalamus.

Multiple unit recording in cells of the reticular formation (the brain stem circuit mediating arousal) in the rat indicated that responsiveness was modified by the pituitary–adrenal axis. Elevated corticosteroid levels or ACTH can diminish the effect of a stimulus in the reticular system or cause it to become inhibitory. Other structures in the limbic-midbrain circuit, mediating emotionality, also were steroid and ACTH sensitive (Taylor *et al.*, 1971). Exploratory behavioral activity showed a U-shaped correlation with corticosterone production in the rat, extremely high and low scores being associated with high corticosterone production levels. The facilitatory or in-hibitory effects of adrenal steroids in active avoidance-acquisition behavior depends on dose and time (Endroczi, 1971; De Wied *et al.*, 1972).

2. Biochemical Correlates

a. Stress. The adrenal cortex is involved in a defense mechanism to all types of stress by liberation of corticosteroids through ACTH (adrenocor-ticotropic hormone) secretion (Sayers, 1950). Human stress is inevitable in the process of everyday living and includes causative agents such as burns, drug intoxication, emotional and nervous stimulation, inadequate food intake, infection, loss of blood, physical work, and trauma. The breakdown in the defense mechanism to stress has been suggested as an etiologic agent to some mental and physical pathology. Certain types of arthritis, duodenal ulcers, and cardiovascular diseases illustrate the latter (Briggs and Brother-ton, 1970). The opponents to the general adaptations syndrome theory (Selye, 1946), which postulates a nonspecific response, point out that in the repair of the damages attributed to stress there are a variety of specific responses characteristic of the cellular level at which they are working.

The marked human 3-fold diurnal rhythm in plasma cortisol levels reaching a low at midnight (Ader and Friedman, 1968) supports in general the role of the corticosteroid in stress; the high liberation period correlated with the high stress period.

b. Affective Illness and Schizophrenia. Administered in high doses, cortisol and its synthetic analogs may cause shifts of mood and occasionally psychotic states. Psychological disturbances are also associated with the excessive secretions of cortisol in Cushing's syndrome or with adrenal insufficiency in Addison's disease. When adrenal disease produces an excess of androgens only, major psychological disturbances do not occur (see Gibbons, 1971). Adrenal insufficiency can lower thresholds for taste, olfaction, and audition; these effects are reversed by glucocorticoid replacement. Cortisol activity as a measure of adrenal function has been considered in schizophrenia (calm chronic versus agitated), manic-depressive states, and endogenous depres-sion. Plasma cortisol levels and urinary 17-hydroxycorticosteroid excretion may be elevated in emotionally disturbed schizophrenic patients but not in emotionally calm chronic schizophrenics (Layne *et al.*, 1962; Hellman *et al.*,

1961). In depression and acute schizophrenic states, high initial plasma cortisol levels show decline to normal during recovery periods in some patients (see Gibbons, 1971). The amounts of urinary tetrahydro derivatives of cortisol (Hellman *et al.*, 1961) and the excretion ratios of three principal 17-oxosteroid cortisol metabolites were similar in nonclinical compared with schizophrenic men (Coppen *et al.*, 1967). Weaknesses in the above studies include different methods of steroid determination, lack of specificity for the steroid measured (cortisol), lack of control for variations in sampling times, and uncontrolled effects from possible shifts in concentration of corticosteroid-binding globulin.

In manic-depressive patients having short cyclothymic alternations, raised plasma levels characteristically accompany the depressed phase with a return to normal or low during the manic phase. Diurnal variation of plasma cortisol persists in depressive illness and the shift toward an earlier peak, sometimes observed, may relate to altered sleep patterns of institutionalized patients. A trend toward elevated (but within the wide normal range) plasma cortisol has been correlated with severity of depression. Decline of cortisol levels following dexamethasone administration to depressive patients indicates that pituitary–adrenal feedback mechanisms are intact. However, the sharp increase in plasma cortisol in response to stress was not observed in patients treated with large doses of tranquilizers and in some cases of hypothalamic diseases. The finding of increased proportion of 17-ketogenic steroids as compared with 17-hydroxycorticosteroids and increased excretion of 11-deoxycorticosteroids in depressive patients has been interpreted as implying the presence of a steroid metabolite with no OH group at C-11 and a different side chain at C-17 (see Gibbons, 1971). The cortisol precursor 17α-hydroxyprogesterone has been suggested.

The relation of protein and steroid hormones to schizophrenic behavior is a controversial subject with conflicting results (see Brambilla and Penati, 1971) largely due to different nosographic classifications of patients. Subjects in initial and chronic stages of the disease were subdivided into hebephrenics, paranoids, and pseudoneurotics (Brambilla and Penati, 1971). A series of measures involving gonadotropin, corticotropin, corticosteroid, androgen and estrogen excretion, and tests for thyroid function and corticotropin reserves (the Metopirone test) were applied to each subgroup. Androgen and estrogen excretion were below normal in all groups. Some pseudoneurotics showed both above- and below-normal gonadotropin levels. Corticotropin reserves were below normal in all groups but the chronic paranoids. Corticosteroid excretion remained in the basal range for all groups after ACTH stimulation and during circadian rhythms. Thyroid function was reported as essentially normal, though the data as presented do not bear this out for the chronic groups. The overall picture indicated that pathologic hypothalamic–pituitary–adrenocortical reactivity to stress was related to reduced psychological adjustment to both external and internal stimuli. The pituitary gonadal functions continued to decrease with chronic hebephrenics. The weakness of the study is in the pooling of the sexes, the small number of paranoids (9) in the initial stage, and presentation of data not amenable to statistical analyses.

A possible direct effect of increased cortisol secretion mediating clinical mood changes in depressives is not favored (Gibbons, 1971) because of the dissimilarity of steroid-induced depressions and those (endogenous) typically encountered clinically. Increased adrenocortical activity observed in some depressives and schizophrenics is attributed to factors of arousal associated with stress. Although this leaves as enigmatic the direct clinical relationship between adrenal function and affective illnesses, the role of stress may be a vital link toward understanding a biological mechanism underlying some forms of mental illness. With early acute agitated schizophrenics, the equivocal results for cortisol excretion are discouraging. However, the finding that pituitary–adrenal feedback mechanisms are intact in depressives (Gibbons, 1971) but not in schizophrenics (Brambilla and Penati, 1971) may have etiological implications. This would be especially important where affective disorders are the prelude to schizophrenia.

The effect of MAO on catecholamine metabolism (see Section IX,C,1,c) and of epinephrine in antagonizing gonadal function point to an indirect but profound relationship between adrenal function and mental illness. Androgens and estrogens may inactivate MAO to a lesser extent than the corticosteroids, which increase under conditions of stress (see Broverman *et al.*, 1974). This possibility led to a therapeutic rationale for large doses of sex steroids that would "outcompete" the adrenal steroids for control of MAO. The schizophrenogenic effects of decreased MAO encountered in conditions of excess adrenal steroids may be involved with a blockade of normal catecholamine metabolism leading to the production of false transmitters such as octopamine (Broverman *et al.*, 1974). MAO may also have a role in the phenomenon of the similarity of amphetamine psychosis and hallucinogenic drug states to schizophrenia. The structural resemblance of many psychotomimetic or hallucinogenic compounds to endogenous biogenic amines (Bryson, 1971) has given rise to the hypothesis of possible abnormal metabolites derived from faulty *O*-methylation of catecholamine metabolism (Osmond and Smythies, 1952). The concept has been extended to cover *N*-methylation of indole amines and is often referred to as the transmethylation hypothesis. Decreased MAO activity would favor the *O*-methylation or *N*-methylation pathways of neurotransmitter metabolism potentiating possible accumulation of transmethylated psychotogens endogenously. This could give rise to amphetamine-psychosis-like states

(Snyder, 1974). The resulting stress from the anxiety induced by unaccountable shifts in perception and mood would further elevate cortisol levels, further depressing MAO activity. This regenerative feedback (Reynolds, 1971) may account for both the cyclicity and intractable nature of the illness. Since regenerative feedback is biologically intolerable for prolonged durations, progressive episodes eventually could favor a decline of pituitary–adrenal function, as has been observed in schizophrenics (Brambilla and Penati, 1971).

The antagonism of gonadal function by stress (see Section IX,C,3,c) could also relate to short-term regenerative feedback processes in mental illness. Increased stress accompanied by raised corticosteroid levels would tend to lower sex-steroid levels and the advantages attributed to their control of MAO regulation of catecholamine metabolism (Broverman et al., 1974). This view would be supported by the observation that defeat in an aggressive encounter or loss of social status (stressful social interactions) can decrease plasma testosterone levels in male rhesus monkeys (Bernstein et al., 1974).

3. Effects of Prenatal Steroidal Action

a. Developmental. The steroid hormones controlling the differentiation of sexual anatomy and of sexual behavioral potentials are elaborated during critical periods of prenatal development. If androgen predominates, masculinization of reproductive physiology, morphology, and behavioral potentials occurs. Morphology and behavior become feminized in the absence of embryonic androgen. This principle of "basic femaleness" proposed by Wiesner (1934) was demonstrated with the female differentiation of male or female rabbit fetuses castrated in utero (Jost, 1947). Nature's rule for critical periods of endocrine influence is that something must be added to make a male (Money and Ehrhardt, 1972). In mammals (heterogametic for males), the chromosomal pairings of XX or XY pass their phyletic program to the undifferentiated fetal gonads determining their destiny as testes (if a Y is present) or ovaries (X's only). In contrast to birds (homogametic for males), the mammalian embryo is subjected to a uterine environment rich in maternal estrogens. For a male phenotype to develop, the Y chromosome functions to induce early stimulation of the embryonic testes (Mittwoch, 1975). This endogenous androgen ensures continuing masculinization of the brain and morphology of the male fetus. In rats, fetal testosterone is detectable by the 14th day of gestation (Price and Ortiz, 1965).

Any condition shifting normal levels of circulating gonadal hormones during embryonic development could alter sexual behavior and morphology (see Section IX,C,3,b). Perinatal testicular secretions integrate genital and gonadotropic tissues with neurobehavioral tissues, ensuring their ability to respond to adult androgen secretions mediating simultaneous activity, a characteristic of males (Feder and Wade, 1974). In females the sequential activation of uterine, gonadotropic, neurobehavioral, and ovarian tissues obviates the necessity of the perinatal organizational action of steroid hormones (see Whalen, 1968). A progesterone–estrogen synergism is a fine tuner of reproductive cyclicity and requires that progesterone rapidly trigger a display of sexual behavior. Unlike estrogen, which can induce female behavior when administered in many species, progesterone administration alone cannot (Young, 1961).

Genetic males deprived of androgen during perinatal development become feminized or demasculinized in behavior. Postnatal deficiencies induced by castration in day-old rats eliminate the potential for ejaculatory behavior in adulthood, and although high levels of incomplete copulatory behavior persist, such males show a high degree of female lordotic patterns following treatment with ovarian hormones (see Ward, 1974). The extent to which neonatal castration in males produces a feminized nervous system remains unsettled. Although similar neural structures appear responsible for ovarian cyclicity in the normal female and the neonatally castrated grafted male (Gorski, 1967), differences in lordic responding may be related to the time of castration and the length of the critical period (Pfaff *et al.*, 1974). Successful surgical castration of male rats *in utero* is not practical, but prenatal cyproterone acetate treatment impairs development of male copulatory behavior and increases the lordotic potential. Castration on the day of birth induces high levels of both lordosis and soliciting behavior, but this period of treatment is too late to produce a male equivalent to normal females (Ward, 1974).

The penis also goes through a critical period of differentiation. Neonatally castrated male rats exhibit incomplete mating and penile development. Stimulation with testosterone in adulthood causes increased glans length and phallic weight only with testosterone pretreatment during infancy. Separate male and female behavior control systems are developmentally and pharmacologically indentifiable in the same gender in rodents. Either incomplete penile or neural differentiation may account for decreased intromission frequency in the neonatally castrated male. The display of mating responses and sexual arousability indicates a functional masculine behavior control system. Hence, completeness of penile development is favored as structuring the behavior (Whalen, 1968).

Testosterone propionate administration to pregnant guinea pigs impairs sexual receptivity in the adult female offspring, which also display male copulatory behavior following testosterone propionate treatment (Phoenix *et al.*, 1959). This classic experiment and those with neonatally androgenized female rats (see Pfaff *et al.*, 1974) raise the question of different mechanisms underlying acyclical gonadotropin release in normal males. In normal or androgenized female rats, either estradiol or testosterone administration followed by progesterone facilitates luteinizing hormone release. Male rats respond similarly if treated with testosterone followed by progesterone, but progesterone is without effect in males primed with estrogen (Taleisnik et al., 1969). Androgenized female rats demonstrate lower lordosis quotient scores than controls following estradiol benzoate treatment alone indicating decreased neuronal sensitivity to estrogen (Whalen et al., 1971). The lordosis quotient score in rats was lower for androgenized females than for controls receiving an estrogen–progesterone sequential combination but not for the estrogen treatment alone, nor for comparison of estrogen-treated males with females castrated as adults. Treatment with progesterone in addition to the estrogen did not increase lordosis frequency for the males as it did with the females (Clemens, 1971). A cortical inhibitory system is postulated which is deactivated by progesterone in the female rat, and which can be suppressed by estrogen priming of males and androgenized females.

The above-postulated circuits may be limited to reflex ovulators. Progesterone levels tend to be lower in spontaneous-ovulating species during behavioral estrus than they are in ovulating rats (see Brown-Grant, 1971). In spontaneous ovulators estrogen priming of the hypothalamic–pituitary system appears to trigger the release of LH. Progesterone of ovarian origin does not initiate the ovulatory surge of gonadotropin but it may have an auxiliary role as a back-up reserve mechanism for LH release.

Mating behavior in male rats may depend on the combined action of estrogens and 5α-dihydro metabolites of circulating testosterone. Specific cytoplasmic receptors for estradiol have been identified in the pituitary and anterior hypothalamus in male rats (Vreeburg et al., 1975).

The effectiveness of neonatal hormone treatment depends not only on the presence of steroid-sensitive receptors, but also on factors of species-specific development at birth. Rats and mice have postnatal periods of hormone susceptibility that are not observed in species whose young are born more fully mature. In the female guinea pig, androgenic stimulation produces inhibition of the female system between 30 and 35 days post conception, similar to the neonatal rat. Periods of critical sensitivity are meaningful only if compared in terms of days post conception rather than days after birth (Young, 1965).

Even with central aromatization effects, differentiation of tissues regulating adult sexual behavior involves the kind of receptor mechanism determining reproductive morphology. Once it has been differentiated or suppressed, a behavior potential cannot be altered in adulthood. Even prolonged estrogen–progesterone treatment is ineffective in activating normal lordotic responding in neonatally androgenized female rats (Whalen et al., 1971). Similarly, prolonged daily testosterone treatment does not restore ejaculatory capacity to neonatally castrated males.

Although it is likely that the suppression of female cyclicity and sexual behavior by neonatal androgen is a CNS-mediated effect, organization of the male control pattern in the neonate may not be. Penile desensitization in cats decreased mounting and intromission frequency, which were initially linked with low seasonal androgen levels, later becoming long-term (Aronson and Cooper, 1968). The strong correlation between pre- and neonatal treatment with androgen, producing enhanced phallic development and more complete masculinization of behavior (Beach, 1971), supports a nonspecific and additive theory of sexual behavior (Beach, 1968).

On the basis of genitosexual anomalies in humans as well as neonatal endocrine influences that permanently alter adult sexual behavior, human psychosexual development is seen to be dependent on genetic and endocrine factors present prior to birth (Diamond, 1968). The organization of the gender personality most frequently parallels that of the external genitalia. Owing to the usual parallel differentiation of the external genitalia and the neural tissues mediating sexual behavior, sexual assignment by parents on the basis of the physical genital appearance usually produces a result concordant with psychosexual development. The genitals function in a role of signaling the prenatal and pubertal endocrine environment, with a hint at later things to come.

In humans, postnatal social ontogenetic experience plays a greater role in psychosexual differentiation than in lower mammals in which sexual behavior is routed in more phyletically determined neurochemical pathways. A serial process of interaction is postulated (Money, 1971). On the basis of experimental and clinical evidence, androgen is regarded as the libido hormone for both male and female adults (see Money and Ehrhardt, 1972). The endogenous androgens of eroticism in nonclinical women may be of adrenal origin or derive from closely related progestins. Androgens of adrenal origin maintain sexual receptivity in female rhesus monkeys (Everitt *et al.*, 1972).

Different androgen receptors in the hypothalamus, one involved with gonadotropin release, the other with male sexual activity, have been implicated. Implantation of cyproterone in the median eminence of rats by blocking testosterone access to the gonadotropin feedback receptor, increased gonadotropin release (Bloch and Davidson, 1967). Cyproterone had a stimulating effect on sexual behavior in castrate rats (Bloch and Davidson, 1971) and administered simultaneously with testosterone propionate demonstrated no antiandrogenic effect on behavior (Whalen and Edwards, 1969). Cyproterone had androgenic effects on the growth of penile papillae, seminal vesicles, and ventral prostate in androgen-sensitive castrated rats. However, given in conjunction with testosterone propionate, cyproterone was antiandrogenic. Competition with testosterone receptors is a suggested mechanism of inhibition. These studies do not consider the possible complication introduced by conversion of testosterone to dihydrotestosterone locally and the respective activity of each of these androgens regarding behavior and anatomical development (see Sections III,A,1; V,D,1,2; IX,A,1, B,1,2).

At this time it is not possible to determine whether the most important site for perinatal action of androgen in the organization of male sexual behavior patterns is the brain or the genitals (Davidson, 1971). An integrative function would actually be a more favorable interpretation, with the appearance of the penis as a final indisputable arbiter of society's assignment of gender, whereas the behavioral potentiation is androgen dependent.

b. *Clinical.* The two known syndromes of altered steroid hormone action in the human fetus demonstrate either a lack or an excess of prenatal androgen. Estrogen apparently is not implicated. These clinical groups were highly predictable on the basis of experimental animal work (Money, 1971). Failure of androgen to act in the genotypic male visibly affects the fetus. Complete failure produces the external anatomical differentiation of a female, as in the complete androgen insensitivity syndrome. Partial failure permits differentiation in the feminine direction as in 46,XY hermaphroditism with partial androgen insensitivity. Other forms of hermaphroditism may relate to partial testicular failure during fetal life but without androgen insensitivity. The effect of fetal androgen-lack in the 46,XY genotype is compatible with sex assignment as a female and postnatal differentiation of a female psychosexual identity. Male assignment creates an identity conflict in the absence of masculine genital sensations and capability. In the genotypic female, absence of androgen is the prerequisite to female anatomical differentiation. No known human clinical syndrome is a product of androgen insufficiency in a genotypic female fetus. No animal models exist for an antiandrogen effect on genetic female fetuses.

Progestin-induced hermaphroditism occurs in some genetic females exposed *in utero* to synthetic progestin, which may be converted to a metabolite having androgenic effects. Although hormone therapy is not required, feminizing surgery may be. In the adrenogenital syndrome, fetal excesses of androgen produce hermaphroditism in genetic females and precocious masculinization (as early as 18 months of age) in genetic males. Girls masculinized by intrauterine exposure to synthetic progestin or with adrenogenital syndrome, appropriately treated, are sufficiently similar to be considered behaviorally as one group. Both have a high probability of differentiating female psychosexual identity but with tomboyish traits. Homosexuality is not characteristic, although high academic motivation predominates over motherhood. This is interpreted (Money, 1971) as a long-term response to a fetal androgen effect on the CNS. An unexpected finding of high intelligence quotient scores among the girls masculinized by intrauterine synthetic progestins may indicate a facilitating effect of androgens in this type of performance measure.

Fractionation studies on urinary 17-ketosteroids indicated that human females have a relatively lower excretion value (Johnsen, 1956) for androsterone than for etiocholanolone. The former is the 5α, the latter the 5β isomer of the 3α-hydroxyandrostan-17-ones. Urine samples from homosexual compared with heterosexual men showed significant differences in the ratio of these androgen metabolites, the homosexual group having ctiocholanolone values greater than for androsterone (Margolese, 1970). Since androsterone levels predominate over etiocholanolone in the urine of heterosexual men, and this ratio is reversed not only for homosexual men, but for nonclinical human females, and in the clinical conditions of diabetes mellitus and depression, it was concluded that the reversed ratio does not in itself determine the direction of sex drive. Some possibly enzymic factor in the intermediate metabolism of androgens may be responsible for both sex drive and androgen metabolite ratios. Metabolic conditions leading to relatively high androsterone values may determine sexual preference for females by members of either sex, whereas a relatively low androsterone level may be associated with sexual preference for males by members of either sex (see Section VIII,C,1,b).

In 47,XYY males, plasma androgen levels do not show a trend toward abnormal elevation and behavior is more characteristically impulsive rather than aggressive. Earlier reports on aggressive predisposition in XYY's have not been confirmed. The absence of all fetal gonadal steroids in Turner's 45,XO syndrome is compatible with female morphology and postnatal psychosexual differentiation (Money, 1971).

Sex offenders have been treated with 300 mg of Depo-Provera every 10 days for about 6 months, after which time there is a gradual tapering off of dosage. The effect is not one of complete chemical castration, but rather one of reduction of ejaculatory frequency from high (4/day) to lower and presumably more manageable (3–4/week) levels (Money, 1971). The present reviewers feel that the use of a drug with long-term effects on the health and general metabolism, including a possible carcinogenic potential (see Section VII,C,2) in human males, raises serious ethical issues.

c. Population Regulation. All general stressors produce certain pituitary–adrenal–gonadal effects in proportion to the severity of the stress (Selye, 1946) including hyperactivity of the pituitary and adrenals and hypoactivity of the gonads. Population density as a possible stressor (Christian, 1950) has been shown to affect endocrine function, being positively correlated with increased adrenocortical activity and adrenal hypertrophy, negatively with gonadal and mammary activity (Thiessen and Rodgers, 1961). These density-dependent behavioral-endocrine factors can, in turn, regulate the size of many populations of mammals (Christian and Davis, 1964). Although the immediate effects of this population-regulating mechanism would be mediated by pituitary–adrenal–gonadal feedback in the adult, *in utero* influences would also occur. Corticosteroids or other hormones injected during pregnancy can influence later behavior (Lieberman, 1963) and brain development (Howard, 1963). Crowding stress has been implicated in decreased RNA and protein synthesis in the C57B1/10 mouse brain (Bell *et al.*, 1971).

Experimentation with neonatal (Krieger, 1972) and embryonic (Levine, 1970; Ward, 1972) rats, with neonatal (Howard, 1963) and prepubertal (Paris and Ramaley, 1974) mice, and with embryonic (Etzel *et al.*, 1974) guinea pigs supports an overview. The sequence of stress, intrauterine and prepubertal influences on adrenal function and central and anatomical development of sexual capabilities links prenatal stress with decreased reproductive function in the adult. The androgens of adrenal origin (Bloch, 1968) are implicated in accessory sex gland development (Price and Ortiz, 1965). Dehydroepiandrosterone sulfate from human adrenals has a role in the development of the phallus (Howard and Migeon, 1962). The secretion of excessive C-19 steroids, possibly including testosterone, from human hyperplastic adrenals produces congenital virilization that may have its origin during fetal life (Soffer *et al.*, 1962). The ACTH–gonadotropin reciprocal hormonal pathway has been proposed as mediating environmental stress developmentally by decreasing fetal testicular secretion (Ward, 1974). However, ACTH is not thought to cross the placental barrier as do the steroid hormones. Increased maternal adrenocortical activity resulting from stress may elaborate additional adrenal androgens at critical periods of embryonic development, altering receptor formation in CNS regions normally sensitive to testosterone or its putative estrogenic metabolites. Such conformational changes in receptor specificity would affect the pharmacodynamics of adult hormonal induction of behavior (Bryson, 1976).

The evolution of density-dependent mechanisms of population regulation would have great adaptational advantage. Their development is indicated in many mammalian species (see Christian and Davis, 1964). Whether crowding stress-induced changes in the intrauterine environment would favor changes in sexual orientation in the direction of bisexuality in humans is not certain (Money and Ehrhardt, 1972). Obviously social and endocrine factors are interactive not only in population regulation but in the development of behavioral pathology (Calhoun, 1962). On the other hand, that which is pathologic social behavior may be culturally relative. In a mature civilization having vastly increased production, leisure time, and a lowered infant-mortality rate, nonreproductive behavior is less likely to be a "socially lethal trait." In the comparison of man to those other mammals which are well regulated in population control, the ecclesiastical suppression of nonreproductive behavior must be added to the list of differences included with agricultural and industrial revolutions leading to the present demographic dilemma.

X. Summary

Steroid hormone determination has progressed from colorimetry and spectrophotometry to fluorometry, radioimmunoassay and related methods, receptor assay, and gas–liquid chromatography with mass fragmentographic analysis. Fluorometry achieves a sensitivity of $1-10$ ng/ml extended to the sub nanogram and picogram range by the subsequent procedures. Bioassay is still the final arbiter when different methodological procedures give discordant results.

The concept that the more biologically active member of an oxo–hydroxy pair among the four major steroid hormone classes was involved in the physiologic activity, the other serving as a precursor, was oversimplified in view of the formation of dihydrotestosterone from testosterone. Progesterone is a link in the steroid hormone synthetic route, but its specific physiologic activity is conjectural. The two types of corticosteroids share both the metabolic and electrolyte-regulating properties in varying degrees that are not mutually exclusive.

Activity related to the stereochemistry of the steroids involves the asymmetric carbon atom, the cis-trans relationship of the four fused rings, and the axial and equatorial relationships of side groups to the steroid plane as a whole. Biologic activity of diethylstilbestrol and reserpine demonstrate that a pentaphenanthrene nucleus is not required.

Estrogens apparently are involved with endergonic enzyme synthetic reactions whereas androgens invoke synthesis of enzyme systems. The cellular protein receptors are in the cytosol fraction when the cells have not been subjected to hormone exposure. Soluble or insoluble receptors appear in the nucleus after exposure. Receptors vary quantitatively during different physiologic conditions, and more than one may appear in any cell. In the brain a distinction between receptor (implying action) and binding site (implying affinity) has been made. Neurons appear to be under direct steroid hormone control, particularly in the case of neurosecretory feedback. Another mechanism of action may involve the activation of steroid-sensitive brain circuits by changes in the level of a specific hormone.

In addition to transport mechanisms and receptor site occupancy, steroid physiology is largely enzymic ranging from synthetic to metabolic routes.

In many steroid hormones or structurally related pharmaceuticals, OH groups have been esterified, alkylated, or otherwise modified. Hydroxy-dehydrogenases involve the interplay with the oxo–hydroxy steroid hormone pairs. Hydroxylates involve synthetic and metabolic routes.

In older women and males, the complete elaboration of nonovarian estrogenic hormones is not accounted for by the adrenal cortex or the testes.

All *in vivo* steroid chemical reactions are not enzyme dependent, as illustrated by the formation of cholesterol hydroperoxides.

Specific plasma transport proteins lower the water-soluble concentration of steroid hormones by noncovalent binding. Sex-binding β-globulin (SBG) plays a major role for the transport of testosterone, estradiol, and the 17β-hydroxy-5α-androstanes; corticosteroid-binding globulin (CBG) for cortisol and during pregnancy for progesterone. α-Acid glycoprotein (AAG) and albumin play intermediate exchange transport roles with CBG and SBG. Albumin is involved primarily with estrone sulfate and some glucosiduronates, also with androstenedione and estrone. The hemoglobin in red cells acts as a transport protein.

Target-site receptor proteins for estradiol are found in the mammary gland, uterus, vagina, pituitary, and hypothalamus; for testosterone in the coagulation gland, epididymis, prostate, seminal vesicles, pituitary, hypothalamus, olfactory bulbs, preoptic and septal regions of the brain; for glucocorticoids in the liver, lymphocytes, mammary gland, and hypothalamus; for the mineral corticoids in the kidney. High corticosteroid levels during stress may involve lympholytic effects ultimately decreasing immune surveillance of error cells associated with ageing and cancer.

The sudden increase in the incidence of a rare tumor type stimulates search for an etiologic agent. The transplacental effect of diethylstilbestrol is correlated with adenocarcinoma of the vagina in young women, and decreased masculinization in young boys. Endometrial carcinoma correlates with estrogen-secreting tumors and with estrogen therapy in women with gonadal dysgenesis. A link between carcinoma of the female breast and reserpine users required large series because this tumor type is common.

Safety testing for carcinogenic hazards with the use of laboratory animals, challenged at a World Health Organization meeting at Geneva, 1973, has enjoyed renewed confidence because of the emergence of cancers with common cross-species etiology.

In brain regions free of cells of mesenchymal origin, the glial cell functions in the defense mechanism against a foreign body analogously to the fibroblast or pericyte in other body areas.

Radiation-induced carcinoma of the skin is linked with local formation of carcinogenic oxidation products of cholesterol.

Chloroderivatives of steroids are under scrutiny for carcinogenic potential.

The estrogen treatment of premature coronary heart disease in males and carcinoma of the prostate was correlated with earlier deaths by heart disease.

The association of female venous thrombosis and pulmonary embolism with the use of "the Pill" prompted reduction of the dose level. Reports of hepatotoxicity are regional. Hypertension usually returns to normal. All the adverse effects are of a low incidence. Associated with the failure of the estrogen–progestogen birth control pill to circumvent pregnancy are vertebral, anal, cardiac, tracheal, esophageal, renal, and limb defects in the offspring.

Marijuana is associated with a low incidence of breast hypertrophy.

Three steroid effects attributed to brain mediation are behavioral phenomena, the organizational influences of perinatal steroids on behavioral patterns and adult endocrine function, and endocrine regulating feedback mechanisms. Electrophysiologic techniques have identified steroid-sensitive central structures and support many uptake studies. Estrogen-sensitive hypothalamic centers control sexual behavior and pituitary gonadotropic function. Androgens function in the brain by way of direct receptor sites and by local aromatization to estrogen. The 5α-reductase functions irreversibly to reduce testosterone to 5α-dihydrotestosterone, which is subject to reversible 3- and 17-dehydrogenase activity.

Perinatal studies with estrogens, androgens, and antiandrogens indicate critical periods in the induction and later susceptibility of receptors in the CNS. Ovulatory cyclicity, mating, and sexual behavioral patterns may be permanently altered in individuals, the implications of which include psychosexual development in humans. The period of brain differentiation, critically susceptible to steroid influences, may be a function of species-specific developmental patterns.

In the brain the aromatization of androgen to estrogen does not involve dihydrotestosterone.

Cortisol is involved in general excitatory effects in the brain, control of ACTH secretion, and stress and nonstress hypothalamic–pituitary–adrenal feedback mechanisms. Steroid interaction with central biogenic amines have clinical implications extending to minimal brain dysfunction in children, affective disorders and depressive states, and schizophrenia. Increased cortisol levels following stress can inhibit monoamine oxidase action. Defects in catecholamine metabolism relating to faulty methylation would be exacerbated, producing possible hallucinogenic compounds.

The immediate effects of crowding stress induce increases in adrenocortical suppression of gonadal function and reproductive behavior in adult mammals including humans. Population-control mechanisms may also involve transplacental effects during periods of critical susceptibility in the development of the pituitary–gonadal–adrenal axis.

ACKNOWLEDGMENTS

The authors gratefully acknowledge the interest and advice of Drs. D. R. Dickson and R. W. Reynolds, and the secretarial assistance of Henrietta Bischoff.

References

Abramson, R. K., and Hutton, J. J. (1975). *Cancer Res.* **35**, 23.
Ader, R., and Friedman, S. B. (1968). *Neuroendocrinology* **3**, 378.
Adlin, E. V., and Channick, B. J. (1966). *Endocrinology* **78**, 511.
Albin, J., Vittek, J., Gordon, G. G., Altman, K., Olivo, J., and Southren, A. L. (1973). *Endocrinology* **93**, 417.
Albrieux, A. S. (1941a). *Proc. Soc. Exp. Biol. Med.* **47**, 381.
Albrieux, A. S. (1941b). *J. Clin. Endocrinol.* **1**, 893.
Anand Kumar, T. C., and Thomas, G. H. (1968). *Nature (London)* **219**, 628.
Antoniades, H. N., McArthur, J. W., Pennell, R. B., Ingersoll, F. M., Ulfelder, H., and Oncley, J. L. (1957). *Am. J. Physiol.* **189**, 455.
A. P. (1974a). *Santa Barbara News Press* April 17, p. E-6.
A. P. (1974b). *Santa Barbara News Press* October 10, p. A-3.
A. P. (1975). *Santa Barbara News Press* April 3, p. A-7.
Arai, Y. (1971). *In* "Steroid Hormones and Brain Function" (C. H. Sawyer and R. A. Gorski, eds.), pp. 185–192. Univ. of California Press, Los Angeles.
Ariëns, E. J. (1954). *Arch. Int. Pharmacodyn. Ther.* **99**, 32.
Armstrong, B., Stevens, N., and Doll, R. (1974). *Lancet* **ii**, 672.
Aronson, L. R., and Cooper, M. L. (1968). *In* "Perspectives in Reproduction and Sexual Behavior" (M. Diamond, ed.), pp. 51–82. Indiana Univ. Press, Bloomington.
Augustinsson, K.-B., and Henricson, B. (1970). *Experientia* **26**, 793.
Augustinsson, K.-B., and Olsson, B. (1961). *Nature (London)* **192**, 969.
Baggett, B., Engel, L. L., Savard, K., and Dorfman, R. I. (1956). *J. Biol. Chem.* **221**, 931.
Bailar, J. C. (1967). *Med. World News* **8**, 27.
Bailey, J. M. (1961). *Proc. Soc. Exp. Biol. Med.* **107**, 30.
Baird, D. T. (1968). *J. Clin. Endocrinol. Metab.* **28**, 244.
Baird, D. T., and Guevara, A. (1969). *J. Clin. Endocrinol. Metab.* **29**, 149.
Baron, D. N., and Abelson, D. (1954). *Nature (London)* **173**, 184.
Barraclough, C. A. (1966). *Recent Prog. Horm. Res.* **22**, 503.
Bartke, A., Steel, R. E., Williams, J. G., and Williams, K. I. H. (1971). *Steroids* **18**, 303.
Bates, R. R., and Prehn, R. T. (1965). *Nature (London)* **205**, 303.
Baulieu, E.-E. (1975). *Clin. Chem.* **21**, 924.
Beach, F. A. (1958). *In* "Biological and Biochemical Bases of Behavior" (H. F. Harlow and C. N. Woolsey, eds.), pp. 263–283. Univ. of Wisconsin Press, Madison.
Beach, F. A. (1968). *In* "Perspectives in Reproduction and Sexual Behavior" (M. Diamond, ed.), pp. 83–131. Indiana Univ. Press, Bloomington.
Beach, F. A. (1971). *In* "Steroid Hormones and Brain Function" (C. H. Sawyer and R. A. Gorski, eds.), p. 212. Univ. of California Press, Los Angeles.
Beall, D. (1940). *Biochem. J.* **34**, 1293.
Becker, H., Kaufmann, J., Klosterhalfen, H., and Voight, K. D. (1972). *Acta Endocrinol. (Copenhagen)* **71**, 589.
Bell, R. W., Miller, C. E., Ordy, J. M., and Rolsten, C. (1971). *J. Comp. Physiol. Psychol.* **75**, 258.
Belleau, B. (1964). *J. Med. Chem.* **7**, 776.
Benagiano, G., Ermini, M., de la Torre, B., Wiqvist, N., and Diczfalusy, E. (1971). *Acta Endocrinol. (Copenhagen)* **66**, 653.

Benedek, T. F., and Rubenstein, B. (1942). "The Sexual Cycle in Women." Natl. Res. Counc., Washington, D.C.

Benirsche, K. (1974). *Acta Endocrinol. (Copenhagen), Suppl.* **185**, 311.

Bergström, S., and Wintersteiner, O. (1941). *J. Biol. Chem.* **141**, 597.

Berliner, V. R. (1974). *Acta Endocrinol. (Copenhagen), Suppl.* **185**, 249.

Bernstein, I. S., Rose, R. M., and Gordon, T. P. (1974). *Hum. Evol.* **3**, 517.

Beyer, C. (1971). *In* "Steroid Hormones and Brain Function" (C. H. Sawyer and R. A. Gorski, eds.), p. 244. Univ. of California Press, Los Angeles.

"Biology of the Laboratory Mouse" (1941). (G. D. Snell, ed.), pp. 212–219. Blakiston, Philadelphia, Pennsylvania.

Bird, C. E., and Clark, A. F. (1973). *J. Clin. Endocrinol.* **36**, 296.

Bischoff, F. (1936). *Am. J. Physiol.* **114**, 483.

Bischoff, F. (1940). *J. Biol. Chem.* **133**, 621.

Bischoff, F. (1956). "Relation of Estronase to Cancer." C-1587 C2. Natl. Advis. Counc., H.E.W., Public Health Serv., Washington, D.C.

Bischoff, F. (1963). *Prog. Exp. Tumor Res.* **3**, 412.

Bischoff, F. (1969). *Adv. Lipid Res.* **7**, 197–211, 230.

Bischoff, F. (1972). *Clin. Chem.* **18**, 869.

Bischoff, F., and Bakhtiar, A. K. (1957). *Endocrinology* **60**, 333.

Bischoff, F., and Bryson, G. (1960). *J. Appl. Physiol.* **15**, 515.

Bischoff, F., and Bryson, G. (1964). *Prog. Exp. Tumor Res.* **5**, 106.

Bischoff, F., and Bryson, G. (1969). *Adv. Lipid Res.* **7**, 186–187.

Bischoff, F., and Bryson, G. (1970). *Fed. Proc., Fed. Am. Soc. Exp. Biol.* **29**, 860.

Bischoff, F., and Bryson, G. (1974a). *Proc. Am. Assoc. Cancer Res.* **15**, 6.

Bischoff, F., and Bryson, G. (1974b). *Chem. Eng. News* **52**, July 15, p. 3.

Bischoff, F., and Jemtegaard, L. M. (1937). *Am. J. Physiol.* **119**, 149.

Bischoff, F., and Katherman, R. E. (1948). *Am. J. Physiol.* **152**, 189.

Bischoff, F., and Katherman, R. E. (1949). *Am. Chem. Soc., Abstr.* March, 6C.

Bischoff, F., and Long, M. L. (1938). *Am. J. Cancer* **32**, 418.

Bischoff, F., and Pilhorn, H. R. (1947). *Am. J. Physiol.* **150**, 444.

Bischoff, F., and Pilhorn, H. R. (1948). *J. Biol. Chem.* **174**, 663.

Bischoff, F., and Stauffer, R. D. (1957). *Am. J. Physiol.* **191**, 313.

Bischoff, F., Maxwell, L. C., and Ullmann, H. J. (1934). *Am. J. Cancer* **21**, 329.

Bischoff, F., Katherman, R. E., Moran, J. J., and Yee, Y. S. (1949). *J. Am. Chem. Soc.* **71**, 4143.

Bischoff, F., Yee, Y. S., Moran, J. J., and Katherman, R. E. (1951a). *J. Biol. Chem.* **189**, 729.

Bischoff, F., Katherman, R. F., and Yee, Y. S. (1951b). *Am. J. Physiol.* **164**, 774.

Bischoff, F., Katherman, R. E., and Favati, V. (1951c). *Am. J. Physiol.* **165**, 667.

Bischoff, F., Katherman, R. E., Favati, V., and Gray, C. L. (1952). *Am. J. Physiol.* **171**, 100.

Bischoff, F., Gray, C. L., and Katherman, R. E. (1953). *Endocrinology* **53**, 321.

Bischoff, F., Stauffer, R. D., and Gray, C. L. (1954). *Am. J. Physiol.* **177**, 65.

Bischoff, F., Torres, A., and Lopez, G. (1957). *Am. J. Physiol.* **189**, 447.

Bischoff, F., Turner, J. G., Jr., and Bryson, G. (1958a). *Am. J. Physiol.* **195**, 81.

Bischoff, F., Turner, J. G., Jr., and Bryson, G. (1958b). *Am. Chem. Soc., Abstr.* September, 54C.

Bischoff, F., Stauffer, R. D., and Bryson, G. (1973). *Fed. Proc., Fed. Am. Soc. Exp. Biol.* **32**, 677.

Black, H. S., and Douglas, D. R. (1972). *Cancer Res.* **32**, 2630.

Black, H. S., and Lo, W.-B. (1971). *Nature (London)* **234**, 306.

Bloch, E. (1968). *In* "Functions of the Adrenal Cortex" (K. W. McKerns, ed.), Vol. 2, pp. 734–735. Appleton, New York.

Bloch, G. J., and Davidson, J. M. (1967). *Science* **155**, 593.

Bloch, G. J., and Davidson, J. M. (1971). *Horm. Behav.* **2**, 11.

Bloch, K. (1965). *Science* **150**, 19.

Böttiger, L. E., and Westerholm, B. (1971). *Acta Med. Scand.* **190**, 455.

Bogdanove, E. M. (1963). *Endocrinology* **73**, 696.

Bogren, H., and Larsson, K. (1963). *Biochim. Biophys. Acta* **75**, 65.

Bongiovanni, A. M., DiGeorge, A. M., and Grumbach, M. M. (1959). *J. Clin. Endocrinol. Metab.* **19**, 1004.

Boot, L. M., and Mühlbock, O. (1956). *Acta Unio Int. Contra Cancrum* **12**, 569.

Boston Collaborative Drug Surveillance Program (1973a). *Lancet* **i**, 1399.

Boston Collaborative Drug Surveillance Program (1973b). *Cancer* **31**, 573.

Boston Collaborative Drug Surveillance Program (1974). *Lancet* **ii**, 669.

Bourgès, M., Small, D. M., and Dervichan, D. G. (1967). *Biochim. Biophys. Acta* **137**, 157.

Bradford-Hill, A. (1974). *Acta Endocrinol. (Copenhagen), Suppl.* **185**, 285.

Brambilla, F., and Penati, G. (1971). *Proc. Int. Soc. Psychoneuroendocrinol., New York* pp. 482–494.

Breuer, H., Vogel, W., and Knuppen, R. (1962). *Z. Physiol. Chem.* **327**, 217.

Briggs, M., and Briggs, M. (1974). *Nature (London)* **252**, 585.

Briggs, M. H., and Brotherton, J. (1970). "Steroid Biochemistry and Pharmacology," p. 146. Academic Press, New York.

Brinkman, A. O., Mulder, E., and van der Molen, H. J. (1970a). "Research on Steroids," Vol. 4, p. 91. Pergamon, Oxford.

Brinkman, A. O., Mulder, E., and van der Molen, H. J. (1970b). *Ann. Endocrinol.* **31**, 789.

Brooks, S. C., Horn, L., Jackson, J., Loud, A. V., and Horwitz, J. P. (1963). *Biochim. Biophys. Acta* **74**, 569.

Broster, L. R. (1946). *Proc. Roy. Soc. Med.* **40**, 35.

Broverman, D. M., Klaiber, E. L., Vogel, W., and Kobayashi, Y. (1974). *Psychol. Bull.* **81**, 672.

Brown-Grant, K. (1971). *In* "Steroid Hormones and Brain Function" (C. H. Sawyer and R. A. Gorski, eds.), pp. 269–288. Univ. of California Press, Los Angeles.

Bryson, G. (1971). *Clin. Chem.* **17**, 5.

Bryson, G. (1976). Personal communication.

Bryson, G., and Bischoff, F. (1963). *Proc. Am. Assoc. Cancer Res.* **4**, 8.

Bryson, G., and Bischoff, F. (1967). *Prog. Exp. Tumor Res.* **9**, 148.

Bryson, G., and Bischoff, F. (1969). *Prog. Exp. Tumor Res.* **11**, 128.

Burch, J. C., and Byrd, B. F. (1971). *Ann. Surg.* **174**, 414.

Bush, I. E. (1957). *Ciba Found. Colloq. Endocrinol. [Proc.]* **11**, p. 263.

Butenandt, A., Tscherning, K., and Hanisch, G. (1935). *Ber. Dsch. Chem. Ges. B* **68**, 2097.

Bye, P. G. T., and Elstein, M. (1973). *Br. Med. J.* **ii**, 389.

Calhoun, J. B. (1962). *Sci. Am.* **206**, 139.

Campbell, H. J. (1965). *J. Physiol. (London)* **181**, 568.

Cancer Res. (1973). **33**, October, Cover Legend.

Candy, J., and Abell, M. R. (1968). *J. Am. Med. Assoc.* **203**, 323.

Carroll, K. K., and Khor, H. T. (1971). *Lipids* **6**, 415.

Carstens, H. B., and Clemmesen, J. (1972). *New Engl. J. Med.* **287**, 198.

Chatterjee, A., and Harper, M. J. K. (1970). *Endocrinology* **87**, 966.

Chem. Eng. News (1973). **51**, January 8, p. 4.

Chem. Eng. News (1974a). **52**, January 28, p. 6.

Chem. Eng. News (1974b). **52**, April 22, p. 5.

Chem. Eng. News (1974c). **52**, July 22, p. 9.

Christian, J. J. (1950). *J. Mammal.* **31**, 247.

Christian, J. J., and Davis, D. E. (1964). *Science* **146**, 1550.

Christine, B. (1971). *New Engl. J. Med.* **285**, 524.

Clark, A. J. (1926). *J. Physiol.* (*London*) **61**, 530, 547.

Clark, J. H., Peck, E. J., and Anderson, J. N. (1974). *Nature* (*London*) **251**, 446.

Clemens, L. G. (1971). *In* "Steroid Hormones and Brain Function" (C. H. Sawyer and R. A. Gorski, eds.), pp. 203–214. Univ. of California Press, Los Angeles.

Coffin, D. E. (1973). *J. Assoc. Off. Agric. Chem.* **56**, 352.

Colby, H. D., and Kitay, J. I. (1972). *Endocrinology* **91**, 1523.

Colby, H. D., Gaskin, J. H., and Kitay, J. I. (1973). *Endocrinology* **92**, 769.

Colombo, J. A., Whitmoyer, D. I., and Sawyer, C. H. (1974). *In* "Biorhythms and Human Reproduction" (M. Ferin, F. Halberg, R. M. Richart, and R. L. Vande Wiele, eds.), pp. 651–656. Wiley, New York.

Committee on Safety of Medicines (1973). *Br. Med. J.* June 2, p. 563.

Coppen, A., Julian, T., Fry, D. E., and Marks, V. (1967). *Br. J. Psychiatry* **113**, 269.

Coronary Drug Project Research Group (1973). *J. Am. Med. Assoc.* **226**, 652.

Critchlow, V. (1971). *In* "Steroid Hormones and Brain Function" (C. H. Sawyer and R. A. Gorski, eds.). pp. 51–58. Univ. of California Press, Los Angeles.

Croxatto, H. B. (1976). *In* "Ovum Transport and Fertility Regulation," pp. 557–562. WHO, Scriptor, Copenhagen.

Csapo, A. (1961). *In* "Mechanism of Action of Steroid Hormones" (C. A. Villee and L. L. Engel, eds.), pp. 126–144. Pergamon, New York.

Curtis, G. C. (1974). *In* "Biorhythms and Human Reproduction" (M. Ferin *et al.*, eds.), pp. 417–423. Wiley, New York.

Cutler, B. S., Forbes, A. P., Ingersoll, F. M., and Scully, R. E. (1972). *New Engl. J. Med.* **287**, 628.

Däring, G. K., and Günther, S. (1959). *Arch. Gynaekol.* **191**, 570.

Dal Monte, E., and D'Amico, M. (1956). *Arch. Soc. Biol. Montevideo* **23**, 89.

Dalton, K. (1972). "The Menstrual Cycle." Warner, New York.

Danielli, J. F., and Davson, H. (1935). *J. Cell. Comp. Physiol.* **5**, 495.

Daughaday, W. H. (1958). *J. Clin. Invest.* **37**, 511.

David, G. F. X., and Anand Kumar, T. C. (1974). *Neuroendocrinology* **14**, 114.

Davidson, J. M. (1966). *Endocrinology* **79**, 783.

Davidson, J. M. (1971). *In* "Steroid Hormones and Brain Function" (C. H. Sawyer and R. A. Gorski, eds.), pp. 355–372. Univ. of California Press, Los Angeles.

Davies, I. J., Naftolin, F., Ryan, K. J., Fishman, J., and Siu, J. (1975). *Endocrinology* **97**, 554.

de Moor, P., Heirweigh, K., Heremans, J. F., and Declerck-Raskin, M. (1962). *J. Clin. Invest.* **41**, 816.

Devenuto, F., Ligon, F., Friedrichsen, D. H., and Wilson, H. L. (1969). *Biochim. Biophys. Acta* **193**, 36.

De Waard, F., Laive, J. W., and Baanders-Van Halewijn, E. A. (1960). *Br. J. Cancer* **14**, 437.

De Wied, D., van Delft, A. M. L., Gispen, W. H., Weijnen, J. A. W. M., and van Wimersma Greidanus, T. B. (1972). *In* "Hormones and Behavior" (S. Levine, ed.), pp. 136–172. Academic Press, New York.

Dhar, A. K., Teng, J. I., and Smith, L. L. (1973). *J. Neurochem.* **21**, 51.

Diamond, M. (1968). *In* "Perspectives in Reproduction and Sexual Behavior" (M. Diamond, ed.). pp. 417–443. Indiana Univ. Press, Bloomington.

Diczfalusy, E., ed. (1970). *Acta Endocrinol.* (*Copenhagen*), *Suppl.* **147**, 11.

Diczfalusy, E. (1974). *Acta Endocrinol.* (*Copenhagen*), *Suppl.* **185**, 221.

Dobberstein, J. (1960). *Abh. Dsch. Akad. Wiss. Berlin, Kl. Med.* **3**, 98.

Doe, R. P., Zinneman, H. H., Flink, E. B., and Ulstrom, R. A. (1960). *J. Clin. Endocrinol. Metab.* **20**, 1484.

Doe, R. P., Fernandez, R. N., and Seal, U. S. (1964). *J. Clin. Endocrinol. Metab.* **24**, 1029.

Dole, V. P., and Hamlin, J. T. (1962). *Physiol. Rev.* **42**, 683.
Dorfman, R. I. (1960). *Endocrinology* **67**, 724.
Dorfman, R. I. (1961). *In* "Mechanism of Action of Steroid Hormones" (C. A. Villee and L. L. Engel, eds.), pp. 148–154. Pergamon, New York.
Doughty, C., Booth, J. E., McDonald, P. G., and Parrott, R. F. (1975). *J. Endocrinol.* **67**, 419.
Drill, V. A. (1974). *Acta Endocrinol. (Copenhagen), Suppl.* **185**, 184.
Drill, V. A., and Calhoun, D. W. (1972). *J. Am. Med. Assoc.* **219**, 593.
Dunn, T. B. (1969). *J. Natl. Cancer Inst.* **43**, 671.
Dunn, T. B., and Green, A. W. (1963). *J. Natl. Cancer Inst.* **31**, 425.
Dziuk, P. J., and Cook, B. (1966). *Endocrinology* **78**, 208.
Eberlein, W. R., and Bongiovanni, A. M. (1956). *J. Biol. Chem.* **223**, 85.
Eik-Nes, K., Schellman, J. A., Lumry, R., and Samuels, L. T. (1954) *J. Biol. Chem.* **206**, 411.
Eisenfeld, A. J., and Axelrod, J. (1967). *Biochem. Pharmacol.* **16**, 1781.
Ekwall, P., and Mandell, L. (1961). *Acta Chem. Scand.* **15**, 140.
Endroczi, E. (1971). *In* "Steroid Hormones and Brain Function" (C. H. Sawyer and R. A. Gorski, eds.), pp. 59–66. Univ. of California Press, Los Angeles.
Etzel, V., Schenck, B., and Neumann, F. (1974). *J. Reprod. Fertil.* **37**, 315.
Everitt, B. J., Herbert, J., and Hamer, J. D. (1972). *Physiol. Behav.* **5**, 409.
Fasal, E., and Paffenbarger, R. S., Jr. (1975). *J. Natl. Cancer Inst.* **55**, 767.
Faure, J., and Vincent, J. D. (1971). *In* "Steroid Hormones and Brain Function" (C. H. Sawyer and R. A. Gorski, eds.), pp. 113–120. Univ. of California Press, Los Angeles.
Feder, H. H., and Silver, R. (1974). *Physiol. Behav.* **13**, 251.
Feder, H. H., and Wade, G. N. (1974). *In* "The Neurosciences Third Study Program" (F. O. Schmitt and F. G. Worden, eds.), pp. 583–588. MIT Press, Cambridge, Massachusetts.
Feherty, P., Farrer-Brown, G., and Kellie, A. E. (1971). *Br. J. Cancer* **25**, 697.
Feldman, S. (1971). *In* "Steroid Hormones and Brain Function" (C. H. Sawyer and R. A. Gorski, eds.), pp. 27–34. Univ. of California Press, Los Angeles.
Fishman, J., and Norton, B. (1975). *Endocrinology* **96**, 1054.
Fleischman, R. W., Hayden, D. W., Rosenkrantz, H., and Braude, C. (1975). *Teratology* **12**, 47.
Flerko, B. (1971). *In* "Steroid Hormones and Brain Function" (C. H. Sawyer and R. A. Gorski, eds.), pp. 161–170. Univ. of California Press, Los Angeles.
Folkman, J. (1971). *New Engl. J. Med.* **285**, 404.
Folkman, J., and Long, D. M., Jr. (1964). *J. Surg. Res.* **4**, 139.
Folley, S. J. (1955). *Br. Med. Bull.* **11**, 145.
Forest, M. G., Rivarola, M. A., and Migeon, C. J. (1968). *Steroids* **12**, 323.
Fotherby, K. (1974). *Acta Endocrinol. (Copenhagen), Suppl.* **185**, 119.
Fragachan, F., Nowaczynski, W., Bertranau, E., Kalina, M., and Genest, J. (1969). *Endocrinology* **84**, 98.
Frantz, A. G., Kleinberg, D. L., and Noel, G. L. (1972). *Recent Prog. Horm. Res.* **28**, 527.
Fried, J. (1961). *In* "Mechanism of Action of Steroid Hormones" (C. A. Villee and L. L. Engel, eds.), pp. 232–234. Pergamon, Oxford.
Ganten, D., Minnich, J. L., Granger, P., Hayduk, K., Breck, H. M., Barbeau, A., Boucher, R., and Genest, J. (1971). *Science* **173**, 64.
Gardner, L., Assemany, S. R., and Neu, R. L. (1970). *Lancet* **ii**, 667.
Gass, G. H., Brown, J., and Okey, A. B. (1974). *J. Natl. Cancer Inst.* **53**, 1369.
Gibbons, J. L. (1971). *In* "Biochemistry, Schizophrenias and Affective Illnesses" (H. E. Himwich, ed.), pp. 308–332. Williams & Wilkins, Baltimore, Maryland.
Giorgi, E. P., Shirley, I. M., Grant, J. K., and Stewart, J. C. (1973). *Biochem. J.* **132**, 465.
Goebelsmann, U., Wiqvist, N., and Diczfalusy, E. (1968). *Acta Endocrinol. (Copenhagen)* **59**, 426.
Gorski, R. A. (1967). *Anat. Rec.* **157**, 63.
Gorski, R. A. (1968). *Endocrinology* **82**, 1001.

Gorski, R. A. (1971). *In* "Steroid Hormones and Brain Function" (C. H. Sawyer and R. A. Gorski, eds)., pp. 1–26. Univ. of California Press, Los Angeles.

Grant, J. K., Giorgi, E., Cowan, R. A., and Pollack, A. (1975). *Clin. Chem.* **21**, 924.

Gray, C. L., and Bischoff, F. (1955). *Am. J. Physiol.* **180**, 279.

Grönroos, M., Kalliomäki, T. O., Keyriläinen, T. O., and Marjanen, P. (1959). *Acta Endocrinol. (Copenhagen)* **31**, 154.

Guériguian, J., and Pearlman, W. H. (1967). *Fed. Proc., Fed. Am. Soc. Exp. Biol.* **26**, 757.

Gyermek, L., Geneher, G., and Fliming, N. (1967). *Int. J. Neuropharmacol.* **6**, 191.

Hagerman, D. D., and Villee, C. A. (1959). *J. Biol. Chem.* **234**, 2031.

Hagerman, D. D., and Villee, C. A. (1961). *In* "Mechanism of Action of Steroid Hormones" (C. A. Villee and L. L. Engel, eds.), p. 180. Pergamon, New York.

Hagino, N., Tima, L., Illei-Donhoffer, A., and Flerko, B. (1975). *Fed. Proc., Fed. Am. Soc. Exp. Biol.* **34**, 340.

Hammerstein, J. (1971). *Symp. Dtsch. Ges. Endokrinol.* **17**, 131.

Harmon, J., and Aliapoulios, M. (1974). *Los Angeles Times* December 11, p. I-4.

Harris, D. N., Lerner, L. J., and Hilf, R. (1968). *Trans. N.Y. Acad. Sci.* **30**, 774.

Harris, G. W., and Michael, R. P. (1964). *J. Physiol. (London)* **171**, 275.

Haukkamaa, M. Karjalainen, O., and Luukkainen, T. (1971). *Am. J. Obstet. Gynecol.* **111**, 205.

Hawker, C. D. (1973). *Anal. Chem.* **45**, 478A.

Heap, R. B., and Deanesly, R. (1966). *J. Endocrinol.* **34**, 417.

Hecker, E., and Marks, F. (1965). *Biochem. Z.* **343**, 211.

Heinonen, O. P., Shapiro, S., Tuominen, L., and Turunen, M. I. (1974). *Lancet* **ii**, 675.

Heller, C. G. (1940). *Endocrinology* **26**, 619.

Hellman, L., Bradlow, H. L., Zumoff, B., and Gallagher, T. F. (1961). *J. Clin. Endocrinol. Metab.* **21**, 1231.

Herbst, A. L., and Scully, R. E. (1970). *Cancer (Philadelphia)* **25**, 745.

Herbst, A. L., Ulfelder, H., and Poskanzer, D. C. (1971). *New Engl. J. Med.* **284**, 878.

Herbst, A. L., Kurman, R. J., Scully, R. E., and Poskanzer, D. C. (1972). *New Engl. J. Med.* **287**, 1259.

Hertig, A. T., and Gore, H. (1960). "Atlas of Tumor Pathology," p. 62. Armed Forces Inst. of Pathol. Washington, D.C.

Heyman, A. (1975). *J. Am. Med. Assoc.* **231**, 718.

Hodges, F. B. (1973). *Los Angeles Times* July 1, p. I-2.

Homburger, F., Bogdonoff, P. D., and Kelley, T. F. (1965). *Proc. Soc. Exp. Biol. Med.* **119**, 1106.

Hooker, C. W., and Forbes, T. R. (1949). *Endocrinology* **44**, 61.

Hooker, C. W., and Pfeiffer, C. A. (1942). *Cancer Res.* **2**, 759.

Horwitz, J. P., Horn, L., Loud, A. V., and Brooks, S. C. (1962). *Experientia* **18**, 414.

Howard, E. (1963). *Fed. Proc., Fed. Am. Soc. Exp. Biol.* **22**, 270.

Howard, E., and Migeon, C. J. (1962). *Handb. Exp. Pharmakol.* **14**, 570.

Immwich, H. (1974). *Lancet* **ii**, 774.

Inano, H., and Tamaoki, B. (1971). *Biochemistry* **10**, 1503.

Inman, W. H. W., and Vessey, M. P. (1968). *Br. Med. J.* **ii**, 193.

Inman, W. H. W., Vessey, M. P., Westerholm, B., and Engelund, A. (1970). *Br. Med. J.* **ii**, 203.

Ito, N., Nagasaki, H., Masayuki, A., and Makiura, S. (1973a). *J. Natl. Cancer Inst.* **51**, 1637.

Ito, N., Nagasaki, H., Arai, M., Sugihara, S., and Makiura, S. (1973b). *J. Natl. Cancer Inst.* **51**, 817.

Jacob, G., and Anspach, M., (1965). *Ann. N.Y. Acad. Sci.* **132**, 536.

Janerich, D. T., Piper, J. M., and Glebatis, D. M. (1974). *New Engl. J. Med.* **291**, 697.

Jensen, E. V., and Jacobson, H. I. (1962). *Recent Prog. Horm. Res.* **18**, 387.

Johansson, H., Terenius, L., and Thoren, L. (1970). *Cancer Res.* **30**, 692.

Johnsen, S. G. (1956). *Acta Endocrinol. (Copenhagen)* **21**, 146.

Jost, A. (1947). *Arch. Anat. Microsc. Morphol. Exp.* **36**, 271.

Kappus, H., Bolt, H. M., and Remmer, H. (1972). *Acta Endocrinol. (Copenhagen)* **71**, 374.

Kappus, H., Bolt, H. M., and Remmer, H. (1973). *Steroids* **22**, 203.

Karavolas, H. J., and Engel, L. L. (1971). *Endocrinology* **88**, 1165.

Karavolas, H. J., and Herf, S. M. (1971). *Endocrinology* **89**, 940.

Kato, T., and Horton, R. (1968). *J. Clin. Endocrinol. Metab.* **28**, 1160.

Kaufman, S., Schwert, G. W., and Neurath, H. (1948). *Arch Biochem.* **17**, 203.

Kawakami, M., Teresawa, E., Ibuki, T., and Manaka, M. (1971). *In* "Steroid Hormones and Brain Function" (C. H. Sawyer and R. A. Gorski, eds.), pp. 79–94. Univ. of California Press, Los Angeles.

Kelch, R. P., Lindholm, U. B., and Jaffe, R. B. (1971). *J. Clin. Endocrinol. Metab.* **32**, 449.

Kemp, T., and Bjergaard, R. (1932). *C.R. Seances Soc. Biol. Paris* **111**, 329.

Kerkay, J., and Westphal, U. (1968). *Biochim. Biophys. Acta* **170**, 324.

Kim, U. (1970). *Science* **167**, 72.

Kim, U., Furth, J., and Yannopoulos, K. (1963). *J. Natl. Cancer Inst.* **31**, 233.

Kimura, T., and Nandi, S. (1967). *J. Natl. Cancer Inst.* **39**, 75.

Kirschstein, R. L., Rabson, A. S., and Rusten, G. W. (1972). *J. Natl. Cancer Inst.* **48**, 551.

Kislak, J. W., and Beach, F. A. (1955). *Endocrinology* **56**, 684.

Klaiber, E. L., and Broverman, D. M. (1967). *Psychopharmacologia* **11**, 320.

Klaiber, E. L., Kobayashi, Y., Broverman, D. M., and Hall, F. (1971). *J. Clin. Endocrinol. Metab.* **33**, 630.

Klaiber, E. L., Broverman, D. M., Vogel, W., and Kobayashi, Y. (1974). *In* "Biorhythms and Human Reproduction" (M. Ferin, F. Halberg, R. M. Richart, and R. L. Vande Wiele., eds.), pp. 353–367. Wiley, New York.

Knapstein, P., David, A., Wu, G. H., Archer, D. F., Flickinger, G. L., and Toughstone, J. C. (1968). *Steroids* **11**, 885.

Kobayashi, T., Kobayashi, Y., and Kato, J. (1966). *In* "Steroid Dynamics" (G. Pincus, T. Nakao, and J. Tait, eds.), p. 305. Academic Press, New York.

Koblinsky, M., Beato, M., Kalimi, M., and Fiegelson, P. (1972). *J. Biol. Chem.* **247**, 7892.

Koch, T. R., Edwards, L., and Chilcote, M. E. (1973). *Clin. Chem.* **19**, 258.

Kodama, M., Kodama, T., Yoshida, M., Totania, R., and Aoki, K. (1975). *J. Natl. Cancer Inst.* **54**, 1275.

Kolanowski, J., and Pizarro, M. A. (1969). *Ann. Endocrinol.* **30**, 177.

Kolodny, R. C., Masters W. H., Kolodner, R. M., and Toro G. (1974). *New Engl. J. Med.* **290**, 872.

Komisaruk, B. A. (1971). *In* "Steroid Hormones and Brain Function" (C. H. Sawyer and R. A. Gorski, eds.), pp. 127–136. Univ. of California Press, Los Angeles.

Kopin, I. J. (1964). *Pharmacol. Rev.* **16**, 179.

Korenbrot, C. C., Paup, D. C., and Gorski, R. A. (1975). *Endocrinology* **97**, 709.

Kornel, L., Moore, J. T., and Noyes, I. (1970). *J. Clin. Endocrinol. Metab.* **30**, 40.

Koshland, D. E., Jr. (1964). *Fed. Proc., Fed. Am. Soc. Exp. Biol.* **23**, 719.

Kozuka, S. (1970). *Cancer Res.* **30**, 1384.

Krieger, D. T. (1972). *Science* **178**, 1205.

Kulin, H. E., and Reiter, E. O. (1972). *J. Clin. Endocrinol. Metab.* **35**, 836.

Lacassagne, A., and Hurst, L. (1963). *C.R. Acad. Sci.* **257**, 1658.

Lacassagne, A., Duplan, J. F., and Buu-Höi, N. P. (1958). *C.R. Acad. Sci.* **247**, 729.

Lacassagne, A., Buu-Höi, N. P., and BaGiao, N. (1970). *C.R. Acad. Sci., Ser. D* **270**, 746.

Lanier, A. P., Noller, K. L., Decker, D. G., and Kurland, L. T. (1973). *Mayo Clin. Proc.* **48**, 793.

Laragh, J. H. (1973). *Los Angeles Times* November 27, p. IV-5. (Knight News Service.)

Laumas, K. R., and Farooq, A. (1966). *J. Endocrinol.* **36**, 95.

Lawson, D. E. M., and Pearlman, W. H. (1964). *J. Biol. Chem.* **239**, 3226.

Layne, D. S., Meyer, C. J., Vaishwanar, P. S., and Pincus, G. (1962). *J. Clin. Endocrinol. Metab.* **22**, 107.

Leach, G. S., Rambaut, P. C., Vernikos-Danellis, J., Winget, C. M., and Campbell, B. O. (1974). *In* "Biorhythms and Human Reproduction" (M. Ferin, F. Halberg, R. M. Richart, and R. L. Vande Wiele., eds.), pp. 409–416, Wiley, New York.

Lebeau, M. C., and Baulieu, E. E. (1970). *J. Clin. Endocrinol. Metab.* **30**, 166.

Lee, L., and Hähnel, R. (1971). *Clin. Chem.* **17**, 1194.

Leonard, B. J. (1974). *Acta Endocrinol. (Copenhagen), Suppl.* **185**, 38.

Levine, S. (1970). *Prog. Brain Res.* **32**, 79.

Lieberman, M. W. (1963). *Science* **141**, 824.

Lilliston, L. (1974). *Los Angeles Times* March 8, View, p. IV-I.

Lin, Y. Y., and Smith, L. L. (1974). *Biochim. Biophys. Acta* **348**, 189.

Linder, H. R. (1961). *J. Endocrinol.* **23**, 161.

Linder, H. R. (1965). *Steroids* **2**, 133.

Lipschutz, A. (1950). "Steroid Hormones and Tumors," p. 174. Williams & Wilkins, Baltimore, Maryland.

Lisk, R. D. (1967). *Neuroendocrinology* **2**, 197.

Lloyd, R. V., and Karavolas, H. J. (1975). *Endocrinology* **97**, 517.

Lo, W.-B., and Black, H. S. (1972). *J. Invest. Dermatol.* **58**, 278.

Longcope, C., Layne, D. S., and Tait, J. F. (1968). *J. Clin. Invest.* **47**, 93.

Los Angeles Times (1974). December 27, News in Brief, p. I-2.

Lurie, A. O., and Weiss, J. B. (1967). *Nature (London)* **215**, 1178.

Lynn, W. S., and Brown, R. H. (1958). *J. Biol. Chem.* **232**, 1015.

Lyons, H. A. (1969). *In* "Metabolic Effects of Gonadal Hormones and Contraceptive Steroids" (H. A. Salhanick, D. M. Kipnis, and R. L. Vande Wiele, eds.), pp. 394–402. Plenum, New York.

McCluer, H. M., and Graham, C. E. (1973). *Lab. Anim. Sci.* **23**, 493.

MacDonald, P. C., Grodin, J. M., and Siiteri, P. K. (1971). "Dynamics of Androgen and Estrogen Secretion. Control of Gonadal Steroid Secretion," pp. 163–169. Univ. of Edinburgh Press, Edinburgh.

McEwen, B. S., Magnus, C., and Wallach, G. (1971). *In* "Steroid Hormones and Brain Function" (C. H. Sawyer and R. A. Gorski, eds.), pp. 247–258. Univ. of California Press, Los Angeles.

Mack, T. M., Pike, M. C., Henderson, B. E., Pfeffer, R. I., Gerkins, V. R., Arthur, M., and Brown, S. E. (1976). *New Engl. J. Med.* **294**, 1262.

MacMahon, B., Cole, P., and Brown, J. (1973). *J. Natl. Cancer Inst.* **50**, 22.

Magoun, H. W. (1958). "The Waking Brain." Thomas, Springfield, Illinois.

Mandell, A., and Mandell, M. (1967). *J. Am. Med. Assoc.* **200**, 792.

Margolese, M. S. (1970). *Horm. Behav.* **1**, 151.

Matthijssen, C., and Mandel, J. E. (1967). *Biochim. Biophys. Acta* **131**, 490.

Maume, B. F., Bournot, P., Lhuguenot, J. C., Baron, C., Barbier, F., Maume, G., Prost, M., and Padieu, P. (1973). *Anal. Chem.* **45**, 1073.

Mayer, G., Meunier, J. M., and Rouault, J. (1958). *C.R. Acad. Sci.* **247**, 524.

Meddleton, W. R. J., and Isselbacher, K. J. (1969). *Proc. Soc. Exp. Biol. Med.* **131**, 1435.

Meites, J., and Nicoll, C. S. (1966). *Annu. Rev. Physiol.* **28**, 57.

Mejer, L. E., and Blanchard, R. C. (1973). *Clin. Chem.* **19**, 710.

Melamed, M. R., Koss, L. G., Flehinger, B. J., Kelisky, R. P., and Dubrow, H. (1969). *Br. Med. J.* **iii**, 195.

Mendelson, J. H., Kuehnle, J., Ellingboe, J., and Babor, T. F. (1974). *New Engl. J. Med.* **291**, 1051.

Mercier-Bodard, C., and Baulieu, E. E. (1968). *Ann. Endocrinol.* **29**, 159.

Mercier-Bodard, C., Alfsen, A., and Baulieu, E.-E. (1970). *Acta Endocrinol. (Copenhagen)*, *Suppl.* **147**, 204.

Merryman, W. (1954). *J. Clin. Endocrinol. Metab.* **14**, 1567.

Meyerson, B. J. (1967). *Endocrinology* **81**, 369.

Meyerson, B. J. (1971). *In* "Steroid Hormones and Brain Function" (C. H. Sawyer and R. A. Gorski, eds.), pp. 237–246. Univ. of California Press, Los Angeles.

Michael, R. P. (1965). *Br. Med. Bull.* **21**, 87.

Migeon, C. J. (1957). *Ciba Found. Colloq. Endocrinol. [Proc.]* **11**, 282.

Mills, I. H. (1961). *Br. Med. Bull.* **18**, 127.

Mittwoch, U. (1975). *In* "Intersexuality in the Animal Kingdom" (R. Reinboth, ed.), pp. 439–446. Springer-Verlag, New York.

Money, J. (1971). *In* "Steroid Hormones and Brain Function" (C. H. Sawyer and R. A. Gorski, eds.), pp. 325–338. Univ. of California Press, Los Angeles.

Money, J., and Ehrhardt, A. A. (1972). *In* "Man & Woman, Boy & Girl," pp. 222–227. Johns Hopkins Press, Baltimore, Maryland.

Moon, R. C., and Turner, C. W. (1959). *Proc. Soc. Exp. Biol. Med.* **101**, 332.

Mosbach, E. H., Neirenberg, M., and Kendall, F. E. (1952). *Am. Chem. Soc., Abstr.* September, C10.

Moshang, T., Jr., Rudd, B. T., Eberlein, W. R., and Bongiovanni, A. M. (1970). *Steroids* **15**, 195.

Mueller, P., and Rudin, D. O. (1969). *Curr. Top. Bioenerg.* **3**, 157–242.

Munck, A., and Brinck-Johnsen, T. (1968). *J. Biol. Chem.* **243**, 5556.

Murphy, B. E. P. (1964). *Nature (London)* **201**, 679.

Murphy, B. E. P. (1967). *J. Clin. Endocrinol. Metab.* **27**, 973.

Murphy, B. E. P. (1968). *Can. J. Biochem.* **46**, 299.

Mustacchi, P., and Gordon, G. S. (1958). *In* "Breast Cancer" (A. Segaloff, ed.), pp. 163–169. Mosby, St. Louis, Missouri.

Naftolin, F., Ryan, K. J., and Petro, Z. (1972). *Endocrinology* **90**, 295.

Nakahara, W. (1961). *Prog. Exp. Tumor Res.* **2**, 158.

Nat. Cancer Inst. (1971). *Monogr.* **34**, 33–87.

Nebert, N. W., Bausserman, L. L., and Bates, R. R. (1970). *Int. J. Cancer* **6**, 470.

Nelson, L. W., Weikel, J. H., Jr., and Reno, F. E. (1973). *J. Natl. Cancer Inst.* **51**, 1303.

Neumann, F., von Berswordt-Wallrabe, R., Elger, W., Steinbeck, H., Hahn, J. D., and Kramer, M. (1970a). *Recent Prog. Horm. Res.* **26**, 337.

Neumann, F., Elger, W., and Steinbeck, H. (1970b). *Lancet* **ii**, 1258.

Neumann, F., von Berswordt-Wallrabe, R., Elger, W., Graf, K.-J., Hasan, S. Mehring, M., Nishino, Y., and Steinbeck, H. (1974). *Acta Endocrinol. (Copenhagen), Suppl.* **185**, 338.

Newball, H. H., and Byar, D. P. (1973). *Urology* **11**, 525.

NIH (1976). *Am. Med. News* April 26, p. 2.

Nissen, E. D., and Goldstein, A. I. (1973). *J. Gynecol. Obstet.* **11**, 138.

Noble, R. L. (1967). *Proc. Am. Assoc. Cancer Res.* **8**, 51.

Noller, K. L., Decker, D. G., Lanier, A. P., and Kurland, L. T. (1972). *Mayo Clin. Proc.* **47**, 629.

Nora, J. J., and Nora, A. H. (1974). *New Engl. J. Med.* **291**, 731.

Nothdurft, H. (1961). "Sarkomerzeugung bei Ratten durch implantierte Fremdkörper," Reprint 8, pp. 262–274. Boehringer, Mannheim.

Novotny, M., Lee, M. L., and Bartle, K. D. (1975). *Chem. Eng. News* **53**, December 8, p. 27.

Oakey, R. E. (1975). *Endocrinology* **97**, 1024.

Oertel, G. W., Knapstein, P., and Heide, K. (1969). *Experientia* **25**, 1192.

Oertel, G. W., Benes, P., and Bohlender, H. (1975). *Clin. Chem.* **21**, 982.

Olds, J. (1958). *Science* **127**, 315.

O'Malley, B. W., Toft, D. O., and Sherman, M. R. (1971). *J. Biol. Chem.* **246**, 1117.

Orellana-Alcalde, J. M., and Dominguez, J. P. (1966). *Lancet* **ii**, 1278.

Osmond, H., and Smythies, J. R. (1952). *J. Ment. Sci.* **98**, 309.

Palka, Y., Ramirez, V. D., and Sawyer, C. H. (1966). *Endocrinology* **78**, 487.

Pan, S. C., and Gardner, W. H. (1948). *Cancer Res.* **8**, 337.

Paris, A. L., and Ramaley, J. A. (1974). *Neuroendocrinology* **15**, 126.

Parvez, H., and Parvez, S. (1973). *J. Neurochem.* **20**, 1011.

Paton, W. D. M., and Payne, J. P. (1968). "Pharmacological Principles and Practice." Churchill, London.

Penfield, W., and Jasper, H. (1954). "Epilepsy and the Functional Anatomy of the Brain." Little, Brown, Boston, Massachusetts.

Peterson, R. E., Wyngarden, J. B., Guerra, L., Brodie, B. B., and Bunim, J. J. (1955). *J. Clin. Invest.* **34**, 1779.

Pfaff, D. W., and Pfaffman, C. (1969). *Brain Res.* **15**, 137.

Pfaff, D. W., Diakow, C., Zigmond, R. E., and Kow, L.-M. (1974). *In* "The Neurosciences Third Study Program" (F. O. Schmitt and F. G. Worden, eds.), pp. 621–646. MIT Press, Cambridge, Massachusetts.

Pfeiffer, C. A., and Allen, E. (1948). *Cancer Res.* **8**, 97.

Phoenix, C. H., Goy, R. W., Gerall, A. A., and Young, W. C. (1959). *Endocrinology* **65**, 369.

Pincus, G. (1965). "The Control of Fertility." Academic Press, New York.

Plager, J. E., and Samuels, L. T. (1954). *J. Biol. Chem.* **211**, 21.

Plattner, P. A., and Uffer, A. (1944). *Helv. Chim. Acta* **28**, 1049.

Plaut, A., and Dreyfuss, M. L. (1946). *Surg. Gynecol. Obstet.* **71**, 756.

Portius, H. J., and Repke, K. (1960). *Arch. Exp. Pathol. Pharmakol.* **239**, 144, 184.

Powers, M. L., and Florini, J. R. (1975). *Endocrinology* **97**, 1043.

Price, D., and Ortiz, E. (1965). *In* "Organogenesis" (R. L. DeHaan and H. Ursprung, eds.), pp. 629–652. Holt, New York.

Puca, G. A., and Bresciani, F. (1969). *Endocrinology* **85**, 1.

Rabinowitz, J. L. (1959). *Atompraxis* **5**, 1.

Rausch-Stroomann, J.-G., Petry, R., Hocevar, V., Mauss, J., and Senge, T. (1970). *Acta Endocrinol. (Copenhagen)* **63**, 595.

Reddy, V. V. R., Naftolin, F., and Ryan, K. J. (1974). *Endocrinology* **94**, 117.

Reed, M. J., Fotherby, K., and Steele, S. J. (1972). *J. Clin. Endocrinol. Metab.* **55**, 351.

Repke, K., and Markwardt, F. (1954a). *Arch. Exp. Pathol. Pharmakol.* **223**, 271.

Repke, K., and Markwardt, F. (1954b). *Naturwissenschaften* **41**, 258.

Reynolds, R. W. (1971). Personal communication.

Reynolds, R. W., and Bryson, G. (1974). *Res. Commun. Chem. Pathol. Pharmacol.* **7**, 715.

Ringold, H. J. (1961). *In* "Mechanism of Action of Steroid Hormones" (C. A. Villee and L. L. Engel, eds.), pp. 200–232. Pergamon, New York.

Rosenthal, H. E., Slaunwhite, W. R., Jr., and Sandberg, A. A. (1969). *J. Clin. Endocrinol. Metab.* **29**, 352.

Rosenthal, H. E., Pietrzak, E., Slaunwhite, W. R., Jr., and Sandberg, A. A. (1972). *J. Clin. Endocrinol. Metab.* **34**, 805.

Ross, M. H., Bras, G., and Lagheer, M. S. (1970). *J. Nutr.* **100**, 177.

Rothblat, G. H. (1969). *Adv. Lipid Res.* **7**, 152.

Rothblat, G. H., and Kritchevsky, D. (1967). *Circulation* **36**, 35. (Abstr.)

Rothchild, L. (1969). *In* "Metabolic Effects of Gonadal Hormones and Contraceptive Steroids" (H. A. Salhanick, D. M. Kipnis, and R. L. Vande Wiele, eds.), pp. 668–675. Plenum, New York.

Royal College General Practitioners (1967). *J. R. Coll. Practit.* **13**, 267.

Ruder, H. J., Loriaux, L., and Lipsett, M. B. (1972). *J. Clin. Invest.* **51**, 1020.

Ryan, K. J., and Engel, L. L. (1953). *Endocrinology* **52**, 287.

Samuels, L. T., Helmreich, M. L., Lasater, M. B., and Reich, H. (1951). *Science* **113**, 490.

Sandberg, A. A., and Slaunwhite, W. R., Jr. (1959). *J. Clin. Invest.* **38**, 1290.

Sandberg, A. A., Slaunwhite, W. R., Jr., and Antoniades, H. N. (1957). *Recent Prog. Horm. Res.* **13**, 209.

Sandberg, A. A., Rosenthal, H., Schneider, S. L., and Slaunwhite, W. R., Jr. (1966). *In* "Steroid Dynamics" (G. Pincus, T. Nakao, and J. F. Tait, eds.), p. 1. Academic Press, New York.

Sartwell, P. E., Masi, A. T., Arthes, F. C., Greene, G. R., and Smith, H. E. (1969). *Am. J. Epidemiol.* **90**, 365.

Sartwell, P. E., Arthes, F. C., and Tomascia, J. A. (1973). *New Engl. J. Med.* **288**, 251.

Sayers, G. (1950). *Physiol. Rev.* **30**, 241.

Scanu, A. M. (1965). *Adv. Lipid Res.* **3**, 67–71.

Schaumburg, B., and Crone, M. (1971). *Biochim. Biophys. Acta* **237**, 494.

Schildkraut, J. J. (1965). *Am. J. Psychiatry* **122**, 509.

Schimke, R. T. (1974). *In* "The Neurosciences Third Study Program" (F. O. Schmitt and F. G. Worden, eds.), p. 818. MIT Press, Cambridge, Massachusetts.

Schindler, A. E., Ebert, A., and Friedrich, E. (1972). *J. Clin. Endocrinol. Metab.* **35**, 627.

Schmidt, C. L., and Greenberg, D. M. (1935). *Physiol. Rev.* **15**, 372.

Schmitt, F. O., Bear, R. S., and Ponder, E. (1938). *J. Cell. Comp. Physiol.* **11**, 309.

Schneider, P. B., Clayton, R. B., and Bloch, K. (1957). *J. Biol. Chem.* **224**, 175.

Schwartz, A. G. (1973). *Cancer Res.* **33**, 2431.

Seal, U. S., and Doe, R. P. (1966). *Steroid Dyn. Proc. Symp. Dyn. Steroid Horm., Tokyo, 1965* p. 63.

Segaloff, A. (1961). Personal communication, cited in Dorfman (1961), p. 152.

Seligman, A. M., Nachlas, M. M., and Mollomo, M. C. (1949). *Am. J. Physiol.* **159**, 337.

Selkirk, J. K., Huberman, E., and Heidelberger, C. (1971). *Biochem. Biophys. Res. Commun.* **43**, 1010.

Selye, H. J. (1946). *J. Clin. Endocrinol. Metab.* **6**, 117.

Sharma, D. C., Forchielli, E., and Dorfman, R. I. (1962). *J. Biol. Chem.* **237**, 1495.

Sharma, D. C., Forchielli, E., and Dorfman, R. I. (1963). *J. Biol. Chem.* **238**, 572.

Sherman, A. I., Goldrath, M., Berlin, A., Nakhariya, V., Banooni, F., Michaels, W., Goodman, P., and Brown, S. (1974). *Obstet. Gynecol.* **44**, 531.

Shimkin, M. B. (1945). *Publ. Amer. Assoc. Advan. Sci.* **22**, 5, 91, 92, 209.

Sih, C. J. (1969). *Science* **163**, 1297.

Siiteri, P. K., and MacDonald, P. C. (1966). *J. Clin. Endocrinol. Metab.* **26**, 751.

Siiteri, P. K., Schwarz, B. E., and MacDonald, P. C. (1974). *Gynecol. Oncol.* **2**, 228.

Skelley, D. S., Brown, L. P., and Besch, P. K. (1973). *Clin. Chem.* **19**, 146.

Slaunwhite, W. R., Jr., and Samuels, L. T. (1956). *J. Biol. Chem.* **220**, 341.

Slaunwhite, W. R., Jr., Rosenthal, H. E., and Sandberg, A. A. (1963). *Arch. Biochem. Biophys.* **100**, 486.

Smith, D. C., Prentice, R., Thompson, D. J., and Herrmann, W. L. (1975). *New Engl. J. Med.* **293**, 1164.

Smith, E. B. (1974). *Adv. Lipid Res.* **12**, 45.

Smith, E. R., and Davidson, J. M. (1967). *Endocrinology* **80**, 725.

Smith, L. L., and Teng, J. I. (1974). *J. Am. Chem. Soc.* **96**, 2640.

Smith, L. L., Teng, J. I., Kulig, M. J., and Hill, F. L. (1973). *J. Org. Chem.* **38**, 1763.

Smith, R. L. (1974). *Acta Endocrinol. (Copenhagen), Suppl.* **185**, 150.

Snyder, S. H. (1974). "Madness and the Brain," pp. 159–162, 200–214. McGraw-Hill, New York.

Sobin, S. S., Tremer, H. M., and Fung, Y. C. (1970). *Circ. Res.* **26**, 397.

Soffer, L. J., Dorfman, R. I., and Gabrilove, J. L. (1962). "The Human Adrenal Gland," pp. 92–105. Lea & Febiger, Philadelphia, Pennsylvania.

Solash, J. (1974). *Fed. Proc., Fed. Am. Soc. Exp. Biol.* **33**, 210.

Soloff, M. S., Creange, J. E., and Potts, G. O. (1971). *Endocrinology* **88**, 427.

Sperry, W. M. (1935). *J. Biol. Chem.* **111**, 467.

Stachenko, J., and Giroud, C. J. P. (1959). *Endocrinology* **64**, 730.

Stauffer, R. D., and Bischoff, F. (1966). *Clin. Chem.* **12**, 206.

Stauffer, R. D., Bryson, G., and Bischoff, F. (1975). *Res. Commun. Chem. Pathol. Pharmacol.* **11**, 515.

Steiner, F. A. (1971). *In* "Steroid Hormones and Brain Function" (C. H. Sawyer and R. A. Gorski, eds.), pp. 43–50, Univ. of California Press, Los Angeles.

Stinson, N. E. (1964). *Br. J. Exp. Pathol.* **45**, 21.

Stitt, S. L., and Kinnard, W. J. (1968). *Neurology* **18**, 213.

Stumpf, W. E. (1968). *Science* **162**, 1001.

Stumpf, W. E., Baerwaldt, C., and Sar, M. (1971). "Basic Actions of Sex Steroids on Target Organs; Autoradiographic, Cellular and Subcellular Localization of Sexual Steroids," pp. 3–20. Karger, Basel.

Swaneck, G. E., Highland, E., and Edelman, I. S. (1969). *Nephron* **6**, 297.

Sweat, M. L., and Bryson, M. J. (1961). *Arch. Biochem. Biophys.* **96**, 186.

Swerdloff, R. S., Walsh, P. C., and Odell, W. D. (1972). *Steroids* **20**, 13.

Sydnor, K. L. (1958). *Endocrinology* **62**, 322.

Szego, C. M. (1953). *Endocrinology* **52**, 669.

Takasugi, N., and Bern, H. A. (1964). *J. Natl. Cancer Inst.* **33**, 855.

Taleisnik, S., Caligaris, L., and Astrada, J. J. (1969). *J. Endocrinol.* **44**, 313.

Tavernetti, R. R., Rosenbaum, W., Kelly, W. G., Christy, N. P., and Roginsky, M. S. (1967). *J. Clin. Endocrinol. Metab.* **27**, 920.

Taylor, A. N., Matheson, G. K., and Dafny, N. (1971). *In* "Steroid Hormones and Brain Function" (C. H. Sawyer and R. A. Gorski, eds.), pp. 67–78. Univ. of California Press, Los Angeles.

Teng, J. I., and Smith, L. L. (1973). *J. Am. Chem. Soc.* **95**, 4060.

Teng, J. I., Kulig, M. J., Smith, L. L., Kan, G., and van Lier, J. E. (1973). *J. Org. Chem.* **38**, 119.

Thiessen, D. D., and Rodgers, D. A. (1961). *Psychol. Bull.* **58**, 441.

Topper, Y. J. (1961). *In* "Mechanism of Action of Steroid Hormones" (C. A. Villee and L. L. Engel, eds.), pp. 111–125. Pergamon, New York.

Townsend, D. (1973). *Los Angeles Times* September 15, p. II-10.

Treloar, O. L., Wolf, R. C., and Meyer, R. K. (1972). *Endocrinology* **90**, 281.

Tuchmann-Duplessis, H. (1974). *Acta Endocrinol. (Copenhagen),* Suppl. **185**, 211, 212.

Tucker, H. A., Larson, B. L., and Gorski, J. (1971). *Endocrinology* **89**, 152.

Udenfriend, S. (1959). *Symp. Catecholamines, NIH, Bethesda, 1958* p. 253.

Ulfelder, H. (1973). *Am. J. Obstet. Gynecol.* **117**, 794.

Ulfelder, H., Poskanzer, D. C., and Herbst, A. L. (1971). *New Engl. J. Med.* **285**, 691.

UPI (1973). *Los Angeles Times* September 21, p. J-6.

Upjohn (1974). "Sterile Aqueous Suspension Depo-Provera (Sterile Medroxyprogesterone Acetate Suspension, U.S.P.)." Upjohn Company, Kalamazoo, Michigan.

USDA Explains New DES Ruling (1975). *Los Angeles Times* February 27, p. VI-12.

van Lier, J. E., and Kan, G. (1972). *J. Org. Chem.* **37**, 145.

Van Nie, R., Benedetti, E. L., and Mühlbock, O. (1961). *Nature (London)* **192**, 1303.

Vernadakis, A., and Woodbury, D. M. (1971). *In* "Steroid Hormones and Brain Function" (C. H. Sawyer and R. A. Gorski, eds.), pp. 35–42. Univ. of California Press, Los Angeles.

Vessey, M. P., and Doll, R. (1969). *Br. Med. J.* **ii**, 651.

Vessey, M. P., Doll, R., Peto, R., and Redman, C. W. G. (1972). *Int. J. Epidemiol.* **1**, 119.
von Uhlig, H. (1959). *Geburstshilfe Frauenheilkd.* **19**, 346.
Vreeburg, J. T. M., Schretlen, P. J. M., and Baum, M. J. (1975). *Endocrinology* **97**, 969.
Wall, R. E., and Migeon, C. J, (1959). *J. Clin. Invest.* **38**, 611.
Ward, I. L. (1972). *Science* **175**, 82.
Ward, I. L. (1974). *In* "Sex Differences in Behavior" (R. C. Friedman, R. M. Richart, and R. L. Vande Wiele, eds.), pp. 3–17. Wiley, New York.
Warren, R. J., and Fotherby, K. (1973). *J. Endocrinol.* **59**, 369.
Watanabe, H. (1971). *Biochim. Biophys. Acta* **231**, 399.
Wedler, H. W. (1943). *Dtsch. Med. Wochenschr.* **69**, 575.
Weil-Malherbe, H., and Szara, S. I. (1971). "The Biochemistry of Functional and Experimental Psychoses," p. 55. Thomas, Springfield, Illinois.
Weiss, N. S., Szekely, D. R., and Austin, D. F. (1976). *New Engl. J. Med.* **294**, 1259.
Weitzman, E. D., and Hellman, L. (1974). *In* "Biorhythms and Human Reproduction" (M. Ferin, F. Halberg, R. M. Richart, and R. L. Vande Wiele, eds.), pp. 371–395. Wiley, New York.
Welsch, C. W. (1970). *Experientia* **26**, 1133.
Welsch, C. W., and Meites, J. (1968). *Int. Congr. Physiol. Sci., 24th, Washington, D.C.* p. 466.
Wender, P. H. (1971). "Minimal Brain Dysfunction in Children," pp. 185–190. Wiley, New York.
West, C. D., Damast, B. L., Sarro, S. D., and Pearson, O. H. (1956). *J. Biol. Chem.* **218**, 409.
Westerholm, B. (1967). *Sven. Laekartidn.* **64**, Suppl. 4, p. 71.
Westerholm, B. (1970). *In* "The Liver and the Pill in Alcoholic Cirrhosis and other Toxic Hepatopathias" (A. Engel and T. Larson, eds.), p. 251. Skandia Group, Nordiska Bokhandelns Förlag, Stockholm.
Westphal, U. (1966). *Hoppe-Seyler's Z. Physiol. Chem.* **346**, 243.
Westphal, U. (1971). *In* "Steroid-Protein Interactions" (F. Gross, A. Labhart, T. Mann, L. T. Samuels, and J. Zander, eds.), Vol. 4, p. 375. Springer-Verlag, Berlin and New York.
Westphal, U., and Carnighan, R. H. (1964). *Proc. Int. Congr. Biochem. 6th, Washington, D.C.* Abstr. No. II-201, p. 187.
Whalen, R. E. (1968). *In* "Perspectives in Reproduction and Sexual Behavior" (M. Diamond, ed.), pp. 303–340. Indiana Univ. Press, Bloomington.
Whalen, R. E. (1971). *In* "Steroid Hormones and Brain Function" (C. H. Sawyer and R. A. Gorski, eds.), pp. 143–144. Univ. of California Press, Los Angeles.
Whalen, R. E., and Edwards, D. A. (1969). *Endocrinology* **84**, 155.
Whalen, R. E., and Hardy, D. F. (1970). *Physiol. Behav.* **5**, 529.
Whalen, R. E., and Luttge, W. G. (1970). *Neuroendocrinology* **6**, 255.
Whalen, R. E., and Rezek, D. L. (1972). *Steroids* **20**, 717.
Whalen, R. E., Luttge, W. G., and Gorzalka, B. B. (1971). *Horm. Behav.* **2**, 83.
White, A., Blecher, M., and Jedeiken, L. A. (1961). *In* "Mechanism of Action of Steroid Hormones" (C. A. Villee and L. L. Engel, eds.), p. 103. Pergamon, New York.
WHO (1971). *W.H.O. Tech. Rep. Ser.* **473**.
Wiesner, B. P. (1934). *J. Obstet. Gynaecol. Br. Emp.* **41**, 867.
Wijmenga, H. G., and von der Molen, H. J. (1969). *Acta Endocrinol. (Copenhagen)* **61**, 665.
Wilkins, L. (1959). *Arch. Anat. Microsc. Morphol. Exp.* **48**, 313.
Wilkinson, C. W., Carlisle, H. J., and Reynolds, R. W. (1976). *Fed. Proc., Fed. Am. Soc. Exp. Biol.* **35**, 481.
Williams, R. H. (1968). "Textbook of Endocrinology," 4th Ed., pp. 443–446. Saunders, Philadelphia, Pennsylvania.
Willis, R. A. (1948). "Pathology of Tumors," p. 184. Butterworth, London.
Wilson, J. D., and Gloyna, R. E. (1970). *Recent Prog. Horm. Res.* **26**, 309.

Wilson, J. D., and Lasnitzki, I. (1971). *Endocrinology* **89**, 659.

Wilson, J. D., and Walker, J. D. (1969). *J. Clin. Invest.* **48**, 371.

Wisner, J. R., Jr., and Gomes, W. R. (1975). *J. Endocrinol.* **65**, 143.

Wittliff, J. L., Hilf, R., Brooks, W. F., Jr., Savlov, E. D., Hall, T. C., and Orlando, R. A. (1972). *Cancer Res.* **32**, 1983.

Woolley, G. (1943). *Science* **97**, 291.

Wotiz, H. H., Lemon, H. M., and Voulgaropoulos, A. (1954). *J. Biol. Chem.* **209**, 437.

Yalom, I. D., Green, R., and Fisk, N. (1973). *Arch. Gen. Psychiatry* **28**, 554.

Young, W. C. (1961). *In* "Sex and Internal Secretions" (W. C. Young, ed.), 3rd Ed., pp. 1173–1239. Williams & Wilkins, Baltimore, Maryland.

Young, W. C. (1965). *In* "Sex and Behavior" (F. A. Beach, ed.), pp. 89–107. Wiley, New York.

Zaffaroni, A. (1974). *Acta Endocrinol. (Copenhagen), Suppl.* **185**, 427.

Zander, J., Forbes, T. R., von Münstermann, A. M., and Neher, R. (1958). *J. Clin. Endocrinol. Metab.* **18**, 337.

Ziel, H. K., and Finkle, W. D. (1975). *New Engl. J. Med.* **293**, 1167.

Zucconi, G., Goebelsmann, U., Wiqvist, N., and Diczfalusy, E. (1967). *Acta Endocrinol. (Copenhagen)* **56**, 71.

Fungal Lipids

MOMTAZ K. WASSEF[1]

Department of Plant Pathology, University of Kentucky, Lexington, Kentucky

I. Introduction

With the exception of yeasts, fungi are among the least studied micro-organisms from the biochemical point of view. Much ignored are the fungal lipid contents and composition or the structure and function of fungal membranes. However, since the development of modern techniques and instrumentation in the 1950s, reliable data on the lipid composition of cells have been reported and biological scientists have come to appreciate the importance of lipids in cell membranes. Only recently, however have studies dealing with fungal lipids been carried out. As a result, information on fungal lipids has been accumulating rapidly, and the need for organizing the data at hand and correlating the reported findings is urgent.

---

[1] Present address: Department of Biochemistry, New York Medical College, Valhalla, New York 10595.

This review will, therefore, attempt to (1) summarize the data available on the nature and composition of lipids in a variety of fungi, and their distribution within the cell; (2) correlate these data, if possible, with fungal taxonomy; and (3) describe some aspects of lipid metabolism, mainly biosynthesis.

Lipids of yeasts have been the subject of reviews by Rattray *et al.* (1975), Mangnall and Getz (1973), Hunter and Rose (1971), Turner (1971), Lynen *et al.* (1968), and Hofmann (1963) and will only be referred to briefly where pertinent. The reader may also refer to the excellent monograph by Weete (1974) and the book by Erwin (1973) for detailed background on fungal lipids and lipids of eukaryotic microorganisms.

II. A Note on Taxonomic Classification

It is extremely difficult to draw distinct boundaries between yeasts and fungi that have yeast-like stages in their life cycle. It is confusing for non-biologists even to distinguish at what stage does a fungus belong to what group or class. Therefore, in this review, fungi will be grouped into Phycomycetes (lower fungi), Ascomycetes, Deuteromycetes (Fungi Imperfecti), and Basidiomycetes (higher fungi). The nomenclature and classification followed here are those used in "The Fungi, An Advanced Treatise" (G. C. Ainsworth, F. K. Sparrow, and A. S. Sussman, eds.), Volumes IV A and B, Academic Press, New York, 1973.

III. Total Lipid Composition

Since the range of the fungi examined in detail for their total lipid composition is rather limited, there are hardly enough data to allow an attempt at correlating certain lipid components of fungi with their taxonomic classification. Earlier attempts were made by Shaw (1966b), who examined the fatty acid composition of a wide range of organisms and reported a positive correlation to exist generally between polyunsaturated fatty acid composition and the taxonomic classification of fungi. The severe lack of data on the overall lipid composition in fungi will limit the present author to attempting a taxonomic classification of fungi with regard to their sterol and fatty acid compositions. There are few factors, however, that might obscure or minimize any latent correlations, namely, the effect of culture conditions and the stage of the fungal growth. These factors will be dealt with in Section III,G.

The data on total lipid content, fatty acid and sterol composition in fungi are summarized in Tables I–IX.

A. FATTY ACID AND STEROL CONTENTS

1. *Phycomycetes*

Several species of Phycomycetes have been analyzed for their fatty acid (Tables I and II), and sterol (Table III) compositions.

a. Fatty Acids. The most significant feature of the fatty acids produced by Phycomycetes is the formation of γ-linolenic acid, C18:3 $\Delta^{6,9,12}$. Other fungi (higher fungi) produce the α-linolenic acid isomer, C18:3 $\Delta^{9,12,15}$. It is striking that none of the zygomycetes synthesizes any ω3 polyenoic fatty acids. However, a chytrid and some members of the Oomycetes do synthesize ω3 polyunsaturated fatty acids, particularly 20:5 ω3. Based on the production of the γ- or α-linolenic acid, Shaw (1966b) suggested that fungi are sharply divided along taxonomic lines. However, analyses of the fatty acid composition of Phycomycetes have been made recently, and these results show that Shaw's hypothesis is applicable to only one order of Zygomycetes, the order Mucorales. With a single exception, all species of Mucorales synthesize only two polyunsaturated fatty acids, α-linoleic and γ-linolenic acids (Table I). The remaining species of Zygomycetes and members of the other two classes of lower fungi (Chytridomycetes and Oomycetes) show more complex fatty acid patterns.

Although few fungi have been examined, lower fungi appear to have the greatest potential for synthesis of long-chain ($>$C18:3) polyunsaturated fatty acid. The long-chain acids C20:2, C20:5, C20:0, C22:0, C20:3 $\Delta^{8,11,14}$, C20:4 $\Delta^{5,8,11,14}$, and C22:3 $\Delta^{7,10,13}$ and other long-chain saturated and polyunsaturated acids were detected in lipids of many species of Chytridomycetes and Oomycetes (Ellenbogen *et al.*, 1969; Shaw, 1965; Weete, 1973).

Fatty acids of the Zygomycetes can be divided into two groups based on the unsaturated fatty acid composition (Tyrrell, 1967). Polyunsaturated fatty acids of chain length up to C18:3 belong to the Mucoraceae and Thamnidaceae group. The second group includes Choanephoraceae and Entomophthraceae, which are capable of producing fatty acids up to the C20:4 level. Tyrrell (1967) further divided Entomophthoraceae into three groups. The first group is characterized by containing 40% of the total fatty acids as C18:1, 16–19% as C16:1, and 12–19% as C20:4. The second group is characterized by high relative amounts of C18:0 (22–34%) and short-chain fatty acids such as C10:0 and C12:0 (20%). The third group is characterized by a high content of saturated fatty acids (50–60%) and high relative amounts of C14:0 (26–30%) and C18:1 (22–25%), as well as tri- and pentadecanoic acids.

The lipid content and fatty acid composition reported for spores of Phycomycetes are given in Table II. Sumner and Morgan (1969) investigated the fatty acid distribution of sporangiospores of several *Mucor* and *Rhizopus* species and reported qualitative and quantitative similarities between the

Table I

TOTAL LIPID CONTENT AND FATTY ACID COMPOSITION OF PHYCOMYCETES (MYCELIA)

Organism	Lipid content (% mycelium dry wt.)	References[a]	12:0	13:0	14:0	15:0	16:0	16:1	17:0	18:0	18:1	18:2	18:3	20:0	20:3	20:4
Class *CHYTRIDOMYCETES*																
Order CHYTRIDIALES																
Dermocystidium sp.[1c]	ND[b]	(1)	—	—	5.9	0.9	26.8	18.8	—	1.4	4.3	2.3	0.7	—	1.6	2.4
Phlyctochytrium punctatum	ND	(1)	—	—	1.4	0.8	25.9	1.6	1.4	10.6	28.7	13.0	3.9	—	3.6	2.8
Rhizophlyctis rosea	ND	(2)	—	—	tr[b]	—	1.3	—	—	6	74	3	3	—	—	—
Order BLASTOCLADIALES																
Allomyces microgynus[2]	ND	(2)	—	tr	1	3	16	4	6	9	36	6	—	4	—	—
Blastocladiella emersonii[3]	8.0	(3)	0.5	—	0.8	—	13.3	2.6	0.8	2.8	39.1	16.9	10.6	0.9	3.2	16.4
Class *HYPHOCHYTRIDOMYCETES*																
Order HYPHOCHYTRIALES																
Hyphochytrium catenoides	ND	(2)	—	—	2	—	22	16	—	—	49	4	—	—	—	—
Rhizidiomyces apophysatus[4]	ND	(2)	—	tr	tr	11	13	5	7	4	11	11	4	—	9	—
Class *OOMYCETES*																
Order PERONOSPORALES																
Pythium acanthicum[5]	ND	(4)	0.9	—	15.2	—	13.5	1.6	—	4.6	31.0	11.5	0.9	1.4	3.1	3.2
Pythium sp. 2142[6] (acanthicum?)	7.4–16	(5)	0.2–0.4	—	6.6–18.7	—	11.5–15.2	1.3–5.0	—	1.8–3.8	25.6–36.8	8.0–15.4	0.8–1.6	1.7–2.6	1.3–6.0	1.3–3.3
P. debaryanum	ND	(6)	—	—	5.5	—	13.0	5.6	—	1.6	13.9	19.7	2.3	—	2.4	12.3
P. debaryanum[7]	ND	(7)	—	—	13.2	—	21.3	7.9	—	4.5	21.3	15.8	4.5	4.3	—	—
P. sp.[8]	11.7	(4)	0.3	—	10.3	—	8.4	0.8	—	5.6	36.3	13.8	0.9	1.6	2.7	1.0
P. ultimum Trow[9]	3–48	(8)	—	—	5.3–9.5	—	14.6–33.6	4.2–11.8	—	3.5–18.0	11.6–21.6	5.8–19.6	1.2–3.6	2.1–3.9	—	—
Phytophthora infestans	ND	(6)	—	—	23.5	—	12.0	3.4	—	2.1	31.2	4.5	tr	—	10.2	7.7
Order SAPROLEGNIALES																
Schizochytrium aggregatum[10]	ND	(1)	—	—	6.7	9.1	18.7	0.8	5.2	8.1	16.7	3.0	tr	0.7	1.5	4.0
Thraustochytrium aureum[11]	ND	(1)	—	—	2.3	4.2	27.1	0.8	1.4	1.3	5.7	2.1	tr	—	tr	4.8
T. roseum[12]	ND	(1)	—	—	0.7	0.9	29.3	1.3	—	4.6	34.6	3.2	0.7	—	tr	1.8

Fatty acid (% of total) — Carbon number and degree of unsaturation

Class ZYGOMYCETES
Order ENTEROMOPHTHORALES

		(n)													
Basidiobolus anarum	ND	(6)	—	—	2.4	—	14.5	10.0	—	3.4	28.9	17.8	23.0	—	—
B. haptosporus	ND	(6)	—	—	5.0	—	16.6	14.1	—	4.6	22.5	14.9	22.3	—	—
B. meristosporus[13]	ND	(6)	—	—	2.4	—	14.3	9.4	1.2	3.2	19.7	23.9	23.2	—	—
Conidiobolus brefeldianus[14] CBS 180/62	23.7	(9)	6.0	0.6	29.0	1.2	12.4	3.2	0.8	0.7	18.5	6.1	7.0	—	—
C. chlamydosporus CBS 167/55	15.7	(9)	5.2	—	14.3	2.5	6.9	7.8	—	11.5	32.1	3.3	1.5	—	8.9
C. denaesporus[15]	ND	(6)	1.1	—	15.2	2.8	10.4	5.4	—	2.5	15.2	1.8	2.1	—	—
C. globuliferus CBS 218/64	21.7	(9)	1.7	—	18.5	0.3	16.9	3.9	—	0.8	22.0	6.6	9.4	0.5	—
C. gonimodes CBS 178/61	17.0	(9)	6.7	—	34.1	2.7	6.1	1.9	—	5.4	22.8	2.8	7.0	—	—
C. hetrosporus[16] ATTC 12941	15.5	(9)	0.1	0.8	9.6	—	8.6	0.8	—	2.3	2.4	0.8	0.5	8.8	19.8
C. hetrosporus[17] CBS 543/63	13.0	(9)	1.2	—	8.3	—	11.5	2.5	—	3.2	5.2	1.7	1.4	2.3	13.0
C. humicola[18] CBS 181/62	18.5	(9)	—	2.5	4.7	5.8	10.2	1.6	1.8	4.1	27.4	9.7	9.7	0.9	2.2
C. lamprauges[19] CBS 183/56	14.5	(9)	2.4	1.6	0.4	0.1	10.6	1.4	2.3	5.1	35.6	2.7	3.2	5.6	10.2
C. megalotocus[20]	12.3	(9)	0.3	6.7	29.6	3.0	20.5	5.5	0.3	0.7	21.7	7.3	4.8	2.6	1.2
C. nanodes[21] CBS 183/62	18.3	(9)	—	—	0.4	0.2	15.2	1.6	0.2	7.0	25.6	3.1	3.1	3.5	16.3
C. paulus[22] CBS 140/57	18.6	(9)	0.1	—	5.1	1.9	8.1	4.2	3.1	8.3	17.3	11.1	9.9	3.3	22.3
C. polytocus[23] CBS 168/55	17.7	(9)	0.6	2.0	5.9	4.6	9.8	0.6	3.1	11.5	41.0	7.1	5.6	0.5	1.0
C. thromboides[24]	ND	(6)	tr	—	5.3	—	12.2	14.9	1.6	3.0	39.1	5.4	2.3	1.2	13.8
C. undulatus[25] CBS 142/57	8.0	(9)	—	0.2	5.2	0.3	14.7	5.4	1.0	10.2	10.2	8.1	10.9	5.6	16.4
Delacroixia coronata[26]	ND	(6)	8.4	—	26.3	1.8	9.3	1.9	—	3.5	21.9	7.3	5.7	2.1	4.8
Entomophthora apiculata	ND	(6)	11.0	2.2	29.9	tr	6.8	1.8	—	1.8	25.2	7.6	4.0	7.8	1.9
E. conglomerata[27]	ND	(6)	—	—	6.6	—	12.5	16.2	1.1	2.8	34.4	5.0	2.8	1.0	13.0
E. coronata	44.4–44.8	(6)	9.1	3.3	30.4	1.4	9.1	1.7	—	1.5	25.0	6.0	4.2	4.5	3.8
E. coronata	ND	(10)	7.7	—	33.5	0.6	12.4	0.7	tr	1.2	21.9	18.2	2.2	0.5	4.6
E. coronata (CM 131278)	ND	(7)	10.6	—	24.4	—	5.0	8.5	—	2.8	35.1	7.4	6.2	—	—
E. exitialis	ND	(6)	3.2	14.2	14.5	8.4	6.1	2.7	—	3.1	24.4	6.9	6.1	—	10.4
E. ignobilis	ND	(6)	1.4	—	20.9	—	10.3	tr	—	7.8	16.8	6.0	3.9	5.8	27.1
E. megasperma[28]	ND	(6)	6.1	—	11.8	tr	10.6	6.0	—	1.7	38.6	4.6	1.8	tr	19.1
E. muscae[29]	ND	(6)	27.1	—	21.3	—	13.4	1.4	—	6.6	7.0	1.7	1.8	1.1	8.4
E. obscura	ND	(6)	—	—	5.9	—	13.8	16.6	1.5	2.6	37.9	4.9	1.7	tr	13.5
E. sp.	ND	(6)	8.6	—	3.0	—	5.2	tr	—	32.2	3.3	tr	tr	1.1	4.0
E. sp.[30]	ND	(6)	tr	—	7.5	—	10.4	18.3	1.2	2.9	38.3	4.2	1.9	tr	12.3
E. sp.	ND	(6)	11.8	—	3.8	—	8.0	tr	—	34.1	5.1	1.3	2.3	3.1	13.5
E. sp.	ND	(6)	21.0	—	14.6	—	10.7	1.3	—	22.5	3.6	2.7	5.0	2.8	13.3
E. thaxteriana	ND	(6)	tr	—	4.6	2.0	10.5	16.6	—	1.6	35.5	5.4	1.7	1.8	14.1

(continued)

163

Table I (*Continued*)

Organism	Lipid content (% mycelium dry wt.)	References[a]	12:0	13:0	14:0	15:0	16:0	16:1	17:0	18:0	18:1	18:2	18:3	20:0	20:3	20:4
								Fatty acid (% of total) — Carbon number and degree of unsaturation								
E. tipula[31]	ND	(6)	tr	—	6.8	tr	10.8	18.4	2.0	7.2	29.8	5.6	2.4	—	1.0	12.4
E. virulenta[32]	ND	(6)	tr	—	6.5	—	9.2	19.3	1.6	1.5	38.3	4.0	2.5	—	tr	14.1
Order MUCORALES																
Choanephora cucuribitarum[33]	21.9	(11)	0.2	—	2.9	0.3	31.2	3.8	0.2	7.8	19.9	20.2	10.8	0.3	tr	—
C. cucuribitarum	ND	(7)	6.6	—	9.1	—	13.1	10.0	—	6.2	24.5	15.6	14.9	—	—	—
Cokeromyces potrasii[34]	ND	(12)	25.8–	—	19.7–	—	20.2–	2.1–	—	9.5–	8.9–	4.2–	2.1–	—	—	—
			0.6		4.9		10.7	2.5		0.0	36.1	26.5	18.0			
Cunninghamella blakesleeanus	ND	(13)	0.8	—	1.0	—	11.9	3.0	—	6.5	34.0	23.3	19.5	—	—	—
Heliocostylium pyriforme	ND	(7)	—	—	1.2	—	29.1	1.9	—	7.3	44.0	8.0	8.5	—	—	—
Mortierella ienispora[35]	4.8	(4)	—	—	1.0	0.6	14.7	0.5	—	8.3	21.1	8.2	6.1	0.8	5.5	26.7
Mucor genevensis (NRRL 1407)	ND	(14)	0.2–	—	1.8–	—	14.6–	1.7–	0.5–	1.4–	20.0–	12.7–	16.8–	—	—	—
			0.4		3.0		23.1	8.1	1.0	3.7	40.0	20.0	32.2			
M. globosus	16.7	(15)	2.1	—	7.6	—	26.1	7.7	—	6.9	25.8	8.3	15.6	—	—	—
M. hiemalis (+)	18.0–18.8	(16, 17)	tr	—	1.8	tr	15.2	3.2	tr	9.6	36.8	19.4	14.8	—	—	—
M. hiemalis (−)	15.1–19.3	(16, 17)	tr	—	2.4	tr	14.8	3.1	tr	9.7	32.6	18.8	19.2	—	—	—
M. javanicus	ND	(7)	—	—	3.6	—	20.3	4.7	—	8.3	26.8	12.6	13.7	—	—	—
M. miehei	7.8–25.1	(16)	—	—	1.8	tr	27.7	3.0	—	6.3	48.0	10.3	2.0	—	—	—
M. mucedo	12.0–15.2	(16)	tr	—	1.1	tr	16.8	1.4	tr	11.3	30.5	32.9	6.4	—	—	—
M. oblongiosporus (CBS 173.27)	2.5–20.0	(16)	tr	—	7.2	tr	14.5	2.4	tr	14.3	28.1	19.6	14.0	—	—	—
M. oblongiosporus (CBS 220.29)	4.5–17.2	(16)	tr	—	8.0	tr	16.0	1.9	tr	10.8	26.6	20.0	19.7	—	—	—
M. pusillus	18.3	(15)	—	—	—	—	23.5	1.2	—	2.9	59.4	11.2	1.1	0.8	—	—
M. racemosus	8.2–19.0	(16)	tr	—	2.7	tr	16.9	2.9	tr	4.6	36.5	16.6	19.4	—	—	—
M. rammannianus	15.2–19.8	(16)	tr	—	1.6	tr	18.5	2.6	tr	4.4	28.0	13.5	30.9	—	—	—

M. sp. I	13.2–35.9	(16)	0.8	—	—	22.5	3.2	—	2.3	55.1	12.6	3.1	—
M. sp. II	8.4–36.4	(16)	tr	—	—	29.1	2.9	—	3.8	57.8	10.1	3.2	—
M. strictus (CBS 575.66)	7.8–24.4	(16)	7.9	tr	tr	16.2	2.4	tr	8.0	34.6	12.7	18.1	—
M. strictus (CBS 576.66)	11.1–21.4	(16)	5.9	tr	tr	22.4	1.9	tr	9.2	34.8	11.6	14.2	—
M. strictus (CBS 100.66)	13.2–20.4	(16)	8.3	tr	tr	15.0	2.4	tr	9.3	32.7	12.0	20.0	—
Phycomyces blakesleeanus ATTC 6200	ND	(18)	tr	—	—	10.9	1.7	—	20.5	29.8	34.9	2.1	—
P. blakesleeanus	ND	(7)	2.0	1.0	—	19.9	3.5	—	7.4	40.6	15.8	9.8	—
Rhizopus arrizus	0.66–4.9	(19)	5.8	—	—	17.2	0.9	—	8.5	36.9	12.5	13.1	—
R. arrhizus	ND	(7)	2.0	1.0	—	19.9	3.5	—	7.4	40.6	15.8	9.8	—
R. arrhizus	ND	(20)	1.2	tr	0.2	18.4	3.7	—	11.0	29.4	16.3	0.2	16.2
R. nigricans	ND	(6)	tr	—	—	15.7	3.4	—	3.9	30.4	19.1	27.5	—
R. stolonifer (syn. R. nigricans)	ND	(7)	5.5	4.9	—	20.8	3.9	—	5.2	34.3	7.8	15.6	—
R. sp. I	11.6–45.3	(16)	tr	tr	—	23.3	3.0	tr	18.6	34.9	21.8	5.1	—
R. sp. II	20.8–32.8	(16)	tr	tr	—	24.3	3.0	tr	7.9	33.8	24.4	6.3	—
R. sp. III	8.8–32.5	(16)	1.6	—	—	30.0	3.2	—	7.0	43.5	15.3	3.3	—

[a] Key to references: (1) Ellenbogen et al. (1969); (2) Howell and Fergus (1964); (3) Sumner (1970); (4) Haskins et al. (1964); (5) Brushaber et al. (1972); (6) Tyrrell (1967); (7) Shaw (1965); (8) Bowman and Mumma (1967); (9) Tyrrell (1971); (10) Mumma and Bruszewski (1970); (11) White and Powell (1966); (12) Rogers and Gleason (1974); (13) Shaw (1966b); (14) Mantle et al. (1969); (15) Mumma et al. (1970); (16) Sumner et al. (1969); (17) Jones (1969); (18) Jack (1966); (19) Gunasekaran et al. (1972b); (20) Weete et al. (1970a).

[b] ND = not determined; tr, trace.

[c] Superscript numbers: key to fatty acid composition not listed in columns 4–17: [1] $C20:2(23.8\%)$, $C20:5(5.2\%)$, unknown (2.2%), $C22:2(0.9\%)$; [2] $C16:2(tr)$, $C17:1(6\%)$, $C17:2(5\%)$, $C19:0(tr)$, $C19:1(tr)$, $C19:2(tr)$, $C20:1(1\%)$; [3] $C_218:3(1.2\%)$, $C20:2(0.8\%)$; [4] $C17:1(8\%)$, $C17:2(10\%)$, $C19:2(2\%)$, $C18:3(4\%)$; [5] $C14:1(0.4\%)$, $C20:2(2.2\%)$, $C20:5(9.1\%)$, unidentified (1.5%); [6] $C14:1(0.3–1.3\%)$, $C20:2(tr)$, $C20:5(9.5–14.6\%)$, unknowns (0.1–1.9%); [7] $C22:0(6.6\%)$; [8] $C14:1(0.1\%)$, $C20:2(5.3\%)$, $C20:5(10.2\%)$, unidentified (2.1%); [9] $C20:1(0–3.2\%)$, $C22:0(0–2.6\%)$, $C22:1(0–11.7\%)$, $C22:0(0–17.0\%)$; [10] $C17:1(2.9\%)$, $C20:2(1.9\%)$, $C20:5(4.1\%)$, $C22:2(1.7\%)$, $C22:5(2.9\%)$, $C22:6(11.2\%)$; [11] $C20:5(5.9\%)$, $C22:2(0.8\%)$, $C22:5(9.5\%)$, $C22:6(34.1\%)$; [12] $C20:5(6.1\%)$, $C22:5(6.6\%)$, $C22:6(10.8\%)$; [13] $C16:2(1.5\%)$; [14] branched-chain 12-methyl tri- and tetradecanoic and 14-methyl pentadecanoic acids (35%); [15] $C20:1(1.0\%)$, $C20:2(0.4\%)$; [16] $C17:1(2.3\%)$, $C20:1(3.1\%)$; [17] $iC14:0(43\%)$, $aC15:0(11.6\%)$, $iC16:0(4.8\%)$; [18] $C17:1(1.8\%)$, $C20:1(2.8\%)$; [19] $C17:1(0.9\%)$, $C20:1(1.0\%)$; [20] $C17:1(0.5\%)$; [21] $C20:1(16.1\%)$, $C20:2(1.7\%)$; [22] $C20:1(15.9\%)$, $C20:2(0.9\%)$; [23] $C17:1(0.7\%)$; [24] $C20:1(1.2\%)$; [25] $C17:1(2.3\%)$, $C20:1(3.1\%)$, $C20:2(3.6\%)$; [26] $iC14:0(30.3\%)$, $aC15:0(9.5\%)$, $iC16:0(4.4\%)$; [27] $C14:1(1.2\%)$, $C16:2(2.3\%)$, $C20:1(1.1\%)$; [28] $C10:0(7.1\%)$, $C22:0(3.1\%)$; [29] $C10:0(16.2\%)$, $C14:1(1.0\%)$, $C22:0(24.4\%)$; [30] $C10:0(10.5\%)$, $C22:0(6.5\%)$; [31] $C14:1(tr)$, $C16:2(2.1\%)$, $C20:1(1.5\%)$; [32] $C14:1(tr)$, $C16:2(1.5\%)$, $C17:1(1.7\%)$, $C20:1(1.5\%)$; [33] $C10:0(0.2\%)$, $C14:1(tr)$, $C16:2(0.6\%)$, $C20:1(0.1\%)$; [34] $C10:0(7.6–0.7\%)$; [35] $C20:2(1.6\%)$, unidentified acids (4.9%).

Table II

TOTAL LIPID CONTENT AND FATTY ACID COMPOSITION OF SPORANGIOPHORES FROM PHYCOMYCETES

Organism	Lipid content (% tissue dry wt.)	References[a]	Fatty acids (% of total) Carbon number and degree of unsaturation									
			14:0	15:0	16:0	16:1	17:0	18:0	18:1	18:2	18:3	20:0
Blastocladiella emersonii[b]	11	(1)	—	—	28	4	—	9	32	—	12	—
Mucor hiemalis	8.4	(2)	2.0	—	15.0	2.1	—	17.1	28.0	17.9	18.0	—
M. miehei	11.3–19.4	(2, 3)	5.6	—	24.4	3.9	—	11.3	32.6	13.1	9.3	—
M. mucedo	3.7	(2)	2.5	—	21.3	3.5	—	12.6	27.2	21.0	12.0	—
M. pusillus	16.1–19.3	(2, 3)	1.0	—	25.4	3.0	—	4.8	42.2	19.0	4.5	—
M. racemosus	4.1	(2)	4.9	—	21.8	3.8	—	9.1	31.4	14.9	14.1	—
M. ramannianus	7.6	(2)	4.1	—	18.7	3.4	—	5.5	31.2	14.1	20.9	—
Rhizopus arrhizus	2.7	(4)	1.0	0.8	16.8	1.7	—	19.9	42.4	7.7	0.1	6.9
Rhizopus sp.	10.4–16.1	(2, 3)	6.0	—	27.3	2.9	—	12.1	28.8	10.6	12.1	—

[a] Key to references: (1) Mills and Cantino (1974); (2) Sumner and Morgan (1969); (3) Jones (1969); (4) Weete et al. (1970a).
[b] Percentage of fatty acid in total lipids; C20:4 (7%).

spores and the parent mycelia with lower degree of unsaturation in spore fatty acids. Incubation temperature influenced the fatty acids of the spores and the mycelia to the same extent, i.e., lipids were more unsaturated when the fungus was grown at lower temperatures.

b. Sterols. Only recently have the sterol contents of Phycomycetes been examined (McCorkindale *et al.*, 1969). Thus, in addition to members of the Mucorales (chitin cell wall), members of the orders Saprolegniales and Leptomitales (cellulose cell wall) were also examined (Table III). Only cholesterol was detected in all three groups. Desmosterol, 24-methylcholesterol, and fucosterol were detected in both Saprolegniales and Leptomitales. In the Mucorales species, ergosterol and 22-dihydroergosterol were identified (Table III).

In four aquatic fungi studied by Bean *et al.* (1973), several sterols were identified as cholesterol, 24-ethylcholesterol, 22-dehydrocholesterol, 24-methylcholesterol, and 24-ethyl-22-dehydrocholesterol. In the Mucorales species, ergosterol, 22-dihydrocrgosterol, episterol, and ergosta-$\Delta^{5,7,24}$-trienol were detected (McCorkindale *et al.*, 1969; Blank *et al.*, 1962; Goulston *et al.*, 1967). In lipid extracts of *Rhizopus arrhizus*, fungisterol, 5-dihydroergosterol, and ergosta-$\Delta^{5,7,14}$-trienol were identified (Weete *et al.*, 1973a).

In support of the separation of Saprolegniales and Leptomitales from the rest of the Phycomycetes based on taxonomic criteria is the observation that C27, C28, and C29 sterol derivatives are present in the Saprolegniales and Leptomitales, while only the 24-methyl derivatives (with the exception of cholesterol in two species) are found in the other Phycomycetes. These two orders are considered among the most primitive of the Phycomycetes.

Although few studies are reported, it appears that the sterol composition of spores is very similar qualitatively to mycelial sterols (Weete *et al.*, 1973a,b; Weete and Laseter, 1974). Ergosterol is not detected, whereas fungisterol is the predominant sterol and is usually accompanied by some minor sterols. Saturated C28 and C29 sterols are also found in spores of *R. arrhizus* and *Linderina pennispora* (Weete *et al.*, 1973a,b). *Plasmodiophora brassicae* is the only phycomycete whose spores contained no sterols that were considered to be mycelial products (Hebert *et al.*, 1973).

2. Ascomycetes and Deuteromycetes (Fungi imperfecti)

This group is divided morphologically into two subclasses: the Hemiascomycetes and the Euascomycetes. The former is considered more primitive than the latter. The yeasts, yeast-like fungi, and certain parasitic mycelial forms belong to the Hemiascomycetes, whereas other mycelial forms belong to the Euascomycetes. Several species representing both subclasses have been analyzed for their fatty acid (Tables IV and V) and sterol (Table VI) contents.

Table III
Sterols Identified in Lipid Extracts from Phycomycetes

Fungus	1	2	3	4	5	6	7	8	9	10	11	12	13	14	15	References
Order MUCORALES																
Mucor hiemalis											±		+		+	McCorkindale et al. (1969)
M. dispersus													+		+	McCorkindale et al. (1969)
Rhizopus stolonifer													+		+	McCorkindale et al. (1969)
Absidia glauca											±		+		+	McCorkindale et al. (1969)
Phycomyces blakesleeanus	±	±										+	+		+	McCorkindale et al. (1969)
Rhizopus arrhizus				+		+	+				±	+	+		+	Weete et al. (1973a)
Rhizidiomyces apophysatus					+			+			±	+	+		+	Bean et al. (1973)
Hypochytrium catenoides						+		+			±	+	+		+	Bean et al. (1973)
Rhizophylctis rosea										+	±	+	+		+	Bean et al. (1973)
Order SAPROLEGNIALES																
Saprolegnia megasperma								+			+	±	−	+	−	McCorkindale et al. (1969)
Aplanopsis terrestris								+			+	+	−	+	−	McCorkindale et al. (1969)
Achlya caroliniana								−			+	+	−	±	−	McCorkindale et al. (1969)
Pythiopsis cymosa								+			+	−	−	+	−	McCorkindale et al. (1969)
Order LEPTOMITALES																
Apodachlya minima								±			+	±	−	+	−	McCorkindale et al. (1969)
A. brachynema								+			+	−	−	+	−	McCorkindale et al. (1969)
Apodachlyella completa								+			+	−	−	+	−	McCorkindale et al. (1969)

a Key to numbers: (1) lanosterol; (2) 24-methylene-24-dihydrolanosterol; (3) fecosterol; (4) 24(28)-dehydrosterol; (5) 24-methylcholesterol; (6) fungisterol; (7) 5-dihydroergosterol; (8) fucosterol; (9) stigmasterol; (10) 22-dehydrocholesterol; (11) cholesterol; (12) desmosterol; (13) ergosterol; (14) 24-methylene cholesterol; (15) 22-dihydroergosterol.

a. Fatty Acids. Considering the variations in culture conditions, isolates of the same species and analytical techniques employed, there are, with a few exceptions, no apparent significant differences in the fatty acid distribution among the Ascomycetes taxa. The total lipid content and the fatty acid composition of several species of Ascomycetes and Deuteromycetes are given in Table IV. Generally, C16:0 is the predominant saturated fatty acid, and C18:1 and C18:2 are the predominant unsaturated fatty acids. C18:3 accumulates in relatively low concentrations except in a few species, and the fatty acids above C18 are not abundant in this group (Table IV).

The Hemiascomycetes tend to accumulate monoenoic acids. *Saccharomyces* species contain 1% or less C18:3 ω3 whereas C16:1 is present at unusually high concentrations of 26–60% of the total fatty acid content. Yeasts and yeast-like fungi, on the other hand, contain 0–28% of their total fatty acid content as C18:3 ω3; *Candida, Torulopsis,* and *Rhodotorula* species have low levels of C16:1 or C18:3 (Table IV).

Mumma *et al.* (1970) reported that oleic acid is the most abundant fatty acid in most thermophilic fungi, while C18:2 is predominant in the mesophiles. It was concluded, however, that thermophilicity could not be explained by differences in the fatty acid composition when thermophiles were compared to closely related mesophilic species.

Generally, branched-chain fatty acids are scarce in fungi, but branched fatty acid isomers of C16 and C18 were detected in lipids extracted from *Penicillium pulvillorum* and *P. cyaneum* (Nakajima and Tanenbaum, 1968; Koman *et al.*, 1969).

The total lipid content and fatty acid composition of conidia produced by Ascomycetes are shown in Table V. Hebert *et al.* (1973) reported that 10% of the total lipid content (23%) of the ascospores of *Byssochlamys fulva* is in the spore wall. Fatty acids of chain length greater than C18 and C18:1 are the predominant fatty acids. Long-chain fatty acids (>C18), particularly C22:0, were found to comprise the bulk of the fatty acids of spores from *Erysiphe graminis* and *Sphaerotheca humili* (Weete, 1974).

b. Sterols. Reports on the sterols of Ascomycetes and Deuteromycetes are very scarce. Only the yeast sterols have been extensively examined, and they are included in a recent review by Rattray *et al.* (1975). Ergosterol appears to be the principal sterol of these fungi. Other sterols detected in extracts of Ascomycetes are listed in Table VI.

Cholesterol, unexpectedly, was identified as the only sterol in extracts of *Penicillium funiculosum* (Chen and Haskins, 1963). Brassicasterol was identified in varying concentrations in extracts of several dermatophytic fungi (Blank *et al.*, 1962). Ergosterol peroxide and its oxidation product, cerevisterol, have been reported as natural sterol products of some fungi, but many investigators have provided evidence that those two products are artifacts

Table IV

Total Lipid Content and Fatty Acid Composition of Ascomycetes and Deuteromycetes (Fungi Imperfecti) (Mycelia)

Organism	Lipid content (% mycelium dry wt.)	References[a]	Fatty acid (% of total) Carbon number and degree of unsaturation													
			12:0	13:0	14:0	15:0	16:0	16:1	17:0	18:0	18:1	18:2	18:3	20:0	20:3	20:4
Ascomycetes																
Order EUROTIALES																
Aspergillus dauci	2.3	(1)	—	1.3	1.8	1.1	40.1	4.0	—	5.9	25.0	17.6	2.0	tr[b]	—	—
A. flavus	ND[b]	(2)	—	—	0.5	—	24.0	2.4	—	21.5	25.3	23.7	—	2.6	—	—
A. flavus	1.2	(3)	0.5	—	0.4	—	12.6	—	—	17.6	37.0	31.9	—	—	—	—
A. fresenius	ND	(4)	tr	—	tr	—	16	—	—	3	20	53	—	—	—	—
A. fumigatus	ND	(5)	—	—	—	—	19.0	0.8	—	3.1	35.2	41.9	0.2	3.8	—	—
A. nidulans	45	(6)	—	—	0.7	—	20.9	1.2	—	15.9	40.3	17.0	11.4	1.2	—	—
A. niger	ND	(7)	1.5	—	1.4	0.4	22.2	3.2	tr	5.2	7.2	46.1	—	—	—	—
A. niger	1.6	(8)	1.8	—	1.5	—	14.2	2.0	—	8.2	27.8	35.6	8.9	—	—	—
A. niger	ND	(9)	—	—	0.3	0.2	15.8	0.7	—	7.2	21.3	37.8	15.6	—	—	—
Cephalosporium acremonium		(10)	—	—	—	—	7.0–8.9	4.7–5.9	—	—	61.2–75.4	11.9–25.5	—	—	—	—
C. diospyri		(11)	—	—	—	—	11.0	—	—	0.0	27.0	61.0	—	—	—	—
Penicillium atrovenetum	ND	(12)	—	—	0.2	0.6	14.5	1.2	1.3	4.6	30.5	43.0	0.8	1.7	—	—
P. chrysogenum	ND	(13)	—	—	3.2	—	10.3	—	—	4.9	46.2	17.5	—	3.5	—	—
P. chrysogenum		(3)	3.9	—	3.1	—	12.8	—	—	11.9	18.8	43.1	6.4	—	—	—
P. chrysogenum	9.8	(14)	—	—	—	—	12.2	—	—	5.5	10.9	65.4	6.0	—	—	—
P. chrysogenum	ND	(15)	—	—	—	—	14	—	—	4	6	54	21	—	—	—
P. chrysogenum	4.3–19.0	(16)	tr	tr	tr	1.8	23.8	3.1	tr	9.0	4.7	48.0	—	4.5	—	—
P. crustosum	12	(17)	—	—	—	—	34.4	—	—	6.7	47.0	11.7	—	—	—	4.2
P. cyaneum[1 c]	9.6	(18)	1.2–5.4	—	0.9–2.8	—	15.4–18.9	3.0–4.8	1.4–2.1	6.8–8.6	10.9–14.2	31.4–45.8	2.8–4.5	—	—	0.4–2.1
P. dupontii	14.8	(14)	—	—	—	—	25.2	—	—	10.8	42.2	21.8	—	—	—	—
P. javanicum	18–35	(19)	—	—	—	—	20.3	0.6	—	17.4	25.1	31.8	0.5	—	—	—
P. lanosum	ND	(3)	—	—	0.3	—	26.4	2.2	—	5.9	42.1	23.1	—	—	—	2.1

170

Species		(no.)														
P. lilacinum	ND	(20)	—	—	0.1	—	32.3	3.4	—	9.4	38.6	13.4	—	2.8	—
P. notatum	ND	(3)	0.6	—	1.5	—	19.6	3.0	—	5.7	13.8	53.5	2.3	—	—
P. pulvillorum[2]	ND	(21)	—	—	1.4	1.9	13.7	1.2	1.6	7.0	19.1	50.2	1.0	—	—
P. roqueforti	ND	(22)	—	—	—	—	12	1	—	4	11	50	17	—	—
P. sophi		(7)	—	—	0.9	tr	19.9	2.3	0.8	4.5	8.8	49.6	13.2	tr	—
P. sopimulosum	41.6	(23)	—	—	—	—	18.0	3.8	—	11.9	43.3	21.1	0.3	1.6	—
P. soppi		(24)	—	—	0.4	—	23.6	3.6	—	7.3	44.1	19.6	0.3	1.1	—
P. tardum		(11)	—	—	—	—	10.0	—	—	2.0	50.8	37.2	—	—	—
Stilbella sp.	17.0	(14)	—	—	—	—	19.5	1.4	—	2.3	13.4	58.3	5.0	—	—
S. thermophila	38.1	(14)	—	—	2.1	—	42.5	1.9	—	13.7	25.4	14.3	—	—	—
Trychophyton rubrum	ND	(25)	4	—	1	0.6	21	3	1	15	15	45	—	1.2	—
Order SPHAERIALES															
Botryosphaeria ribis	ND	(3)	—	—	1.3	—	31.7	—	—	20.6	15.3	19.8	11.3	—	—
Ceratocystis coerulescens strain 431	ND	(26)	—	—	3.0–17.4	—	10.1–16.3	1.0–6.0	—	2.1–18.7	9.1–22.8	10.1–38.6	7.2–18.3	2.4–20.4	—
C. fagacearum[3]	ND	(27)	8.2	—	6.0	3.0	12.0	2.0	2.2	13.7	16.0	17.1	3.0	2.4	—
Chaetomium globosum	ND	(3)	—	—	0.4	—	19.2	1.7	—	8.3	17.0	46.4	7.0	—	—
C. globosum	54.1	(14)	—	—	1.4	1.–	30.6	10.8	—	9.6	9.7	35.6	1.3	—	—
C. thermophile	9.4	(14)	—	—	—	—	57.8	3.1	—	4.4	8.0	26.8	—	—	—
Cochliobolus miyabeanus[4] (*Helminthosporium oryzae*)		(28)	—	—	—	—	22	—	—	3	7	59	9	—	—
Mycosphaerella musicola	ND	(3)	1.9	—	2.1	—	16.0	2.3	—	5.6	16.8	48.7	5.4	1.2	—
Neurospora crassa	10	(29)	—	—	—	—	10–12	2	—	2.4	4–5	40–42	32–34	—	—
N. crassa	5.1–8.1	(30)	—	—	5.2	—	17.8	4.3	—	3.4	9.8	54.7	9.4	tr	—
N. crassa (mutant)	5–8	(30)	—	—	3.6	—	12.4	5.5	—	1.0	5.4	50.0	20.7	tr	—
N. crassa	ND	(3)	2.8	—	3.8	—	18.2	2.5	—	7.9	11.1	42.3	7.7	3.7	—
N. crassa	ND	(31)	—	—	—	—	26–27.8	—	—	2–9.3	5.4–16.4	44.1–61.5	2.6–14.1	—	—
Sepedonium ampullosporum		(11)	0.2–0.3	—	—	—	30.4	—	—	9.1	16.1	44.3	—	—	—
Stemphylium dendriticum	2.4	(32)	—	—	0.6	—	18.6	1.6	0.1	3.6	17.2	51.5	6.2	0.1	—
Order HELOTIALES															
Botrytis cinerea	ND	(3)	3.4	—	3.4	—	19.0	1.3	—	3.8	11.0	16.4	41.7	—	—
B. cinerea	2.6	(33)	—	—	0.2	0.2	16.5	0.9	—	4.9	22.6	44.2	9.4	0.3	—

(continued)

171

Table IV (*Continued*)

Organism	Lipid content (% mycelium dry wt.)	References[a]	12:0	13:0	14:0	15:0	16:0	16:1	17:0	18:0	18:1	18:2	18:3	20:0	20:3	20:4
Order HYPOCREALES																
Claviceps gigantea	ND	(34)	—	—	—	—	17	3	—	3	56	20	—	—	—	—
C. paspali	ND	(34)	—	—	—	—	19	7	—	2	57	15	—	—	—	—
C. purpurea[5]	ND	(34)	—	—	—	—	20	7	—	4	23	14	—	—	—	—
C. purpurea[6]	ND	(35)	0.1	—	0.4	0	33.4	4.0	0.2	5.1	21.3	12.3	0.4	1.0	—	—
C. purpurea[7]	ND	(36)	—	—	0.9	—	23.9	3.8	—	3.2	20.9	12.3	—	0.9	—	—
C. purpurea (M₁)	20–30	(37)	—	—	0.2	—	19.5	6.6	0	3.3	38.0	32.4	—	—	—	—
C. purpurea (M₃)[8]	20–30	(37)	—	—	1.0	—	23.4	6.0	—	3.6	30.1	14.5	—	—	—	—
C. purpurea (M₂)[9]	20–30	(37)	—	—	4.6	—	20.0	4.6	—	5.1	40.9	18.9	—	—	—	—
C. purpurea (M₄)[10]	20–30	(37)	—	—	0.6	—	24.2	5.4	—	7.2	23.5	10.0	—	—	—	—
C. purpurea (M₅)[11]	20–30	(37)	—	—	0.5	—	22.7	6.0	—	2.3	18.7	8.0	—	—	—	—
C. purpurea (33F16, 1/1)	1.9–31.3	(38)	—	—	0.3	—	23.2	5.7	—	3.2	36.3	31.3	1	—	—	—
C. purpurea (33F16, 2/4)[12]	1.9–31.3	(38)	—	—	0.5	—	24.1	5.9	—	2.5	14.2	12.7	2	—	—	—
C. sp.	ND	(34)	—	—	—	—	34	2	—	7	39	14	—	—	—	—
C. sulcata[13]	ND	(34)	—	—	—	—	11	1	—	5	13	5	1	—	—	—
Fusarium aquaeductuum	ND	(39, 40)	—	—	—	—	11	—	—	4	25	58	1	—	—	—
F. aquaeductuum var. *medium*	ND	(39, 40)	—	—	—	—	12	—	—	6	29	47	2	—	—	—
F. moniliforme	ND	(3)	—	—	2.1	—	14.4	—	—	11.0	29.7	41.6	1.2	—	—	—
F. oxysporum	ND	(41)	—	—	tr	—	11.0	—	—	16.6	35.7	33.4	3.8	—	—	—
F. oxysporum f. *lini*	ND	(3)	0.8	—	1.6	—	18.2	2.2	—	12.0	11.0	41.7	12.5	—	—	—
F. roseum	ND	(41)	—	—	tr	—	17.5	—	—	5.3	29.1	39.7	8.2	—	—	—
F. sambucinum	ND	(39, 40)	—	—	—	—	12	0	—	7	33	39	4	—	—	—
F. solani	54	(33)	—	—	0.5	0.2	18.5	1.0	—	13.6	24.0	36.5	5.1	0.9	—	—
F. solani f. *phaseoli*	21	(1)	—	—	1.3	0.5	28.0	5.4	—	10.0	28.1	21.6	1.0	tr	—	—
F. sp.	35	(33)	—	—	0.6	0.1	20.8	1.0	0	10.6	22.8	29.7	13.2	0.9	—	—
Nectria achroleuca	ND	(3)	—	—	—	—	19	—	—	14	24	37	5	—	—	—
Order DIAPORTHALES																
Glomerella cingulata	ND	(42)	—	—	1.1	—	43.7	2.2	—	5.8	26.4	19.8	1.2	—	—	—

	(n)															
Order TAPHRINALES																
Taphrina deformans	ND	(3)	2.1	—	4.8	—	21.2	6.7	—	—	4.6	51.5	7.0	2.1	—	—
Order PEZIZALES																
Pyronema domesticum	ND	(3)	0.4	—	0.4	—	13.6	—	—	—	21.2	29.5	35.1	—	—	—
Order ENDOMYCETALES																
Saccharomyces cerevisiae	ND	(43)	0.2	—	1.0	—	12.5	37.0	—	—	5.0	43.9	—	—	—	—
Deuteromycetes (Fungi Imperfecti*)																
*Beauveria bassiana	7.8	(44)	—	—	—	—	20	—	—	—	5	33	40	2	—	—
*B. tenella[14]	ND	(45)	0.4	—	1.2	—	20.4	—	1.0	—	9.2	25.6	23.7	1.5	1.2	—
*Candida lipolytica	6.6–8.5	(46)	—	—	—	—	19	12	1	—	1	45	21	—	—	—
*C. scotti (AL25)	8.2	(46)	—	—	—	—	15	2	tr	—	3	17	34	28	—	—
*C. scotti (5AAP)	10.7	(46)	—	—	—	—	12	2	tr	—	2	16	51	17	—	—
*C. sp (No. 5)	4.8	(46)	—	—	—	—	14	18	tr	—	1	14	40	11	—	—
*Cephalosporium acremonium corda		(10)	—	—	—	—	7	6	—	—	—	75	12	—	—	—
*C. subverticallatum	ND	(3)	0.9	—	1.6	—	21.6	2.7	—	—	6.8	28.3	35.0	3.1	—	—
*Cylindrocarpon radicicola	ND	(3)	3.5	—	3.1	—	22.4	1.7	—	—	7.0	24.6	25.5	9.2	2.1	—
*C. radicicola	7.5	(32)	0.1	—	0.3	0.1	23.8	0.7	0.3	—	8.0	27.4	29.3	9.8	tr	—
Epicoccum nigrum		(39)	—	—	3	2	15	3	—	4	7	18	34	4	—	—
*Epicoccum nigrum		(39)	—	—	—	—	15	3	—	—	7	18	34	4	—	—
Humicola brevis	14.6	(14)	—	—	—	—	28.8	1.9	—	—	3.7	20.4	41.3	4.0	—	—
H. grisea (mesophile)	10.8	(14)	—	—	—	—	15.3	—	—	—	1.5	30.9	33.9	18.5	—	—
H. grisea v. thermoidea	13.0	(14)	—	—	—	—	28.8	—	—	—	2.2	40.4	28.5	—	—	—
H. insoleus	14.2	(14)	—	—	—	—	29.9	—	—	—	1.1	37.3	31.8	—	—	—
H. lanuginosa	17.2	(14)	—	—	—	—	21.4	—	—	—	4.5	65.2	8.6	—	—	—
H. nigrescens	8.0	(14)	—	—	—	—	20.5	—	—	—	3.6	29.2	34.3	12.2	—	—
*Isvaia farinosa	8.0	(44)	tr	—	—	—	17	1	—	—	6	41	34	—	—	—
*Macrophomina phaseolina[15]	4–13.1	(47)		0–1.8	2.6–2.9	tr	—	tr	tr	—	tr–4.6	tr	tr–1.3	15.9–30.8	tr–1.2	
Malbranchea pulchella v. sulfurea (thermophile)	24.8	(14)	—	—	—	—	26.2	—	—	—	7.5	35.0	31.3	—	—	—
M. pulchella	26.5	(14)	—	—	—	—	11.3	—	—	—	11.4	26.6	50.7	—	—	—
*Metarrhizium anisopliae	12.2	(44)	—	—	—	—	21	1	—	—	9	23	47	—	—	—
*Microsporum gipseium	10.5	(48)	—	—	—	—	17.2	—	—	—	7.7	10.4	64.4	—	—	—
*Pithomyces chartarum	4–6	(49)	0.5	—	1.4	0.2	29.5	0.7	tr	—	8.1	15.0	41.3	1.1	—	—
*Pullularia pullulaus	11.2	(50)	—	—	1.6	—	47.1	—	—	—	3.6	25.2	5.7	16.8	—	—

(continued)

173

Table IV (*Continued*)

Organism	Lipid content (% mycelium dry wt.)	References[a]	Fatty acid (% of total) Carbon number and degree of unsaturation												
			12:0	13:0	14:0	15:0	16:0	16:1	17:0	18:0	18:1	18:2	18:3	20:0	20:3	20:4
P. pullulaus	11	(51)	—	—	—	—	31	3	—	8	46	11	—	—	—	—
P. pullulaus	10.5–11.0	(52)	—	—	0.5	tr	24.7	4.4	0.4	6.3	47.8	14.8	0.9	—	—	—
Rhodotorula glutinis	12	(46)	—	—	—	7	9	1	3	4	58	2	—	6	—	—
R. graminis	31.7–37.2	(53)	0.4	—	5.0	—	31.9	0.3	—	3.2	37.2	10.2	4.6	—	—	—
Sclerotium bataticola	26–46	(54)	—	—	6.2–	—	14.6–	14.2–	—	1.3–	48.0–	14.6–	0.1–	0.2–	—	—
					0.4		18.2	17.7		2.1	51.4	16.6	0.4	0.3		
S. rolfsii	2.8	(1)	1.2	—	5.7	1.0	23.9	tr	—	10.2	17.5	40.1	0.5	tr	—	—
Sporotrichum exile	9.5	(14)	1.4	1.	1.9	—	17.0	2.1	—	8.8	8.3	58.4	—	2.1	—	—
S. thermophile	15.5	(14)	—	—	—	—	28.4	—	—	6.8	2.7	35.1	—	—	—	—
Trichophyton mentagrophytes	12.3	(17)	0.1	—	0.3	0.9	23.8	0.2	—	11.2	17.0	45.2	—	—	—	—
T. rubrum	10	(55)	—	—	0.8	2.1	23.8	—	0.1	7.4	13.1	52.4	—	—	—	—
T. viride	4.8–9.6	(56)	—	—	—	—	17	—	—	5	26	46	3.5	tr	—	—
Verticillium albo-atrum (spores)	14	(57)	2.1	—	0.6	0.3	31.7	0.4	0.4	35.1	21.0	6.5	0.4	—	—	—

[a] Key to references: (1) Gunasekaran and Weber (1972); (2) Singh (1957); (3) Shaw (1965); (4) Stone and Hemming (1968); (5) Kaufmann and Viswanathan (1965); (6) Singh *et al.* (1955); (7) Salmonowitz and Niewiadomski (1965); (8) Shaw (1966b); (9) Sumner (1970); (10) Huber and Redstone (1967); (11) Ando *et al.* (1969); (12) Van Etten and Gottlieb (1965); (13) Abe (1952); (14) Mumma *et al.* (1970); (15) Bennett and Quackenbush (1969); (16) Divakaran and Modia (1968); (17) Audette *et al.* (1961); (18) Koman *et al.* (1969); (19) Coots (1962); (20) Singh *et al.* (1956); (21) Nakajima and Tanenbaum (1968); (22) Kubeczka (1968); (23) Shimi *et al.* (1959); (24) Singh *et al.* (1957); (25) Kostiw et al. (1966); (26) Sprechter and Kubeczka (1970); (27) Collins and Kalnins (1968); (28) Gribanovski-Sassu and Beljak (1971); (29) Todd *et al.* (1957); (30) Hardesty and Mitchell (1963); (32) Brady and Nye (1970); (32) Hartman *et al.* (1962); (33) Haskins *et al.* (1964); (34) Morris (1967); (35) Thiele (1964); (36) Bharusha and Gunstone (1957); (37) Morris and Hall (1966); (38) Mantle *et al.* (1969); (39) Foppen and Gribanovski-Sassu (1968); (40) Gribanovski-Sassu and Foppen (1968); (41) Rambo and Bean (1969); (42) Jack (1966); (43) Light *et al.* (1962); (44) Tyrrell (1969); (45) Molitoris (1963); (46) Kates and Baxter (1962); (47) Wassef *et al.* (1975); (48) Wirth *et al.* (1964); (49) Hartman *et al.* (1960); (50) Merdinger (1966); (51) Merdinger *et al.* (1968); (52) Merdinger and Cwiakala (1967); (53) Hartman *et al.* (1959); (54) Gottlieb and Van Etten (1966); (55) Wirth and Anand (1964); (56) Ballance and Crombie (1961); (57) Walker and Throneberry (1971).

[b] ND, not determined; tr, trace.

[c] Superscript numbers: Key to fatty acid composition not listed in columns 4–17: [1] C14:1(2.1–3.4%), C20:2(0.3–4.2%), C22(0.5–2.0%); [2] iC16:0(0.4%), iC18:0(1.0%), C17:1(1%), C20:1(0.3%), C20:2(0.2%), C23:0(1%), C24:0(4.9%), C26:0(1.1%); [3] C19:0(1.2%), C21(1%), C22:0(2%), C23:0(1.6%), C14:1(0.9%); [4] C24:0(4.9%), C26:0(1,1%); [5] OH—C18:0(33%); [6] OH—C18:0(22.0%); [7] OH—C18:0(34.1%); [8] OH—C18:1(21.5%); [9] OH—C18:1(5.9%); [10] OH—C18:1(29.1%); [11] OH—C18:1(41.8%); [12] OH—C18:1(40.1%); [13] 9, 10-kihydroxy C18:0(64%), C20:1(tr); [14] C20:1(013–017%), C22:0(1.3%), C24:0(0.8%); [15] C8:0(tr–1.7%), C10:0(6.6–37.2%), C20:1(tr), C22:1(10.8–14.3%), C24:1(16.1–39.0%).

[d] Asterisks indicate Fungi Imperfecti. When the type of spore formation (sexual stage) has not yet been described, the organism is consigned to the Deuteromycetes (Fungi Imperfecti). Spores of many organisms have not been described, but are listed under Ascomycetes because they are related to forms whose sexual stage has been demonstrated to characterize them as Ascomycetes.

Table V

TOTAL LIPID CONTENT AND FATTY ACID COMPOSITION OF CONIDIA FROM FUNGI IMPERFECTI

Organism	Lipid content (% tissue, dry wt.)	References	Fatty acid (% of total) Carbon number and degree of unsaturation										
			14:0	15:0	16:0	16:1	17:0	18:0	18:1	18:2	18:3	20:0	22:0
Aspergillus niger[1]	ND	(1)	1.7	—	30.6	0.8	—	5.3	33.3	27.4	—	tr[b]	—
Curvularia sp.[2]	ND	(2)	0.5	0.6	27.9	3.3	—	9.4	21.7	27.8	1.8	0.7	2.4
Erysiphe graminis[3]	ND	(3)	0.8	0.3	8.8	1.0	—	2.0	4.3	6.0	5.1	0.3	1.7
Fusarium oxysforum	ND	(4)	tr	—	14.2	—	—	39.5	28.9	17.4	tr	—	—
Fusarium roseum	ND	(4)	tr	—	22.5	—	—	tr	43.4	34.1	tr	—	—
Pithomyces chartarum (Sporidesmium bakeri)	14	(5)	0.8	tr	21.6	1.3	—	6.4	15.9	53.4	—	—	0.4
Sphaerotheca humili[4] var. fuliginia		(3)	1.1	—	5.3	1.0	—	2.2	4.5	7.0	4.3	13.0	1.7

[a] Key to references: (1) Morris (1967); (2) Bharusha and Gunstone (1956); (3) Weete (1974); (4) Chisholm and Hopkins (1957); (5) Hartman et al (1962).

[b] ND, not determined; tr, trace.

[c] Superscript numbers: Key to fatty acid composition not given in column 4–14: [1] C14:1(1.4%), C24:0(4.6%), C12:0(0.8%); [2] C20:1(1.8%), C22:1(0.8%), C24:0(2.4%), C22:1(9.0%); [3] C22:0(5%), C24:1(7.1%), C24:0(7.6%), C24:1(6.5%), unknowns(44.1%); [4] C12:0(0.2%), C22:0(41.7%), C22:1(1.7%), C24:0(10%), unknowns(8%).

175

Table VI

STEROLS IDENTIFIED IN LIPID EXTRACTS FROM ASCOMYCETES AND DEUTEROMYCETES

Fungus	Sterol[a]																References
	1	2	3	4	5	6	7	8	9	10	11	12	13	14	15	16	
Yeast	+			+		+	+	+	+		+		+	+	+	+	Mercer and Johnson (1969); Barton et al. (1968); Goulston et al. (1967)
Saccharomyces cerevisiae		+													+		Wieland and Stanley (1931)
Aspergillus fumigatus			+												+		Goulston and Mercer (1969)
A. niger					+										+		Barton and Bruun (1951)
Claviceps purpurea								+							+		Breivak et al. (1954)
Pullularia pullulans												+			+		Merdinger et al. (1968)
Penicillium funiculosum													+		+		Haskins (1963)

[a] Key to numbers: (1) lanosterol; (2) 4-α-methyl-24-methylene-24-dihydrozymosterol; (3) 24-methylenelophenol; (4) fecosterol; (5) 14-dehydroergosterol; (6) 24(28)-dehydroergosterol; (7) 22-dihydroergosterol; (8) 5-dihydroergosterol; (9) episterol; (10) brassicasterol; (11) ascosterol; (12) stigmasterol; (13) desmosterol; (14) zymosterol; (15) ergosterol; (16) ergosta-$\Delta^{8(9),22}$-dienol.

(see Vacheron and Michel, 1968; Breivak *et al.*, 1954; Tanahashi and Takahashi, 1966; Clarke and McKenzie, 1967; Adam *et al.*, 1967; Sharratt and Madhausing, 1967).

In the few investigations reported, the sterol compositions in spores are very similar to those of the mycelia. Weete and Laseter (1974) reported that ergosterol, the most abundant sterol in the conidia of imperfect fungi, was accompanied by lower proportions of di- and tetraunsaturated C28 sterols. They also isolated ergosta-$\Delta^{5,7,14,22}$-tetraenol from both the conidia and the mycelium of *Aspergillus niger*. Conidia from *Penicillium claviforme* differ from those of other imperfect fungi by having fungisterol as the most abundant sterol. The mycelium of *Penicillium funiculosum* contained cholesterol as the sole sterol (Chen and Haskins, 1963).

3. *Basidiomycetes*

a. Fatty Acids. In spite of the many variations in culture conditions or age of the cultures, the fatty acid distribution of Basidiomycetes reported by various authors are qualitatively surprisingly similar. The total lipid content and fatty acid distribution of Basiomycetes are given in Table VII. Basidiomycetes produce linoleic and α-linolenic acids, and there are no other apparent characteristics to distinguish them from Ascomycetes and Deuteromycetes. In a few cases, small amounts of dienoic and trienoic 20- and 22-carbon atom compounds are found (Table VII), but these are probably chain elongation products of linoleic and α-linolenic acids.

Shaw (1966a,b) reported differences in the fatty acid distribution between the stipe and pileus of *Collybia* sp.; however, he suggested that the distribution in the stipe may be intermediate in fatty acid composition between that of the mycelium and pileus. Furthermore, because of the differences in fatty acid composition between the neutral and polar lipids, Shaw (1967) suggested that the overall fatty acid distribution depends on the relative proportion of these lipids. This hypothesis was supported by the work of Holtz and Schisler (1971) on *Aspergillus bisporus*.

The total lipid content and fatty acid composition of several species of basidiomycete spores are shown in Table VIII. Tulloch and Ledingham (1960, 1962) reported considerable variation in the fatty acid composition of spores from numerous basidiomycetous fungi and concluded that the data were not sufficient to be useful for taxonomic classification. However, generally C16:0, C18:1, and C18:2 are the predominant fatty acids in these spores. Fatty acids with chain length greater than C18 are often present. Rust spores are characterized generally by having a high abundance of unsaturated fatty acids, and this may be due to the unusually high levels of C18:3 and to the presence of 9,10-epoxy-*cis*-octadecanoic acid.

The fatty acid composition of spores from smut fungi have been reported by several investigators. The major predominant unsaturated fatty acids

Table VII

TOTAL LIPID CONTENT AND FATTY ACID COMPOSITION OF BASIDIOMYCETES (MYCELIA)

Organism	Lipid content (% mycelium dry wt.)	References[a]	Fatty acid (% of total) Carbon number and degree of unsaturation													
			12:0	13:0	14:0	15:0	16:0	16:1	17:0	18:0	18:1	18:2	18:3	20:0	20:3	20:4
Order AGARICALES																
Agaricus bisporus (Lange) Sing[d] strain 310[1c]	ND[b]	(1)	2.6	—	4.1	—	20.5	7.6	2.5	6.9	15.5	38.1	—	—	—	—
A. bisporus (Lange) Sing[d] strain 314	ND	(1)	8.3	—	4.9	—	20.9	6.6	7.6	6.0	16.2	29.3	—	—	—	—
A. bisporus (Lange) Sing[d] strain 320[2]	ND	(1)	4.3	—	2.5	—	18.8	8.3	6.4	4.8	15.6	33.0	—	—	—	—
A. bisporus (Lange) Sing[d] strain 322	ND	(1)	4.8	—	3.8	—	21.4	4.9	6.8	7.0	13.7	37.4	—	—	—	—
A. campestris (white variety)		(2)	2.5	—	1.8	—	11.9	—	1.1	5.5	2.6	63.4	—	9.0	—	—
A. campestris (wild)	ND	(3)	2.2	—	2.8	—	15.0	4.0	—	3.0	5.0	65.5	—	2.5	—	—
Amanita muscaria	ND	(4)	—	—	0.5	1.4	10.1	1.6	—	8.0	39.6	52.7	—	—	—	—
Auricularia auriculajadae	ND	(5, 6)	—	—	—	—	19	—	—	4	32	42	1	—	—	—
Clitocybe illudeus	0.9	(7)	—	—	tr	—	18.6	1.5	—	1.8	42.8	34.8	—	—	—	—
Collybia sp.	ND	(3)	2.5	—	3.2	—	13.1	1.9	—	1.7	6.3	54.3	17.0	—	—	—
Coprinus comatus (ATCC 12640)	ND	(8)	—	—	0.7	—	22.5	2.3	—	9.6	20.4	42.0	2.5	—	—	—
Corticium solani	ND	(9)	5.5	—	3.5	—	13.4	2.2	—	7.3	22.3	28.4	14.9	—	—	—
Daedaleopsis confragosa	ND	(5, 6)	—	—	—	—	22	4	—	7	18	5	18	—	—	—
D. tricolor	ND	(5, 6)	—	—	—	—	21	9	—	11	16	34	—	—	—	—
Exobasidium vexans	ND	(9)	2.4	—	2.5	—	16.4	2.6	—	5.6	23.1	34.2	13.2	—	—	—

Species		Ref[a]											
Fomes annosus	5.3–6.7	(10)	—	—	—	21	—	—	37	10	29	—	—
F. fomentarius	ND	(11)	—	—	—	35	3	—	10	17	4	1	—
F. igniarius[3]	ND	(12)	—	1.5	—	12.3	—	1.2	12.6	—	—	1.0	—
F. sp.	ND	(3)	1.2	2.2	—	12.4	2.1	—	3.1	4.5	70.3	4.2	—
Polyporus sulphureus	ND	(5, 6)	—	—	—	2	2	—	3	35	30	—	—
Rhizoctonia lamellifera	ND	(9)	3.6	4.2	—	21.4	2.6	—	9.7	12.3	29.5	13.5	—
R. solani	6.1–6.9	(13)	—	tr	tr	11.7–14.5	tr–3.2	—	2.4–3.9	15.7–24.9	54.4–66.6	—	—
Tricholoma nudum (NRRL 1371)	3.1–49.1	(14)	—	0.4–1.0	—	17.6–29.0	1.1–1.6	—	6.2–12.6	12.3–33.0	29.0–35.2	0.5–26.1	—
Order TREMELLALES													
Stilbum zacallo-canthum	ND	(9)	0.6	1.0	—	21.8	4.3	—	3.7	21.5	41.4	3.8	—
Order LYCOPERDALES													
Calvita gigantium	ND	(7)	—	+	—	+	+	—	+	+	75	—	—
Order USTILLAGINALES													
Tilletia controversa[4]	5.8	(15)	1.0	1.7	1.7	9.2	2.5	—	0.2	10.6	66.2	1.7	—
Ustilago scitaminca[5]	ND	(9)	1.0	2.0	—	19.7	3.0	—	7.3	28.8	32.3	1.7	—
Order APHYLLOPHORALES													
Trametes orientalis		(11)	—	—	—	19	—	—	42	—	15	—	—

[a] Key to references: (1) Holtz and Schisler (1971); (2) Hughes (1962); (3) Shaw (1967); (4) Talbot and Vining (1963); (5) Yokokawa (1969); (6) Yokokawa (1970); (7) Bentley et al. (1964); (8) Jack (1966); (9) Shaw (1965); (10) Gunasekaran et al. (1970); (11) Ishida and Mitsuhashi (1970); (12) Epstein et al. (1966); (13) Gottlieb and Van Etten (1966); (14) Leegwater et al. (1962); (15) Trione and Ching (1971).

[b] ND = not determined; tr, trace.

[c] Superscript number: Key to fatty acid composition not listed in columns 4–17: [1] $C10:0(4.1\%)$; [2] $C10:0(6.1\%)$; [3] $C17:1(1.1\%)$, $C19:0(1\%)$, $C21:0(1\%)$, $C22:0(24.8\%)$, $C23:0(1\%)$, $C24:0(26\%)$, $C25:0(4.4\%)$, $C26:0(15.4\%)$, $C27:0(1.9\%)$, $C28:0(23.9\%)$, $C30:0(tr)$, $C32:0(tr)$; [4] free acids $C6:0(6.3\%)$, $C8:0(4.4\%)$, $C16:2(1.3\%)$; [5] $C20:1(4.2\%)$.

[d] Values are average of the fatty acids of neutral and polar lipids.

Table VIII

TOTAL LIPID CONTENT AND FATTY ACID COMPOSITION OF SPORES FROM BASIDIOMYCETES

Organism	Lipid contents (% tissue, dry wt.)	References[a]	Fatty acid (% of total) Carbon number and degree of unsaturation											
			14:0	15:0	16:0	16:1	17:0	18:0	18:1	18:2	18:3	20:0	22:0	Epoxy
Agarigus bisporus (Lange) Sing[c] strain 310	ND[b]	(1)	tr[b]	—	9.7	tr	—	3.1	2.7	83.7	—	—	—	—
strain 314	ND	(1)	2.5	—	17.9	tr	—	4.9	6.1	68.8	—	—	—	—
strain 320	ND	(1)	tr	—	11.4	tr	—	4.1	4.5	80.0	—	—	—	—
strain 322	ND	(1)	tr	—	10.6	tr	—	2.2	1.7	85.5	—	—	—	—
Cronartium comandrae (aeciospore)[1]	17	(2)	1.3	1.5	21.6	2.4	—	2.8	6.8	6.2	12.1	0.6	—	39.1
C. hasknessii (aeciospore)[2]	12.5	(2)	1.1	0.8	17.7	1.2	—	4.8	6.9	5.2	12.1	0.5	1	38.0
C. ribicola (aeciospore)[3]	18	(2)	0.7	0.9	21.6	1.6	—	4.0	5.9	8.0	19.1	1.1	—	34.4
Frommea obtusa var. *duchesneae* (aeciospore)	19	(2)	0.5	0.1	16.3	0.8	—	73.1	9.6	4.2	9.7	0.9	1.9	42.9
Gymnosporangium juvenescens[4]	6.3	(3)	0.6	0.7	11.6	1.0	—	9.6	2.9	7.7	54.6	2.9	3.3	—
Hemileia vastatrix (uredospore)	24	(2)	—	—	5.0	1.0	—	3.0	2.0	7.0	1.0	2.0	1.0	78
Melampsora lini (uredospore)[5]	14.5	(3)	0.6	0.4	11.1	0.3	—	3.1	2.2	2.0	3.0	1.1	1.4	74.2
M. medusae (uredospore)[6]	14.6	(3)	1.3	0.6	32.0	1.3	0.4	5.7	7.0	6.7	7.8	0.7	1.2	30.8
Peridermium stalactiforme (aeciospore)[7]	15	(2)	1.0	1.1	19.7	3.2	—	2.5	8.0	5.0	10.9	—	—	39.4
Phragmidium andersonii (teliospore)	13	(2)	0.1	—	6.6	0.7	—	2.6	20.1	23.0	43.9	0.3	—	1.7
P. speciosum (teliospore)	9.5	(2)	0.4	—	10.4	0.6	—	3.0	14.7	20.1	42.3	0.4	0.7	7.5
Puccinia aspargi (teliospore)	13	(2)	0.6	0.5	18.8	1.9	—	2.7	18.7	8.6	40.6	1.0	2.2	4.4

P. asteris (teliospore)	10	(2)	0.4	0.3	8.5	0.8		0.6	62.3	10.7	12.6	—	0.4	3.4
P. carthami	9.0	(3)	0.4	0.4	17.5	0.5		3.2	28.4	22.2	22.6	—	—	4.8
P. corconata (aeciospore)	37	(2)	1.4	0.8	21.4	0.8		5.3	13.1	18.0	2.2	0.2	0.3	36.5
(teliospore)	9	(2)	0.8	0.6	14.1	0.9		1.4	25.8	22.2	16.3	1.2	1.5	15.2
P. graminis														
P. g. avenae (uredospore)	16	(2)	1.9	0.2	35.5	0.5		6.0	11.4	6.1	8.0	—	—	29.5
P. g. avenae (uredospore)[8]	ND	(4)	2.2	—	31.6	1.0	3.1	5.6	1.0	3.6	6.8	2.8	30.0	8.3
P. g. avenae (aeciospore)	21	(2)	1.6	0.7	28.2	0.4		6.4	7.8	6.1	8.2	—	—	30.1
P. g. avenae (teliospore)	10	(2)	0.8	0.5	23.1	0.4		3.5	15.0	4.6	8.3	—	—	41.0
P. g. tritici (uredospore)[9]	18	(2)	2.8	0.2	42.9	1.4		4.7	5.9	4.5	11.2	—	—	26.3
P. g. tritici (aeciospore)	17	(2)	2.1	0.3	33.6	1.8		5.2	16.9	10.0	12.6	—	—	17.5
P. g. tritici (teliospore)	10	(2)	1.4	0.6	20.6	1.4		3.1	17.6	9.6	21.6	—	—	23.0
P. helianthi (teliospore)	13.3	(3)	1.0	0.9	23.3	1.3		4.1	15.0	11.9	23.0	0.3	—	16.4
P. hieracii (uredospore)	8.4	(3)	0.3	0.4	16.3	0.5		5.5	11.7	21.1	33.7	1.0	—	9.5
(teliospore)	7.3	(3)	0.3	0.4	17.1	0.3		4.6	15.1	19.2	34.0	0.5	—	8.5
P. pulsatillae (teliospore)	23	(2)	0.2	0.2	11.9	3.7		3.8	6.7	63.7	3.1	3.1	1.2	0.7
P. recondita (aeciospore)	31	(2)	0.9	0.2	18.8	0.9		3.4	36.2	5.6	6.6	0.4	0.2	26.8
P. sorghi, race 4-1 (uredospore)	21	(2)	0.7	0.3	25.8	0.9		7.5	18.7	11.3	32.6	1.2	1.0	—
(teliospore)	10	(2)	1.7	—	25.6	1.2		9.3	13.2	9.5	37.5	1.0	1.0	—
Ravenelia hobsoni (teliospore)[10]	18.8	(2)	0.8	0.6	23.7	1.6		9.2	46.1	6.4	3.0	1.8	1.9	—
Spacelotheca reiliana[11]	ND	(5)	—	—	15.9	1.8	8.0	8.0	29.0	27.8	2.4	0.9	2.4	—
Tilletia caries	ND	(6)	2.0	—	36.9	26.6		2.4	4.6	14.3	13.2	—	—	—
T. controversa	ND	(6)	3.4	—	63.1	9.7		4.2	4.9	11.2	3.6	—	—	—
T. controversa[12]	35.0	(7)	0.9	—	16.0	2.1		1.3	14.4	49.4	3.2	—	—	—
T. foetida	ND	(6)	5.7	—	67.3	7.6		6.0	7.6	5.8	0.3	—	—	—
T. foeteus[13]	20.0	(3)	0.5	—	14.6	3.0		1.0	8.8	63.2	—	—	0.4	—
Urocystis agropyri[14]	ND	(5)	—	—	8.6	—		6.3	18.0	7.7	—	0.3	—	—
Uromyces hedysariobscuri (teliospore)	14	(2)	0.5	0.2	15.8	0.5		3.5	7.5	40.9	27.7	0.3	2.0	—

(continued)

Table VIII (*Continued*)

Organism	Lipid contents (% tissue, dry wt.)	References[a]	Fatty acid (% of total) Carbon number and degree of unsaturation											
			14:0	15:0	16:0	16:1	17:0	18:0	18:1	18:2	18:3	20:0	22:0	Epoxy
U. phaseoli (uredospore)	20	(2)	1.1	0.6	25.4	0.7	—	11.5	32.7	8.3	17.4	0.3	2.0	—
U. psoraleae (aeciospore)[15]	10.2	(2)	0.9	0.3	19.9	1.4	—	8.8	40.9	5.2	15.6	—	1.1	1
Ustilago bullata[16]	0.6	(8)	3.4	1.8	16.9	14.2	0.5	4.8	29.7	24.9	0.3	0.9	—	—
U. levis[17]	14.5	(3)	1.1	0.9	19.8	6.8	—	3.9	42.0	19.0	1.6	—	0.2	—
U. maydis	0.4	(8)	0.5	0.2	18.2	3.2	tr	1.4	39.6	30.7	2.6	3.7	—	—
U. maydis[18]	ND	(5)	1.5	4.1	15.0	1.9	6.7	6.4	23.1	22.6	3.5	2.8	1.5	—
U. nigra[19]	4.0	(3)	1.4	1.2	24.9	5.7	—	5.5	35.0	22.0	1.6	0.5	0.4	—
U. tritici[20]	5.0	(3)	0.3	2.7	26.9	9.7	—	4.7	30.2	16.4	—	1.0	—	—
U. zeae[21]	22.0	(3)	0.4	0.2	9.3	5.2	—	2.6	53.8	17.4	—	2.3	1.2	—

[a] Key to references: (1) Holtz and Schisler (1971); (2) Tulloch and Ledingham (1962); (3) Tulloch and Ledingham (1960); (4) Laseter and Valle (1971); (5) Weete *et al.* (1969); (6) Laseter *et al.* (1968b); (7) Trione and Ching (1971); (8) Gunasekaran *et al.* (1972a).

[b] ND, not determined; tr, trace.

[c] Values are average of the fatty acids of neutral and polar lipids.

[d] Superscript numbers: Key to fatty acid composition not listed in columns 4–15. [1] C20:1(3.6%), others (2.0%); [2] C20:1(1.6%), unknowns (9.1%); [3] C20:1(0.8%), others (1.9%); [4] unknowns(5.1%); [5] C20:1(0.6%); [6] unknowns(4.2%); [7] C20:1(4.6%), others(4.6%); [8] C24:1(6.0%); [9] C24:0(1.5%), C22:1(6.3%); [10] unknown(4.9%), others (1.9%); [11] C24:0(4.6%); [12] C6:0(6.3%), C8:0(4.4%), C10–13:0(1.1%); [13] C16:2(1.2%), C20:1(1.2%), C24:1(6.0%); [14] unknown #1(41.4%), unknown #2 (18.0%); [15] unknowns(5.9%); [16] C14:1(2.4%); [17] C20:1(3.2%), unknown(1.5%); [18] C14:1(1.2%), C22:1(tr), C24:0(tr); [19] C20:1(1.0%), unknown(0.8%); [20] C20:1(1.9%), unknown(3.5%); [21] C20:1(7.6%). [22] C6:0(6.3%), C8:0(4.4%), C10–13:0(1.1%).

were reported to be C18:1 and C18:2 (Tulloch and Ledingham, 1962; Morris, 1967) In some smut species, C16:1 was present in high concentrations (Weete *et al.*, 1970a).

b. Sterols. Few basidiomycetes have been examined for their sterol composition. Ergosterol has been reported in a number of basidiomycetes (Milazzo, 1965; Holtz and Schisler, 1971). A number of other sterols, methyl and dimethyl sterols have been identified in several basidiomycetes species (Table IX). A number of lanosterol derivatives in which the methyl substituent at C-20 has been oxidized to either CH_2OH or $COOH$ are characteristic of *Polyporus* sp. (Guider *et al.*, 1954; Beereboom *et al.*, 1957; Halsall and Sayer, 1959).

Spores of rust fungi have a sterol profile that is considerably different from that of other fungi. The most striking difference is the absence of ergosterol and the presence of C29 sterols in abundance. The major sterol component of wheat stem rust and *P. graminis* uredospores is stigmast-Δ^7-enol with lesser amounts of stigmasterol and cholesterol (Nowak *et al.*, 1972; Weete and Laseter, 1974). Jackson and Frear (1968) identified stigmast-Δ^7-enol and stigmasta-$\Delta^{7,24(28)}$-dienol as the two principal sterols of *Melampsora lini* (flax rust) with small concentrations of stigmasta-$\Delta^{5,7}$-dienol.

Table IX
STEROLS IDENTIFIED IN LIPID EXTRACTS FROM BASIDIOMYCETES

Fungus	Sterol[a]							References
	1	2	3	4	5	6	7	
Ganaderma applanatum	+						+	Strigina *et al.* (1971)
Puccinia graminis		+					+	Hougen *et al.* (1958)
Polyporus paragamenus		+					+	Barton and Cox (1949)
Daedalea quercina			+				+	Breivak *et al.* (1954)
Fomes applanatus			+				+	Holtz and Schisler (1972)
Polyporus pinicola			+				+	Weiland and Bened (1943)
G. applanatum				+			+	Strigina *et al.* (1971)
Melampsora lini					+	+	+	

[a] Key to numbers: (1) fungisterol; (2) 22-dihydroergosterol; (3) 5-dehydroergosterol; (4) Episterol; (5) stigmasta-$\Delta^{7,24(28)}$-dienol; (6) stigmasta-$\Delta^{5,7}$-dienol; (7) ergosterol.

B. HYDROCARBONS

The composition and distribution of fungal aliphatic hydrocarbons were the subject of a review by Weete (1972), and their distribution in the spores of some fungi is shown in Table X. Generally the alkane carbon chain lengths range from C18 to C35 with C27, C29, and C31 the principal hydrocarbons. Even-numbered carbon chain alkanes are present in small concentrations

Table X

HYDROCARBON DISTRIBUTION IN THE SPORES OF SOME FUNGAL SPECIES

Fungal species	Hydrocarbon chain length (% of total)												References
	C21	C22	C23	C24	C25	C26	C27	C28	C29	C30	C31	C33	
Puccinia graminis tritici	—	—	3.1	7.2	7.3	8.1	17.6	7.3	29.4	1.3	16.2	2.3	Laseter and Valle (1971)
P. striiformis	—	—	3.9	3.2	7.9	2.2	20.5	2.5	23.9	1	23.9	3.4	Laseter and Valle (1971)
Spacelotheca reiliana[1 a]	—	—	2.1	—	3.2	1.1	9.1	3.8	34.2	13.1	16.2	2.5	Weete et al. (1969)
Tilletia caries[2]	0.1	0.2	5.4	0.5	9.7	1.0	23.5	4.3	34.8	1.6	13.7	1.5	Laseter et al. (1968b)
T. controversa[3]	0.4	0.2	3.9	0.9	11.4	0.4	24.7	2.7	25.6	1.3	21.5	2.7	Laseter et al. (1968b)
T. foetida[4]	0.3	0.3	3.2	1.0	11.9	1.3	24.7	5.7	28.8	1.9	15.2	1.7	Laseter et al. (1968b)
Urocystis agropyri[5]	1.5	—	2.0	1.2	3.3	1.0	12.2	0.9	46.3	1.2	23.7	—	Gunasekaran et al. (1972a)
Ustilago bullata[6]	11.3	4.3	21.8	—	23.5	—	1.1	—	0.4	—	—	—	Gunasekaran et al. (1972a)
Ustilago maydis[7]	1.3	1.3	3.1	1.5	11.0	3.0	36.0	7.0	13.0	5.0	4.0	—	Gunasekaran et al. (1972a)
Ustilago maydis[8]	—	—	1.9	1.3	11.1	2.1	33.4	7.7	13.8	3.8	—	3.6	Weete et al. (1969)

[a] Superscript numbers: Key to chain lengths not listed in columns 2–13: [1] iso C25(1.8%), iso C27(2.8%), iso C24(8.3%), iso C31(5.1%), C32(2.7%); [2] iso C27(1.0%), iso C29(1.3%), iso C31(1.1%); [3] iso C27(0.8%), iso C29(1.9%), iso C31(1.7%); [4] iso C27(0.9%), iso C29(1.6%), iso C31(1.3%); [5] C19(1.1%), iso C25(1.6%); [6] C9 to C18(23.1%), C19(10.3%), C20(3.8%); [7] C14 to C18(9.7%), C19(1.6%), C20(1.6%), C32(1.0%); [8] C19(1.1%), C20(1.5%), C27(8.4%), iso C29(6.9%), C32(1.7%), iso C31(3.1%).

whereas branched-chain isomers are reported for only few species (Weete *et al.*, 1970 a,b; Oro *et al.*, 1966; Laseter and Valle, 1971).

The spore hydrocarbon distributions of several fungal species were analyzed to determine their potential as a chemotaxonomic tool. Gunasekaran *et al.* (1972a), reported that short-chain hydrocarbons were most prevalent in the teliospores of *U. bullata*, C23 and C25 being the most abundant alkanes. The uredospores of *P. graminis avenae* were reported to contain C23 as the principal hydrocarbon whereas C29 was predominant in *P. graminis tritici* (Laseter and Valle, 1971). Also a single race (6AF stem rust) and a mixture of leaf rust races can be readily distinguished; nC23 comprises 50% of the leaf rust hydrocarbon while C23, C25, C27, and C29 range from 14 to 17% each in the stem rust spores. Total hydrocarbon concentrations range from 40 to 150 ppm for various rust and smut species (Oro *et al.*, 1966; Laseter and Valle, 1971). These differences may be characteristic and can be used as a chemotaxonomic character to delimit fungal species. However, to warrant any definite conclusions, quantitative data for many more species produced under a wide varieties of conditions are needed.

Paraffinic hydrocarbons were detected in the mycelia of *Penicillium* sp., *Aspergillus* sp., and *Trichoderma viride* grown in liquid media (Clenshaw and Smedley-Maclean, 1929; Jones, 1969; Jones and Young, 1970). A homologous series of alkanes ranging from nC15 to nC36 were detected in all three species, but *Penicillium* sp. and *Aspergillus* sp. contained major components ranging from nC27 to nC30 and no significant odd-carbon components. *Trichoderma viride*, on the other hand, possessed nC22 and nC24 as the predominant alkanes with odd: even carbon chain-length ratio of less than one.

The hydrocarbon content of yeasts has recently been reviewed by Rattray *et al.* (1975) and will not be covered here in detail. Both straight- and branched-chain hydrocarbons were detected in yeasts, and the predominant chain lengths ranged between C10 and C19 (Baraud *et al.*, 1967). Generally, no alkanes were identified, but Merdinger and Devine (1965) reported alkanes ranging in carbon chain lengths from C16 to C39. Hexadecatriene, a polyunsaturated alkane, was identified in *Candida utilis* grown anaerobically in a defined medium, while squalene (comprising 50% of total hydrocarbons) was present only in the plasma membrane fraction (Fabre-Joneau *et al.*, 1969).

C. GLYCERIDES AND GLYCOLIPIDS

1. *Acylglycerides*

Although the relative proportions of lipid classes vary with the environmental parameters, the triacylglycerides (triglycerides) are often the most abundant class in lipid extracts of fungi. The fatty acid composition of tri-glycerides isolated from several fungal species are shown in Table XI. Note the qualitative similarity of the total fatty acid distribution listed in Tables I, II, IV, V, VII, and VIII and that of the triglycerides, Table XI. The fatty acid components of triglycerides have carbon chain lengths ranging between C8 and C24 with C16:0, C18:1, and C18:2 as the predominant fatty acids.

Morris and Hall (1966) reported that lipids of *Claviceps purpurea* contain up to 44% ricinoleic acid (D-12-hydroxy-*cis*-Δ^9-octadecenoic acid), the hydroxyl groups of which are esterified to long-chain fatty acids. Thus, glycerides containing, 1, 2, or 3 molecules of ricinoleic acid may exist as tetra-, penta-, or hexa-acid glycerides, respectively. These lipids are called estolides and may be referred to as mono-, di-, or triestolide triacylglycerides. The fatty acids in estolides are generally highly saturated as compared to those directly esterified to glycerols.

In a typical triglyceride, unsaturated fatty acids (usually oleic and linoleic acids) are most often found esterified in the 2 position of the glycerol, whereas saturated acids are found to be esterified in the 1 and 3 positions.

Butane-1,3-diol and a C5-diol are two new types of neutral lipids isolated from the yeast *Lipomyces starkey* (Bergel'son *et al.*, 1966; Vaver *et al.*, 1967).

Mono- and diglycerides are generally present as minor constituents of fungal lipid extracts. The fatty acids of the monoacylglycerides are usually saturated (96%) with C14:0 and C16:0 the predominant acids (Gunasekaran *et al.*, 1972b). The fatty acid distribution of the diacylglycerides is very similar to that of the triacylglycerides except that while C18:2 and C18:3 are present in the triacylglyceride in the proportions of 13.2% and 8.1%, respectively, C18:2 is only 1.5% in the diacylglyceride. The diacylglyceride detected in *Candida* sp. is reported to be probably a mixture of 1,2-diacyl- and 1,3-diacyl-*sn*-glycerols (Kates and Baxter, 1962).

2. *Glycolipids and Sulfolipids*

Very little information is available on the glycolipids of fungi. Mono-galactosyl diglyceride was detected in lipid extracts of *Saccharomyces cerevisiae* together with sulfatides and sterol glycosides (Baraud *et al.*, 1970a). Other sulfur-containing lipids have also been detected, but their structures have not been fully elucidated (Collier and Kennedy, 1963; Jack, 1964; Suomalainen, 1969). Wassef *et al.* (1975) tentatively identified mono- and diglycosyl and diglycerides in lipid extracts of *Macrophomina phaseolina*.

3. *Simple Esters*

Methyl and ethyl esters of long-chain fatty acids (palmitic, oleic, and stearic) have been detected in fungi (Weete *et al.*, 1970b; Laseter and Weete,

1971; Laseter *et al.*, 1968a,b). However, the extent to which methyl and ethyl esters are distributed among the fungi is unknown and their functions are uncertain.

Sterol esters are widely distributed in nature and are reported to be present in fungi (Jack, 1964; Adams and Parks, 1967; Madyastha and Parks, 1969). Generally, the sterol ester fraction consist of fatty acids, ranging in chain length between C14 and C18, esterified primarily to ergosterol. In yeast, C16:1 is the most abundant fatty acid; therefore the predominance of ergosteryl palmitoleate is to be expected. Madyastha and Parks (1969) reported that, in yeast, ergosterol was esterified to fatty acids in relative abundance in the descending order of: C16:1 > C18:1 > C16:0 > C18:0 > C14:0 > C14:1. Ergosteryl oleate seems to be the major sterol ester in other fungal species.

D. PHOSPHOLIPIDS

Kates and Wassef (1970) reviewed the distribution of phospholipids in various tissues. The phospholipid distribution in yeasts was reviewed by Hunter and Rose (1971) Mangnall and Getz (1973), and Rattray *et al.* (1975). The phospholipid content in several fungal species is shown in Table XII.

Phosphatidylcholine (PC) and phosphatidylethanolamine (PE) were detected in all fungi examined (Table XII). Although not detected in the mycelia of *Agaricus bisporus* (Griffin *et al.*, 1970), PC is usually the predominant phospholipid both in yeast and mycelial forms of fungi and comprises 35–50% of the total phospholipids. 1,2-Dipalmitoyl-*sn*-glycero-3-phosphoryl-choline was detected in yeasts (Kates and Baxter, 1962; Kates and Paradis, 1973; Hanahan and Jayoko, 1952; Haskell and Snell, 1965; Shafai and Lewin, 1968). The PE content ranged from 14–35% of the total phospholipids and *N*-methyl- and *N,N*-dimethyl-PE were minor components in lipids from *S. cerevisiae* (Letters, 1966) and *Neurospora crassa* (Hall and Nye, 1959, 1961).

Phosphatidylserine (PS) was detected in most fungi and comprised 4–20% of the total phospholipids. Phosphatidylinositol (PI) was found in most fungi studied, especially yeasts, and its concentration ranged from 8–23% of the total phospholipids. The di- and triphosphate isomers of PI, PI-4-phosphate and PI-4,5-diphosphate have been characterized in lipids of *S. cerevisiae* (Prottey *et al.*, 1970; Lester and Steiner, 1968).

Jack and Laredo (1968) examined spore phospholipids of three fungal species and reported the presence of equal relative proportions of PC, PE, PS and an unknown phospholipid. However, the fatty acid compositions of the phospholipids of the three species differed considerably with respect to the contents of C16, C18, and C20 unsaturated acids.

Table XI

Fatty Acid Composition of Fungal Acylglycerides

Fungus	References	C14:0	C16:0	C16:1	C18:0	C18:1	C18:2	C18:3
					Fatty acids (% of total)			
Phycomyces blakesleeanus[a]	(1)	tr	28.8	tr	15.7	29.2	15.2	tr
Lipomyces lipoferus[a]	(1)	tr	11.9	2.8	5.6	76.7	2.8	tr
Glomerella cingulata	(1)	tr	40.8	1.0	4.2	30.1	20.7	3.2
Coprinus comatus[a]	(1)	4.2	28.1	1.8	17.3	23.4	25.7	tr
Fusarium culmorum[b]	(2)	0.3	24.0	0.5	11.0	31.0	33.2	—
Claviceps purpurea[c]	(3)	0.7	28.0	3.7	6.4	19.6	17.4	—
Claviceps purpurea[d]	(3)	0.2	19.5	6.6	3.3	38.0	32.4	—
Tricholoma nudum[e]	(4)	—	24.3	—	12.5	34.2	26.5	—
R. arrhizus[f]	(5)	0.3	20.5	0.8	24.5	43.1	5.5	—
R. arrhizus[g]	(6)	8.2	22.9	tr	31.3	16.4	13.2	8.1
R. arrhizus[h]	(6)	38.6	49.0	8.8	1.0	1.8	0.9	—
R. arrhizus[i]	(6)	17.4	22.0	1.0	34.8	23.2	1.5	—
Choanephora cucurbitarum[j]	(7)	2.9	31.2	3.8	7.8	19.9	20.2	10.8
Alternaria dauci[k,l]	(8)	1.2	62.0	tr	2.8	9.0	23.9	—
Fusarium solani[k,m]	(8)	1.6	45.2	4.1	0.8	15.0	30.5	2.9
Sclerotium rolfsii[k,n]	(8)	1.3	51.5	tr	4.5	6.6	31.5	tr
Candida petrophillum[o]	(9)	0.8	5.0	8.2	1.6	41.9	39.6	—
Ceratocystis coerulescens[p]	(10)	—	8.0	3.0	18.0	9.6	14.4	11.0
C. coerulescens[q]	(10)	—	10.0	1.1	8.1	24.7	35.2	11.6
C. coerulescens[r]	(10)	—	5.1	0.7	14.0	5.3	13.7	7.5
Pithomyces chartarum[s]	(11)	2.6	33.9	0.4	8.6	17.6	35.6	0.9
Stemphylium dentriticum[s,t]	(11)	0.7	21.9	2.0	2.9	21.7	47.7	2.7
Cylindrocarpon radicicola[s]	(11)	0.3	23.5	0.6	8.2	28.6	27.9	10.9
Sclerotinia sclerotiorum[u]	(12)	2.1	22.7	1.8	2.6	20.9	39.3	10.1
S. sclerotiorum[v]	(12)	0.3	16.1	0.8	1.9	20.9	45.0	15.6
S. sclerotiorum[w]	(12)	0.2	13.0	0.5	4.0	28.0	47.3	6.2
S. sclerotiorum[x]	(12)	0.4	7.4	1.0	1.1	31.1	49.6	9.3

[a] Either C20:0 and λC18:3 or both.

[b] Conidia.

[c] Sclerotia, OH—C18:1(24.1–35.5%); varies with isolate.

[d] Mycelia, OH—C18:1(0–41.8%); varies with isolate.

[e] 4-Day-old culture.

[f] C15(tr): C20:0(3.9%), C22:0(1.0%).

[g] 96-Hour culture.

[h] Monoglycerides, 72-hour culture (monoglyceride fraction below detectable limits at 96 hr).

[i] Diglycerides, 96-hour culture.

[j] C10(0.2%, C12(0.2%), C14:1(0.06%), C15(0.3%), C16:2(0.6%), C16:3(0.2%), C17(0.2%), C20:1(0.1%), C20:2(0.2%), C20:3(0.06%), C22:1(0.09%), C22:2(0.03%), C24(0.03%), C24(0.1%), C22:2(0.06%).

[k] Fatty acid constituents of neutral lipids.

[l] C12(1.0%), C14:1(tr), C20:0(tr).

[m] C12(tr), C14:1(tr).

[n] C12(0.8%), C15(0.8%).

[o] Grown on glucose substrate, C15(0.8%), C17:1(2.1%).

[p] Submerged culture, <C16 (including C17) (14.2%), >C18(20.0%).

[q] Surface culture, <C16 (including C17) (2.8%), >C18(5.6%).

[r] Diglycerides, surface culture, <C16 (including C17) (7.4%), >C18(46.1%).

[s] Neutral "glycerides" C15(0.1–0.4%).

[t] C12(0.3%).

[u] Neutral lipids (21% of total lipid), mycelia from laboratory culture, C17(0.2%).

[v] Neutral lipids (87% of total lipid), natural sclerotia, C17(0.2%).

[w] Neutral lipids (70% of total lipid), cultured sclerotia, 7 days old, C17(0.4%).

[x] Neutral lipids (27% of total lipid), cultured sclerotia, 84 days old, C17(0.2%).

[y] Key to references: (1) Jack (1965); Marchant and White (1967); (3) Bergel'son *et al.* (1966); (4) Leegwater *et al.* (1962); (5) Weete *et al.* (1970a); (6) Gunasekaran *et al.* (1972a); (7) White and Powell (1966); (8) Gunasekaran and Weber (1974); (9) Mizuno *et al.* (1966); (10) Sprechter and Kubeczka (1970); (11) Hartman *et al.* (1962); (12) Summer and Colotelo (1970).

Table XII

CONTENT OF FUNGAL PHOSPHOLIPIDS

Fungal species	Phospholipids[a] (% of total)					References
	PC	PE	PI	DPG	PS	
Saccharomyces cerevisiae[b]	46.4	14.9	12.7	—	9.5	Getz *et al.* (1970)
Yeast	42	35	9	12	—	Vignais *et al.* (1970)
Saccharomyces cerevisiae (Guiness 1164)	42.5	22.6	20.9	2.5	7.2	Letters (1966)
Yeast (commercial, cy 1)	42.4	18.3	22.6	7.1[c]	—	Trevelyan (1966)
Yeast (commercial, sy 1)[d]	38.0	28.0	14.0	4.1[c]	15.1	Trevelyan (1966)
Endomycopsis selenospora	46	23	17	—	14	Graff *et al.* (1968)
Saccharomyces cerevisiae (CBS 712)	44	24	21	—	11	Graff *et al.* (1968)
Hansenula anomala	53	23	9	—	15	Graff *et al.* (1968)
Bullera alba (CBS501)	54	30	8	—	8	Graff *et al.* (1968)
Trigonopsis variabilis (CBS 1040)	51	18	15	—	16	Graff *et al.* (1968)
Candida macedoniensis (CBS 600)	41	26	16	—	17	Graff *et al.* (1968)
Brettanomyces truxellensis (CBS 72)	41	21	22	—	16	Graff *et al.* (1968)
Saccharomyces marrianus	42	22	17	—	19	Graff *et al.* (1968)
Claviceps purpurea[e]	26.8	18.9	28.2	—	12.9	Anderson *et al.* (1964)
Saccharomyces cerevisiae[f,i] (D273-10B)	38.5	30.6	8.1	10.9	4.2	Paltauf and Schatz (1969)
S. cerevisiae[g,i]	47.5	19.3	12.6	6.2	10.0	Paltauf and Schatz (1969)
S. cerevisiae[h,i]	34.3	17.9	26.0	8.9	3.9	Paltauf and Schatz (1969)
S. cerevisiae[j]	20	20	35	<5	—	Paltauf and Schatz (1969)
S. cerevisiae[k]	45	15	30	<5	—	Suomalainen (1969)
S. cerevisiae[l]	55	20	15	—	—	Suomalainen and Nurminen (1970)
S. pombe[m]	44.9	19.4	17.6	—	5.7	White and Hawthorne (1970)
S. cerevisiae[n]	27	29	23[n]	—	—	Longley *et al.* (1968)
S. cerevisiae	45.2	16.7	19.8	—	9.3	Deierkauf and Booij (1968)

[a] PC, phosphatidylcholine; PE, phosphatidylethanolamine; PI, phosphatidylinositol; PS, phosphatidyl serine; LPE, lysophosphatidylethanolamine; PGP, polyglycerophosphate; PG, diphosphatidylglycerol DMPE, dimethylphosphatidylethanolamine; PA, phosphatidic acid; LPC, lysophosphatidylcholine; DPG diphosphatidylglycerol (cardiolipin).

[b] Percentage of phospholipid phosphorus, stationary cultures, DPG (7.5%), traces of LPE, DMPE, PA LPC, PG, and PGP.

[c] Fast running (paper chromatography) cardiolipin-like material.

[d] Grown on synthetic media.

[e] Respiratory particles, LPC (6.7%).

[f] Mitochondria from cells grown in presence of lipids, PA (3.2%).

[g] Mitochondria from cells grown without lipids.

[h] Promitochondria from cells grown without lipids.

[i] Percent of total phosphorus.

[j] Plasma membrane, value for PI represents PI + PS, unidentified 10%.

[k] Cell wall, value for PI represents PI + PS, unidentified 5%.

[l] Whole cells, PI represents PI + PS, 5% unknown.

[m] Methyl glycerophosphate 3.9%.

[n] PI + PS, 23%.

Saccharomyces cerevisiae showed phospholipid composition changes at various stages of growth (Getz *et al.*, 1970). Log-phase yeast had more PC, PE, and PI contents than stationary-phase. Regardless of the strain, aerobic or anaerobic growth, the phospholipid composition of log-phase yeast cells was very similar. Stationary wild-type yeast grown aerobically, however, contained less PC, PE, and cardiolipin and more PI than aerobically grown cells. *Schizosaccharomyces pombe* showed no notable differences (White and Hawthorne, 1970). The cardiolipin present in yeasts was found to be almost exclusively mitochondrial, and its amount was related to the degree of mitochondrial development (Jakovcic *et al.*, 1971). The relationship between the respiratory activity, phospholipids and mitochondria is discussed by Mangnall and Getz (1973) and will not be covered here.

Reports on the fatty acids of individual phospholipids are very scarce. However, the fatty acid content of the total phospholipid fraction are reported to have the same pattern as those of total fatty acids. Yeast fungi generally contain C16:1 as the predominant fatty acid. In other fungi, C16:0, C18:1 and in some cases C16:1 are the most common acids found. Other saturated and unsaturated homologs are generally present in smaller concentrations.

E. Sphingolipids

The ceramides and cerebrosides isolated from representatives of mycelial fungi comprised between 0.2 and 0.7% of the dry cell weight (Weiss and Stiller, 1972; Weiss *et al.*, 1973). Generally, the long-chain base moieties are similar in the species examined with normal, branched (iso isomers), saturated, and unsaturated phytosphingosine homologs ranging in chain length between C17 and C22. The relative proportions of each base varies between the ceramide and the cerebroside fractions and among each of the species examined. However, C18-phytosphingosine is the predominant base in the ceramide fraction. The bases containing iso-C21 and nC22 are present in higher relative concentrations in the Basidiomycetes examined. The iso C21-phytosphingosines are abundant in *P. blakesleeanus* and *F. lini* (Weiss and Stiller, 1972; Weiss *et al.*, 1973).

Yeasts were among the first fungi studied for their sphingolipids, which was the subject of a recent review by C. Rattray *et al.* (1975).

Saturated, unsaturated, normal, and branched-chain fatty acids ranging in chain-length between C12 and C26 are hydrolysis products of fungal sphingolipids. α-Hydroxy-C26 and α-hydroxy-C24 acids of the D-configuration (Karlsson, 1966) have been identified in yeast and other fungi (Sweeley, 1959; Sweeley and Moscatelli, 1959; Stanacev and Kates, 1963; Wagner and Zofcsik, 1966a,b; Kaufman *et al.*, 1971; Nurminen and Suomalainen, 1971).

Wagner and Zofcsik (1969b) isolated a "mycoglycolipid" cerebroside from yeast which contained 2-hydroxy-C24, 2-hydroxy-C22, C26, C24, C22, and C20 acids. Other fatty acids identified in sphingolipid fraction are generally those typical of most fungi, C16:0, C18:0, C18:1.

Cerebrosides, which are glycosphingolipids or contain a monosaccharide moiety in the 1-position of the long-chain base (primarily D-glucosyl ceramides) are produced by many fungi (Kaufman et al., 1971; Weiss and Stiller, 1972; Weiss et al., 1973). Although galactose was identified as a component of the sphingolipids of one fungal species, mannose-inositol- phosphate-ceramide and mannose-(inositol-phosphate)$_2$-ceramide were identified in S. cerevisiae (Wagner and Zofcsik, 1966b) and baker's yeast (Steiner et al., 1969), respectively.

Wassef and Hendrix (1977) showed that the lipid composition of Pythium prolatum differed radically from lipids of other fungi. In addition to the classical diacyl phospholipids, PC and PE were found to be present in the glyceryl and alken-1-yl ether analogs. Furthermore, a new phospholipid comprising 12–16% of the total phospholipid fraction was isolated and identified as ceramide aminoethyl phosphonate. This is the first report of a phosphonolipid in fungi.

F. LIPIDS OF SCLEROTIA

Generally, sclerotia contain a relatively low total lipid content and have fatty acids with carbon chain lengths ranging from C14 to C18. Palmitic acid seems to be the predominant saturated acid, whereas the unsaturated acids vary in relative abundances depending on the species and method of culture. Total lipid content and fatty acid composition of sclerotia from a few fungi are shown in Table XIII.

The fatty acid distribution in sclerotia produced by Sclerotinia borealis, S. sclerotiorum, and Botrytis tulipae was reported to be qualitatively identical (Sumner and Colotelo, 1970; Weete et al., 1970a). However, the sclerotia grown on their natural host contain fatty acids with a higher degree of unsaturation, which may be due to the relatively high content of C18:1 (Sumner and Colotelo, 1970).

Sclerotia produced by Claviceps purpurea and related species are different from those of other fungi in that they contain 20–30% oil (Morris, 1967), (Table XIII). The fatty acids in sclerotia of this group are characterized by the presence of little or no C18:3 and by having high levels of ricinoleic acid (D-12-hydroxy-cis-Δ^9-octadecenoic acid). The hydroxy acid is not present in the mycelia, however, and corresponding increases in relative proportions of C18:2 and C18:3 are noticed (Mantle et al., 1969).

Exceptionally, there are some *Claviceps* sp. in which ricinoleic acid does not accumulate above 1% (Table XIII). In these cases, other unusual acids such as epoxy-C18 and 9,10-dihydroxyoctadecanoic acids are present (Morris, 1967).

Sclerotial lipids of *Macrophomina phaseolina* differed considerably from the mycelial lipids (Wassef *et al.*, 1975). Neutral lipid contents were low in mycelia and high in sclerotia. This was not unexpected in view of the fact that sclerotia are structures that exist in a dormant condition for long periods of time. Since storage lipids are usually neutral, it is conceivable that the neutral lipids of sclerotia may serve as carbon and energy reserves. Cardiolipin was reported to be absent from sclerotial phospholipids, and present in the mycelia of *M. phaseolina* (Wassef *et al.*, 1975). Also mycelial lipids were rich in C24:1, C18:3, and C22:1 fatty acids whereas sclerotia contained C18:1, C18:2, C22:1, C20:0, and C16:1 as major acids.

G. Factors Affecting Total Lipid Composition

The lipid content of vegetative hyphae varies between 1 and 50%, of spores between 1 and 35%, and of yeast cells between 7 and 15% of the tissue dry weights. The amount of lipids produced by a given species of fungus depends to a great extent on the developmental stage of growth and on the culture conditions. The total lipid abundance of many fungi at different growth stages were the subject of a recent monograph by Weete (1974). Culture parameters that influence the growth and the lipid contents of fungi have been found to be temperature, carbon source, pH, inorganic salts, and vitamins.

1. *Temperature*

Reports on the effect of temperature on the lipid content of fungi seem inconclusive. While increasing growth temperature, within certain ranges, usually is accompanied by increasing lipid content of fungi (Shaw, 1966a,b; Bowman and Mumma, 1967; Sumner and Morgan, 1969; Cantrell and Dowler, 1971), studies on yeasts show that decreasing growth temperature increases lipid content (Sumner *et al.*, 1969; Kates and Baxter, 1962; Kates and Paradis, 1973). With few exceptions (Bowman and Mumma, 1967; Hunter and Rose, 1972) probably the most pronounced effect of temperature on fungal lipids is the relative increase of unsaturation of fatty acids of fungi grown under lower temperature conditions (Sumner and Morgan, 1969; Sumner *et al.*, 1969; Brown and Rose, 1969). This phenomenon has usually been given an ecological interpretation. The increased degree of unsaturation alters the physical properties of lipids, e.g., melting point, resulting in a

Table XIII

TOTAL LIPID CONTENT AND FATTY ACID COMPOSITION OF SCLEROTIAL LIPIDS

Organism	Lipid contents (% tissue, dry wt.)	References[a]	Fatty acid (% of total) Carbon number and degree of unsaturation											
			14:0	15:0	16:0	16:1	17:0	18:0	18:1	18:2	18:3	20:0	OH–C18:1	diOH–C18:1
Botrytis tulipae														
natural	3.3	(1)	0.4	—	13.2	1.1	—	2.2	15.7	62.8	4.7	tr[b]	—	—
cultured	2.9	(1)	2.5	—	19.6	3.3	—	6.8	22.2	43.6	1.6	tr	1	1
Claviceps gigantea	ND[b]	(2)	0.2	—	17.2	2.6	—	2.7	55.6	19.6	tr	tr	1	tr
C. paspali	ND	(2)	0.2	—	19.0	7.4	—	2.1	56.7	14.5	—	tr	tr	—
C. purpurea	ND	(3)	0.1	—	19.9	6.5	—	4.3	22.5	14.3	—	—	32.3	—
C. purpurea (S$_1$ U.S.A.)	20–30	(4)	0.7	—	28.0	3.7	—	6.4	19.6	17.4	—	—	24.1	—
C. purpurea (S$_2$ U.K.)	20–30	(4)	0.2	—	26.0	4.8	—	4.1	24.1	13.2	—	—	27.5	—
C. purpurea (S$_3$ U.K.)	20–30	(4)	0.1	—	19.9	6.5	—	4.3	22.5	14.3	—	—	32.5	—
C. purpurea (S$_4$ Spain)	20–30	(4)	1.2	—	25.1	4.3	—	4.6	20.0	9.8	—	—	34.9	—
C. purpurea (S$_5$ Rumania)	20–30	(4)	0.4	—	22.9	3.1	—	5.4	17.0	15.8	—	—	35.5	—
C. purpurea	ND	(2)	0.1	—	19.9	6.5	—	4.3	22.5	14.3	tr	tr	32.5	tr
C. sp.	ND	(2)	0.3	—	34.1	2.4	—	7.3	38.6	14.4	—	tr	1	2
C. Sulcata	ND	(2)	0.1	—	11.1	0.8	—	4.9	12.8	5.1	0.1	1.4	tr	63.6

Macrophomina phaseolina[c]	0.9–4.2	(5)	—	tr–13.1	tr–17.2	—	tr–6.4	tr–16.2	3.5–49.0	1.30–23.4	1.9–38.4	—
Sclerotinia borealis (SB$_3$)												
natural	2.7	(1)	1.7	15.5	6.0	—	3.3	18.5	41.7	12.3	tr	—
cultured	2.6	(1)	1.2	20.8	1.8	—	9.8	15.0	47.1	2.5	tr	—
S. borealis (SB$_4$)												
natural	3.3	(1)	0.3	10.5	1.0	—	1.1	7.2	56.5	23.3	tr	—
cultured	3.6	(1)	0.4	10.7	0.5	—	0.9	5.8	80.5	1.5	tr	—
S. rolfsii[d]	ND	(6)	3.3	18.6	3.2	—	5.1	7.3	60.7	—	—	—
S. sclerotiorum[e]	ND	(7)	tr	12.9	0.5	1.3	5.0	37.5	37.9	4.7	—	—
S. sclerotiorum[f]	ND	(7)	0.6	16.3	1.9	1.2	5.9	16.6	25.8	26.7	0.7	—
S. sclerotiorum												
natural	2.5	(1)	0.3	11.2	1.4	—	1.4	21.2	50.0	15.1	tr	—
cultured	5.6	(1)	0.3	11.2	0.6	—	1.0	32.4	50.4	4.3	tr	—

[a] Key to references: (1) Sumner and Colotelo (1970); (2) Morris (1967); (3) Mantle *et al.* (1969); (4) Morris and Hall (1966); (5) Wassef *et al.* (1975); (6) Howell and Fergus (1964); (7) Weete *et al* (1970a).

[b] ND, not determined; tr, trace.

[c] Variation due to change in carbon:nitrogen ratio of the medium. C10:0(tr–5.8%); C20:1(tr); C22:1(tr–52.4%).

[d] C8:0(0.4%); C10:0(0.54%); C12:0(1.08%).

[e] Grown on sucrose–salts medium.

[f] Collected from peas.

physiological adaptive response that facilitates survival of the organism at that temperature (Hunter and Rose, 1972; Knipprath and Mead, 1968; Caldwell and Vernberg, 1970). It follows, therefore, that the order of increasing unsaturation in lipids from fungi with increasing temperature optima should be: psychrophile (10°–20°C) > mesophile (25°–30°C) > thermophile (50°C or more). If the alteration in the degree of unsaturation were strictly an adaptive response, one might expect to find a linear correlation between growth temperature and the degree of unsaturation. However, the data available are insufficient and incomplete and do not clearly demonstrate a linear change.

An explanation for the increased unsaturation of fatty acids of fungi at lower incubation temperature was suggested by James (1969). It is well established that oxygen is required during the dehydrogenation of fatty acids (Yuan and Bloch, 1961; Bennett and Quackenbush, 1969); therefore, decreased temperatures that increase oxygen solubility may affect the rate of desaturation. Increased oxygen tension was shown to be in direct proportion to the increased unsaturation obtained at low incubation temperatures (James, 1969).

Using *Candida lipolytica*, Kates and Paradis (1973) observed a reciprocal relationship between percentages of 18:1 and 18:2 acids during growth at 10°C or 25°C in all the phosphatides, particularly phosphatidylcholine. These reciprocal changes were found to be a reflection of changes in the proportions of tetraenoic, trienoic, and dienoic molecular species of the phosphatides. Positional distribution studies showed that desaturation during growth at either temperature occurred in fatty acids esterified both at the 1- and 2-positions of phosphatidylcholine, but specifically in the 2-position of phosphatidylethanolamine. Calculations of the probable distribution of molecular species during growth suggested that desaturation of lecithin to a tetraenoic species occurs at both temperatures by stepwise desaturation of dienoic and trienoic molecular species. A similar mechanism, namely, the desaturation *in situ* of oleoyl-PC to linoleoyl-PC was demonstrated by Gurr *et al.* (1969) to take place in *Chlorella* chloroplasts. These reactions are presumed to take place early in the growth cycle where the desaturating enzymes are most active. Inhibition or repression (at high temperatures) of the enzyme(s) involved in desaturation would result in low contents of unsaturated fatty acids. On the other hand, decreased inhibition or derepression of these enzymes at lower temperatures would result in a higher degree of unsaturation.

2. Carbon Source

Many investigators reported that carbohydrates were the best carbon substrates for fungal growth and 15–18% of the sugar available in the media was converted into lipids (Ripple, 1940; Enebo *et al.*, 1946; Pan,

1949; Pan *et al.*, 1949; Agarwall and Peterson, 1949). Glucose is the most commonly used sugar and is efficiently converted to lipids by a number of fungi. The ability to convert sugars into fats varies in individual fungi, but the best carbohydrates found for lipid production by most fungi are, in decreasing order: glucose > sucrose > fructose.

The ratio of saturated to unsaturated fatty acids produced by *Blakeslea trispora* varied inversely with sugar concentration (Dedyukhina and Bekhtereva, 1969). However, other culture conditions, such as the carbon to nitrogen ratio, have profound effects on contents of fatty acids (McElroy and Stewart, 1967; Bentley *et al.*, 1964; Leegwater *et al.*, 1962; Talbot and Vining, 1963; Wassef *et al.*, 1975). The requirements for dietary fatty acids and other lipids are not uncommon among fungi and have been discussed in detail by Keith *et al.* (1973).

3. *Inorganic Nutrients*

The inorganic nutrients influencing lipid production by fungi have been reviewed by Woodbine (1959). Phosphate and NaCl seem to influence lipid accumulation and increase production in *Saccharomyces cerevisiae* (Nielsen and Nilsson, 1950; Mass-Forster, 1955; Combs *et al.*, 1968), whereas calcium, sodium, and iron have no effect (Steinberg and Ordal, 1954).

In some species, organic nitrogen is best for mycelial growth, but is far inferior to the inorganic (specially NH_4^+) form for fat production. Exception to that rule occurred when *Aspergillus nidulans* was grown on asparagine (Naquib and Saddik, 1960) and *Penicillium lilacinum* was grown on glycine (Singh *et al.*, 1956; Osman *et al.*, 1969).

The carbon:nitrogen (C:N) ratio is an important factor for lipid production by fungi. The C:N ratio has a very wide range, varying from one fungus to the other. The optimum ratio found best for fungal growth and fat production was 65:1 and 80:1 for *P. lilacinum* (Osman *et al.*, 1969) and *M. vinacea* (Chesters and Peberdy, 1965), respectively. On the other hand, some yeasts produced the highest lipid content when grown on nitrogen-deficient media (Starkey, 1946). The C:N ratio also alters the fatty acid content as mentioned above (Wassef *et al.*, 1975).

4. *pH*

The optimum pH value for the growth of most fungi are between 6.0 and 7.0. However, during fungal growth in an unbuffered media, the pH level falls with increasing age until a value is reached which results in growth inhibition. At a given temperature, the best pH value for lipid production varies with the species but lipid content is almost unchanged between pH 5.9 and 7.5 (Cantrell and Dowler, 1971). Few fungi were reported that can grow and produce the same lipid content at lower and higher pH values (pH 4.0 and 8.0) (Kessell, 1968; Gad and El-Nockrashy, 1960).

The effect of pH and CO_2 levels on lipid content of yeast were reported by Castelli *et al.* (1969). At pH 5.5, high concentration of bicarbonate and pCO_2 caused a 27% increase in total lipid content of *Saccharomyces cerevisiae*. No significant increase in total lipid contents, however, was observed by raising the pH to 6.0 while other parameters were constant.

5. *Aeration*

Many investigators have reported that culture aeration allows fungi to grow more rapidly than nonaerated cultures and to utilize most of the available carbon source (usually glucose) by the end of the growth period. However, no significant differences were found in the total content or nature of the lipids produced from a number of aerated or nonaerated fungi (Starkey, 1946). An exception, however, was observed by Enebo *et al.* (1944), who reported that higher fat yields were obtained from aerated cultures of *Rhodotorula gracilis* compared to nonaerated ones.

6. *Vitamins*

Many fungi require vitamins for growth and reproduction. The relationship between lipid production and vitamin addition is not yet established, but generally, vitamin deficiencies cause reductions in lipid content. *Hanseniospora vallbyensis* produced 40% less lipids in pyridoxine-deficient medium than in the presence of the vitamin (Haskell and Snell, 1965). *Saccharomyces cerevisiae* contained less lipids when grown under pantothenate-deficient conditions (Klein and Lipmann, 1953). Biotin-deficient medium caused accumulation of C16 acids and reduction in C18 acid contents (Suomalainen and Keranen, 1968). Inositol-deficient medium, on the other hand, caused an abnormally high lipid content in a *Saccharomyces* species (Johnston and Paltauf, 1970; Lewin, 1965). The increase in the lipid content of inositol-deficient cells was due to higher levels of triglycerides and other nonpolar lipids. Phosphatide content in general decreased with a significant decrease in the levels of phosphatidylethanolamine and phosphatidylcholine (Shafai and Lewin, 1968). The exact role of inositol in fungal lipids is not clearly understood.

H. Lipid Composition and Taxonomic Classification

1. *Fatty Acid Composition*

Shaw (1966b) was the first to attempt to correlate polyunsaturated fatty acid composition of fungi with their taxonomic classification. The fatty acid spectra obtained for the limited number of the fungi examined at the time indicated that such an attempt was feasible. However, examination of a wide range of fungal species and positive identification of fatty acids with modern techniques forced a great deal of alteration of Shaw's hypothesis. Members of the same group had qualitatively, reasonably similar fatty acid composition, but group differences occurred. Summary data of fatty acid and sterol composition in fungi as related to taxonomic classification are shown in Table XIV.

a. Phycomycetes. Examination of the data in Tables I and II shows that lower Phycomycetes (classes Chytridomycetes and Oomycetes) contain higher levels of long-chain polyenoic fatty acids ($>$C18:3) than do higher Phycomycetes (class Zygomycetes). Furthermore, members of the class Oomycetes produce long-chain polyenoic fatty acids ranging between C16:1 to C20:4 and C22:3. However, some members of the order Entomoph-thorales belonging to the class Zygomycetes are capable of producing greater abundances of polyenoic fatty acids having chain lengths of C20 and C22. Some members have an abundance of C14:0. Almost all other members of the Zygomycetes produce polyunsaturated fatty acids up to chain lengths of C18, and with not more than three double bonds. Fatty acid composition of the spores are very much the same as those of the parent mycelia.

With few exceptions, most of the Phycomycetes produce C18:3 $\Delta^{6,9,12}$ (γ-linolenic acid, or the ω6 isomer), which is the predominant isomer produced by higher animals and a number of plants.

b. Ascomycetes and Deuteromycetes (Fungi Imperfecti). Most species belonging to this group produce C18:3 $\Delta^{9,12,15}$ (α-linolenic acid or ω3 isomer) rather than the ω6 isomer produced by Phycomycetes. However, fatty acids having chain lengths above C18 are not abundant in this group. From the data presented in Tables IV and V, with few exceptions, no apparent significant differences appear in the fatty acid distribution among the different species of this group, i.e., C16:0, C18:1, and C18:2 are the predominant acids. However, true yeasts contain few or no long-chain polyenoic acids, but tend to accumulate monoenoic acids, particularly C16:1. The hydroxy analogs of linoleic and ricinoleic acids have been detected in large amounts in few members of the order Hypocreales (Claviceps sp.). Epoxy acids were also identified in the same order.

c. Basidiomycetes. Members of this group produce the α-linolenic acid rather than the γ-isomer. However, the long-chain polyunsaturated acids are seldom reported for Basidiomycetes. Examination of the data in Tables VII and VIII indicates that there are no apparent characteristics of the fatty acid composition of Basidiomycetes that may establish their chemotaxonomic importance. The considerable variation in the data on fatty acids among the species and for the same species grown under various conditions prevents any meaningful taxonomic conclusion to be drawn.

Table XIV

SUMMARY OF DATA ON FATTY ACID AND STEROL COMPOSITION OF FUNGI ACCORDING TO THEIR TAXONOMIC CLASSIFICATION

Fungal group	Fatty acids[a]	Sterols
Phycomycetes		
Zygomycetes — Entomophthoraceae	C14:0, C16:1, C18:1, C18:2, (ω6)C18:3, C20:4	Cholesterol, campesterol, ergosterol, 22-dihydroergosterol, fungisterol, 24-methyl-$\Delta^{5,7,24(28)}$-cholestatrienol, episterol, fucosterol
Zygomycetes — Other orders	C16:0, no more than C18, (ω6)C18:3, C18:2	
Chytridomycetes	ω3(C18:3, C18:4, C20:5) ω6(C18:3, C20:4)	
Oomycetes	ω3(C20:5, C22:6), ω6(C18:3, C20:4), C20:0, C22:0, C20:3, C22:3	Cholesterol, ergosterol, brassicasterol, stigamasterol
Ascomycetes and Deuteromycetes (Imperfect fungi)		
True yeasts	No polyenoic acids of the methylene interrupted type, C18:2, (ω3)C18:3, C16:1	
Claviceps sp.	Hydroxy and epoxy long-chain acids	
Slime molds	ω6(C20:2, C20:3, C20:4)	
Basidiomycetes	Nonspecific, too much variation; no (ω6)C18:3	Ergosterol, 5-dihydroergosterol, 24-ethyl-$\Delta^{5,7}$-cholestadienol, 24-ethyl-Δ^{7}-cholesterol, Δ^{7}-avenasterol

[a] Almost all fungi tested contained C16:0, C18:1, and C18:2 as major fatty acids.

2. *Sterol Composition*

Reports on sterol composition are too few to allow the formulation of well-defined conclusions concerning the sterol distribution among the various taxonomic groups of fungi. However, a few species representing the major fungal taxa (Phycomycetes, Ascomycetes, and Basidiomycetes) have been carefully examined, and the following generalizations may be justified:

1. Most species produce C28 sterols, ergosterol tending to be present abundantly.

2. Fungisterol is present in most fungi and is associated with large amounts of ergosterol.

3. Sterols with unsaturation in Δ^7-position are predominant in most fungi. However, certain lower classes of Phycomycetes produce C27, C28, and C29 sterols with unsaturation predominantly in Δ^5-position.

4. The rust fungi are unique in that C29 sterols accumulate in their spore oils.

5. Some species in certain groups belonging to the class Oomycetes apparently do not produce sterols.

6. Ergosterol is not produced by either the aquatic Phycomycetes or the rust fungi.

IV. Intracellular Distribution of Lipids

A. PREPARATION OF CELL FRACTIONS

1. *Preparation of Cytoplasmic (Plasma) Membranes*

Methods for the preparation and identification of yeast plasma membranes were reported recently (Schibeci *et al.*, 1973a,b). There are two general procedures: (a) Enzymic digestion of the cell wall, osmotic lysis of the protoplast, and recovery of the plasma membrane by isopycnic centrifugation (Boulton, 1965; Longley *et al.*, 1968; Baraud *et al.*, 1970a; Schibeci *et al.*, 1973a); (b) mechanical disintegration of the cells and recovery of the cell envelope (cell wall plus plasma membrane). Plasma membrane-rich fractions can then be obtained by differential centrifugation either before (Matile, 1970) or after removal of the cell wall by enzymic digestion (Suomalainen and Nurminen, 1973). However, procedure (b) was reported to produce a high degree of contamination due to entrapment of intracellular components (Dube *et al.*, 1973). Ultracentrifugal methods, however, have permitted the isolation of nuclei (Rozijn and Tonino, 1964), vacuoles (Matile and Wiemken, 1967; Indge, 1968; Holley and Kidby, 1973; Van der Wilden *et al.*, 1973), "promitochondria" (Schatz, 1965; Griddle and Schatz, 1969), mitochondria (Accoceberry and Stahl, 1972; Bandlow, 1972; Chappell and Hansford,

1972; Bednarz-Prashad and Mize, 1974), and the inner and outer mitochondrial membrane (Accoceberry and Stahl, 1972; Bandlaw, 1972; Chappell and Hansford, 1972).

2. Preparation of Cell Walls

A cell wall preparation is usually obtained by rupturing the cell (usually mechanically) and removing the intracytoplasmic components and plasma membrane by centrifugation and repeated washing (Kanetsuna et al., 1969; Domer and Hamilton, 1971; Safe and Caldwell, 1975). The possibility of contamination by particles of plasma membrane is usually high and should always be taken into consideration.

B. LIPIDS OF THE CELL WALL

This topic was the subject of a review by Bartnicki-Garcia (1968). Generally, the fungal cell wall is composed of 80–90% polysaccharides with the remainder consisting of lipid and protein. Total cellular lipids and total cell wall lipids of various fungi have been compiled by Weete (1974).

A significant quantity of the cell wall lipid occurs in a bound form and is present in 2- to 3-fold higher levels than the freely extractable lipids. Kidby and Davies (1970) have discussed the biological activity of the cell wall in terms of a proposed structure, but the role of the lipid component has not yet been resolved. However, Shah and Knights (1968) suggested a structural or protective role of lipids against drying out of the cell wall, since morphological distortion was observed when the walls of dermatophytic fungi were extracted with organic solvents. Also, it was proposed that lipids play a role in the pathogenicity of dermatophytes (Peck, 1947), but that role was challenged by Elinor and Zaikina (1963).

Several investigators reported that yeast cell wall lipids are composed mainly of tri- and diacylglycerols with various amounts of free fatty acids, sterols, sterol esters, phospholipids, and sphingolipids (Kanetsuna et al., 1969; Suomalainen, 1969; Bianchi, 1967; Chattaway et al., 1968; Domer and Hamilton, 1971). Exceptionally, the principal components of the cell walls of three filamentous forms of C. albicans were sterols and sterol esters, which comprised 40–60% of the cell wall total lipids (Bianchi, 1967). Phospholipids were the next most abundant group of lipids in these organisms.

C. LIPIDS OF THE PLASMA MEMBRANE

The total lipid contents of fungal plasma membranes range between 30 and 50% of the total weight. Lipids of the plasma membrane and whole cell are qualitatively similar, but differ quantitatively with respect to individual lipid components.

Several investigators analyzed the cytoplasmic membranes of different yeast species (Anderson *et al.*, 1964; Boulton, 1965; Mendoza and Villanueva, 1967; Matile *et al.*, 1967; Longley *et al.*, 1968; Nurminen *et al.*, 1970). Generally, the plasma membrane contained 40% lipid, 50% protein, 6% sterols, and various concentrations of RNA and carbohydrates (glucan and mannan). The principal structure components were phospholipids ranging from 15 to 25% of the membrane and consisting of PC, LPC, PE, PI, and PS. The major fatty acids were C16:0, C16:1, and C18:1. Mono-, di-, and triglycerides, sphingolipids, and glycolipids were also present with various amounts of sterols and sterol esters. Some of these lipids were present in a lipoprotein complex to form the functional membrane structure. It was suggested that a mannan–protein complex existed that played an important role in the budding of yeast and providing an interface between the plasma membrane and the cell wall (Matile *et al.*, 1967).

D. Lipids of Mitochondria

The yeast mitochondrial lipid composition was found to be very similar to that of typical mammalian mitochondria.

The composition of the respiratory particles isolated from *Claviceps purpurea* contained 25.7% lipid and 2.2% ergosterol (Anderson *et al.*, 1964). The phospholipids were PI (28%), PC (27%), PS (13%), PE (18%), and cardiolipin (7%).

The lipid composition of normal mitochondria and promitochondria from yeast grown under different culture conditions were analyzed (Paltauf and Schatz, 1969). The respiratory particles were found to contain similar levels of neutral lipids. However, normal mitochondria contained smaller quantities of phospholipids but 70% more ergosterol than the promitochondrial particles. Significant differences in mitochondrial fatty acids and phospholipids, reviewed recently by Mangnall and Getz (1973) and Rattray *et al.* (1975) are pointed out in the corresponding sections.

V. Extracellular Lipids

Extracellular lipids produced by many fungi, particularly yeast, were the subject of a review by Stodola *et al.* (1967). The qualitative and quantitive nature of the extracellular lipids are influenced considerably by the different growth parameters. Depending on the media composition, these lipids may be found at concentrations up to 1–2 gm/liter and may be present in crystalline form.

The extracellular lipids identified in a large number of yeast strains include polyol fatty acid esters, glycolipids, with hydroxy fatty acids, sugar alcohols, acetylated sphingosines, and acetylated fatty acids (Haskins *et al.*, 1955; Ruinen and Deinema, 1964; Stodola *et al.*, 1967). Acetic acid was often a major product of hydrolysis, suggesting that the hydroxyl groups of the hydroxy acids are acetylated. Two such acids have been identified as extracellular lipid products of a yeast, NRRL YB-2501 (Stodola *et al.*, 1965), and a *Rhodotorula* sp. (Stodola *et al.*, 1967). Both species also produced the triacetate of 8,9,13-trihydroxydocosanoic acid and the keto acid 13-oxo-8,9-diacetoxydocosanoic acid (Vesonder and Stodola, 1969).

Rhodotorula graminis and *R. glutinis* produced extracellular glycolipids containing D-mannitol, D-arabitol, and xylitol esterified to 3-D-hydroxypalmitic and 3-D-hydroxystearic acids, in a molar ratio of 1:1 (Tulloch and Spencer, 1964). The acids were present in molar ratio of about 5–7:1 and were partially acetylated.

An extracellular glycolipid produced by the osmophilic yeast *Torulopsis magnoliae* (*T. apicola*) was found to be composed of the disaccharide (2-*O*-β-D-glucopyranosyl-D-glucopyranose) glycosidically linked to the OH group of 17-L-hydroxyoctadecanoic or 17-L-hydroxyoctadecenoic acids (Gorin *et al.*, 1961). The C_{22} acid, 13-hydroxydocosanoic, was isolated from the extracellular glycolipid products of *Candida bogoriensis* (Stodola *et al.*, 1967).

The crystalline extracellular lipid produced by *Ustilago zeae* PRL 119 was found to be a mixture of glycolipids containing the hydroxy acids 15,16-dihydroxypalmitic or 2,15,16-trihydroxypalmitic acids glycosidically linked to β-D-cellobiopyranoside units (Lemieux, 1951; Lemieux and Giguese, 1951).

VI. Biosynthesis of Lipid Components

A. FATTY ACIDS

1. *Saturated, Straight-Chain Fatty Acids*

The overall equation for fatty acid biosynthesis is known to be:

$$\text{Acetyl-CoA} + n \text{ malonyl-CoA} + 2n \text{ NADPH} + 2n \text{ H}^+ \longrightarrow$$
$$\text{CH}_3(\text{CH}_2-\text{CH}_2)_n - \text{CO} - \text{CoA} + n \text{ CO}_2 + n \text{ CoA} + 2n \text{ NADP} + n \text{ H}_2\text{O} \quad (1)$$

This equation represents a series of sequential reactions (see Fig. 1) responsible for producing fatty acids of various chain lengths (C_{12}–C_{20}) that are present in most living cells. However, the principal product of these reactions is palmitic and stearic acids.

The initial reactang of fatty acid synthesis is the thiol ester of coenzyme A (CoA) and acetate (acetyl-SCoA), which is produced primarily through the decarboxylation of pyruvate in the mitochondria. Fatty acid-synthesizing

1. $CH_3-CO-S-CoA + ACP-SH \rightleftharpoons CH_3-CO-S-ACP + CoA-SH$
   acetyl-SCoA   acetyl-SACP

2. $HOOC-CH_2-CO-S-CoA + ACP-SH \rightleftharpoons HOOC-CH_2-CO-S-ACP + CoA-SH$
   malonyl-SCoA   malonyl-SACP

3. $HOOC-CH_2-CO-S-ACP + CH_3-CO-SACP \rightleftharpoons CH_3-CO-CH_2-CO-SACP$
   malonyl-SACP   acetyl-SACP   acetoacetyl-SACP

4. $CH_3-CO-CH_2-CO-SACP + NADPH + H^+$
   acetoacetyl-SACP

   $\rightleftharpoons CH_3-CHOH-CH_2-CO-SACP + NADP^+$
   D-β-hydroxybutyryl-ACP

5. $CH_3-CHOH-CH_2-CO-S-ACP \rightleftharpoons CH_3-CH=CH-CO-SACP + H_2O$
   D-β-hydroxybutyryl-SACP   crotonyl-SACP

6. $CH_3-CH=CH-CO-SACP + NADPH + H^+ \rightleftharpoons CH_3-CH_2-CH_2-CO-SACP + NADP^+$
   crotonyl-SACP   butyryl-SACP

FIG. 1. Pathway of saturated fatty acid biosynthesis. Enzymes involved in the reactions shown are: (i) acetyl transacylase, (ii) malonyl transacylase, (iii) β-ketoacyl-ACP-synthetase, (iv) β-ketoacyl-ACP reductase, (v) enoyl-ACP hydrase, (vi) enoyl-ACP reductase. ACP, acyl carrier protein.

enzymes are located in the cell cytoplasm. Therefore, acetyl-SCoA must be transferred to the cytoplasm to allow fatty acid synthesis to occur. Mitochondrial membranes, however, are impermeable to acetyl-SCoA and the C_2 unit must be modified for transport across the mitochondrial membrane. This is accomplished in one of three ways: (1) the C_2 moiety of acetyl-SCoA can be transferred to carnitine and the resulting ester transported through the membrane, (2) acetyl-SCoA may be shuttled through the TCA cycle and the citrate or glutarate (via α-ketoglutarate) produced is transported through the membrane, or (3) acetyl-SCoA may be broken down, and the free acetate may cross the mitochondrial membrane. Acetyl-SCoA can then be regenerated from these compounds in the cytoplasm. Two of the enzymes involved in the generation of acetyl-SCoA have been detected: (a) the citric acid cleavage enzyme which catalyzes the reaction

$$\text{Citrate} + ATP + CoASH \rightleftharpoons \text{acetyl-SCoA} + \text{oxaloacetate} + ADP + \qquad (2)$$

and (b) acetic thiokinase (acetyl-SCoA sythetase) which catalyzes the reaction

$$\text{Acetate} + ATP + CoASH \xrightarrow{Mg^{2+}} \text{acetyl-SCoA} + AMP + PP_i \qquad (3)$$

The supernatant of cellular homogenates can be separated into two fractions: one contains the fatty acid-synthesizing enzymes, and the other requires bicarbonate, malonic acid, and biotin for fatty acid synthesis, suggesting a carboxylation reaction in the preparation of the initial substrate (Wakil, 1958). Acetyl-CoA carboxylase has been isolated from yeast (Matsuhashi, 1969) that catalyzes the transcarboxylation of acetyl-SCoA to give rise to malonyl-SCoA. This is a biotin-containing enzyme, which is first carboxylated in an ATP-dependent reaction followed by the transcarboxylation of acetyl-CoA to malonyl-CoA (Lynen, 1967) as follows:

$$CO_2 + \text{biotin} - \text{Enz} + \text{ATP} \rightleftharpoons CO_2 - \text{biotin} - \text{Enz} + \text{ADP} + H_3PO_4$$

$$\overset{\text{acetyl-CoA carboxylase}}{CO_2 - \text{biotin} - \text{Enz} + \text{acetyl} - \text{CoA} \rightleftharpoons \text{biotin} - \text{Enz} + \text{malonyl} - \text{CoA}} \quad (4)$$

The reactions of fatty acid biosynthesis, as they are catalyzed by individual soluble enzymes isolated from *Escherichia coli*, were described by Vagelos *et al.* (1969) and are outlined in Fig. 1. The essential features of this mechanism had, however, been originally postulated by Lynen (1961) on the basis of experiments with the fatty acid synthetase system of yeast. The substrates, intermediates, and products in fatty acid biosynthesis are acyl-ACP (acyl carrier protein) derivatives (Fig. 1). Thus the initial reactions in fatty acid synthesis consist of the transfer of acetate and malonate from their CoA to ACP coenzyme carriers [Eqs. (i) and (ii), Fig. 1]. Acetyl-ACP and Malonyl-ACP condense to form acetoacetyl-ACP, which is then reduced to butyryl-ACP [Eqs. (iii) and (iv), Fig. 1]. Butyryl-ACP can then condense with a second molecule of malonyl-ACP, and the series of condensation and reduction reactions [Eqs. (iii) to (vi), Fig. 1] continues until a long-chain fatty acid results (Fig. 1).

Malonate supplies all the carbon atoms of the long-chain fatty acid with the exception of the two methyl-terminal carbons, which are derived from acetate (Lynen, 1961). The use of acetate as the primer results exclusively in the formation of even-chain fatty acids (Lynen, 1961) (Fig. 1). Substitution of propionate for acetate as primer results in the formation of odd-chain fatty acids. Supplementing the growth medium with isobutyrate, leucine, valine, or isoleucine produces iso and anteiso branched-chain fatty acids (Baraud *et al.* 1970b).

ACP was originally isolated from *E. coli* as a heat-stable protein with a 4'-phosphopantetheine as a prosthetic group. ACP has not been separated or purified from fungi although protein containing 4'-phosphopantetheine and with properties generally similar to those of *E. coli* ACP has been shown to be present in yeast (Wells *et al.*, 1966; Lynen *et al.*, 1968).

The reactions of the fatty acid synthetase system that produces long-chain fatty acids via the serial condensation of malonyl-ACP units appear to constitute the universal and exclusive mechanism for the *de novo* synthesis of long-chain fatty acids in microorganisms. In *Saccharomyces cerevisiae*, the fatty acid synthesizing enzymes are found in a highly organized particle that (1) is distinct from ribosomes, (2) can be sedimented by centrifugation, and (3) is nonmembranous (Klein *et al.*, 1967a,b,c). Lynen and his co-workers (1968; Lynen, 1961) have isolated this particulate system from yeast and studied its organization and operation. They found that it is a multienzyme complex consisting of one of each of the synthetase enzymes, which are grouped around a central SH-containing "core" protein, this core was identified as the yeast ACP (Lynen *et al.*, 1968). Under the electron microscope, it appears as an oval particle with a longitudinal diameter of 250 Å and a cross diameter of 210 Å. Molecular weight, calculated on the basis of β-alanine content, was 16,000.

Sumper and Lynen (1972) reported that yeast fatty acid synthetase (FAS) reversibly dissociates into subunits of 250,000 molecular weight (MW). Schweizer *et al.* (1973) reported that the yeast synthetase consisted of two nonidentical subunits of MW 179,000 and 185,000. They further suggested that the FAS of animal and yeast origin were aggregates of enzymes and ACP held together by noncovalent interactions. On the other hand, studies by Stoops *et al.* (1975) on chicken and rat livers and on yeast FAS indicated that the subunits consisted of a single polypeptide chain of MW 185,000–200,000 containing the 4'-phosphopantetheine group and binds acetyl and malonyl groups. The size (about 200,000 daltons) of the subunit comprising the yeast FAS seems to be essentially the same as reported from different laboratories. However, Stoops *et al.* (1975) observed that, when the FAS was treated with denaturing agents (sodium dodecyl sulfate or guanidine HCl), it produced many peptide fractions; this led them to suspect a proteolytic effect on the synthetase. Inactivation of the protease resulted into the possibility of dissociating the FAS into two identical polypeptide chains of equal molecular weight. The polypeptide contained the 4'-phosphopantetheine group and was capable of binding acetyl and malonyl groups. These observations indicate that in the FAS complex, ACP and the multicatalytic activities of the fatty acid biosynthesizing enzymes are associated only with the two polypeptide chains suggesting a novel structural organization for multienzyme complexes. The exposure of the FAS to proteolysis may explain the presence of many proteins reported to be present in attempts to purify yeast or animal ACP and the isolation of a pantetheine-containing polypeptide of MW 10,000–16,000 (Lynen, 1961, 1967; Willecke *et al.*, 1969; Schweizer *et al.*, 1970; Yang *et al.*, 1967; Qureshi *et al.*, 1974; Roncari, 1974).

2. *Chain Elongation*

Palmitic and stearic acids are usually the product of the fatty acid synthetase system studied in fungi. Labeled palmitic acid supplied to the growth media of yeasts was found to be incorporated into longer-chain fatty acids without extensive breakdown suggesting the presence of a chain elongation system in yeast (Erwin *et al.*, 1964; Korn *et al.*, 1965; Meyer and Holtz,

1966). Fulco (1967) reported that the yeasts *Saccharomyces cerevisiae* and *Candida utilis* can chain-elongate arachidic acid to docosahexanoic and 2-hydroxyeicosanoic acids, but the nature of the enzymes involved is unknown. Orme *et al.* (1972) showed that a mutant of *S. cerevisiae* deficient in fatty acid synthetase was capable of elongating dietary fatty acid (C13 to C17) by two carbon units or more. The extent of elongation was dependent on the fatty acid chain length added to the growth medium, and no acids greater than C18 were produced.

Two types of enzyme systems have been isolated that chain-elongate pre-existing fatty acids by addition of two carbon units. One system was found in the mitochondria of animals (Wakil, 1961; Fulco and Mead, 1961; Harlan and Wakil, 1964; Levis and Mead, 1964) and plants (Martin and Stumpf, 1959; Barron *et al.*, 1961; Hitchcock and James, 1964) that utilized acetyl-CoA but not malonyl-CoA as the source of C2 units. The second system was found in the microsomal fraction of animal cells and employs malonyl-CoA as the source of C2 units and produces CoA-bound intermediates (Nugleren, 1965; Schiller and Bensch, 1971). Studies on the chain-elongation enzymes in fungi are very limited, and no system has been isolated or specifically identified.

3. *Monounsaturated*

The biosynthetic reactions involved in formation of unsaturated fatty acids have been elucidated largely through the investigations of Bloch and co-workers; the subject has been thoroughly reviewed by Wakil (1962), Kates (1964, 1966), Vagelos (1964), Mead (1960, 1961, 1963), Bloch *et al.* (1961), O'Leary (1962), Hofmann (1963), Erwin (1973), Weete (1974), and Gurr (1974). The discussion here will be limited to the biosynthesis of monounsaturated fatty acids only in fungi, with very brief reference to other biological systems where pertinent.

Two separate mechanisms are known for the biosynthesis of unsaturated fatty acids, one is a direct desaturation of corresponding saturated acids requiring both oxygen and NADH or HADPH, the other an anaerobic system restricted to bacteria involves chain elongation of shorter-chain unsaturated fatty acids.

a. Aerobic Pathway. Monounsaturated acids could be formed by desaturation of corresponding saturated acids. The desaturase system, which appeared to be an aggregate of enzymes associated with the microsomal fraction of the cell, required both molecular oxygen and NADPH and acted only on the CoA derivatives of the fatty acids (Bloomfield and Bloch, 1960; Yuan and Bloch, 1961; Meyer and Bloch, 1963). Direct demonstration of this reaction was reported by Bloomfield and Bloch (1960), who showed that the particulate fraction from *S. cerevisiae* converted C16:0 to *cis*-C16:1-

Δ^9 and C18:0 to *cis*-C18:1-Δ^9 via their CoA derivatives, according to Eqs. (5) and (6). A similar type of desaturase system was found in yeast (Schultz and Lynen, 1971), *Neurospora crassa* (Bennett and Quackenbush, 1969) and in *Penicillium chrysogenium* (Howling *et al.*, 1972).

$$CH_3(CH_2)_{14}-CO-SCoA \xrightarrow{O_2, NADPH} CH_3(CH_2)_5=CH(CH_2)_7-CO-SCoA \quad (5)$$
$$\text{(palmitic)} \qquad\qquad\qquad \text{(palmitoleic)}$$

$$CH_3(CH)^1_6-CO-CoA \xrightarrow{O_2, NADPH} CH_3(CH_2)_7CH=CH(CH_2)_7-CO-SCoA \quad (6)$$
$$\text{(stearic)} \qquad\qquad\qquad \text{(oleic)}$$

The desaturases are specific for introducing a Δ^9 double bond regardless of the chain length of the fatty acid-CoA substrate. This specificity may arise from binding of the enzyme at the activated carboxyl end of the substrate, thus allowing the 9- and 10-methylene groups to be properly positioned at the active center (Howling *et al.*, 1972; Brett *et al.*, 1971). However, Schultz and Lynen (1971), suggested that the formation of a certain monoene is governed not by the desaturase, but by the specificity of the enzyme(s) that provides the thiol ester substrates.

Reports by Gurr *et al.* (1969) and Baker and Lynen (1971) have suggested a specific dehydrogenation of phospholipid-bound oleic acid to linoleate. Talamo *et al.* (1973) and Pugh and Kates (1973) demonstrated desaturation of phospholipid-linked oleic acid with cell-free microsomal systems from yeasts. Similarly, ethanolamine plasmalogen was shown by Wykle *et al.* (1972) and Paltauf and Holasek (1973) to be synthesized by dehydrogenation of the corresponding 1-0-alkyl-2-acyl-glycerophosphorylethanolamine. Although Pugh and Kates (1975) reported few studies on the characterization of the microsomal-bound phospholipid desaturase system in *Candida lipolytica*, several properties of this desaturase system remained to be determined.

The fact that the desaturase system was not sensitive to cyanide and that methylene blue could not replace molecular oxygen suggested the participation of an oxygenase reaction. The desaturase was visualized as proceeding by way of a hydroxyacid (either the 9- or 10-hydroxy derivative), the dehydration of which would yield the desired unsaturated acid (Bloch *et al.*, 1961; Bloomfield and Bloch, 1960). Although 9- or 10-hydroxy-C18:0 could fully substitute for oleic acid as a growth factor for anaerobically grown yeast, neither of the hydroxy acids was later found to be an intermediate in the biosynthesis of oleic acid (Bloch *et al.*, 1961; Light *et al.*, 1962). The hydroxystearic acids apparently are converted to ethyl esters of the acylated acids by the anaerobically grown cells (Keeney *et al.*, 1962).

Marsh and James (1962) demonstrated the formation of hydroxystearate from stearate by yeast. Keto acids (Keeney *et al.*, 1962; Bloch, 1963), the phosphate ester of 10-hydroxystearate (Bloch *et al.*, 1961), 9,10-dihydroxy-stearate, (Bloch, 1963) 9,10-*cis*-epoxystearate (Bloch, 1963), and stearolic acid (Meyer and Bloch, 1963) have been suggested as possible intermediates in the biosynthesis of monounsaturated fatty acids but were shown not to be converted to oleic acid.

Light *et al.* (1962) suggested an alternative mechanism for the desaturase system that involved a direct abstraction of a hydrogen from each of carbon atoms 9 and 10 in palmitic or stearic acids, with oxygen serving as the electron acceptor without entering into covalent linkage with a carbon atom of the acid. Schroepfer and Bloch (1964) showed that the desaturating enzyme system from *Corynebacterium diphtheriae* stereo specifically removes one particular hydrogen atom, having the D configuration, from each pair of hydrogens at carbon atoms 9 and 10 during conversion of C18:0 to C18:1 Δ^9, and the hydrogen removal at C-9 probably precedes that at C-10. Clarification of the intermediate reactions and the roles played by oxygen, NADH and NADPH must await purification of individual enzymes, attempts at which have so far been unsuccessful (Light *et al.*, 1962).

b. Anaerobic Pathway. This pathway for the formation of monounsaturated fatty acids, which appears to be restricted to bacteria of the orders Eubacteriales and Pseudomonadales, has not been detected in fungi and has been the subject of several extensive reviews (Bloch *et al.*, 1961; Hofmann, 1963; Kates, 1964, 1966; Erwin, 1973; Weete, 1974). In this pathway, the biosynthesis of monounsaturated fatty acids occurs by chain elongation of existing short-chain unsaturated fatty acid precursors. Saturated fatty acid formation proceeds as usual until the C16 level is reached. At this point, the enzyme, β-hydroxydecanoyl thioester dehydrase acts upon hydroxydecanoyl-ACP (dehydration and double-bond isomerization) to produce *cis*-Δ^3-decenoyl-ACP and *trans*-Δ^2-decenoyl-ACP.. The trans isomer undergoes chain elongation to the preferred saturated product. On the other hand, the cis isomer has the wrong configuration for reduction by enoyl-ACP reductase; therefore it continues in the elongation reactions as an unsaturated intermediate and remains bound to the ACP of the synthetase. This pathway offers an explanation for the existance of Δ^7, Δ^9, and Δ^{11} unsaturated acids detected in bacteria.

4. Polyunsaturated Fatty Acids

Polyunsaturated fatty acid biosynthesis was studied in *Candida utilis* (Yuan and Bloch, 1961) and *Penicillium chrysogenum* (Bennett and Quackenbush, 1969) and was found to proceed via sequential desaturations of C18:1 Δ^9 and chain elongation. The polyunsaturated fatty acids produced have the all-cis configuration and are of the methylene-interrupted type, which falls into three families—$\omega 3$, $\omega 6$, and $\omega 9$—classified according to the number of methylene groups between the terminal methyl group and the first double bond toward the carboxyl end.

The $\omega 3$ type of desaturation usually produces linoleic and α-linolenic acids from oleate by introducing double bonds at C-12, C-13, and C-15, C-16, as follows:

$$18:1\omega 9 \xrightarrow{\text{O}_2} 18:2\omega 6 \longrightarrow 18:3\omega 3 \tag{7}$$

or it could be expressed as

$$\text{C18:1 } \Delta^9 \xrightarrow{\text{O}_2} \text{C18:2 } \Delta^{9,12} \xrightarrow{\text{O}_2} \text{C18:3 } \Delta^{9,12,15}$$
$$\text{oleate} \qquad\qquad\qquad\qquad \alpha\text{-linolenate}$$

α-Linolenate may accumulate in some organisms or it may undergo carboxyl desaturation coupled with chain elongation as follows:

$$
\begin{array}{c}
\qquad\qquad \xrightarrow{\text{O}_2} \;\; 18:3\omega 3 \;\; \xrightarrow{\text{C}_2} \\
18:4\omega 3 \longleftarrow \qquad\qquad\qquad\qquad \longrightarrow 20:3\omega 3 \\
\qquad\qquad\qquad\qquad\qquad\qquad\qquad\qquad \downarrow \text{O}_2 \\
22:6\omega 3 \xleftarrow{\text{O}_2} 22:5\omega 3 \xleftarrow{\text{C}_2} 20:5\omega 3 \xleftarrow{\text{O}_2} 20:4\omega 3
\end{array}
\tag{8}
$$

The $\omega 6$ type of polyunsaturated fatty acids are synthesized from linoleic acid via chain elongation and desaturation. However, here all double bonds are introduced exclusively toward the carboxyl end of the molecule, as follows:

$$
\begin{array}{c}
\qquad\qquad 20:2\omega 6 \\
\qquad\qquad \text{C}_2 \uparrow \quad \searrow \text{O}_2 \\
18:1\omega 9 \xrightarrow{\text{O}_2} 18:2\omega 6 \qquad 20:3\omega 6 \xrightarrow{\text{O}_2} 20:4\omega 6 \\
\text{(C18:}\Delta^9\text{)} \quad \text{(C18:2 } \Delta^{9,12}\text{)} \qquad\qquad\qquad \text{C20:4 } \Delta^{5,8,11,14} \\
\qquad \downarrow \text{O}_2 \quad \nearrow \text{C}_2 \qquad\qquad\qquad \text{arachidonic acid} \\
\qquad\quad 18:3\omega 6 \qquad\qquad\qquad\qquad \downarrow \\
\text{(C18:3 } \Delta^{6,9,12}\text{)} \qquad\qquad\qquad\qquad 22:4\omega 6 \\
\qquad\qquad\qquad\qquad\qquad\qquad\qquad\qquad\qquad \downarrow \text{O}_2 \\
\text{(}\gamma\text{-linolenic acid)} \quad 22:5\text{W6} \longleftarrow
\end{array}
\tag{9}
$$

Arachidonic acid, usually encountered in fungi, may be produced via either of two routes: desaturation of linoleic acid (C18:2 $\Delta^{9,12}$) to γ-linolenic (C18:3 $\Delta^{6,9,12}$) followed by chain elongation; or alternatively, chain elongation of linoleic acid to $20:2\omega 6$ followed by carboxyl-directed desaturation. The first pathway is predominant in animals and certain algae. The second route is the major one in the slime mold *Physarum polycephalum* (Korn *et al.*, 1965) and certain protozoa (Erwin, 1973).

The $\omega 9$ family of polyunsaturated fatty acids are produced by vertebrates. Most organisms specialized for carboxyl-directed desaturation retain the ability to produce linoleic acid from oleic acid. When this ability is lacking, as in vertebrates, linoleic acid becomes a dietary requirement. In the absence of linoleic acid from the diet, vertebrates carry out a carboxyl-directed desaturation sequence that starts with oleic acid and produces an $\omega 9$ polyenoic acid as follows: hydroxyl, epoxy, aldehyde, . . . , etc. The biosynthetic pathway of acetylenic acids is not well established and will not be covered here. The reader is referred to articles by Bu'lock (1966) and Turner (1971) for discussion and review of the subject.

5. *Hydroxy Acids*

The hydroxy fatty acids present in fungal lipids include 12-OH-C18:1, 17-OH-C16:0, 17-OH-C18:0, 2-OH-C16:0, and most important, D-12-hydroxy-Δ^9-octadecenoic acid (ricinoleic acid). The biosynthestic pathway for ricinoleic acid has been reviewed by Morris (1970). In fungi, ricinoleic acid is biosynthesized by direct hydration of linoleic acid according to Eq. 10.

$$CH_3(CH_2)_4CH{=}CH{-}CH_2{-}CH{=}CH{-}(CH_2)_7{-}COOH \xrightarrow{\text{hydration}}$$
linoleic acid

$$CH_3{-}(CH_2)_4{-}\overset{\displaystyle \overset{OH}{\diagdown}}{\underset{\displaystyle |}{\underset{\displaystyle H}{C}}}H{-}CH{-}CH_2{-}CH{=}CH{-}(CH_2)_7{-}COOH \qquad (10)$$
ricinoleic acid

Ricinoleic acid usually occurs as glycerol esters, and the -OH group is further esterified to a long-chain fatty acid (estolides). It was suggested that linoleic acid was not simply hydrated to ricinoleic acid, but instead, long-chain fatty acids are gound directly across the double bond of linoleic acid, producing the estolide structure (Morris, 1970).

Other hydroxy fatty acids are the 17-L-OH-C18 acids that occur as glycosides bound in extracellular glycolipids. In *Torulopsis* sp., the hydroxy acid is bound glycosidically to the disaccharide sophorose. In the biosynthesis of the glycolipid, the hydroxy acids are formed first and then are linked to sophorose. Heinz *et al.* (1970) showed that L-17-OH-C18:0 is formed by the direct hydroxylation of stearate without the formation of an unsaturated intermediate, and molecular oxygen and NADPH are cofactors.

2-Hydroxy fatty acids are known to occur as amides of phytosphingosine in yeasts and other fungi (Stanacev and Kates, 1963). However, little is known about the biosynthesis of these acids in fungi, and the subject was reviewed recently by Morris (1970). Fulco (1967) reported that an enzyme from *Candida utilis* cell-free preparation can convert hexacosanoic acid (C26) to 2-OH-C26. The hydroxylation process is associated with the α-decarboxylation pathway in this yeast.

3-Hydroxy acids are present in yeasts as their D isomers and usually occur as ester-bound or glycoside-bound extracellular lipids (Kates, 1964, 1966).

D-3-OH-C16 and -C18 acids are present as mannitol or pentitol esters in *Rhodotorula* sp. (Tulloch and Spencer, 1964). D-3-OH acids are synthesized as intermediates in the biosynthesis of saturated fatty acids by the malonyl-CoA pathway, but apparently remain enzyme bound and do not accumulate. A separate system for their synthesis and transformation into glycolipids thus probably exists, but no hard evidence is available on this point. A cell-free enzyme preparation from *D. discoideum* was shown to effect the conversion of C14, C16, and C18 fatty acyl-CoA to the corresponding 3-hydroxy acids by hydration of the intermediate *trans*-2-enoic acids (Davidoff and Korn, 1964) as shown in Eq. (11).

$$R\text{—}CH_2CH_2CO\text{—}SCoA \longrightarrow$$

$$\underset{\overset{|}{H}}{R\text{—}C}{=}\underset{\overset{|}{H}}{C}\text{—}CO\text{—}SCoA \rightleftharpoons R\text{—}\underset{\overset{|}{H}}{CH}\text{—}CH_2\text{—}CO\text{—}SCoA \qquad (11)$$

The 3-hydroxy acids accumulate in this *in vitro* system. However, *in vivo*, other enzymes dehydrate the 3-hydroxy acids back to the *trans*-2-enoic acids and further to *cis*- and *trans*-3-enoic acids, which are then further metabolized (Davidoff and Korn, 1964).

6. Epoxy Acids

cis-9,10-Epoxystearic acid is a major fatty acid of *Puciinia graminis* and has the L configuration. There is no hard evidence indicating the precise route for the biosynthesis of epoxy fatty acids in fungi. However, based on the results of the incorporation of stearate and oleate (Knoche, 1971; Powell *et al.*, 1967), the following pathway starting from stearic acid produced from the fatty acid synthetase is proposed for the biosynthesis of *cis*-9,10-epoxy-stearic acid:

$$\underset{\text{Stearic acid}}{CH_3(CH_2)_{16}COOH} \xrightarrow{\text{desaturation}} \underset{\text{Oleic acid}}{CH_3(CH_2)_7CH{=}CH(CH_2)_7COOH}$$

$$\underset{\textit{cis}\text{-9,10-Epoxystearic acid}}{CH_3(CH_2)_7\text{—}\overset{\displaystyle O}{\overset{\displaystyle /\,\backslash}{CH\text{—}CH}}(CH_2)_7COOH} \qquad \underset{\substack{\downarrow \\ \text{Epoxy lipids}}}{\text{Oleyl lipids}}$$

The immediate substrate for the enzyme synthesizing the epoxy acid is uncertain. However, over 95% of the epoxide is located in the triglyceride and phospholipid fractions of the fungus. It has, therefore, been proposed that the substrate for the epoxide-forming enzymes may be the complex acyl lipids rather than the free or thiol ester acids.

B. Biosynthesis of Complex Lipids

1. *Phospholipids*

Biosynthesis of phospholipids in plants, animals, and microorganisms including yeast has been extensively reviewed (Kates, 1966; Rossiter, 1968; Lennarz, 1970; Hunter and Rose, 1971; Mangnall and Getz, 1973; Kates and Marshall, 1975), but little attention has been given to the formation of phospholipids in fungi other than yeast (Hunter and Rose, 1971). The pathways for the biosynthesis of phospholipids in fungi, mainly yeasts, are summarized in Fig. 2.

Phosphatidic acid (PA) is shown to be formed by the specific acylation of *sn*-glycero-3-phosphate (White and Hawthorne, 1970; Steiner and Lester, 1972). PA in the form of its nucleotide derivative cytidine diphosphate diglyceride (CDP-diglyceride) appears to be the key intermediate for the biosynthesis of phospholipids (Steiner and Lester, 1972; Hutchinson and Cranan, 1968). However, phosphatidylethanolamine (PE) (Steiner and Lester,

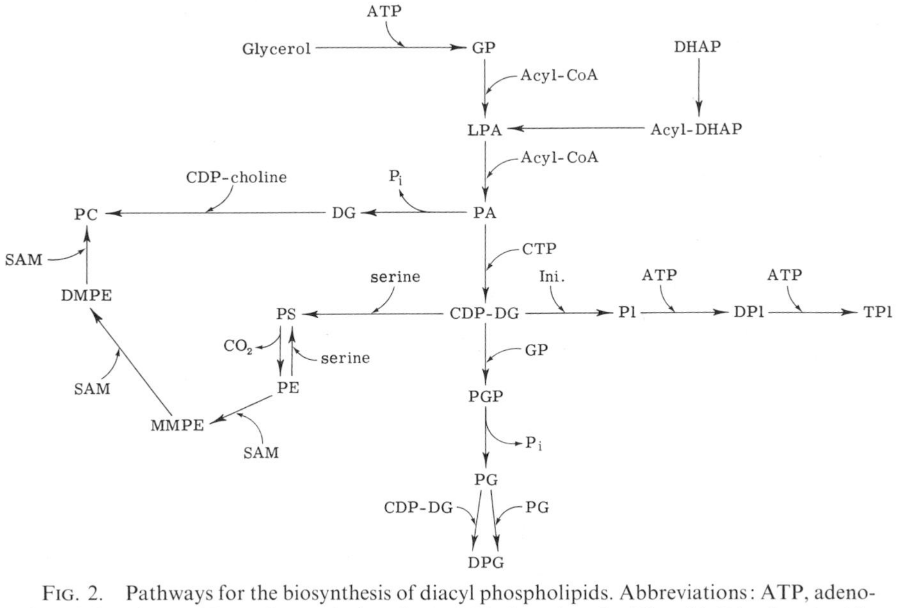

FIG. 2. Pathways for the biosynthesis of diacyl phospholipids. Abbreviations: ATP, adenosine triphosphate; GP, *sn*-glycero-3-phosphate; LPA, lysophosphatidic acid; PA, phosphatidic acid; DHAP, dihydroxyacetone phosphate; Acyl-DHAP, acyl dihydroxyacetone phosphate; CTP, cytidine triphosphate; CDP-DG, cytidine diphosphate diglyceride; Ini, inositol; PI, phosphatidylinositol; DPI, diphosphoinositide; TPI, triphosphoinositide; PS, phosphatidylserine; PE, phosphatidylethanolamine; PC, phosphatidylcholine; MMPE, monomethyl-PE; DMPE, dimethyl-PE; SAM, *S*-adenosylmethionine; DG, diglyceride; PGP, phosphatidylglycerol phosphate; PG, phosphatidylglycerol; DPG, diphosphatidylglycerol (cardiolipin); P, inorganic phosphate.

1972) and phosphatidylcholine (PC) (Wagner *et al.*, 1969, Waechter and Lester, 1971) were shown also to be synthesized through reactions with 1,2-diacylglycerol and either CDP-ethanolamine or CDP-choline, respectively. An alternative pathway for PC formation is the stepwise methylation of PE, monomethyl-PE and dimethyl-PE, but the process is depressed in the presence of PC (Wagner *et al.*, 1969). An alternative pathway for PE synthesis is through the decarboxylation of phosphatidylserine (PS) (Steiner and Lester, 1972). Serine or inositol react with CDP-diglyceride to form PS or phosphatidylinositol (PI), respectively. However, an alternative but undefined mechanism has been considered to be of major importance for PI information in *S. pombe* (Hutchison and Cronan, 1968). Synthesis of diphosphatidylglycerol (cardiolipin, DPG) in *S. cerevisiae* has been found (Cobon *et al.*, 1974) to involve reaction of CDP-diglyceride and phosphatidyl-glycerol (PG), although Stanacev *et al.* (1973) suggested other possible routes for polyglycero-phospholipid synthesis. PG may be synthesized by the condensation of CDP-diglyceride and *sn*-glycero-3-phosphate and dephos-phorylation of the produced phosphatidylglycerol phosphate (PGP). This reaction has not been demonstrated in fungi. An interconversion (via CDP-diglyceride) between PI and PS (PE also by implication) has been demon-strated by Steiner and Lester (1972).

Cobon *et al.* (1974) have shown that yeast microsomal fractions contain the two general pathways for PC synthesis and the systems for the formation of PA, PS, and PI. The systems for the biosynthesis of DPG, PE, and PG are restricted to the mitochondria. The PI conversion to diphosphatidylino-sitol (DPI) catalyzed by the enzyme PI-kinase may be associated with the plasma membrane (Wheeler *et al.*, 1970).

2. Glycolipids

There is very little known about the distribution or biosynthesis of glyco-lipids in fungi. The pathway for mono- and digalactosyl diglyceride formation was investigated in plants by Mudd *et al.*, (1969), Ongun and Mudd (1970), and Mudd and Garcia (1975) and found to proceed according to Eqs. (12) and (13).

$$\text{1, 2-diacylglycerol} + \text{UDP-galactose} \xrightarrow{\text{UDP}} \text{MGDG (monogalact-osyldiglyceride)} \quad (12)$$

$$\text{MGDG} \xrightarrow{\text{UDP-galactose}} \text{DGDG (digalactosyldiglyceride)} \quad (13)$$

The initial reaction involves the transfer of a galactose from UDP-galactose to a 1,2-diglyceride to form MGDG. DGDG is produced by a subsequent transfer of another galactose molecule to MGDG. MGDG is produced at a slower rate than DGNG, and each reaction appears to be catalyzed by a different enzyme.

3. *Sphingolipids*

The biosynthesis of spingolipids has been intensely investigated and was the subject of several recent reviews (Carter *et al.*, 1965; Stoffel, 1971, 1973; Morell and Braun, 1972).

Using the microsomal fraction of a cell-free preparation from *Hansenula ciferrii*, Braun and Snell (1967, 1968), demonstrated the formation of *erythro*-sphingosine and *erythro*-dihydrosphingosine from palmityl-CoA and serine in the presence of NADPH and pyridoxal phosphate. In the absence of NADPH, 3-ketodihydrosphingosine and 3-ketosphingosine accumulate, suggesting that the 3-keto compounds are intermediates formed by a condensation reaction shown to be separate from the NADPH-requiring reduction reaction (Stoffel, 1973). This reaction occurs via a displacement of CO_2 by palmityl-CoA from pyridoxal phosphate and serine, and does not require NADPH. The next reaction is the stereospecific reduction of the 3-keto intermediate to the D-*erythro* isomer in presence of NADPH (Braun and Snell, 1968; Snell *et al.*, 1970).

DiMari *et al.* (1971) demonstrated that (a) 3-ketodihydrosphingosine is converted exclusively by *H. ciferrii* cell-free preparation to dihydrosphingosine; (b) the condensing enzyme does not differentiate between palmityl-CoA and *trans*-2-hexadecenoyl-CoA; and (c) palmitic acid is converted to *trans*-2-hexadecenoic acid by the cell-free preparation enzyme. These results suggest that saturated and unsaturated sphingosines are formed via different pathways controlled or regulated at a point prior to reduction of the carbonyl intermediates in the formation of the 3-keto compounds.

The exact mechanism of phytosphingosine (4-hydroxysphinganine) biosynthesis is not completely elucidated. Green *et al.* (1965) demonstrated the incorporation of [3-^{14}C]serine and [^{3}H]palmitic acid into tetraacetyl-4-D-hydroxysphinganine by *H. ciferrii*. In the same yeast, dihydrosphingosine was reported to be converted to phytosphingosine by two different routes (Weiss and Stiller, 1967; Stoffel *et al.*, 1968). Stoffel *et al.* (1968) reported that phytosphingosine is formed by the loss of a hydrogen at C-3 of dihydrosphingosine to form the corresponding ketone, which is hydroxylated at C-4 and then reduced to the trihydroxy base. Weiss and Stiller (1967), on the other hand, concluded that phytosphingosine produced from [4,5-^{3}H]dihydrosphingosine was converted intact to its trihydroxy isomer by the same organisms, which contradicts Stoffel's findings. The exact biosynthetic mechanism for phytosphingosine remains uncertain.

4. *Cerebrosides*

Studies on the biosynthesis of ceramides and cerebrosides in animal systems have been reviewed recently by Morell and Braun (1972). Cerebrosides are biosynthesized by the addition of a monosaccharide either to a ceramide or to a long-chain base followed by N-acylation. In either case, ceramide must be produced first before the addition of the sugar to form a cerebroside. This is achieved by the condensation of a long-chain base and acyl-CoA catalyzed by the enzyme acyl-CoA long-chain base acyltransferase (Morell and Radin, 1970). The same authors assumed that hydroxy fatty acid-containing ceramides are formed in a similar manner. They also presented some evidence for the existence of two enzyme systems for the formation of hydroxy and nonhydroxy fatty acid-containing ceramides.

The carbohydrate donor for cereboside formation is glycosyl-UDP. Both reactions leading to the cerebroside synthesis can be summarized by Eqs. (14) and (15):

$$\text{Long-chain base } + \text{ glycosyl-UDP} \rightarrow \text{psychosine } + \text{ UDP}$$
$$\text{glycosylceramide } + \text{ CoA} \xleftarrow{\quad \text{acyl-CoA} \quad} \qquad (14)$$

$$\text{Ceramide } + \text{ glycosyl-UDP} \rightarrow \text{glycosylceramide } + \text{ UDP} \qquad (15)$$

Galactose and glucose are the sugars most often encountered as part of the cerebroside structure.

Mycoglycolipids and more complex ceramide oligoglycosides are probably formed by the stepwise transfer of sugar molecules to preformed ceramide mono-, di-, or oligoglycosides. These reactions were not demonstrated in fungi, but have been shown to occur in brain preparations (Hay and Gray, 1970; Handa and Burton, 1969).

Sphingomyelin was not detected in fungi, and its synthesis will not be covered here. However, for a review on the subject in mammalian systems, see Morell and Braun (1972).

5. Sterols

The first key intermediate in sterol biosynthesis is mevalonic acid whose biosynthesis from acetate is well established and appears to involve the same intermediates in animal, plant, and fungal systems (Folkers *et al.*, 1959). The overall pathway from acetate to mavalonate to squalene and the first cyclized product, lanosterol, is shown in Fig. 3.

Mevalonic acid biosynthesis involves the condensation of acetyl-SCoA (I) and malonyl-SCoA (II) to form acetoacetyl-SCoA (III) which can be incorporated into fatty acids (see Section VI,A1) or 3-hydroxymethylglutaryl-SCoA (IV). Mevalonic acid (V) results from reduction of the carbonyl group of hydroxy methylglutaryl-CoA and the release of the reduced compound from the enzyme (Fig. 3) (Brodie *et al.*, 1963; Clayton, 1965).

Squalene formation involves phosphorylation of mevalonic acid to mevalonic acid 5-phosphate by the enzyme mevalonic kinase, followed by a second phosphorylation to produce the corresponding pyrophosphate in

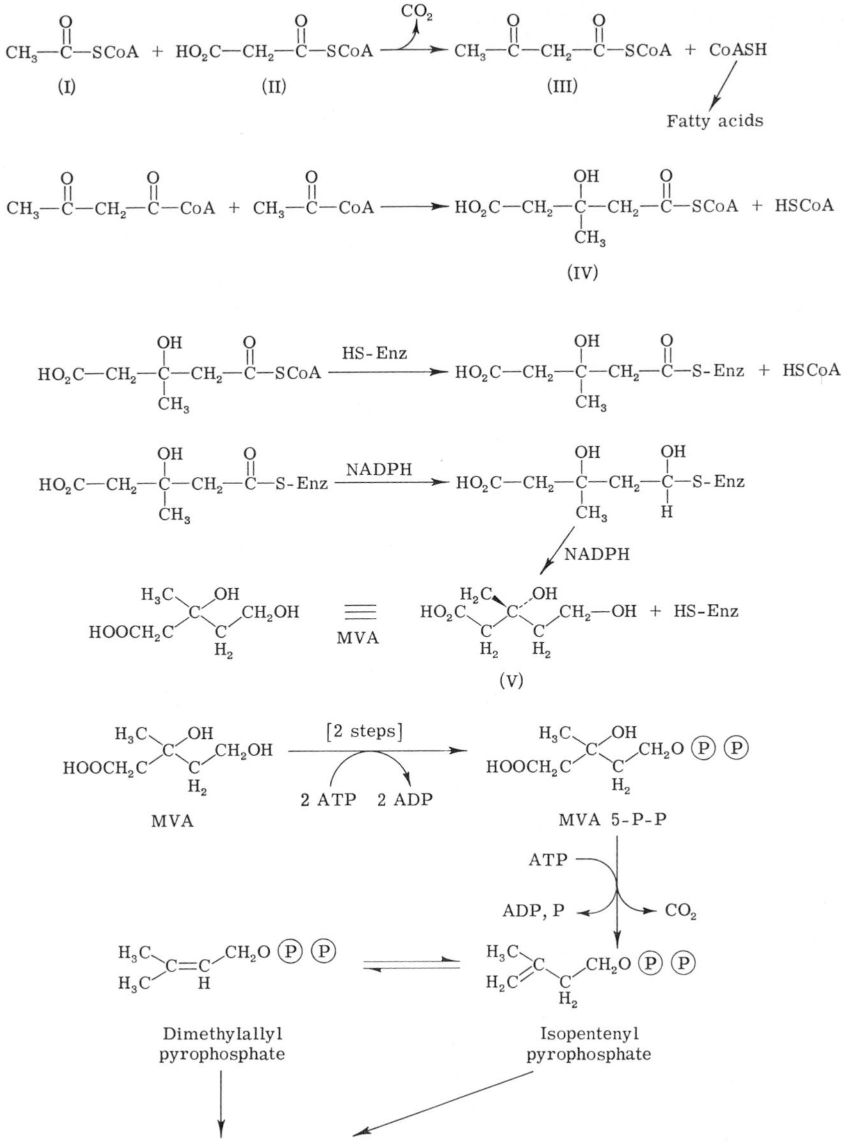

FIG. 3.   Caption on following page.

presence of ATP and Mn^{2+}. Isopentenyl pyrophosphate is formed by a trans decarboxylation and elimination of the 3-hydroxyl group (Fig. 3).

Isopentenyl pyrophosphate is isomerized to dimethylallyl pyrophosphate by the enzyme isopentenyl pyrophosphate isomerase. This is a reversible reaction and Agranoff *et al.* (1960) showed that the equilibrium ratio is about 1:9. Isopentenyl pryophosphate condenses with dimethylallyl pyrophosphate to form geranyl pyrophosphate (Fig. 3). This condensation involves the addition of an allylic group to the C-4 of isopentenyl pyrophosphate with loss of a proton from the C-2 and an inversion of the configuration around the C-1 of the allylic pyrophosphate (Cornforth *et al.*, 1966; Popjak, 1970). Farnesyl pyrophosphate is formed by head-to-tail condensation of two

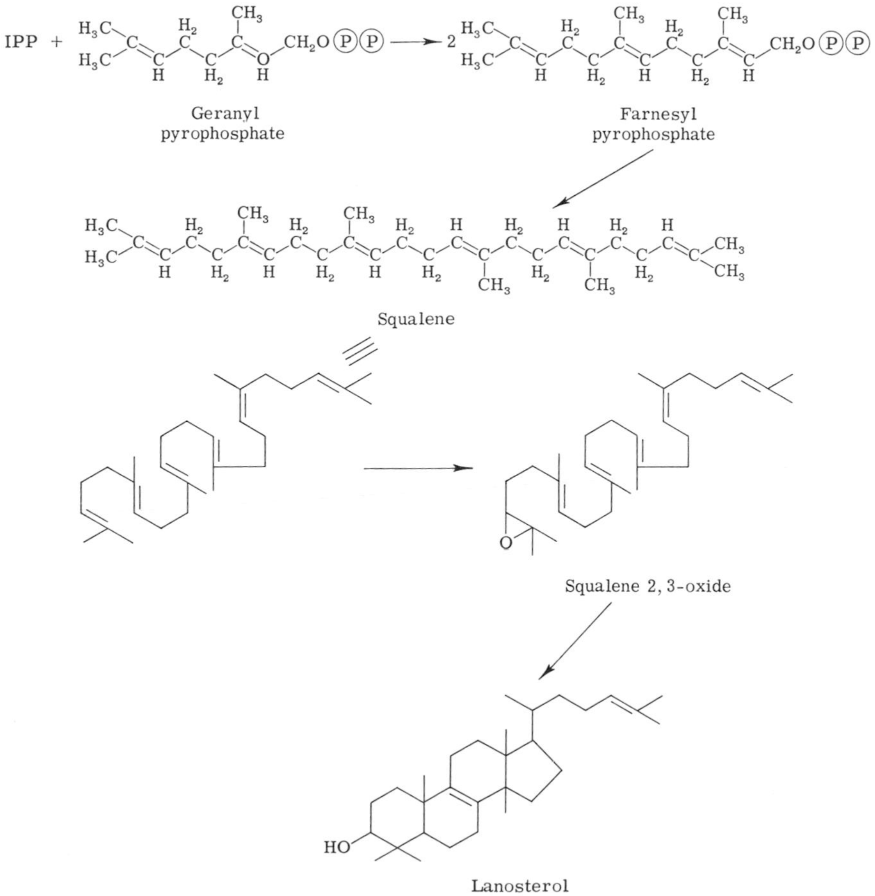

Geranyl
pyrophosphate

Farnesyl
pyrophosphate

Squalene

Squalene 2,3-oxide

Lanosterol

FIG. 3.   Biosynthesis of lanosterol from acetyl-SCoA, MVA, mevalonic acid.

molecules of geranyl pyrophosphate (Fig. 3). This pathway for the formation of C10 and C15 intermediates was detected in yeast (Lynen *et al.*, 1958a,b, 1959).

Tail-to-tail condensation of two farnesyl pyrophosphate molecules results into the formation of squalene. Popjak and Cornforth (1966) have shown that in this condensation the pro-S-hydrogen from C-1 of a farnesyl pyrophosphate molecule (from C-5 of mevalonate) is removed and a hydrogen from the B side of reduced pyridine nucleotide is inserted stereospecifically. This reaction was demonstrated to occur in yeast (Amdur *et al.*, 1957; Lynen *et al.*, 1958b), and Shechter and Bloch (1971) isolated the *trans*-farnesyl pyrophosphate-squalene synthetase. Rilling (1966) isolated a phosphorylated C30 intermediate from subcellular yeast particles deficient in NADPH, called "presqualene," which was later renamed presqualene pyrophosphate by Epstein and Rilling (1970), who confirmed its structure to be 2-(2,6,10-trimethyl-1,6,9-undecatriene)-3-methyl-3-(4,8-dimethyl-3,7-nonadiene)-cyclo propylcarbinylpyrophosphate. Altman *et al.* (1971) reported the conversion of presqualene to squalene by yeast subcellular particles in the presence of NADPH and Mg^{2+}.

Squalene is oxidized by molecular oxygen to 2.3-oxidosqualene (Fig. 3) followed by cyclization to lanosterols through a postulated intermediate (protosterol) (Mulheirn and Caspi, 1971). The cyclization reaction is catalyzed by the enzyme 2,3-oxidosqualene-sterol cyclase (Dean *et al.*, 1967; Mercer and Johnson, 1969; Shechter *et al.*, 1970), which has optimal activity at low ionic strengths (Shechter *et al.*, 1970).

It is well established that lanosterol is present in fungi and that, as in animals but not in photosynthetic plants, it is a precursor of sterols. Generally, the major sterol present in fungi is ergosterol, which is usually accompanied by fungisterol. Therefore, the characteristic structural features of a fungal sterol would be (1) a $\Delta^{5,7}$-diene system, (2) a trans Δ^{22} double bond, and (3) a 24-β-methyl group. However, the aquatic phycomycetes were devoid of ergosterol, but other C28 sterols and the Δ^5 derivatives of C27, C28, and/or C29 sterols were present and might act as precursors of ergosterol. The conversion of lanosterol to the major 4-demethyl sterol products will be dealt with next. The reader may refer to the excellent article by Weete (1973) on the biosynthesis of ergosterol by fungi.

There are 13 sterols that have been isolated from fungi, identified, and considered either as end products or possible biosynthetic compounds with lanosterol as the key intermediate (Barton *et al.*, 1972, 1973, 1974). The proposed pathways for the production of these sterols is shown in Fig. 4. Information on the sequence of action of the enzymes involved is generally lacking, but evidence for a multiplicity of sterol biosynthesis pathways in fungi (yeasts) has been presented (Weete, 1973).

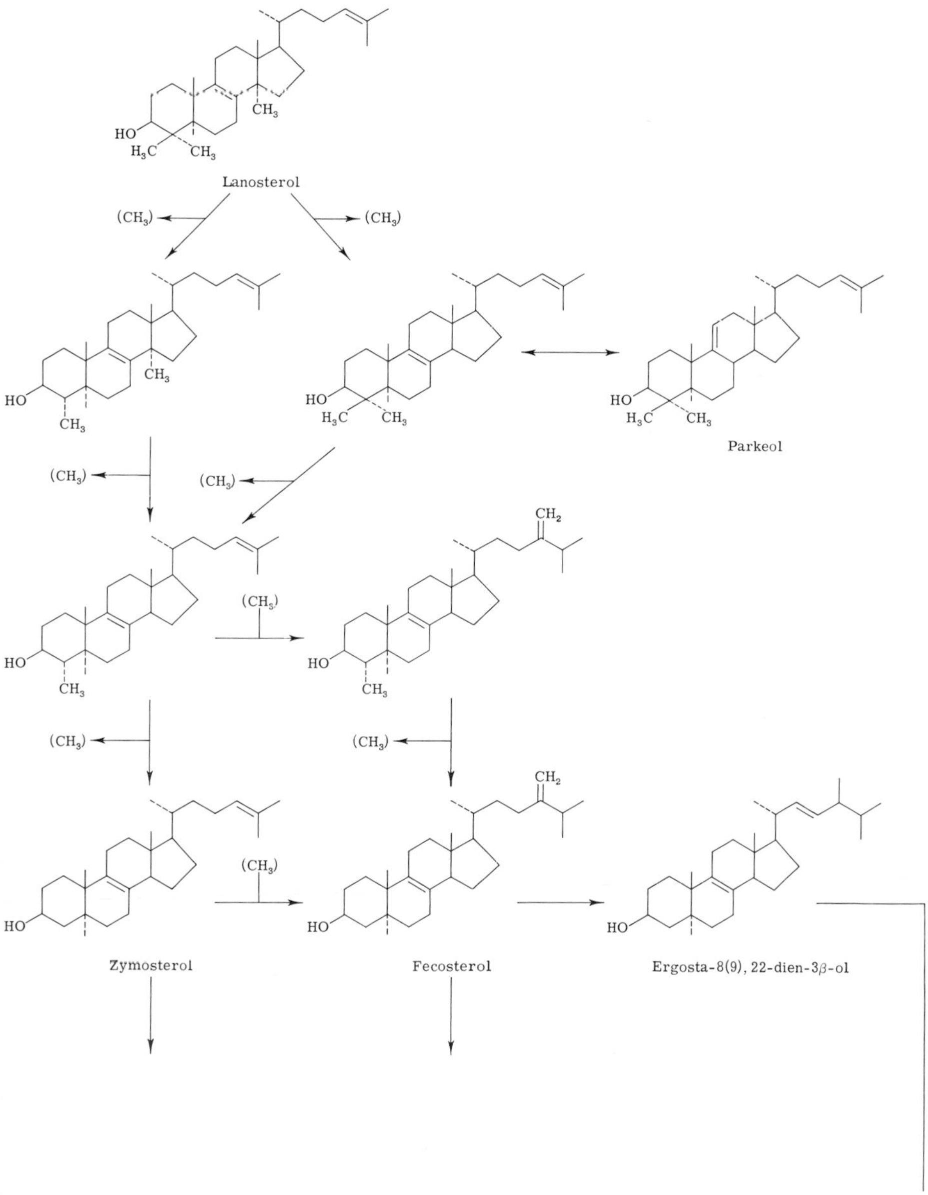

FIG. 4.   Caption on the following page.

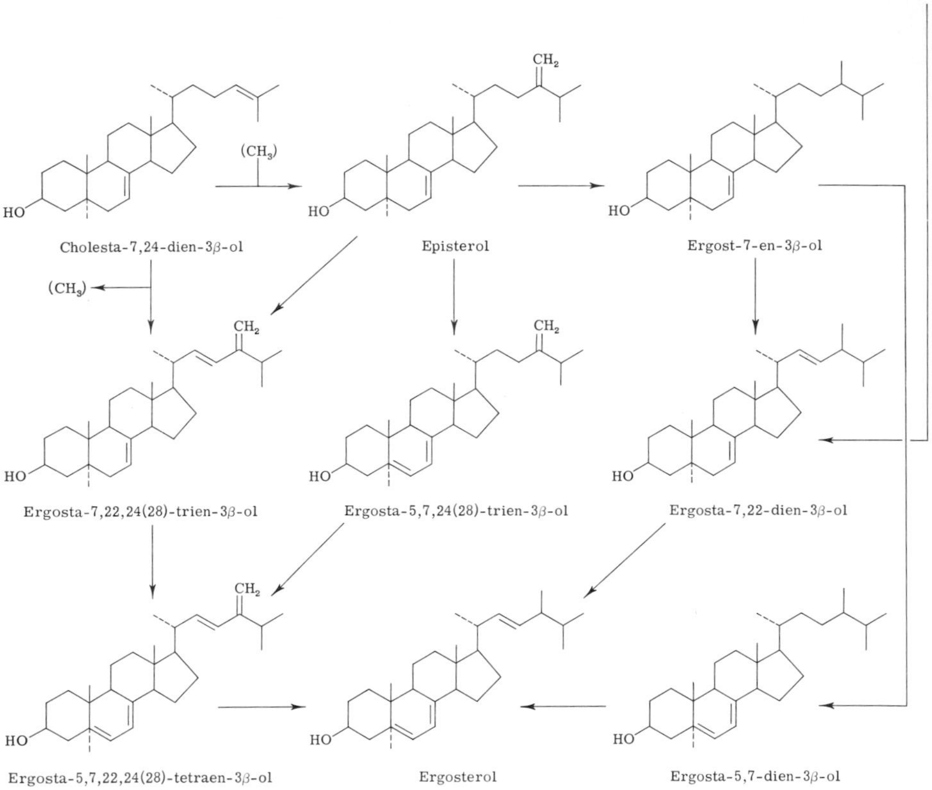

FIG. 4. Possible pathways of metabolic conversion of sterols in yeast; named compounds have been isolated from *Saccharomyces cerevisiae*. Reproduced from Rattray *et al.* (1975) by kind permission of J. B. M. Rattray and the American Society for Microbiology.

The first step in sterol biosynthesis from lanosterol involves the removal of the two CH_3 groups at position 4 and the one at position 14. However, accumulation of 4,14-dimethyl sterol derivatives because of the inability to remove one of the CH_3 groups from position 4 and that of position 14 (Trocha *et al.*, 1974) suggests that the other 4-methyl group is subject to earlier removal. S-Adenosylmethionine: Δ^{24} sterol methyltransferase (C24-methyltransferase) methylates at position 24 sterols carrying a CH_3 group at position 4. This enzyme is located in promitochondria or mitochondria of *S. cerevisiae* (Thompson *et al.*, 1973) and is specific for cholesta-7, 24-dien-3β-ol (Hatanaka *et al.*, 1974) although zymosterol is also used (Moore and Gaylor, 1970). Cholesta-7,24-dien-3β-ol is also produced from zymosterol by the enzyme $\Delta^8: \Delta^7$-isomerase (Barton *et al.*, 1974).

There are multiple possible enzymic pathways for the conversion of fecosterol and episterol to ergosterol. The molecular events presumably involve a 5,6-dehydrogenase for the introduction of additional unsaturation in ring B, a 22,23-dehydrogenase for the dehydrogenation of the side chain, and a methylene reductase for the reduction of the methylene group at position 24. The lack of any of these systems would result in the accumulation of a different sterol. A major biosynthetic route producing ergosterol from episterol involved the sequential introduction of unsaturation at position 22,23, and then at position 5,6, followed by the reduction of the methylene group at position 24 (Fryberg *et al.*, 1972, 1973). The known *in vivo* enzymes present and their sterol products were summarized by Rattray *et al.* (1975) and Gaylor (1974).

ACKNOWLEDGMENTS

The author is grateful to Drs. M. Kates, G. Rouser, H. Wheeler, and J. Kuc for reading the manuscript. Sincere gratitude is also due to Dr. Nabila Wassef for her valuable help and assistance in preparing this chapter. The typing and preparing of the manuscript by Mrs. Libbie Jones and Madeline Cummings are greatly appreciated.

References

Abe, Y. (1952). *Yushi Kagaku Kyokaishi* **1**, 132.
Accoceberry, B., and Stahl, A. (1972). *C.R. Acad. Sci., Ser. D* **274**, 3135.
Adam, H. K., Campbell, I. M., and McCorkindale, N. J. (1967). *Nature (London)* **216**, 397.
Adams, B. G., and Parks, L. W. (1967). *J. Cell. Physiol.* **70**, 161.
Agarwall, P. N., and Peterson, W. H. (1949). *Arch. Biochem.* **20**, 29.
Agranoff, B. W., Eggerer, H., Henning, V., and Lynen, F. (1960). *J. Biol. Chem.* **235**, 326.
Altman, L. J., Kowerski, R. C., and Rilling, H. C. (1971). *J. Am. Chem. Soc.* **93**, 1782.
Amdur, B. H., Rilling, H. C., and Bloch, K. (1957). *J. Am. Chem. Soc.* **79**, 2646.
Anderson, J. A., Sun, F., McDonald, J. K., and Cheldelin, V. H. (1964). *Arch. Biochem. Biophys.* **107**, 37.
Ando, K., Kato, A., Tamura, G., and Arima, K. (1969). *J. Antibiot.* **22**, 23.
Audette, R. C. S., Baxter, R. M., and Walker, G. C. (1961). *Can. J. Microbiol.* **7**, 282.
Baker, N., and Lynen, F. (1971). *Eur. J. Biochem.* **19**, 200.
Ballance, P. E., and Crombie, W. M. (1961). *Biochem. J.* **80**, 170.
Bandlow, W. (1972). *Biochim. Biophys. Acta* **282**, 105.
Baraud, J., Cassagne, C., Genevois, L., and Joneau, M. (1967). *C.R. Acad. Sci.* **265**, 83.
Baraud, J., Maurice, A., and Napias, C. (1970a). *Bull. Soc. Chim. Biol.* **52**, 421.
Baraud, J., Demassieux, S., and Maurice, A. (1970b). *Rev. Fr. Corps Gras.* **17**, 155.
Barron, E. J., Squires, C. L., and Stumf, P. K. (1961). *J. Biol. Chem.* **236**, 2610.
Bartnicki-Garcia, S. (1968). *Annu. Rev. Microbiol.* **22**, 87.
Barton, D. H. R., and Bruun, T. (1951). *J. Chem. Soc.* p. 2728.
Barton, D. H. R., and Cox, J. D. (1949). *J. Chem. Soc.* p. 214.
Barton, D. H. R., Harrison, D. M., and Widdowson, D. A. (1968). *Chem. Commun.* p. 17.
Barton, D. H. R., Kempe, U. M., and Widdowson, D. A. (1972). *J. Chem. Soc., Perkin Trans.* *1* **1**, 513.

Barton, D. H. R., Corrie, J. E. T., Marshall, P. J., and Widdowson, D. A. (1973). *Bioorg. Chem.* **2**, 363.

Barton, D. H. R., Corrie, J. E. T., Widdowson, D. A., Bard, M., and Woods, R. A. (1974). *J. Chem. Soc., Chem. Commun. January*, p. **30**.

Bean, G. A., Patterson, G. W., and Mottee, J. J. (1973). *Comp. Biochem. Physiol. B* **43**, 935.

Bednarz-Prashad, A. J., and Mize, C. E. (1974). *Biochemistry* **13**, 4237.

Beereboom, J. J., Fazakerley, H., and Halsall, T. G. (1957). *J. Chem. Soc.* p. 3437.

Bennett, A. S., and Quackenbush, F. W. (1969). *Arch. Biochem. Biophys.* **130**, 567.

Bentley, R., Lavate, W. V., and Sweeley, C. C. (1964). *Comp. Biochem. Physiol.* **11**, 263.

Bergel'son, L. D., Vaver, V. A., Prokozova, N. V., Ushakov, A. N., and Popkova, G. A. (1966). *Biochim. Biophys. Acta* **116**, 511.

Bharusha, K. E., and Gunstone, F. D. (1956). *J. Sci. Food Agric.* **7**, 606.

Bharusha, K. E., and Gunstone, F. D. (1957). *J. Chem. Soc.* p. 610.

Bianchi, D. E. (1967). *Antonie van Leeuwenhoek*; *J. Microbiol. Serol.* 33, 324.

Blank, F., Shorland, F. E., and Just, G. (1962). *J. Invest. Dermatol.* **39**, 91.

Bloch, K. (1963). *In* "The Control of Lipid Metabolism" (J. K. Grant, ed.), p. 1. Academic Press, New York.

Bloch, K., Baronowsky, P. E., Goldfine, H., Lennarz, W. J., Light, R., Norris, A. T., and Scheuerbrandt, G. (1961). *Fed. Proc., Fed. Am. Soc. Exp. Biol.* **20**, 921.

Bloomfield, D. K., and Bloch, K. (1960). *J. Biol. Chem.* **235**, 537.

Boulton, A. A. (1965). *Exp. Cell Res.* **37**, 343.

Bowman, R. D., and Mumma, R. O. (1967). *Biochim. Biophys. Acta* **144**, 501.

Brady, S., and Nye, J. F. (1970). *J. Bacteriol.* **104**, 780.

Braun, P. E., and Snell, E. E. (1967). *Proc. Natl. Acad. Sci. U.S.A.* **58**, 298.

Braun, P. E., and Snell, E. E. (1968). *J. Biol. Chem.* **243**, 3775.

Breivik, O. N., Owades, J. L., and Light, R. (1954). *J. Org. Chem.* **19**, 1734.

Brett, D., Howling, D., Morris, L. J., and James, A. T. (1971). *Arch. Biochem. Biophys.* **143**, 535.

Brodie, J. D., Wasson, G., and Porter, W. (1963). *J. Biol. Chem.* **238**, 1294.

Brown, C. M., and Rose, A. H. (1969). *J. Bacteriol.* **99**, 371.

Brushaber, J. A., Child, J. J., and Haskins, R. H. (1972). *Can. J. Microbiol.* **18**, 1059.

Bu'lock, J. D. (1966). *In* "Biosynthesis of Antibiotics" (J. F. Sneel, ed.,) p. 141. Academic Press, New York.

Caldwell, R. S., and Vernberg, F. J. (1970). *Comp. Biochem. Physiol.* **34**, 179.

Cantrell, H. F., and Dowler, W. M. (1971). *Mycologia* **63**, 31.

Carter, H. E., Johnson, P., and Weber, E. J. (1965). *Annu. Rev. Biochem.* **34**, 109.

Castelli, A., Littarru, G. P., and Barbaresi, G. (1969). *Arch. Mikrobiol.* **66**, 34.

Chappell, J. B., and Hansford, R. G. (1972). *In* "Preparation of Mitochondria from Animal Tissues and Yeasts" (G. D. Birnie, ed.), 2nd Ed. of "Subcellular Components, Preparation and Fractionation," p. 77. Butterworth, London.

Chattaway, F. W., Holmes, M. R., and Barlow, A. J. E. (1968). *J. Gen. Microbiol.* **51**, 367.

Chen, Y. S., and Haskins, R. H. (1963). *Can. J. Chem.* **41**, 1647.

Chesters, C. G., and Peberdy, J. F. (1965). *J. Gen. Microbiol.* **41**, 127.

Chisholm, M. R., and Hopkins, C. Y. (1957). *Can. J. Chem.* **35**, 358.

Clarke, S. M., and McKenzie, M. (1967). *Nature (London)* 213, 504.

Clayton, R. B. (1965). *Quart. Rev., Chem. Soc.* **19**, 168.

Clenshaw, E., and Smedley-Maclean, I. (1929). *Biochem. J.* **23**, 107.

Cobon, G. S., Crowfoot, P. D., and Linnane, A. W. (1974). *Biochem. J.* **144**, 265.

Collier, R., and Kennedy, G. Y. (1963). *J. Mar. Biol. Assoc. U.K.* **43**, 605.

Collins, R. P., and Kalnins, K. (1968). *Mycopathol. Mycol. Appl.* **36**, 214.

Combs, T. J., Guarneri, J. J., and Pisano, M. A. (1968). *Mycologia* **60**, 1233.

Coots, R. H. (1962). *J. Lipid Res.* **3**, 84.

Cornforth, J. W., Cornforth, R. H., Donninger, C., and Popjak, G. (1966). *Proc. Roy. Soc., Ser. B* **163**, 492.

Davidoff, F., and Korn, E. D. (1964). *J. Biol. Chem.* **238**, 3199.

Dean, P. D. G., Ortiz de Montellano, P. R., Bloch, K., and Corey, E. J. (1967). *J. Biol. Chem.* **242**, 3014.

Dedyukhina, E. G., and Bekhtereva, M. N. (1969). *Mikrobiologiya* **38**, 775.

Deierkauf, F. A., and Booij, H. L. (1968). *Biochim. Biophys. Acta* **150**, 214.

DiMari, S. J., Brady, R. N., and Snell, E. E. (1971). *Arch. Biochem. Biophys.* **143**, 553.

Divakaran, P., and Modia, M. J. (1968). *Experientia* **24**, 1102.

Domer, J. E., and Hamilton, J. G. (1971). *Biochim. Biophys. Acta* **231**, 465.

Dubé, J., Setterfield, G., Kiss, G., and Lusena, C. V. (1973). *Can. J. Microbiol.* **19**, 285.

Elinor, N. P., and Zaikina, N. A. (1963). *Vopr. Med. Khim.* **9**, 177.

Ellenbogen, B. B., Aaronson, S., Goldstein, S., and Belsky, M. (1969). *Comp. Biochem. Physiol.* **29**, 805.

Enebo, L., Lundin, H., and Myrback, K. (1942) *Osterr. Chem.—Ztg.* **45**, 9.

Enebo, L., Anderson, L. G., and Lundin, H. (1946). *Arch. Biochem.* **11**, 383.

Epstein, W. W., and Rilling, H. C. (1970). *J. Biol. Chem.* **245**, 4597.

Epstein, W. W., Avoyagi, E., and Jennings, P. W. (1966). *Comp. Biochem. Physiol.* **18**, 225.

Erwin, J. (1973). *In* "Lipids and Biomembranes of Eukaryotic Microorganisms" (J. Erwin, ed.), p. 41. Academic Press, New York.

Erwin, J., Hulanicka, D., and Bloch, K. (1964). *Comp. Biochem. Physiol.* **12**, 191.

Fabre-Joneau, M., Baraud, J., and Cassagne, C. (1969). *C. R. Acad. Sci., Ser. D* **268**, 2282.

Folkers, K., Skunk, C. H., Linn, B. O., Robinson, F. M., Wittreich, P. E., Huff, J. W., Gilfillan, J. L., and Skeggs, H. R. (1959). "Biosynthesis of Terpenes and Sterols." Little, Brown, Boston, Massachusetts.

Foppen, F. H., and Gribanovski-Sassu, O. (1968). *Biochem. J.* **106**, 97.

Fryberg, M., Oehlschlager, A. C., and Unran, A. M. (1972). *Biochem. Biophys. Res. Commun.* **48**, 593.

Fryberg, M., Oehlschlager, A. C., and Unran, A. M. (1973). *J. Am. Chem. Soc.* **95**, 5747.

Fulco, A. J. (1967). *J. Biol. Chem.* **242**, 3608.

Fulco, A. J., and Mead, J. F. (1961). *J. Biol. Chem.* **236**, 2416.

Gad, M. A., and El-Nockrashy, S. (1960). *J. Chem. U.A.R.* **3**, 57.

Gaylor, J. L. (1974). *In* "Biochemistry of Lipids" (T. W. Goodwin, ed.), Biochemistry Series One, Vol. 4, pp. 1–37. Butterworth, London.

Getz, G. S., Jakovcic, S., Heywoof, J., Frank, J., and Rabinowitz, M. (1970). *Biochim. Biophys. Acta* **218**, 441.

Gorin, P. A. J., Spencer, J. F. T., and Tulloch, A. P. (1961). *Can. J. Chem.* **39**, 846.

Gottlieb, D., and Van Etten, J. L. (1966). *J. Bacteriol.* **91**, 161.

Goulston, G., and Mercer, E. I. (1969). *Phytochemistry* **8**, 1945.

Goulston, G., Goad, L. J., and Goodwin, T. W. (1967). *Biochem. J.* **102**, 15C.

Graff, G. L. A., Vanderkelen, B., Guening, C., and Humpers, J. (1968). *Soc. Belge Biol.* 1635.

Green, M. L., Kaneshiro, T., and Law, J. H. (1965). *Biochim. Biophys. Acta* **98**, 582.

Gribanovski-Sassu, O., and Beljak, J. (1971). *Ann. Ist Super. Sanita* **7**, 95.

Gribanovski-Sassu, O., and Foppen, F. H. (1968). *Arch. Microbiol.* **62**, 251.

Griddle, R. S., and Schatz, G. (1969). *Biochemistry* **8**, 322.

Griffin, P. F. S., Bonennan, P. J., and Losel, D. M. (1970). *Biochem. J.* **119**, 11 P.

Guider, J. M., Halsall, T. G., and Jones, E. R. H. (1954). *J. Chem. Soc.* p. 4471.

Gunasekaran, M., and Weber, D. J. (1972). *Phytochemistry* **11**, 3367.

Gunasekaran, M., and Weber, D. J. (1974). *Mycopathol. Mycol. Appl.* **52**, 261.

Gunasekaran, M., Raju, P. K., and Lyda, S. A. (1970). *Phytopathology* **60**, 1027.

Gunasekaran, M., Bushnell, J. L., and Weber, D. J. (1972a). *Res. Commun. Chem. Pathol. Pharmacol.* **3**, 621.

Gunasekaran, M., Weber, D. J., and Hess, S. L. (1972b). *Lipids* **7**, 430.

Gurr, M. I. (1974). *In* "Biochemistry of Lipids" (T. W. Goodwin, ed.), Biochemistry Series One, Vol. 4, pp. 181–235. Butterworth, London.

Gurr, M. I., Robinson, M. P., and James, A. T. (1969). *Eur. J. Biochem.* **9**, 70.

Hall, M. O., and Nye, J. F. (1959). *J. Am. Chem. Soc.* **81**, 2275.

Hall, M. O., and Nye, J. F. (1961). *J. Lipid Res.* **2**, 321.

Halsall, T. G., and Sayer, G. C. (1959). *J. Chem. Soc.* p. 2031.

Hanahan, D. J., and Jayoko, M. E. (1952). *J. Am. Chem. Soc.* **74**, 5070.

Handa, S., and Burton, R. M. (1969). *Lipids* **4**, 589.

Hardesty, B. A., and Mitchell, H. K. (1963). *Arch. Biochem. Biophys.* **100**, 330.

Harlan, W. R., and Wakil, S. J. (1964). *J. Biol. Chem.* **239**, 2489.

Hartman, L., Hawke, J. C., Shorland, F. B., and di Menna, M. E. (1959). *Arch. Biochem. Biophys.* **81**, 346.

Hartman, L., Hawke, J. C., Morice, I. M., and Shorland, F. B. (1960). *Biochem. J.* **75**, 274.

Hartman, L., Morice, I. M., and Shorland, F. E. (1962). *Biochem. J.* **82**, 76.

Haskell, B. E., and Snell, E. E. (1965). *Arch. Biochem. Biophys.* **112**, 494.

Haskins, R. H. (1963). *Can. J. Microbiol.* **9**, 451.

Haskins, R. H., Thorn, J. A., and Boothroyd, D. (1955). *Can. J. Microbiol.* **1**, 749.

Haskins, R. H., Tulloch, A. P., and Micetich, R. G. (1964). *Can. J. Microbiol.* **10**, 187.

Hatanaka, H., Ariga, N., Nagai, J., and Katsuki, H. (1974). *Biochem. Biophys. Res. Commun.* **60**, 787.

Hay, J. B., and Gray, G. M. (1970). *Biochem. Biophys. Res. Commun.* **38**, 527.

Hebert, R. J., Hart, L. T., Dimopoullos, G. T., and Larson, A. D. (1973). *Abstr. Soc. Microbiol., Annu. Meet.* p. 19.

Heinz, E., Tulloch, A. P., and Spencer, J. F. T. (1970). *Biochim. Biophys. Acta* **202**, 49.

Hitchcock, C., and James, A. T. (1964). *Biochem. J.* **93**, 22.

Hofmann, K. (1963). "Fatty Acid Metabolism in Microorganisms," p. 78. Wiley, New York.

Holley, R. A., and Kidby, D. K. (1973). *Can. J. Microbiol.* **19**, 113.

Holtz, R. B., and Schisler, L. C. (1971). *Lipids* **6**, 176.

Holtz, R. B., and Schisler, L. C. (1972). *Lipids* **7**, 251.

Hougen, F. W., Craig, B. M., and Ledingham, G. A. (1958). *Can. J. Microbiol.* **4**, 521.

Howell, D. Mc B., and Fergus, C. L. (1964). *Can. J. Microbiol.* **10**, 616.

Howling, D., Morris, L. J., Gurr, M. I., and James, A. T. (1972). *Biochim. Biophys. Acta* **260**, 10.

Huber, F. M., and Redstone, M. O. (1967). *Can. J. Microbiol.* **13**, 332.

Hughes, D. H. (1962). *Mushroom Sci.* **5**, 540.

Hunter, K., and Rose, A. H. (1971). *In* "The Yeasts" (A. H. Rose and J. S. Harrison, eds.), Vol. 2, p. 8. Academic Press, New York.

Hunter, K., and Rose, A. H. (1972). *Biochim. Biophys. Acta* **260**, 639.

Hutchison, H. T., and Cronan, J. E., Jr. (1968). *Biochim. Biophys. Acta* **164**, 606.

Indge, K. J. (1968). *J. Gen. Microbiol.* **51**, 441.

Ishida, Y., and Mitsuhashi, J. (1970). *Yokagaku* **19**, 93.

Jack, R. C. M. (1964). *Contrib. Boyce Thompson Inst.* **22**, 311.

Jack, R. C. M. (1965). *J. Am. Chem. Soc.* **42**, 1051.

Jack, R. C. M. (1966). *J. Bacteriol.* **91**, 2101.

Jack, R. C. R., and Laredo, J. L. (1968). *Lipids* **3**, 459.

Jackson, L. L., and Frear, D. S. (1968). *Phytochemistry* **7**, 654.

Jakovcic, S., Getz, G. S., Rabinowitz, M., Jakob, H., and Swift, H. (1971). *J. Cell Biol.* **48**, 490.

James, A. T. (1969). *Biochim. Biophys. Acta* **187**, 13.

Johnston, J. M., and Paltauf, F. (1970). *Biochim. Biophys. Acta* **218**, 431.

Jones, J. G. (1969). *J. Gen. Microbiol.* **59**, 152.

Jones, J. G., and Young, B. V. (1970). *Arch. Mikrobiol.* **70**, 82.

Kanetsuna, F., Carbonell, L. M., Moreno, R. E., and Rodriguez, J. (1969). *J. Bacteriol.* **97**, 1036.

Karlsson, K. A. (1966). *Acta Chem. Scand.* **20**, 2884.

Kates, M. (1964). *Adv. Lipid Res.* **2**, 17.

Kates, M. (1966). *Annu. Rev. Microbiol.* **20**, 13.

Kates, M., and Baxter, R. M. (1962). *Can. J. Biochem. Physiol.* **40**, 1213.

Kates, M., and Marshall, M. O. (1975). *In* "Recent Advances in Chemistry and Biochemistry of Plant Lipids" (T. Galliard and E. I. Mercer, eds.), pp. 115–159. Academic Press, New York.

Kates, M., and Paradis, M. (1973). *Can. J. Biochem.* **51**, 184.

Kates, M., and Wassef, M. K. (1970). *Annu. Rev. Biochem.* **39**, 323.

Kaufman, B., Basu, S., and Roseman, S. (1971). *J. Biol. Chem.* **246**, 4266.

Kaufmann, H. P., and Viswanathan, C. V. (1965). *Fette, Seifen, Anstrichm.* **67**, 7.

Keeney, M., Katz, I., and Schwartz, D. P. (1962). *Biochem. Biophys. Acta* **62**, 615.

Keith, A. D., Wisieski, B. J., Henry, S., and Williams, J. C. (1973). *In* "Lipids and Biomembranes of Eukaryotic Microorganisms" (J. Erwin, ed.), p. 259. Academic Press, New York.

Kessell, R. H. J. (1968). *J. Appl. Bacteriol.* **31**, 220.

Kidby, D. K., and Davies, R. (1970). *J. Gen. Microbiol.* **61**, 327.

Klein, H. P., and Lipmann, F. (1953). *J. Biol. Chem.* **203**, 95.

Klein, H. P., Volkmann, C. M., and Leaffer, M. A. (1967a). *J. Bacteriol.* **94**, 61.

Klein, H. P., Volkmann, C. M., and Weibel, J. (1967b). *J. Bacteriol.* **94**, 475.

Klein, H. P., Volkmann, C. M., and Chao, F. C. (1967c). *J. Bacteriol.* **93**, 1966.

Knipprath, N. G., and Mead, J. F. (1968). *Lipids* **3**, 121.

Knoche, H. W. (1971). *Lipids* **6**, 581.

Koman, V., Betina, V., and Barath, Z. (1969). *Arch. Mikrobiol.* **65**, 172.

Korn, E. D., Greenblatt, C. L., and Less, A. M. (1965). *J. Lipid Res.* **6**, 43.

Kostiw, L. L., Vicher, E. E., and Lyon, I. (1966). *Mycopathologia* **29**, 145.

Kubeczka, K. H. (1968). *Arch. Mikrobiol.* **60**, 139.

Laseter, J. L., and Valle, R. (1971). *Environ. Sci. Technol.* **5**, 631.

Laseter, J. L., and Weete, J. D. (1971). *Science* **172**, 864.

Laseter, J. L., Weete, J. D., and Weber, D. J. (1968a). *Phytochemistry* **1**, 1177.

Laseter, J. L., Hess, W. M., Weete, J. D., Stocks, D. L., and Weber, D. J. (1968b). *Can. J. Microbiol.* **14**, 1149.

Leegwater, D. C., Youngs, C. G., Spencer, J. F. T., and Craig, B. M. (1962). *Can. J. Biochem. Physiol.* **40**, 847.

Lemieux, R. V. (1951). *Can. J. Chem.* **31**, 396.

Lemieux, R. V., and Giguese, J. (1951). *Can. J. Chem.* **29**, 678.

Lennarz, W. J. (1970). *Annu. Rev. Biochem.* **39**, 359.

Lester, R. L., and Steiner, M. R. (1968). *J. Biol. Chem.* **243**, 4889.

Letters, R. (1966). *Biochim. Biophys. Acta* **116**, 489.

Levis, G. M., and Mead, J. F. (1964). *J. Biol. Chem.* **239**, 77.

Lewin, L. M. (1965). *J. Gen. Microbiol.* **41**, 215.

Light, R., Lennarz, W. J., and Bloch, K. (1962). *J. Biol. Chem.* **237**, 1793.

Longley, R. P., Rose, A. H., and Knights, B. A. (1968). *Biochem. J.* **108**, 401.

Lynen, F. (1961). *Fed. Proc., Fed. Am. Soc. Exp. Biol.* **20**, 941.

Lynen, F. (1967). *Biochem. J.* **102**, 381.

Lynen, F., Eggerer, H., and Henning, V. (1958a). *Angew. Chem.* **70**, 638.
Lynen, F., Eggerer, H., Henning, V., and Kessel, I. (1958b). *Angew. Chem.* **70**, 738.
Lynen, F., Agranoff, B. W., Eggerer, H., Henning, V., and Moslein, E. M. (1959). *Angew. Chem.* **71**, 657.
Lynen, F., Oesterhelt, D., Schweizer, E., and Willecke, K. (1968). *In* "Cellular Compartmentalisation and Control of Fatty Acid Metabolism" (F. C. Grain, ed.), pp. 1–24. Academic Press, New York.
Maas-Forster, M. (1955). *Arch. Mikrobiol.* **22**, 115.
McCorkindale, N. J., Hutchinson, S. A., Pursey, B. A., Scott, W. T., and Wheeler, R. (1969). *Phytochemistry* **8**, 861.
McElroy, F. A., and Stewart, H. B. (1967). *Can. J. Biochem.* **45**, 171.
Madyastha, P. B., and Parks, L. W. (1969). *Biochim. Biophys. Acta* **176**, 858.
Mangnall, D., and Getz, G. S. (1973). *In* "Lipids and Biomembranes of Eukaryotic Microorganisms" (J. A. Erwin, edr.), p. 145. Academic Press, New York.
Mantle, P. G., Morris, L. J., and Hall, S. W. (1969). *Trans. Br. Mycol. Soc.* **53**, 441.
Marchant, R., and White, M. F. (1967). *J. Gen. Microbiol.* **48**, 65.
Marsh, J. B., and James, A. T. (1962). *Biochim. Biophys. Acta* **60**, 320.
Martin, R. O., and Stumpf, P. K. (1959). *J. Biol. Chem.* **234**, 2548.
Matile, P. (1970). *FEBS (Fed. Eur. Biochem. Soc.) Symp.* **20**, 39.
Matile, P., and Wiemken, A. (1967). *Arch. Mikrobiol.* **56**, 148.
Matile, P., Moor, H., and Muhlethaler, K. (1967). *Arch. Mikrobiol.* **58**, 201.
Matsuhashi, M. (1969). *In* "Lipids" (J. M. Lowenstein, ed.), Methods in Enzymology, Vol. 14, p. 3. Academic Press, New York.
Mead, J. F. (1960). *In* "Lipid Metabolism" (K. Bloch, ed.), p. 41. Wiley, New York.
Mead, J. F. (1961). *Fed. Proc., Fed. Am. Soc. Exp. Biol.* **20**, 952.
Mead, J. F. (1963). *Annu. Rev. Biochem.* **32**, 241.
Mendoza, C. G., and Villanueva, J. R. (1967). *Biochim. Biophys. Acta* **135**, 189.
Mercer, E. I., and Johnson, M. W. (1969). *Phytochemistry* **8**, 2329.
Merdinger, E. (1966). *Can. J. Microbiol.* **12**, 206.
Merdinger, E., and Cwiakala, C. (1967). *Lipids* **2**, 276.
Merdinger, E., and Devine, E. M., Jr. (1965). *J. Bacteriol.* **89**, 1488.
Merdinger, E., Kohn, P., and McClain, R. C. (1968). *Can. J. Microbiol.* **14**, 1021.
Meyer, F., and Bloch, K. (1963). *Biochim. Biophys. Acta* **77**, 671.
Meyer, H., and Holtz, G. G. (1966). *J. Biol. Chem.* **241**, 5000.
Milazzo, F. H. (1965). *Can. J. Bot.* **43**, 1347.
Mills, G. L., and Cantino, E. C. (1974). *J. Bacteriol.* **118**, 192.
Mizuno, M., Shimojima, Y., Iguchi, T., Takeda, I., and Senoh, S. (1966). *Agric. Biol. Chem.* **30**, 506.
Molitoris, H. P. (1963). *Arch. Mikrobiol.* **47**, 104.
Moore, J. T., Jr., and Gaylor, J. L. (1970). *J. Biol. Chem.* **245**, 4684.
Morell, P., and Braun, P. E. (1972). *J. Lipid Res.* **13**, 293.
Morell, P., and Radin, N. S. (1970). *J. Biol. Chem.* **245**, 342.
Morris, L. J. (1967). *Lipids* **3**, 260.
Morris, L. J. (1970). *Biochem. J.* **118**, 681.
Morris, L. J., and Hall, S. W. (1966). *Lipids* **1**, 188.
Mudd, J. B., and Garcia, R. (1975). *In* "Recent Advances in Chemistry and Biochemistry of Plant Lipids" (T. Galliard and E. I. Mercer, eds.), p. 162. Academic Press, New York.
Mudd, J. B., Van Vliet, H. H. D. M., and Van Deenen, L. L. M. (1969). *J. Lipid Res.* **10**, 623.
Mulheirn, L. J., and Caspi, E. (1971). *J. Biol. Chem.* **246**, 3948.
Mumma, R. O., and Bruszewski, T. E. (1970). *Lipids* **5**, 115.
Mumma, R. O., Fergus, C. L., and Sekura, R. D. (1970). *Lipids* **5**, 100.

Nakajima, S., and Tanenbaum, S. W. (1968). *Arch. Biochem. Biophys.* **127**, 150.

Naquib, K., and Saddik, K. (1960). *Can. J. Bot.* **38**, 613.

Nielsen, H., and Nilsson, N. G. (1950). *Arch. Biochem. Biophys.* **25**, 316.

Nowak, R., Kim, W. K., and Rohringer, R. (1972). *Can. J. Bot.* **50**, 185.

Nugleren, D. H. (1965). *Biochim. Biophys. Acta* **106**, 280.

Nurminen, T., and Suomalainen, H. (1971). *Biochem. J.* **125**, 963.

Nurminen, T., Oura, E., and Suomalainen, H. (1970). *Biochem. J.* **116**, 61.

O'Leary, W. M. (1962). *Bacteriol. Rev.* **26**, 421.

Ongun, A., and Mudd, J. B. (1970). *Plant Physiol.* **45**, 255.

Orme, T. W., McIntyre, J., Lynen, F., Kuhn, L., and Schweizer, E. (1972). *Eur. J. Biochem.* **24**, 407.

Oro, J., Laseter, J. L., and Weber, D. J. (1966). *Science* **154**, 399.

Osman, H. G., Abdel-Akher, M., El-Refai, A. M. H., and Nashat, M. A. (1969). *Z. Allg. Mikrobiol.* **9**, 283.

Paltauf, F., and Holasek, A. (1973). *J. Biol. Chem.* **248**, 1609.

Paltauf, F., and Schatz, G. (1969). *Biochemistry* **8**, 335.

Pan, S. C. (1949). *Chem. Dig.* **8**, 5.

Pan, S. C., Andreason, A. A., and Kolachor, P. (1949). *Arch. Biochem.* **20**, 29.

Peck, R. J. (1947). *In* "Biology of Pathogenic Fungi" (W. J. Nickerson, ed.), p. 1. Ronald Press, New York.

Popjak, G. (1970). *Biochem. Soc. Symp.* **29**, 17.

Popjak, G., and Cornforth, J. W. (1966). *Biochem J.* **101**, 553.

Powell, R. G., Smith, C. R., and Wolff, I. A. (1967). *Lipids* **2**, 172.

Prottey, C., Seidman, M. M., and Ballou, C. E. (1970). *Lipids* **5**, 463.

Pugh, E. L., and Kates, M. (1973). *Biochim. Biophys. Acta* **316**, 305.

Pugh, E. L., and Kates, M. (1975). *Biochim. Biophys. Acta* **380**, 442.

Qureshi, A. A., Lornitzo, F. A., and Porter, J. W. (1974). *Biochem. Biophys. Res. Commun.* **60**, 158–165.

Rambo, G. W., and Bean, G. A. (1969). *Can. J. Microbiol.* **15**, 967.

Rattray, J. B. M., Schibeci, A., and Kidby, D. K. (1975). *Bacteriol. Rev.* **39**, 197.

Rilling, H. C. (1966). *J. Biol. Chem.* **241**, 3233.

Ripple, A. (1940). *Arch. Mikrobiol.* **11**, 271.

Rogers, P. J., and Gleason, F. H. (1974). *Mycologia* **66**, 919.

Roncari, D. A. K. (1974). *J. Biol. Chem.* **249**, 7035.

Rossiter, R. J. (1968). *In* "Metabolic Pathways" (D. M. Greenberg, ed.), Vol. 2, p. 69. Academic Press, New York.

Rozijn, T. H., and Tonino, G. J. M. (1964). *Biochim. Biophys. Acta* **91**, 105.

Ruinen, J., and Deinema, M. H. (1964). *Antonie van Leeuwenhoek; J. Microbiol. Serol.* **30**, 377.

Safe, S., and Caldwell, J. (1975). *Can. J. Microbiol.* **21**, 79.

Salmonowitz, J., and Niewiadomski, H. (1965). *Rev. Fr. Corps Gras* **12**, No. 5.

Schatz, G. (1965). *Biochim. Biophys. Acta* **96**, 342.

Schibeci, A., Rattray, J. B. M., and Kidby, D. K. (1973a). *Biochim. Biophys. Acta* **311**, 15.

Schibeci, A., Rattray, J. B. M., and Kidby, D. K. (1973b). *Biochim. Biophys. Acta* **323**, 532.

Schiller, H., and Bensch, K. (1971). *J. Lipid Res.* **12**, 248.

Schroepfer, G. J., Jr., and Bloch, K. (1964). *J. Biol. Chem.* **240**, 54.

Schultz, J., and Lynen, F. (1971). *Eur. J. Biochem.* **21**, 48.

Schweizer, E., Willecke, K., Winnewisser, W., and Lynen, F. (1970). *Vitam. Horm. (N.Y.)* **28**, 329.

Schweizer, E., Kniep, B., Castorph, H., and Holzner, U. (1973). *Eur. J. Biochem.* **39**, 353.

Shafai, T., and Lewin, L. M. (1968). *Biochim. Biophys. Acta* **152**, 787.

Shah, V. K., and Knights. S. C. (1968). *Arch. Biochem. Biophys.* **127**, 229.

Sharratt, A. N., and Madhausing, C. (1967). *Can. J. Microbiol.* **13**, 1351.

Shaw, R. (1965). *Biochim. Biophys. Acta* **98**, 230.

Shaw, R. (1966a). *Comp. Biochem. Physiol.* **18**, 325.

Shaw, R. (1966b). *Adv. Lipid Res.* **4**, 107.

Shaw, R. (1967). *Nature (London)* **213**, 86.

Shechter, I., and Bloch, K. (1971). *J. Biol. Chem.* **246**, 7690.

Shechter, I., Sweat, F. W., and Bloch, K. (1970). *Biochim. Biophys. Acta* **220**, 463.

Shimi, I. R., Singh, J., and Walker, T. K. (1959). *Biochem. J.* **72**, 184.

Singh, J. (1957). *J. Sci. Ind. Res.* **16**, 113.

Singh, J., Walker, T. K., and Meara, M. L. (1955). *Biochem. J.* **61**, 85.

Singh, J., Shah, S., and Walker, T. K. (1956). *Biochem. J.* **62**, 222.

Singh, J., Philip, S. E., and Walker, T. K. (1957). *J. Sci. Food Agric.* **8**, 697.

Snell, E. E., DiMari, S. J., and Brady, R. N. (1970). *Chem. Phys. Lipids* **5**, 116.

Sprechter, E., and Kubeczka, K. H. (1970). *Arch. Mikrobiol.* **73**, 337.

Stanacev, N. Z., and Kates, M. (1963). *Can. J. Biochem. Physiol.* **41**, 3130.

Stanacev, N. Z., Davidson, J. B., Stuhne-Sekalec, L., and Domazet, Z. (1973). *Can. J. Biochem.* **51**, 286.

Starkey, R. L. (1946). *J. Bacteriol.* **51**, 33.

Steinberg, M. P., and Ordal, Z. J. (1954). *J. Agric. Food Chem.* **2**, 873.

Steiner, M. R., and Lester, R. L. (1972). *Biochim. Biophys. Acta* **260**, 222.

Steiner, S., Smith, S., Waechter, C. J., and Lester, R. L. (1969). *Proc. Natl. Acad. Sci. U.S.A.* **64**, 1042.

Stodola, F. H., Vesonder, R. F., and Wickerham, L. J. (1965). *Biochemistry* **4**, 1390.

Stodola, F. H., Deinema, M. H., and Spencer, J. F. T. (1967). *Bacteriol. Rev.* **31**, 194.

Stoffel, W. (1971). *Annu. Rev. Biochem.* **40**, 57.

Stoffel, W. (1973). *Chem. Phys. Lipids* **11**, 318.

Stoffel, W., Sticht, G., and LeKim, D. (1968). *Hoppe-Seyler's Z. Physiol. Chem.* **349**, 1149.

Stone, K. J., and Hemming, F. W. (1968). *Biochem. J.* **109**, 877.

Stoops, J. K., Arslanian, M. J., Oh, Y. H., Aune, K. C., Vanaman, T. C., and Wakil, S. J. (1975). *Proc. Natl. Acad. Sci. U.S.A.* **72**, 1940.

Strigina, L. I., Elkin, Y. N., and Elyakov, G. B. (1971). *Phytochemistry* **10**, 2361.

Sumner, J. L. (1970). *Can. J. Microbiol.* **16**, 1161.

Sumner, J. L., and Colotelo, N. (1970). *Can. J. Microbiol.* **16**, 1171.

Sumner, J. L., and Morgan, E. D. (1969). *J. Gen. Microbiol.* **59**, 215.

Sumner, J. L., Morgan, E. D., and Evans, H. C. (1969). *Can. J. Microbiol.* **15**, 515.

Sumper, M., and Lynen, F. (1972). *Colloq. Ges. Biol. Chem.* **23**, 365.

Suomalainen, H. (1969). *Antonie van Leeuwenhoek*; *J. Microbiol. Serol.* **35**, Suppl., 83.

Suomalainen, H., and Keranen, A. J. A. (1968). *Chem. Phys. Lipids* **2**, 296.

Suomalainen, H., and Nurminen, T. (1970). *Chem. Phys. Lipids* **4**, 247.

Suomalainen, H., and Nurminen, T. (1973). *In* "Yeast, Mould and Plant Protoplasts" (J. R. Villaneuva, J. Garcia-Acha, S. Gascon, and F. Urubura, eds.), p. 1. Academic Press, New York.

Sweeley, C. C. (1959). *Biochim. Biophys. Acta* **36**, 268.

Sweeley, C. C., and Moscatelli, E. A. (1959). *J. Lipid Res.* **1**, 40.

Talamo, B., Chang, N., and Bloch, K. (1973). *J. Biol. Chem.* **248**, 2738.

Talbot, G., and Vining, L. C. (1963). *Can. J. Bot.* **41**, 639.

Tanahashi, Y., and Takahashi, T. (1966). *Bull. Chem. Soc. Jpn.* **39**, 848.

Thiele, O. W. (1964). *Biochim. Biophys. Acta* **84**, 483.

Thompson, E. D., Knights, B. A., and Parks, L. W. (1973). *Biochim. Biophys. Acta* **304**, 132.

Todd, D., Stone, D., Hechter, O., and Nussbaum, A. (1957). *J. Biol. Chem.* **229**, 527.

Trevelyan, W. E. (1966). *J. Inst. Brew., London* **72**, 184.
Trione, E. J., and Ching, T. M. (1971). *Phytochemistry* **10**, 227.
Trocha, P. J., Jasne, S. J., and Sprinson, D. B. (1974). *Biochem. Biophys Res. Commun.* **59**, 666.
Tulloch, A. P., and Ledingham, G. A. (1960). *Can. J. Microbiol.* **6**, 425.
Tulloch, A. P. and Ledingham, G. A. (1962). *Can. J. Microbiol.* **8**, 379.
Tulloch, A. P. and Spencer, J. F. T. (1964). *Can. J. Chem.* **42**, 830.
Turner, W. B. (1971). "Fungal Metabolites," p. 66. Academic Press, New York.
Tyrrell, D. (1967). *Can. J. Microbiol.* **13**, 755.
Tyrrell, D. (1969). *Can. J. Microbiol.* **15**, 818.
Tyrrell, D. (1971). *Can. J. Microbiol.* **17**, 1115.
Vacheron, M. J., and Michel, G. (1968). *Phytochemistry* **7**, 1645.
Vagelos, P. R. (1964). *Annu. Rev. Biochem.* **33**, 139.
Vagelos, P. R., Albert, A. W., and Majerus, P. W. (1969). *In* "Lipids" (J. M. Lowenstein, ed.), Methods in Enzymology, Vol. 14, p. 39. Academic Press, New York.
Van der Wilden, W., Matile, P., Schellenberg, M., Meyer, J., and Wiemken, A. (1973). *Z. Naturforsch. C* **28**, 416.
Van Etten, J. L., and Gottlieb, D. (1965). *J. Bacteriol.* **89**, 409.
Vaver, V. A., Prokazova, N. V., Ushakov, A. N., Golovkina, L. S., and Bergel'son, L. D. (1967). *Biokhimya* **32**, 310.
Vesonder, R. F., and Stodola, F. H. (1969). *Can. J. Chem.* **47**, 1247.
Vignais, P. M., Nachbaur, J., Huet, J., and Vignais, P. V. (1970). *Biochem. J.* **116**, 42P.
Waechter, C. J., and Lester, R. L. (1971). *J. Bacteriol.* **105**, 837.
Wagner, F., Kleeman, T., and Zahn, W. (1969). *Biotechnol. Bioeng.* **11**, 393.
Wagner, H., and Zofcsik, W. (1966a). *Biochem. Z.* **346**, 333.
Wagner, H., and Zofcsik, W. (1966b). *Biochem. Z.* **346**, 334.
Wakil, S. J. (1958). *J. Am. Chem. Soc.* **80**, 6465.
Wakil, S. J. (1961). *J. Lipid Res.* **2**, 1.
Wakil, S. J. (1962). *Annu. Rev. Biochem.* **31**, 369.
Walker, R. F., and Throneberry, G. O. (1971). *Phytochemistry* **10**, 2979.
Wassef, M. K., and Hendrix, J. W. (1977). *Biochim. Biophys. Acta* **486**, 172.
Wassef, M. K., Ammon, V., and Wyllie, T. D. (1975). *Lipids* **10**, 185.
Weete, J. D. (1972). *Phytochemistry* **11**, 1201.
Weete, J. D. (1973). *Phytochemistry* **12**, 1845.
Weete, J. D. (1974). *In* "Fungal Lipid Biochemistry, Monographs in Lipid Research" (D. Kritchevsky, ed.), Ch. 2, p. 39. Plenum, New York.
Weete, J. D., and Laseter, J. L. (1974). *Lipids* **7**, 575.
Weete, J. D., Laseter, J. L., Weber, D. J., Hess, W. M., and Stocks, D. L. (1969). *Phytopathology* **59**, 545.
Weete, J. D., Weber, D. J., and Laseter, J. L. (1970a). *J. Bacteriol.* **103**, 536.
Weete, J. D., Weber, D. J., and LeTourneau, D. (1970b). *Arch. Mikrobiol.* **75**, 59.
Weete, J. D., Laseter, J. L., and Lawler, G. C. (1973a). *Arch. Biochem. Biophys.* **155**, 411.
Weete, J. D., Hart, L. T., Dimopoullos, G. T., and Larson, A. D. (1973b). *Abstr. Soc. Microbiol., Annu. Meet.* p. 19.
Weiland, H., and Bened, W. (1943). *Justus Liebigs Ann. Chem.* **554**, 1.
Weiss, B., and Stiller, R. L. (1967). *J. Biol. Chem.* **242**, 2903.
Weiss, B., and Stiller, R. L. (1972). *Biochemistry* **11**, 4522.
Weiss, B., Stiller, R. L., and Jack, R. C. M. (1973). *Lipids* **8**, 25.
Wells, W. N., Schultz, J., and Lynen, F. (1966). *Proc. Natl. Acad. Sci. U.S.A.* **56**, 633.
Wheeler, G. E., Michell, R. H., and Rose, A. H. (1970). *Biochem. J.* **127**, 64P.
White, G. L., and Hawthorne, J. N. (1970). *Biochem. J.* **117**, 203.

White, H. B., and Powell, S. S. (1966). *Biochim. Biophys. Acta* **116**, 388.
Wieland, H., and Stanley, W. M. (1931). *Justus Liebigs Ann. Chem.* **489**, 31.
Willecke, K., Ritter, E., and Lynen, F. (1969). *Eur. J. Biochem.* **8**, 503.
Wirth, J. C., and Anand, S. R. (1964). *Can. J. Microbiol.* **10**, 23.
Wirth, J. C., Annand, S. R., and Kish, Z. L. (1964). *Can. J. Microbiol.* **10**, 811.
Woodbine, M. (1959). *Prog. Ind. Microbiol.* **1**, 179.
Wykle, R. L., Blank, M. L., Malone, B., and Snyder, F. (1972). *J. Biol. Chem.* **247**, 5442.
Yang, C. P., Butterworth, P. H. W., Bock, R. M., and Porter, J. W. (1967). *J. Biol. Chem.* **242**, 3501.
Yokokawa, H. (1969). *Yukagaku* **18**, 258.
Yokokawa, H. (1970). *Yukagaku* **19**, 97.
Yuan, C., and Bloch, K. (1961). *J. Biol. Chem.* **236**, 1277.

The Biochemistry of Plant Sterols

WILLIAM R. NES

Department of Biological Sciences,
Drexel University,
Philadelphia, Pennsylvania

I. Introduction

Plants are a diverse group of organisms that differ from animals by not possessing a nervous system. They can be grouped into two great categories: those with and those without photosynthetic capacity. The photosynthetic group are comprised in turn by four subgroups: the autotrophic bacteria; the algae, including the phytoflagellates, which resemble protozoa; the bryophytes; and the more familiar tracheophytes (vascular plants, such as trees). The nonphotosynthetic group include the heterotrophic bacteria, mycoplasmas, protozoa, slime molds, fungi, and probably the sponges. In the present review, an attempt will be made to summarize the present state of our knowledge of the structure, biosynthesis, and function of the sterols of this varied biological spectrum. In addition, other questions arise. What taxonomic and evolutionary correlations exist? How does sterol biochemistry differ in plants and animals? What happens when a plant ingests or absorbs or is experimentally presented with a sterol that it does not itself make? What metabolic pathways are present or can be induced? What kinds of mechanisms exist to govern what can happen either in *de novo* biosynthesis or as a resultant of sterol presentation? What governs the mechanisms that exist? How did they arise? And why? Do all plants biosynthesize sterols *de novo*? Are there any developmental phenomena? Is there a distinction between the function of "dominant sterols" and some of the "trace sterols"? Are some of the "trace sterols" the resultant of "dead-end metabolism"? This chapter will also explore some of these and other areas where fact or theory present an opportunity for rational development. But first we must examine the details of structure itself.

II. Structure and Stereochemistry

A. ORIENTING REMARKS

The steroidal structure is composed of two very different units. They are the tetracyclic "nucleus" in which all the carbon atoms are in rings (annular) and three types of nonannular (acyclic) carbon atoms (Fig. 1). The first of the acyclic types is comprised by three C_1 groups, usually in a completely reduced state, two of which are attached to C-4 and one to C-14. Residual atoms from the hexaisopentenoid precursor (squalene) are composed of 30

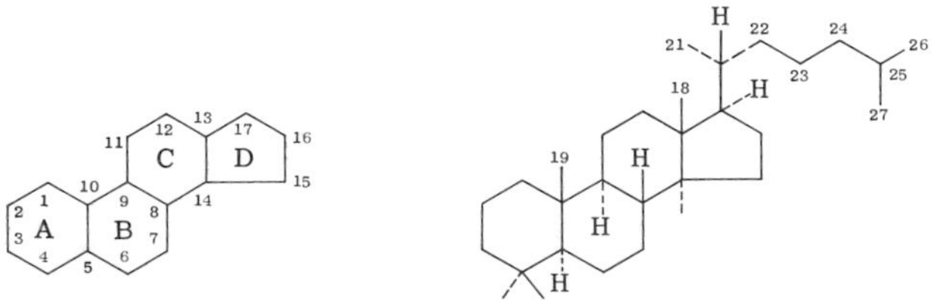

Tetracyclic nucleus
of steroids

Nucleus with all C_1 groups
and C_8 side chain

FIG. 1. Steroid structure and stereochemistry. H and CH_3 groups attached to the nucleus and shown with an interrupted line are designated α and project away from the observer; those with a solid line are designated β and project toward the observer. The convention is different in the side chain. See Figs. 4 and 5 and consult the text.

carbon atoms; these C_1 groups are removed in the biosynthetic process and only rarely appear among the dominant sterols of either plants or animals. Two axial methyl groups, one on C-10 and one on C-13, constitute the second acyclic type. Since they project out from the nucleus (toward the observer in Fig. 1) at an angle of 90° relative to the coplanar arrangement of alternate nuclear atoms, they are referred to as "angular methyls." They are present in all dominant sterols with the exception of the sponge *Axinella polypoides*, which contains a mixture primarily composed of 24-methyl and 24-ethyl sterols lacking C-19 (Minale and Sodano, 1974). In some intermediates the methyl group (C-19) on C-10 is modified, as will be seen in the biosynthetic section. This modification (9,19-cyclo grouping appearing biosynthetically first in cycloartenol) distinguishes photosynthetic from non-photosynthetic organisms. The third acyclic carbon type is attached to C-17. Present in all dominant sterols, this group of atoms, known as the "side chain," numbers commonly from eight in the "C_{27}-sterols" to ten in the "C_{29}-sterols" and occasionally is larger. The side chain has two features not present in the other two acyclic types of carbon atom. Being a chain, it can presumably assume a multitude of conformations. Second, being a branched chain, it allows for asymmetry beyond the asymmetry intrinsic in the nucleus and its attached C_1 groups. Asymmetry commonly exists at C-20 and C-24.

The term "steroid" was coined by Fieser and Fieser (1949) and was intended to refer to any structure that was like ("-oid") cholesterol, cholestanol, the latter's C-5 epimer (coprostanol), the bile acids, etc., in that the structure in question has the same nuclear skeleton as cyclopentanophenanthrene. This skeleton is shown in Fig. 1. The Fieser and Fieser definition, while useful, unfortunately ignores stereochemistry and would, for instance, include euphol (Fig. 2) and its relatives within the steroid family. Euphol has inverted stereochemistry at C-13, C-14, and C-17 compared to true steroids and is an epimer of one of the steroid intermediates, lanosterol. Furthermore, since terpenes have been defined by the number of multiples of a C_{10} unit present in their structures (monoterpene, C_{10}; sesquiterpene, C_{15}; etc.), the 4,4,14-trimethylsterols with thirty carbon atoms, such as lanosterol, have often also been referred to as "triterpenoids" and grouped together with euphol. In order to be more exacting, we shall use the term "steroid" to imply only those compounds that originate in squalene or its oxide by a cyclization process forming four rings of the cyclopentanophenanthrene type in which the molecule approximates trans-syn-trans-anti-trans-anti stereochemistry in the transition state (Fig. 2). As will be seen more fully in the section on biosynthesis, this definition includes both lanosterol and cycloartenol as well as cholesterol, sitosterol, cholestanol, its C-5 epimer, bile acids, and estrone, but it excludes euphol. With reference to a polycycle

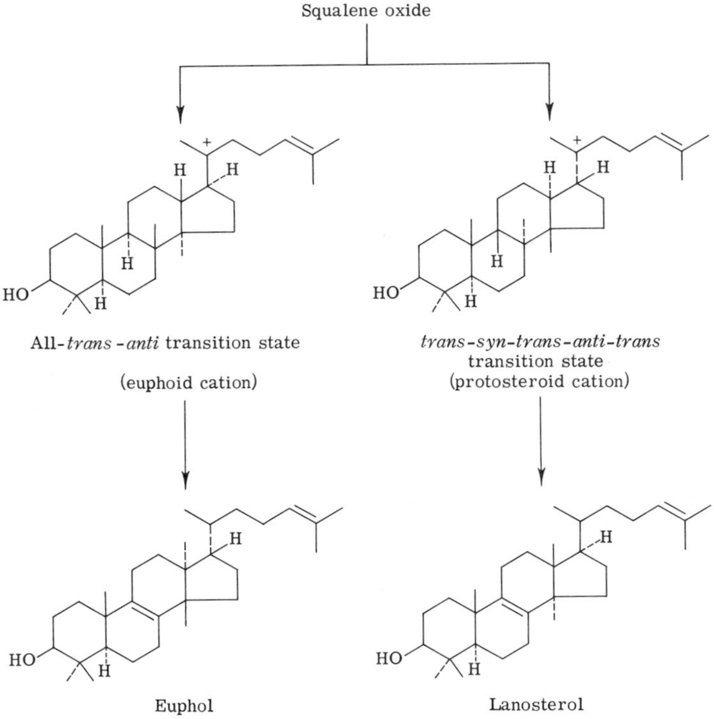

FIG. 2.   Tetracyclic triterpenoid and steroid pathways.

derived from squalene, the term "triterpenoid" will be reserved for a compound derived through an all-trans-anti transition state (Fig. 2). Both the tetracyclic euphol and the pentacyclic tetrahymanol fall into this category. The term "sterol," never given a precise definition, will be used to imply a steroid bearing a hydroxy group at C-3 and a lipophilic character. The lipophilic character restricts the number of polar groups. Thus, estrone, bile acids, and the hormone metabolite tetrahydrocortisol, with five hydroxyl groups, are not lipophilic, having much greater solubility in water than the sterol, cholesterol, from which they are metabolically derived. Consequently, they would not be "sterols." 22-Hydroxycholesterol, however, which is present in lilies, would be a sterol. The definition of a sterol here given could be made more precise as occasion demands by placing limiting numbers on solubility or other lipid characteristic(s). Until this is done, the question as to whether the ecdysones, some of which are biosynthesized by plants, or the hydroxyvitamin D metabolites should be called sterols is a bit equivocal. We shall presently assume them to be too polar and not discuss them in detail. Nearly all sterols are derivatives of 5α-cholestan-3β-ol, which is shown in Fig. 3 together with sterols possessing the three most common

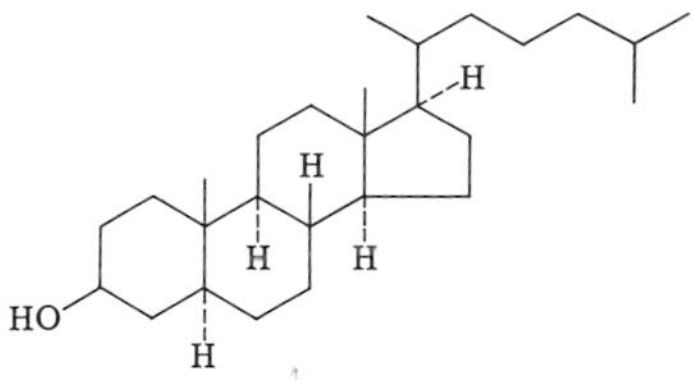

5α-Cholestan-3β-ol
(cholestanol)

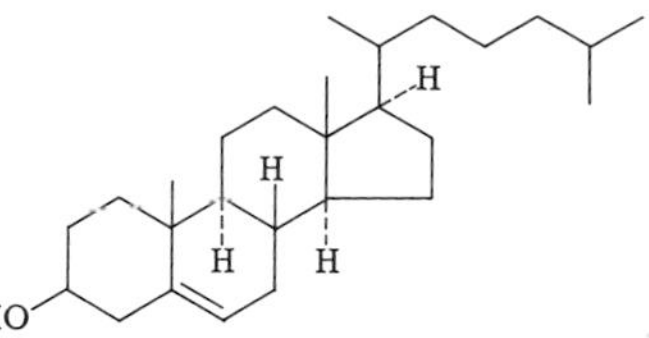

Cholest-5-en-3β-ol
(cholesterol)

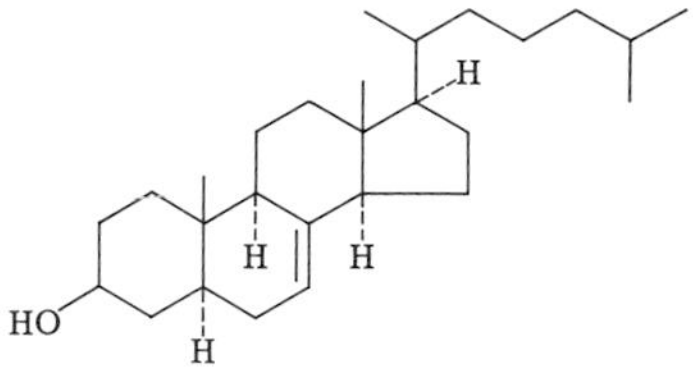

Cholest-7-en-3β-ol
(lathosterol)

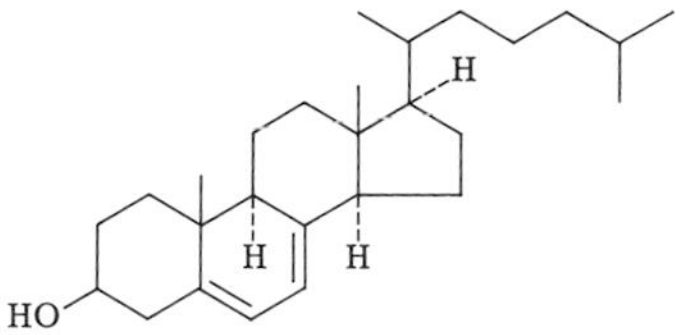

Cholesta-5,7-dien-3β-ol
(7-dehydrocholesterol)

FIG. 3.   Basic sterol structures.

types of nuclear unsaturation (Δ^5 as in cholesterol, Δ^7 as in lathosterol, and $\Delta^{5,7}$ as in 7-dehydrocholesterol). The figure also illustrates systematic nomenclature. Table I lists the trivial names that have been assigned to various sterols.

B. NUCLEAR STEREOCHEMISTRY

There is no new information on nuclear stereochemistry. The older literature that was definitive has been elegantly reviewed by Fieser and Fieser (1949, 1959) for animal sterols. The presumption that plant sterols have the same nuclear configurations as those in animals has been documented in several cases also reviewed by the Fiesers (1949, 1959). Examples are chemical conversion of plant sterols to pregnenolene (the 20-ketone corresponding to cleavage of cholesterol, sitosterol, etc., between C-20 and C-22) or to deoxycorticosterone (the Δ^4-3-ketone corresponding to 20-hydroxypregnenolene), which are derived biologically from cholesterol without alterations in the nuclear skeleton and without stereochemical inversion.

C. SIDE-CHAIN STEREOCHEMISTRY

The side chains of plant sterols, not previously well investigated, have been the subject of much interest in recent years at biosynthetic and structural levels as well as in relation to phylogenetics. Two dominant varieties exist:

Table I

TRIVIAL NAMES OF STEROLS

Names	Structure based on changes or additions to 5α-cholestan-3β-ol (cholestanol)
Coprostanol	5β-H
24-Epiergostanol (campestanol)	24α-Methyl
Ergostanol	24β-Methyl
24-Epistigmastanol (poriferastanol)	24β-Ethyl
Stigmastanol	24α-Ethyl
Cholesterol	Δ^5
Campesterol (24α-methylcholesterol)	Δ^5-24α-Methyl
22-Dihydrobrassicasterol (24β-methylcholesterol; Δ^5-ergostenol)	Δ^5-24β-Methyl
Sitosterol (24α-ethylcholesterol)	Δ^5-24α-Ethyl
Clionasterol (24β-methylcholesterol)	Δ^5-24β-Ethyl
Clerosterol (25(27)-dehydroclionasterol)	$\Delta^{5,25(27)}$-24β-ethyl
22-Dehydrocholesterol	$\Delta^{5,trans-22}$
Diatomsterol (crinosterol) (pincsterol)	$\Delta^{5,trans-22}$-24α-Methyl
Brassicasterol	$\Delta^{5,trans-22}$-24β-Methyl
Stigmasterol	$\Delta^{5,trans-22}$-24α-Ethyl
Poriferasterol	$\Delta^{5,trans-22}$-24β-Ethyl
Lathosterol	Δ^7
Epifungisterol (24α-methyllathosterol)	Δ^7-24α-Methyl
Fungisterol (24β-methyllathosterol; Δ^7-ergostenol)	Δ^7-24β-Methyl
22-Dihydrospinasterol (24α-ethyllathosterol; schottenol; Δ^7-stigmastenol)	Δ^7-24α-Ethyl
22-Dihydrochondrillasterol (24β-ethyllathosterol)	Δ^7-24β-Ethyl
22-Dehydrolathosterol	$\Delta^{7,trans-22}$
22-Dehydroepifugisterol	$\Delta^{7,trans-22}$-24α-Methyl
22-Dehydrofungisterol (5-dihydroergosterol)	$\Delta^{7,trans-22}$-24β-Methyl
Spinasterol	$\Delta^{7,trans-22}$-24α-Ethyl
Chondrillasterol	$\Delta^{7,trans-22}$-24β-Ethyl
7-Dehydrocholesterol	$\Delta^{5,7}$
22-Dihydroepiergosterol (7-dehydrocampesterol)	$\Delta^{5,7}$-24α-Methyl
22-Dihydroergosterol (7-dehydro-Δ^5-ergostenol)	$\Delta^{5,7}$-24β-Methyl
24-Epiergosterol	$\Delta^{5,7,trans-22}$-24α-Methyl
Ergosterol	$\Delta^{5,7,trans-22}$-24β-Methyl
7-Dehydrositosterol	$\Delta^{5,7}$-24α-Ethyl
7-Dehydroclionasterol	$\Delta^{5,7}$-24β-Ethyl
7-Dehydrostigmasterol	$\Delta^{5,7,trans-22}$-24α-Ethyl
7-Dehydroporiferasterol	$\Delta^{5,7,trans-22}$-24β-Ethyl
Lichesterol	$\Delta^{5,8,trans-22}$-24β-Methyl

Table I (*Continued*)

Names	Structure based on changes or additions to 5α-cholestan-3β-ol (cholestanol)
Ostreasterol (chalinasterol; 24-methylenecholesterol)	Δ^5-24-Methylene
Fucosterol	Δ^5-*cis*-24-Ethylidene
28-Isofucosterol (Δ^5-avenasterol)	Δ^5-*trans*-24-Ethylidene
Episterol (24-methylenelathosterol)	Δ^7-24-Methylene
Fecosterol (24-methylenezymosterol)	Δ^8-24-Methylene
5-Dehydroepisterol	$\Delta^{5,7}$-24-Methylene
Δ^7-Avenasterol	Δ^7-*trans*-24-Ethylidene
Vernosterol	$\Delta^{8(9),\ 14(15)}$-*trans*-Ethylidene
Haliclonasterol	Δ^5-20-Epi-24α-methyl
Sargosterol	Δ^5-20-Epi-*cis*-24-ethylidene
22-Hydroxycholesterol	Δ^5-(22S)-22-Hydroxy
Saringosterol	Δ^5-24-Hydroxy-24-vinyl
Carpesterol	Δ^7-6-Keto-22α-hydroxy-4α-methyl-24α-ethyl
Peniocerol	Δ^8-6α-Hydroxy
Macdougallin	Δ^8-6α-Hydroxy-14α-methyl
Pollinastanol	9,19-Cyclo-14α-methyl
Lophenol	Δ^7-4α-Methyl
Citrostadienol (24-ethylidenelophenol)	Δ^7-4α-Methyl-*trans*-ethylidene
Obtusifoliol	Δ^8,4,14α-Dimethyl-24-methylene
Cycloeucalenol	9,19-Cyclo-4α,14α-dimethyl-24-methylene
Desmosterol	$\Delta^{5,24}$
Zymosterol	$\Delta^{8,24}$
Ascosterol	$\Delta^{8,23}$
Celsianol	$\Delta^{5,9(11)}$-24α-Ethyl
Codisterol	$\Delta^{5,25(27)}$-24β-Methyl
Clerosterol	$\Delta^{5,25(27)}$-24β-Ethyl
Elasterol	$\Delta^{7,16,25}$-24α-Ethyl
Indosterol	$\Delta^{9(11),22}$-24α-Ethyl
Lanosterol	$\Delta^{8,24}$-4,4,14α-Trimethyl
Parkeol	$\Delta^{9(11),24}$-4,4,14α-Trimethyl
Cycloartenol	Δ^{24}-9,19-Cyclo-4,4,14α-trimethyl
Cyclobranol (24-methylcycloartenol)	Δ^{24}-9,19-Cyclo-4,4,14α,24-tetramethyl
Cyclosadol	Δ^{23}-9,19-Cyclo-4,4,14α,24-tetramethyl
Cyclolaudenol	$\Delta^{25(27)}$-9,19-Cyclo-4,4,14α,24β-tetramethyl
Gramisterol (24-methylenelophenol)	Δ^7-4α-Methyl-24-methylene

those with and those without a Δ^{22} bond, and those with 0, 1, or 2 carbon atoms at C-24. The latter two types possess an asymmetric (chiral) center at C-24. A chiral center also exists at C-20.

Two conventions of nomenclature are currently in use to describe the stereochemistry of the side chain. One is the sequence rule described by

Cahn *et al.* (1956, 1966). Since it employs excessive empirical "priorities" and even then uses opposite notations for the same configuration at C-24 when there is or is not a Δ^{22} bond, the sequence rule will not be used in this chapter. Instead we will use an extension of the Fieser and Fieser (1959) modification of the Fischer and Plattner conventions as described in the next paragraph.

Assume each of the carbon atoms in the side chain to have been rotated such that all those carbon atoms proceeding from C-17 in a linear array lie in a single plane passing perpendicularly through C-17. Assume further that the side chain is oriented away from the observer who is looking toward the β-face of the nucleus held in the plane of the paper with C-3 at the bottom left and that every fourth carbon atom of the side chain is cis-oriented with respect to each other. If now the C—C—C angle is forced into a 180° arrangement (flattened), a Fischer projection is obtained, and atoms to the left are said to be β-oriented and those to the right to be α-oriented (Fig. 4). This is the Fischer–Plattner–Fieser-and-Fieser convention. We will modify it slightly in the following way. Instead of flattening the side chain, let us simply rotate it 90° around the C-17,20 bond such that it appears on our right. Those atoms, then, that are in front of the plane of the chain (which is more or less that of the paper and the nucleus) are α-oriented, and those projecting to the rear are β-oriented (Fig. 4). The notation for configuration is then the same as before, but it relates more closely to a real conformer rather than to an artificially flattened system of carbon atoms. If the side chain is next placed in the staggered conformation, which is the one we normally write, the α,β designations with respect to front and back, respectively, remain the same except at C-23, where α refers to the substituent toward the rear. In order to avoid all complication, we shall simply use the staggered conformer as a standard (Fig. 5). Groups in front of the plane are α-oriented; those in back are β-oriented. Except at C-23 the designations

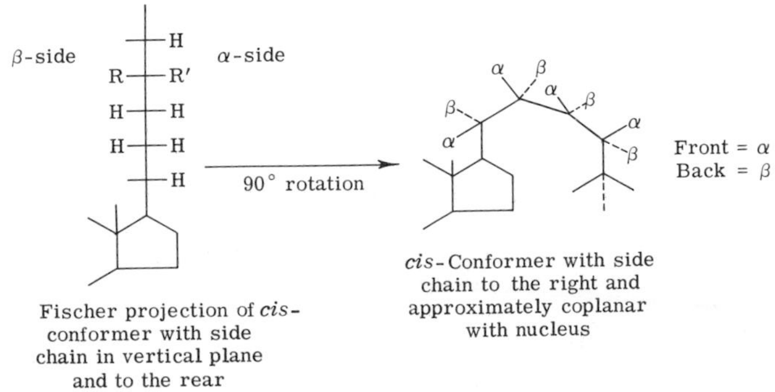

FIG. 4.   Earlier conventions of stereochemical nomenclature.

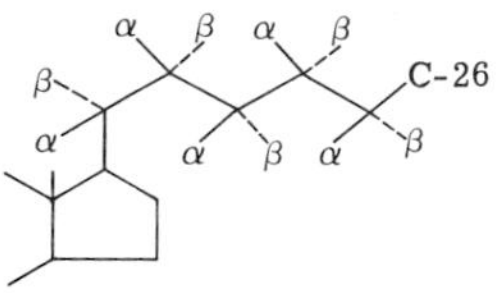

Staggered conformation

FIG. 5. Nomenclature convention used in this chapter.

are the same as in the older convention. The configuration at C-25 remains equivocal unless we specify which of the two methyl groups is to be placed in the plane of the paper. We will arbitrarily take it to be the one that is trans-oriented with respect to C-23 in squalene. This is the methyl group bearing label from $[2-^{14}C]$-mevalonate. We will also assume this C atom to be number 26. With this convention, the 25-H atom can be assigned an α or β designation.

24α-Methyl sterols possessing no Δ^{22} bond are designated $(24R)$-24-methyl sterols by the sequence rule, but in the Δ^{22} series 24α-methyl sterols have the S notation. Conversely, 24β-methyl sterols in the saturated series have the S notation, but in the 22,23-dehydro case they are assigned the R configuration. The cis-Δ^{22} bond is described by the letter Z (zusammen, German for together) and the $trans$-Δ^{22} bond by E (entgegen, German for opposite) in the nomenclature derived from the sequence rule. Since there is but one

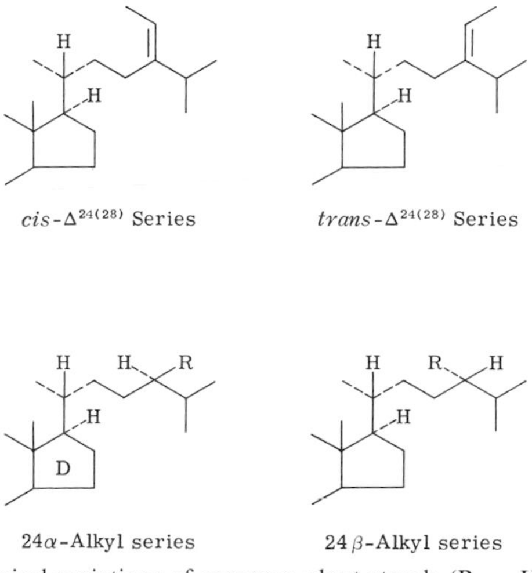

cis-$\Delta^{24(28)}$ Series

$trans$-$\Delta^{24(28)}$ Series

24α-Alkyl series

24β-Alkyl series

FIG. 6. Stereochemical variations of common plant sterols ($R = $ H, CH_3, or C_2H_5). In the sequence rule nomenclature, the cis-$\Delta^{24(28)}$ series is designated E, the $trans$ series Z, the 24α-alkyl series R, the 24β series S, the Δ^{22}-24α-alkyl series S, and the Δ^{22}-24β-alkyl series R. The Δ^{22} bond when present is usually trans-oriented, and is also designated E.

substituent on each of the carbon atoms of the double bond, the cis–trans and E–Z notations always agree for the Δ^{22} bond, but for the $\Delta^{24(28)}$ bond of sterols with a C_2 group on C-24, the sequence rule gives greater priority to the branched isopropyl group (C-25, C-26, and C-27) than to the twenty-three carbon atoms (C-1 through C-23) on the other side of C-24 owing to their proceeding from an unbranched system (C-22 and C-23). Thus, when C-29 is cis-oriented to the large group (C-1 through C-23), it has the E geometry by the notation derived from the sequence rule, although together-ness (of the two larger groups) and a Z notation would have been expected had branching not to be considered (Fig. 6). Consequently, we will use the more direct cis–trans nomenclature for the sterols without implying that the sequence rule is not useful in other cases. Where possible we will also use the α,β-notation instead of the "pro-R,S" notation that follows from the sequence rule. While the latter designation allows correlations with non-steroidal materials, it complicates correlations within the side chain itself.

A "pro-R" or "pros-S" H atom is one in a formally nonchiral carbon atom that would confer the R or S designation on the atom if the H atom were deuterium and such a change conferred chirality on the atom. Thus, at C-24 the pro-R-H atom has the α configuration in the 24-dealkyl series, because, viewed from the 24β-H atom toward C-24, the substituents D, CH_2-R, and $CH(CH_3)_2$ are found with decreasing priority in a clockwise ("Rectus") rather than counterclockwise ("Sinister") order. At C-23 the pro-R-H atom also has the α configuration, but only in the 24-dealkyl series. The same α-oriented H atom in the 24-alkyl series is given the pro-S designation. On the other hand, at C-22 the α-H atom is the pro-S-H atom in the 24-alkyl as well as in the 24-dealkyl series. These complicated reversals, each of which requires substantial intellectual gymnastics to follow, are made unnecessary simply by using the α,β convention derived from the staggered conformation (Fig. 5). Consequently, where possible, data recorded in the literature in the pro-R,S convention will be transferred to the α,β convention.

D. Isolation and Identification

The isolation and identification of a particular compound falls into the general realm of structural elucidation, which can become quite complicated, especially for an unusual sterol. However, for the common dominant struc-tures recent advances in chromatography and spectroscopy now allow a relatively simple procedure. Except in rare cases, the neutral lipid chro-matographing on alumina or silica gel with approximately the same rate of movement as cholesterol is nearly all 4,4,14-trisdemethylsterol. Δ^{7}- and $\Delta^{5,7}$-Sterols move very slightly slower than cholesterol, and sterols retaining the 4-methyl and 4,4-dimethyl groups move, respectively, somewhat faster and a great deal faster than cholesterol. Crystallization from a minimum volume of methanol will not usually alter the relative amounts of the major components but will remove xanthophylls, which frequently are trace contaminants of the 4,4,14-trisdemethyl fraction. Thus, a sterol fraction of substantial purity is readily available.

Subsequent separation according to the number and position of double bonds can be achieved by argentation chromatography, which is especially useful for the separation of sterols with a $\Delta^{24(28)}$ bond. The order of increasing rate is sterols with a methylene group, ethylidene group, and no $\Delta^{24(28)}$ bond. $\Delta^{5,7}$-Sterols can also be separated from Δ^{5}-sterols by argentation chromatography, but the diene system sometimes undergoes changes in the presence of silver ion. A good method for the isolation of these sterols not causing artifacts is chromatography on the recently introduced lipophilic Sephadex (Ellingboe *et al.*, 1970), on which they move substantially faster than their Δ^{5} analogs. Lipophilic Sephadex also allows the separation of the homologous series of sterols with a 24-H atom, 24-methyl group, and 24-ethyl group. While the homologous series can be separated by reversed-phase chromatography (de Souza and Nes, 1969) and gas–liquid chromatography (Patterson, 1971a), the Sephadex system is preferable for preparative work (Nes *et al.*, 1976). Gas–liquid chromatography is an excellent way to identify and quantitate individual sterols in a mixture (Knights, 1973; Patterson, 1971a).

Mass spectroscopy, recently reviewed by Brooks and Middleditch (1973), then defines a number of structural parameters. Among them are the empirical formula and molecular weight, which follow from the molecular ion and isotopic distribution. Judicious use of the fragmentation pattern reveals, *inter alia*, the presence of a double bond (Δ^{5} or Δ^{8}) allylic to C-19, the presence of a $\Delta^{5,7}$ system, the presence of methyl groups in the nucleus, the presence of alkyl groups in the side chain, and the presence and position of double bonds in the side chain. Ultraviolet spectroscopy proves the presence and position of conjugated diene structures, and infrared absorption is distinctive for the *trans*-Δ^{22} bond.

Proton magnetic resonance (PMR) spectroscopy is similarly useful for the elucidation of many of these same structural features, and it is unique among physical methods in allowing us to distinguish the epimeric structures at C-24 (Thompson *et al.*, 1972; Mulheirn, 1973; Nes *et al.*, 1976). Slight differences in optical rotation are reported in the older literature for the epimers, but the purity of the samples is in question, substantial amounts are necessary, and mixtures cannot be analyzed. While differences in melting points of esters of the epimers also are reported, melting point data have drawbacks similar to those mentioned for optical rotations. They are all obviated by PMR spectroscopy. The configuration of the 24β-methyl group in ergosterol and the configuration of the 24α-ethyl group in stigmasterol have been firmly established by degradation followed by correlation of the C-24-containing fragment with standard small molecules (Tsuda *et al.*, 1960). Proton magnetic resonance spectroscopy has now shown that 24β-methyl-cholesterol (dihydrobrassicasterol) prepared from ergosterol has a markedly different spectrum from that of its epimer, campesterol, and a few percent of the latter in the former can be quantitatively analyzed. In the case of 24-ethylcholesterol, the spectrum also allows unequivocal configurational assignment. Neither the presence of a Δ^{22} bond nor of a $\Delta^{5,7}$-diene system interfere with the determination, and it can be carried out on as little as 3 mg. In fact, the PMR absorption of methyl groups alone is so finely influenced by structural features that the spectrum is essentially a "fingerprint" of the entire sterol. Since the method has become so useful recently, some of the more important features dealing with the common sterols are described in what follows.

At 220 MHz, cholesterol exhibits two distinct though incompletely resolved doublets even for the two *gem*-dimethyl groups (C-26 and C-27). Since these two are formally equivalent, their separation in the spectrum shows the subtle influence of the asymmetric environment provided not closer than five carbons away in the remainder of the molecule. Wing *et al.* (1974) have shown similar resolution of C-26 and C-27 in vitamin D_3 at 330 MHz. The introduction of a 24α-methyl group (campesterol) results (at 220MHz) in a further separation (7 Hz) of the doublet for C-26 and C-27. All four doublets ($J = 6$–7 Hz) expected for the four methyl groups in the side chain are readily seen (C-21, 200 Hz; C-26 and C-27, 187 and 188 Hz; C-28, 177 Hz), although the left- and right-hand peaks fall at the same place in one case experimentally, yielding seven instead of eight peaks with a single peak of double intensity at 173 Hz. The doublet for C-21 is unchanged from the position in cholesterol at 200 Hz, but it is moved strongly downfield in the Δ^{22} derivative which along with a shift in the signal from C-18 is diagnostic for the Δ^{22} bond. When the configuration at C-24 is inverted (dihydrobrassicasterol), all four of the doublets now are completely separated and the eight expected peaks occupy discrete places in the spectrum. The failure to have any overlap, as there is in campesterol, is due to a shift of 5 Hz upfield for the campesterol doublet at 177 Hz (C-28). A shift (3 Hz downfield) also occurs in the doublet for C-21. These shifts are immensely valuable for diagnostic purposes (Nes, 1974a; Nes *et al.*, 1976; Rubinstein *et al.*, 1976).

The introduction of a 24α-ethyl group (sitosterol) alters the PMR spectrum of cholesterol dramatically through a shift in and further separation of the doublets for C-26 and C-27 together with introduction of a triplet for C-29. The J value for the triplet is 7 Hz, and all three peaks are seen to be centered at 186 Hz. The two doublets for C-26 and C-27 are assignable at 184 and

179 Hz. A doublet at 203 Hz is derived from C-21, because it is shifted downfield to 225 Hz in stigmasterol owing to the allylic effect of the Δ^{22} bond. Much smaller shifts (2–4 Hz) occur in the doublets for C-26 and C-27 of stigmasterol, since they are separated by two carbon atoms from the Δ^{22} bond. While inversion of the configuration at C-24 (sitosterol to clionasterol) results in much less change in the spectrum than is observed in the epimeric 24-methyl sterols, the doublet for C-21 is shifted slightly (1 Hz) downfield, and the triplet for C-29 is moved downfield by 2 Hz. The doublets for C-26 and C-27 are almost unchanged. The net result is that the central part of the triplet (186 Hz) which was 2 Hz to the left is now (at 188 Hz) further to the left (by 5 Hz) of the most fully downfield peak (at 183 Hz) for C-26 and C-27, and the right-hand peak of the triplet observable in sitosterol at 179 Hz has now disappeared under one of the *gem*-dimethyl peaks at 182 Hz.

Introduction of a Δ^{22} bond into the epimeric 24-ethyl sterols does not prevent the differences due to inversion of the configuration from being manifest. The expected seven peaks for the triplet for C-29 (177 Hz, $J = 7$) and for the two doublets (186 and 175 Hz) for C-26 and C-27 are seen in stigmasterol, although one of the peaks (183 Hz) for C-26 or C-28 is only a shoulder. In the epimeric poriferasterol only six of the seven peaks are separate (including a shoulder at 177 Hz for one of the C-26 or C-27 doublets), and the positions are shifted very slightly (ca. 1 Hz). As in the 22,23-dihydro cases (sitosterol and clionasterol), the two doublets for C-26 and C-27 are also shifted only slightly (within 1 Hz) owing to inversion of the configuration. These small shifts, however, induce major changes in the appearance of the spectrum. The downfield shift of about 1 Hz in the triplet for C-29 in proceeding from stigmasterol to poriferasterol reduces two peaks to one by overlap and intensification of the right-hand portion (171 Hz) of the triplet with the right-hand portion of one of the doublets for C-26 or C-27. It also results in emergence of the left-hand portion of the triplet as a completely resolved peak at 185 Hz. A similarly small downfield shift in the relationship between the doublet for C-21 and the singlet for C-19 occurs in going from the 24α-ethyl- to the 24β-ethyl-Δ^{22}-sterol. Since the peak for C-19 bifurcates the doublet, the small shift results in different overlapping and alterations in the apparent intensities of the peaks for C-21.

The spectra of 24β-methyl-Δ^{22}-cholesterol (brassicasterol) and its 7,8-dehydro derivative (ergosterol) show discrete peaks for all the doublets. Within 1 Hz the six peaks for C-26, C-27, and C-28 are identical in the two sterols, but the presence of the Δ^7 bond in the $\Delta^{5,7}$-diene strongly shifts the four peaks for C-18, C-19, and C-21. The spectrum of 24-epiergosterol shows a shift in the signal for C-21 comparable to that found in campesterol compared to dihydrobrassicasterol. The spectra of the $\Delta^{24(28)}$-sterols (ostreasterol and fucosterol) show the expected allylic downfield shifts for C-26

Table II
AMOUNTS OF STEROLS IN PLANTS

Plant	Part	Percent of wet (W) or dry (D) weight	References
Cyanophyta			
Phormidium luridum	Whole	0.003 W	de Souza and Nes (1968)
Charophyta			
Nitella flexilis	Whole	0.09 D	Patterson (1972)
Chara vulgaris		0.06 D	Patterson (1972)
Chlorophyta			
Enteromorpha intestinalis	Whole	0.027 W	Gibbons _et al._ (1968)
Ulva lactuca	Whole	0.020 W	Gibbons _et al._ (1968)
Chlorella (5 species)	Whole	0.2 D	Patterson (1969)
Green algae (13 species)	Whole	0.05–0.38 D	Patterson (1974)
Codium fragile	Whole	0.0076 W	Rubinstein and Goad (1974a)
Phaeophyta			
Ascophyllum nodosa	Whole	0.10 D	Safe _et al._ (1974)
Furcellaria fastigiata	Whole	0.02 D	Safe _et al._ (1974)
Fucus vesiculosus	Whole	0.1 W	Nes _et al._ (unpublished observations)
Nine species	Whole	0.02–0.24 D	Ikekawa _et al._ (1968)
Chrysophyta			
Diatoms (11 species)	Whole	0.06–0.57 D	Orcutt and Patterson (1975)
Ochromonas malhamensis	Whole	1.3 D	Gershengorn _et al._ (1968)
Ochromonas danica	Whole	0.33 W	Gershengorn _et al._ (1968)
Fungi			
Yeast (69 species)	Whole	Less than 0.1 to 10 D	Dulaney _et al._ (1954)
Neurospora crassa	Whole	0.032 W	Nes _et al._ (unpublished observations)
Agaricus sp.	Whole	0.021 W	Nes _et al._ (unpublished observations)
Phycomycetes			
(4 species)	Whole	0.003–0.26 D	Bean _et al._ (1973)
(22 species)	Mycelia	0.005–0.25 D	McCorkindale _et al._ (1969)
Slime molds			
Dictyostelium discoideum	Whole	0.3 D	Heftmann _et al._ (1960)
Tracheophyta			
Castanea vulgaris	Pollen	0.13 D	Hugel _et al._ (1964)

Table II (*Continued*)

Plant	Part	Percent of wet (W) or dry (D) weight	References
Hypocheris radiata	Pollen	0.9 D	Hugel *et al.* (1964)
Zea mays	Pollen	0.15 D	Hugel *et al.* (1964)
Pinus montana	Pollen	0.14 D	Hugel *et al.* (1964)
Saguaro sp.	Pollen	1.0 D	Nes *et al.* (unpublished observations)
Pinus pinea	Seeds	0.125 Ungerminated	van Aller *et al.* (1969)
Pisum sativum	Seeds	0.072 Ungerminated	Baisted *et al.* (1962)
Pisum sativum	Seeds	0.030 Germinated	Baisted *et al.* (1962)
Cucurbita pepo	Seeds	0.026 Ungerminated	Sucrow and Reimerdes (1968)
Cucurbita pepo	Leaves	0.02 W	Nes *et al.* (unpublished observations)
Cucumis sativus	Seeds	0.062 Ungerminated	Sucrow and Reimerdes (1968)
Brassica oleracea	Leaves	0.003 W	Nes *et al.* (unpublished observations)
Podophyllum peltatum	Leaves	0.027 W	Nes *et al.* (unpublished observations)
Liriodendron tulipifera	Leaves	0.032 W	Nes *et al.* (unpublished observations)
Dryopteris novaboracensis	Leaves	0.064 W	Nes *et al.* (unpublished observations)
Lycopodium complanatum	Leaves	0.042 W	Nes *et al.* (unpublished observations)

and C-27. In fucosterol C-26 and C-27 yield coincident doublets, and there is a more dramatic downfield shift in the doublet for C-21. The spectra of the completely saturated stigmastanol and cholestanol show the expected strong upfield shift (46 Hz) for C-19, which is no longer influenced by the Δ^5 bond. The absorptions for C-26, C-27, and C-29 are not significantly changed, but the singlets for C-18 and the doublets for C-21 are both moved upfield several Hz. Δ^7-Sterols can be distinguished from Δ^5-sterols by a shift in the signal for C-18 from 150 Hz in the latter to 118 Hz in the former as in the change from cholesterol to lathosterol.

III. The Dominant Sterols

A. Orienting Remarks

Sterols are present in both plants and animals in amounts varying between approximately 0.01 and 0.1% of wet weight in the majority of cases for which data are available (Table II). This means that 1 kg of fresh material will usually contain sterols in the amount of 100–1000 mg. Specimens that are physiologically dry, such as seeds or pollen, tend not only toward the higher limit, but as in the case of pollen, which approaches 1% sterol, may considerably surpass it. The lower limit is reached or exceeded in leaves of some but not all plants and in some algae, especially Phycomycetes and Cyanophyta. However, surprisingly little information on the quantity of sterols is available. More data would be of great value in the interpretation of function and other biological parameters.

The sterols comprising ca. 90% of the mixture have been called the "dominant sterols" (Nes, 1974b). In practically all cases these are principally composed of the 4,4,14-trisdemethyl derivatives. In addition, there are sterols in smaller quantities including trace amounts. In this category one usually finds sterols bearing one or more of the three methyl groups on C-4 and C-14 as well as others, e.g., sterols with a Δ^7, Δ^8, or $\Delta^{24(28)}$ bond. Examples of these minor components in higher plants are cycloartenol, pollinasterol, 24-methylenecycloartanol, lophenol, isofucosterol, and Δ^7-avenasterol. In fungi, examples are fungisterol, dihydroergosterol, and zymosterol. These compounds may be intermediates, although the evidence is not by any means unequivocal. As will be discussed subsequently, the problems involved here of biosynthetic sequence vs dead end pathways become quite serious and have not been resolved.

B. TRACHEOPHYTA

There are four subphyla of the Phylum Tracheophyta (vascular plants). In increasing order of evolutionary development, they are the Psilopsida, Lycopsida, Sphenopsida, and Pteropsida. Examples of the first, second, and third are, respectively, *Psilotum nudum* (the whisk fern), *Lycopodium complanatum*, and *Equisetum* (a horsetail). While not common, they can be found and have been partially investigated. They constituted an important part of the flora in earlier times. The highest subphylum has three classes, the Filicineae (ferns), Gymnospermae (conifers and allies), and Angiospermae (flowering plants). It is these that dominate the usual landscape, and they have been especially well investigated.

Sterols were isolated from the higher tracheophytes as early as the turn of the present century. In the case of stigmasterol, which was discovered by Windaus and Hauth (1906) in the early part of the present century in *Physostigma venenosum* (the Calabar bean) from which its name is derived, a double bond (Δ^{22}) present in the side chain permitted easy chemical degradation and correlation with animal steroids. The compound consequently played an important part in the evolution of our general knowledge of the steroid field. This early work among other things showed that sterols similar to cholesterol are present in photosynthetic plants. However, as well known as stigmasterol is, it is not commonly a major constituent of the dominant sterol mixture of tracheophytes. Only in rare cases, e.g., ivy, *Hedera helix*, (Hillman *et al.*, 1975), where it is indeed the major sterol, and soybean, where it is a 20% component, does it represent more than 10% of the sterol mixture. It has simply been easy to isolate through the insoluble character of its tetrabromide from which it can be regenerated. In the mid-1920s its 22,23-dihydro derivative, sitosterol, was isolated from wheat germ oil (Greek, *sito-*, grain) by Anderson *et al.* (1926). A quarter of a century later, sitosterol was still thought to be a "less common sterol" (Fieser and Fieser, 1949), and as late as 1959 only a brief paragraph is devoted to it in the most authoritative book in the field (Fieser and Fieser, 1959). However, evidence has been accumulating for a more prominent status. It appears to be the major component of the dominant sterol mixture of most higher plants. Exceptions include the families *Theaceae* and *Cucurbitaceae* in which Δ^7-sterols are not only dominant but apparently exclusive. The advent of gas–liquid chromatography, along with argentation and lipophilic Sephadex chromatography, mass spectrometry, and nuclear magnetic resonance (NMR) spectroscopy, has made it possible in the last decade not only to determine structures easily, but to quantitate relative amounts of different sterols. Information on composition from some representative investigations and covering a wide variety of plants is given in Tables III–V.

The older literature uses the name "β-sitosterol" for 24α-ethylcholesterol. The Greek letter was not meant to imply configuration, but to distinguish it from α- and γ-sitosterol. Since the latter two "compounds" are not discrete entities, having been shown to be mixtures (Thompson *et al.*, 1963; Bates *et al.*, 1968), modern usage is to drop the β. Sitosterol has recently been shown (Nes *et al.*, 1976) by NMR spectroscopy to have the 24α configuration without any epimer as contaminant in the New York fern (*Dryopteris noveboracensis* [L.]), the seeds of the stone pine (*Pinus pinea*), the leaves of the tulip tree (*Liriodendron tulipifera* [L.]), May apple (*Podophyllum peltatum* L.), cabbage (*Brassica oleracea* L.), and the seeds of peas (*Pisum sativum* L.) and soybeans (*Glycine max* [L.] Merr.). Similarly, 24-ethylcholesterol occurring in *Kalmia latifolia* (Nes and Nes, unpublished observations) and *Lycopodium complanatum* (Nes *et al.*, unpublished observations) has only the α configuration. In these plants, which represent all the classes within the Pteropsida, sitosterol was the major component of the sterol mixture. The epimer of sitosterol (24β-ethylcholesterol, clionasterol) has never been identified in tracheophytes and presumably is not biosynthesized in them. Chemical degradation (Tsuda *et al.*, 1960) of stigmasterol has established that it has the 24α-ethyl group, and its epimer (22-dehydro-24β-ethylcholesterol, poriferasterol) has also never been found in tracheophytes. On the other hand, 24β-ethyl sterols do exist in vascular plants, but those that are

Table III

SEEDS CONTAINING MOSTLY Δ^5-STEROLS

Plant	Sterol composition (%) Nomenclature base: cholesterol						References
	24-H	24-CH$_3$	24-C$_2$H$_5$	Δ^{22}-24-CH$_3$	Δ^{22}-24-C$_2$H$_5$	Other	
Corn	Trace	23	66	Trace	6	5	Itoh et al. (1973)
Rice	Trace	28	49	Trace	15	8	Itoh et al. (1973)
Wheat	Trace	22	67	Trace	Trace	11	Itoh et al. (1973)
Coconut	1	8	58	Trace	13	6	Itoh et al. (1973)
Palm	3	9	70	Trace	11	7	Itoh et al. (1973)
Peanut	Trace	15	64	Trace	9	12	Itoh et al. (1973)
Soybean	Trace	20	53	Trace	20	7	Itoh et al. (1973)
Sunflower	Trace	8	60	Trace	8	23	Itoh et al. (1973)
Safflower	—	14	52	Trace	9	24	Itoh et al. (1973)
Olive	—	2	87	Trace	1	9	Itoh et al. (1973)
Castor	Trace	10	44	Trace	22	24	Itoh et al. (1973)
Kapols	Trace	9	86	Trace	2	3	Itoh et al. (1973)
Cottonseed	Trace	4	93	Trace	1	2	Itoh et al. (1973)
Linseed	Trace	29	46	Trace	9	15	Itoh et al. (1973), Middleditch and Knights (1972)
Rapeseed	Trace	25	58	10	Trace	7	Itoh et al. (1973)
Sesame	—	19	62	Trace	10	9	Itoh et al. (1973)
Cocoa	2	9	59	Trace	26	4	Itoh et al. (1973)
Coffee	Trace	19	54	Trace	20	7	Itoh et al. (1973)
Pinus pinea	—	30	70	—	—	—	van Aller et al. (1969)
Pisum sativum	—	15	85	—	—	—	Castle et al. (1967), Knights (1972)
Lactuca sativa	1	14	52	—	12	22	Knights and Berrie (1971)
Arabis albida	1	23	76	—	—	—	Knights and Berrie (1971)
Cheiranthus cheri	15	18	38	—	—	29	Knights and Berrie (1971)
Alyssum maritimum	1	14	79	4	—	2	Knights and Berrie (1971)

Table IV

LEAVES CONTAINING MOSTLY Δ^5-STEROLS

Plant	24-H	24-CH$_3$[a,c,d]	24α-C$_2$H$_5$	Δ^{22}-24α-CH$_3$	Δ^{22}-24α-C$_2$H$_5$	Other	Reference
Lycopodium complanatum	—	8	38	—	16	38	a
Ginkgo biloba	—	minor	major	—	Trace	—	a, b
Dryopteris novaboracensis	11	10	52	—	—	27	a
Podophyllum peltatum	—	—	80	—	11	9	a
Liriodendron tulipifera	—	15	85	—	Trace	—	a
Brassica oleracea	1.4	30	69	—	—	—	a

Composition of sterol mixture (%). Nomenclature base: cholesterol

[a] Nes et al. (unpublished observations).
[b] Kircher (1970).
[c] Nes et al. (1976).
[d] Both α and β configurations are present.

Table V

SOME TRACHEOPHYTES CONTAINING ONLY Δ^7-STEROLS

Plant	Part	Percent of sterol mixture. (Structural base: lathosterol)							References
		24-H	24-CH$_3$	24-C$_2$H$_5$	Δ^{22}-24-C$_2$H$_5$	$\Delta^{24(28)}$-24-C$_2$H$_5$	$\Delta^{25(27)}$-24-C$_2$H$_5$	$\Delta^{22,25(27)}$-24-C$_2$H$_5$	
Camelia japonica	Seeds	—	3	45	45	6	—	—	[a]
Camelia sasangua thunb.	Seeds	—	2	30	62	6	—	—	[a]
Thea sinensis	Seeds	—	4	59	33	2	—	—	[a]
Alfalfa	Seeds	—	7	46	40	5	—	—	[a]
Garden balsam	Seeds	—	6	59	27	8	—	—	[a]
Spinach	Seeds	—	8	35	45	8	—	—	[a]
Shea fat	Seeds	—	6	43	37	11	—	—	[a]
Cucurbita pepo	Leaves	Trace	Trace	37	42	16	4(?)	—	[b]
Cucurbita pepo	Seeds	—	—	—	23	—	54	23	[c]
Cucumis sativus	Seeds	—	—	—	10	—	10	80	[c]
Cucumis melo	Seeds	—	—	—	13	—	26	61	[c]
Citrullus vulgaris	Seeds	—	—	—	15	—	27	58	[c]
Cucurbita pepo	Fruit	Essentially the same distribution as in leaves							[b]
Cucumis melo	Fruit	Nearly all Δ^{22}-24-ethyl							[c]
Citrullus vulgaris	Fruit	Nearly all Δ^{22}-24-ethyl							[c]

[a] Itoh et al. (1974).
[b] Nes et al. (unpublished observations).
[c] Sucrow and Reimerdes (1968).

known have a double bond ($\Delta^{25(27)}$) at the end of the side chain. Thus, 24β-ethylcholesta-7,22,25(27)-trien-3β-ol has been found. Along with its 22-dihydro derivative, it occurs as the major constituent in seeds of the Cucurbitaceae (Sucrow and Girgensohn, 1970; Sucrow *et al.*, 1971), and its Δ^5-isomer is reported (Bolger *et al.*, 1970) to be the major sterol of *Clerodendrum compellii*. This strongly suggests that there is selection operating with respect to the configuration depending on whether there is or is not a $\Delta^{25(27)}$ bond as discussed in Section VII.

As a first approximation, in those plants that contain sitosterol as the major constituent of the sterol mixture, 24-methylcholesterol is next in amount. The ratio varies considerably. Cottonseed and the fronds of the New York fern (*D. noveboracensis*) are examples of plant parts with very little 24-methyl component. More commonly, though, gymnosperms and angiosperms contain 24-methylcholesterol in amounts of 10–30% of the dominant sterol mixture. Contrary to earlier assumption, and unlike the situation with the 24-ethyl analog (sitosterol), 24-methylcholesterol occurs as both the 24α and 24β epimers. This has been demonstrated (Nes *et al.*, 1976) by NMR spectroscopy in the same plants mentioned in the preceding paragraph, in which sitosterol was shown to have only the 24α-configuration, as well as in corn (Mulheirn, 1973). 24α-Methylcholesterol is known as campesterol. 24β-Methylcholesterol has no real trivial name and is referred to variously, for instance, as dihydrobrassicasterol and Δ^5-ergostenol. In the investigated cases both epimers are present in a ratio (24α:24β) greater than unity except in seeds of the Brassica family, where only the 24α epimer is found (Mulheirn, 1974). In place of the 24β epimer [which is present in leaves (Nes *et al.*, 1976)] is its 22-dehydro derivative (brassicasterol). While the significance of the epimeric ratio is not yet understood, a reasonable explanation for the substitution of the Δ^{22} derivative exists and is discussed in Section VII.

During the investigations in the 1930s and 1940s of the vitamin D problem, $\Delta^{5,7}$-sterols (provitamins D) were found by ultraviolet spectroscopy or bioassay in various photosynthetic plants at levels ranging from 0.05% to 0.3% of the sterol mixture. The plants included both monocots and dicots. Examples are cottonseed, ryegrass, spinach, horse chestnut, carrot, and cabbage. The data have been summarized by Bills (1954). The amounts are inconsequential relative to sitosterol or the other dominant sterols. However, in the lower tracheophyte, *Lycopodium complanatum*, ergosterol constitutes a significant part (2–25%) of the dominant sterol mixture (Nes *et al.*, 1975b). It is accompanied by a lesser amount of a sterol with the NMR spectrum of the corresponding 24α epimer. The major sterol, as usual, however, is sitosterol. The Rangpur lime (*Citrus reticulata*) also contains a 24-methyl $\Delta^{5,7,22}$-sterol (Yokoyama and White, 1968).

From those tracheophytes that contain Δ^7-sterols, two have been encountered often. They are the Δ^7 analog of 24-ethylcholesterol and its Δ^{22} derivative. The latter is known as "α-spinasterol," but the prefix "α" will be dropped, since "β-spinasterol" has been shown to be a mixture (Takeda et al., 1958). The stereochemistry at C-24 has not been the subject of rigid study, but it is claimed (Fieser et al., 1949) that 7-dehydrostigmasterol upon reduction at C-5,6 yields spinasterol, which was first isolated from spinach (Hart and Heyl, 1932). On the assumption that this is correct, spinasterol becomes the Δ^7 analog of stigmasterol. Spinasterol has also been isolated from, among others, senega root, alfalfa, *Monmordica cochinchinensis*, and *Aster baccharoides* (see also Table V). Spinasterol is usually accompanied by its 22-dihydro derivative (dihydrospinasterol, Δ^7-stigmastenol, Δ^7-sitostenol, schottenol—all terms being equivalent), which is also present, for instance, in the cactus, *L. schotti* and in the chloroplasts of *Spinacia oleracea* as well as being a 3% component in wheat germ oil. The corresponding Δ^7-24-methyl sterol (24α-methyllathosterol) when present constitutes a much smaller part of the mixture than would be expected from the composition of Δ^5-sterols. From Tables III–V it will also be seen that, in the plants containing only Δ^7-sterols there, the percentage of the Δ^{22}-24-ethyl sterol (spinasterol) compared to the 22-dihydro analog is higher than is usually found in Δ^5-sterol-containing plants. Δ^7-Sterols with a 24-H atom (lathosterol), 24-methyl or 24-ethyl groups, are, in rare cases such as the fern, minor companions of the corresponding Δ^5-sterols.

While campestanol and stigmastanol have been reported in *Zea mays* (Kemp and Mercer, 1968) and *Physarum polycephalum* (Lenfant et al., 1970) and a few other plants, the stanols corresponding to cholesterol, 24-methyl-, and 24-ethylcholesterol are only very rarely found in tracheophytes. On the other hand, cholesterol itself is present in many higher plants, as first observed by Johnson et al. (1963, 1966) and Heftmann (1968). There is no clear understanding, though, as to what taxonomic, developmental, or functional characteristics dictate its presence. It has always been found only as a minor component (from traces to a few percent of the sterol mixture).

On occasion, one also finds $\Delta^{24(28)}$-sterols with a Δ^5 or Δ^7 bond. Some well documented cases are the following. Seeds of the pine, *Pinus pinea*, contain the *trans*-24(28)-dehydro derivative (isofucosterol) of 24α-ethylcholesterol as an 8% component of the sterol mixture (van Aller et al., 1969). Small amounts of the Δ^7 analog (Δ^7-avenasterol) of isofucosterol have been found in various plants (Knights and Laurie, 1967; Frost and Ward, 1968; Itoh et al., 1974). Pollen frequently contains the 24(28)-dehydro derivative of 24-methylcholesterol (24-methylenecholesterol) as its major sterol (Barbier et al., 1960; Hugel et al., 1964; Barbier, 1970). Finally, Δ^{25}-sterols are found, especially in the family Cucurbitaceae (Sucrow and Reimerdes, 1968; Sucrow and Girgensohn, 1970; Sucrow et al., 1971).

In summary, the dominant sterol mixture of most tracheophytes at the level of Pteropsida is the homologous series of Δ^5-sterols with an H atom, CH_3 group, and C_2H_5 group at C-24 (cholesterol and its 24-methyl and 24-ethyl derivatives). When the configuration at C-24 is considered, and assuming the configuration at C-20 always to be the same, we then find four major sterols: cholesterol, 24α- and 24β-methylcholesterol, and 24α-ethylcholesterol. The relative concentrations are nearly always such that the 24α-ethyl-, 24α-methyl-, 24β-methyl-, and 24-H-sterols occur in decreasing order as given. Some notable exceptions are seeds (but not leaves) of the *Brassica* genus in which 24β-methylcholesterol is replaced by its Δ^{22} derivative (brassicasterol), ivy in which 24α-cthylcholesterol is nearly but not completely replaced by its Δ^{22} derivative (stigmasterol), and the families *Theaceae* and *Cucurbitaceae* in which the Δ^5-sterols are completely replaced by their Δ^7 analogs (at least in some cases with the 24β-ethyl configuration). These replacements occur to a lesser extent in certain other cases, leading to a complex mixture composed of the homologous cholesterol series, their Δ^7 analogs, their *trans*-$\Delta^{24(28)}$ analogs, and their *trans*-Δ^{22} derivatives. Furthermore, in the lower tracheophyte, *Lycopodium complanatum*, significant replacement of the Δ^5-24β-methyl component is made by the corresponding $\Delta^{5,7}$-sterol (ergosterol). There is also evidence for some replacement of the Δ^5-24α-methyl component by 24-epiergosterol in the latter plant. This array of sterols is consistent with biosynthetic sequences in which enzymic steps are partially or wholly blocked.

C. BRYOPHYTA

The bryophytes (which differ from tracheophytes in that the gametophyte generation is dominant and no true vascular tissue is present) are found in two classes, the Hepaticae (liverworts) and Musci (mosses). Only the latter seems to have been investigated. 24-Ethylcholesterol and its completely saturated analog have been reported present in species of *Sphagnum* (Ives and O'Neill, 1958) and 24-methyl- and 24-ethylcholesterol in other mosses (Marsili and Morelli, 1968, 1970).

D. ALGAE

Algae are a diverse group of organisms with varying degrees of cellular development and differentiation. Most are obligatorily photosynthetic, but some, notably the euglenoids, can grow in the absence of light. Most also do not have individual modes of locomotion, but again some, e.g., *Ochromonas* species, do. They are classified primarily on the basis of the photosynthetic pigments that lend color to their appearance. In terms of relative evolutionary development little is known about the different phyla, although development within a given phylum is well studied biologically. They differ from embryophytes (bryophytes and tracheophytes) by not possessing an embryonic stage of ontogeny, and no algae have the extent of cellular differentiation that is encountered in the higher embryophytes. Willstätter and Page (1914) were the first to recognize sterols in algae, and Carter *et al.* (1939) were the first to examine the problem in detail. Representative species of all the major algal Divisions (Phyla) of the algae have now been examined except those from the Pyrrhophyta (yellow-brown algae), among which are the dinoflagellates responsible for "red tides."

Although the older literature summarized in part by Miller (1962) reports the presence of sitosterol, fucosterol, cholesterol, etc., in red algae (Phylum Rhodophyta), more than forty species that have been recently examined show the great majority of these organisms to be unique among plants in possessing no 24-alkyl sterols. Primarily cholesterol and desmosterol have been found (Tsuda *et al.*, 1957, 1958a,b; Gibbons *et al.*, 1967; Beastall *et al.*, 1971; Alcaide *et al.*, 1968a, 1969; Saito and Idler, 1966; Idler *et al.*, 1968). Species in seven orders (Porphyridiales, Bangiales, Gelidiales, Cryptonemiales, Gigartinales, Rhodymeniales, and Ceramiales) have been the subject of examination. Most of the work has been summarized by Patterson (1971b). In *Hypnea japonica* only 22-dehydrocholesterol is present. In *Porphyra purpurea* only desmosterol is present. In most of the other species only cholesterol is present, occasionally accompanied by the Δ^{22} or Δ^{24} derivatives. However, in one species (*Rytiphlea tinctoria*) the only sterol is reported to be 24-methylcholesterol. In view of this latter report some of the species recorded in the earlier literature (notably Heilbron, 1942) to possess 24-alkysterols should perhaps be reexamined. This is given further weight by the recent incorporation of label from acetate and methionine into fucosterol, brassicasterol, and 24-methylenecholesterol in *Rhodymenia palmata* (Ferezou *et al.*, 1974). Probably also worth reexamination is the report (Aaronson and Baker, 1961) that *Porphyridium cruentum* when grown on a chemically defined medium lacks sterols altogether.

The brown algae (Phylum Phaeophyta) follow next, at least in a biosynthetic sense. Most of the data have been reviewed by Miller (1962) and Patterson (1971b). The many Phaeophyta species consistently contain 24-ethyl-idenecholesterol as the major sterol. Occasionally it is accompanied by 24-methylenecholesterol. 24-Ethylidenesterol exhibits cis-trans isomerism about the $\Delta^{24(28)}$ bond. Unlike tracheophytes, algae may contain both isomers (but never reported in the same organism). Fucosterol (the cis isomer) was first isolated from *Fucus* species, from which its name is derived (Heilbron *et al.*, 1934). It appears to be characteristic of the brown algae. Isofucosterol is the trans isomer and occurs in some green algae, such as *Enteromorpha intestinalis* and *Ulva lactuca* (Gibbons *et al.*, 1968), where it is the major sterol. The current stereochemical assignments arising from spectroscopy are the reverse of the earlier ones based on deductions from chemical synthesis. Reports (Ikekawa *et al.*, 1968; Patterson, 1968) of the presence of small amounts of cholesterol accompanying the $\Delta^{24(28)}$-sterols in ten species of brown algae are unusual and conceivably represent contamination. Brown algae also have been reported (Ikekawa *et al.*, 1966, 1968; Safe *et al.*, 1974) to contain small amounts of 24-hydroxy-24-vinyl-cholesterol (saringasterol), which would result from electrophilic attack on C-24 of fucosterol of a species, acting as if it were OH^+. Evidence exists for this compound arising as an oxidative artifact (Knights, 1970b). 24-Ketocholesterol, probably also an oxidative artifact, has been isolated from *Laminaria* (Safe *et al.*, 1974). The ketone has been found in other cases, e.g., *Ascophyllum nodosum*, and evidence presented for its not being a true metabolite (Knights, 1970b). Similarly, the early report that *Sargassum ringgoldianum* contains the C-20 epimer of fucosterol (Tsuda *et al.*, 1958c) is probably incorrect. Ikekawa *et al.* (1968) upon reinvestigation of this same species found only fucosterol.

The golden algae and diatoms (Phylum Chrysophyta) and the green algae (Phylum Chlorophyta) differ from the red and brown ones in that a saturated 24-alkyl group is usually but not always (cf. the preceding paragraph) present. This allows chirality at C-24. A quarter of a century ago, Bergmann and Feeney (1950) found that the green alga *Scenedesmus obliquus* contained the 24-epimer (chondrillasterol) of spinasterol. Chondrillasterol had just previously been isolated from a sponge, *Chondrilla nucula* (Bergmann and McTique, 1948), from which the sterol's name is derived. From this and subsequent work it has come to be thought that the 24-alkyl sterols of algae are the 24-epimers of the major tracheophyte sterols. The extent to which this is valid as a generality remains for further work, but in several cases good evidence does exist. Early work on the problem relied on very small differences in the optical rotation of the epimers. In view of the fact that most sterols isolated in the early period were mixtures, this evidence is suspect.

More recently, purity has been achieved chromatographically, and with melting point data and especially PMR spectra it has been possible, beginning with the work of Patterson and Krauss (1965), to show that the sterols of most, but not all, algae examined do indeed have the 24β configuration. The PMR technique is the most certain, and, it is hoped, will allow a more thorough survey to be made in the future. The PMR spectra especially at 220 MHz of the eight Δ^5-sterols derived from adding a 24-methyl, 24-ethyl, and trans-Δ^{22} grouping are all unequivocally different (Thompson *et al.*, 1972; Rubinstein and Goad, 1974b; Nes *et al.*, 1976). The melting points,

when different by 10° or more, also become a clear indicator. While this is
not usually so, it does happen for stigmasterol, m.p. 170°, and its epimer,
poriferasterol, m.p. 156°, although their acetates melt within 3°C of each
other. The reverse is true of sitosterol and its epimer clionasterol (as acetates,
m.p. 120°C and 140°C, respectively). With one or the other or both of these
techniques the dominant sterols of several algae have now been structurally
determined. The sterol content of a variety of species is given in Tables VI–
IX. It will be seen that the green algae do contain 24β-alkylsterols, but either
of the epimers may exist in the golden algae. *Ochromonas* species (Chrysophyceae) biosynthesize sterols with the 24β configuration, but the major
sterol (24-epibrassicasterol) of the diatom *Phaeodactylum tricornutum*
(Bacillariophyceae), formerly *Nitzschia closterium* forma *minutissima*, has
the 24α configuration based on PMR work (Rubinstein and Goad, 1974b).
Similarly, the major sterol of *Amphora exigua* is by melting point clearly
stigmasterol, not poriferasterol (Orcutt and Patterson, 1975). In Table IX
the other sterols for diatoms are tentatively listed as having α configurations
at C-24 by analogy to the Δ^{22}-24α-methyl and Δ^{22}-24α-ethyl sterols of
P. tricornutum and *A. exigua*.

It will be seen from Table IX that considerable variation among the
golden algae exists beyond the configurational question. The Class Xantho-
phyceae seems to be characterized by having cholesterol and 24β-methyl-
cholesterol in all three orders, while the flagellates in the Class Chrysophyceae
primarily possess the 22-dehydro-24β-ethylcholesterol, poriferasterol. The
change to the Class Bacillariophyceae, the diatoms, not only inverts C-24,
but leads to some species with sterols bearing only one carbon atom at
C-24 (24-epibrassicasterol and campesterol).

The green algae clearly belong to several biosynthetic classes depending
on the presence (a) only of Δ^5-sterols, (b) only of Δ^7-sterols, and (c) substantial quantities of $\Delta^{5,7}$-sterols (Patterson, 1969, 1974) together with Δ^5-
or Δ^7-sterols (Tables VI–VIII). Some green algae of the $\Delta^{5,7}$ group also
contain large amounts of cholesterol and its 24-methylene and 24-ethylidene
derivatives, the latter (24-C_2H_4) also being in large amount in the Charophyta
(Patterson, 1972). As in the tracheophytes and brown and golden algae, the
principal sterols of many of the green algae have two carbon atoms at C-24,
but many do not, as in the one species examined in the order Chloro-
sphaerales and most of the algae with $\Delta^{5,7}$-sterols. Some green algae also
contain Δ^{25}-sterols as their major component. A recent example is the
siphonous marine alga *Codium fragile*, in which the dominant sterols are
25-dehydro-24β-ethyl- and 25-dehydro-24β-methylcholesterol. They are
present in the decreasing relative order given and are known, respectively,
as clerosterol and codisterol. In a few algae a $\Delta^{5,7}$-24-methyl sterol replaces
the Δ^5- and Δ^7-sterols. On the assumption that the configuration at C-24 is

Composition of sterol mixture (%). Nomenclature base: cholesterol

Alga	24-H	24β-CH$_3$	24β-C$_2$H$_5$	Δ^{22}-24β-CH$_3$	Δ^{22}-24β-C$_2$H$_5$	Δ$^{24(28)}$-24-CH$_2$	Δ$^{24(28)}$-C$_2$H$_4$	References
Chlorophyta								
Cladophorales								
Cladophora flexuosa	22	2	6	1	2	21	45	a
Pithophora sp.	28	—	10	2	2	40	14	a
Zygnematales								
Spirogyra sp.	11	12	39	6	32	—	—	a
Siphonales								
Halimeda incrassata	2	4	94	—	—	—	—	a
Codium fragile	—	25-Dehydro, 6	25-Dehydro, 94	—	—	—	—	b
Chlorosphaerales								
Cocomyxa elongata	—	48	33	—	19	—	—	a
Chlorococcales								
Chlorella pringsheimii	—	23	1	4	72	—	—	a
Chlorella ellipsoidea (247)	—	Minor	Minor	—	Major	—	—	c
Chlorella saccharophilia	—	Minor	Minor	—	Major	—	—	c
Ulvales								
Enteromorpha intestinales	—	—	—	—	—	—	100	d
Enteromorpha linza	—	—	—	—	—	—	Major	e
Ulva lactuca	—	—	—	—	—	—	100	d
Charophyta								
Charales								
Nitella flexilis	—	—	58	—	—	—	36	f
Chara vulgaris	—	—	58	—	—	—	36	f
Phaeophyta								
Costaria costata	2.5	—	—	—	—	16.5	76	g
Sargassum confusum	0.1	—	—	—	—	2	90	g
Sargassum ringgoldianum	1.7	—	—	—	—	5	92	g
Fucus evanescens	5	—	—	—	—	14	79	g
Dictyopteris divaricata	—	—	—	—	—	2	97	g

[a] Patterson (1974).
[b] Rubinstein and Goad (1974a).
[c] Patterson and Krauss (1965).
[d] Gibbons et al. (1968).
[e] Tsuda and Sakai (1960).
[f] Patterson (1972).
[g] Ikekawa et al. (1968).

Table VII

GREEN ALGAE CONTAINING Δ^7-STEROLS

	Composition of sterol mixture (%). Nomenclature base: lathosterol					
Alga	24-H	24β-CH$_3$	24β-C$_2$H$_5$	Δ^{22}-24β-CH$_3$	Δ^{22}-24β-C$_2$H$_5$	References
Chlorella fusca	—	21	18	—	61	a
Scenedesmus obliquus	—	19	16	—	65	a
Oocystis polymorpha	?	22	8	2	67	b

[a] Patterson (1974).
[b] Orcutt and Richardson (1970).

Table VIII

GREEN ALGAE CONTAINING $\Delta^{5,7}$-STEROLS

	Composition of sterol mixture (%). Nomenclature base: 7-dehydrocholesterol					
Alga	24-H	24β-CH$_3$	24β-C$_2$H$_5$	Δ^{22}-24β-CH$_3$	Δ^{22}-24β-C$_2$H$_5$	References
Chlamydomonas rheinhardi	—	—	—	44	56	a
Chlorella simplex	—	12	—	70	—	b
Chlorella ellipsoidea (246)	—	1	—	35	—	c
Chlorella nocturna	—	12	—	70	—	b
Chlorella sorokiniana	—	12	—	70	—	b
Chlorella vannielii	—	12	—	70	—	b
Chlorella candida	—	12	—	70	—	b

[a] Patterson (1974).
[b] Patterson (1969).
[c] Patterson et al. (1974).

Table IX

STEROLS OF GOLDEN ALGAE

Alga	\multicolumn{8}{Composition of sterol mixture (%). Nomenclature base: cholesterol}
	24-H	24β-CH₃	24β-C₂H₅	Δ²²-24-H	Δ²²-24β-CH₃	Δ²²-24β-C₂H₅	Other	Reference
Xanthophyceae								
Heterosiphonales								
Botrydium granulatum	15	—	85	—	—	—	—	[a]
Heterotrichales								
Tribonema aegnale	33	—	67	—	—	—	—	[a]
Heterococcales								
Monodus subterraneus	34	—	66	—	—	—	—	[a]
Chrysophyceae								
Ochromonas malhamensis	?	—	—	—	?	98	?	[b]
Ochromonas danica	—	6	9	—	13	58	15	[b]

Alga	24-H	24α-CH₃	24α-C₂H₅	Δ²²-24-H	Δ²²-24α-CH₃	Δ²²-24α-C₂H₅	Other	Reference
Bacillariophyceae								
Nitzschia alba	—	—	—	—	90	—	10	[c]
Nitzschia closterium	—	—	—	—	98	—	2	[d]
Phaeodactylum tricornutum	—	—	—	—	91	—	9	[d, e]
Navicula pelliculosa	—	—	—	—	98	—	—	[d]
Nitzschia ovalis	11	—	—	33	54	—	2	[d]
Nitzschia frustulum	42	4	—	—	54	—	—	[d]
Amphora exiqua	—	—	—	17	—	80	3	[d]
Amphora sp.	—	—	—	—	—	99	—	[d]
Nitzschia longissima	89	5	—	—	—	—	6	[d]
Biddulphia aurita	2	39	—	—	21	—	38	[d]
Thalassiosira pseudonana	2	36	—	—	—	—	62	[d]
Fragilaria sp.	1	39	—	—	—	—	60	[d]

[a] Mercer et al. (1974).
[b] Gershengorn et al. (1968).
[c] Tornabene et al. (1974).
[d] Orcutt and Patterson (1975).
[e] Rubinstein and Goad (1974b).

β, the algal $\Delta^{5,7}$-sterol which also bears a Δ^{22} bond is designated as ergosterol. The configuration of the Δ^{22} bond in algal sterols has usually not been determined and is only assumed to be trans oriented. This needs further verification by careful infrared studies. Recently, cis-oriented Δ^{22}-sterols have been isolated from invertebrate animals (Idler and Wiseman, 1971; Teshima et al., 1974); this illustrates the danger in presumptions about stereochemistry.

The prokaryotic blue-green algae (Phylum Cyanophyta), originally thought not to contain sterols (Levin and Bloch, 1964), are now known to possess them. A mixture consisting of 80% of the Δ^7 analogs of 24-ethylcholesterol and its 22-dehydro derivative in a ratio, respectively, of 3:2 was found in Phormidium luridum (de Souza and Nes, 1968). The compounds were, then, either the pair Δ^7-stigmastenol and spinasterol, or their epimers, Δ^7-chondrillastenol and chondrillasterol, but the configuration at C-24 was not elucidated to decide between these two alternatives. Four other sterols comprised the remaining 20% of the mixture. They were 24-ethyl-$\Delta^{5,7}$-cholestadienol, 24-ethyl-$\Delta^{5,7,22}$-cholestatrienol, 24-ethylcholesterol, and cholesterol. Mass spectral and other analyses failed to detect any 24-methyl sterols. In Anacystis nidulans and Fremyella diplosiphon, cholesterol and 24-ethylcholesterol have been reported to be present (Reitz and Hamilton, 1968).

E. LICHENS

Lichens are symbionts between fungi and algae. In certain cases the two organisms (mycobiont and phycobiont) have been separated and effectively cultured individually and also recombined to generate the lichen (Ahmadjian, 1965, 1966). One would therefore expect lichens to possess both typical algal and fungal sterols. The earlier literature reports the presence of "sitosterol" and "ergosterol." Since lichens commonly involve an ascomycete as the mycobiont and since ascomycetes produce ergosterol, the presence of the latter in lichens is expected, but a 24α-ethylsterol ("sitosterol") would be unexpected in the phycobiont. More recently a careful study (Lenton et al., 1973a,b) of the common foliose lichen Xanthoria parietina (L.) has been made. It is composed of the alga Trebouxia decolorans and a fungus of the same name as the lichen. The lichen itself was found to contain primarily poriferasterol, ergosterol, and lichesterol, the $\Delta^{5,8,22}$-isomer of ergosterol. Separate culture proved the C_{29}-sterol to be present in the phycobiont and the C_{28}-sterols in the mycobiont. The former also contained small amounts of clionasterol, brassicasterol, 22-dihydrobrassicasterol, and cholesterol. The mycobiont contained small amounts of $\Delta^{7,22}$-, $\Delta^{7,22,24(28)}$-, and $\Delta^{7,24(28)}$-24β-methyl sterols.

F. Euglenoids

Euglena species have the capacity to grow either photosynthetically or in the absence of light. Ergosterol has been reported in this organism (Stern *et al.*, 1960) as well as in *Astasia ocellata* and *Peranema trichophorum* (Williams *et al.*, 1966). However, in a careful study by Brandt *et al.* (1970), *E. gracilis* was shown to contain Δ^5- and Δ^7-sterols with 24-methyl and 24-ethyl groups.

G. Nonphotosynthetic Plants

The plants lacking photosynthetic capability include the eukaryotic slime molds (Phylum Myxomycophyta) and fungi (Phylum Eumycophyta) and the prokaryotic bacteria (Phylum Schizomycophyta) and mycoplasms. The latter differ from bacteria primarily in the lack of a cell wall. Only two species of slime mold have been investigated, *Dictyostelium discoideum* and *Physarum polycephalum*. The dominant sterols of both species possess a 24-alkyl group. In *D. discoideum* 22-dehydro-24-ethylcholestanol is present (Heftmann *et al.*, 1960). On the basis of a comparison of its melting point and optical rotation with synthetic 5-dihydrostigmasterol, it is believed to have the 24α configuration. The fully saturated analog is also biosynthesized. In *P. polycephalum* only the fully saturated homologs 24-methyl- and 24-ethylcholestanol have been found (Lederer, 1969) in the 4,4-demethyl fraction. On the other hand, more than 150 species of fungi have been studied (Weete, 1973, 1974), and in nearly all cases sterols are present. The exceptions are the vegetative phases of *Pythium* and *Phytophthora* genera (Elliott *et al.*, 1964), which lack sterols. In spores of the primitive parasitic *Plasmodiophora brassicae* (Knights, 1970a) sterols do not appear to be biosynthesized constituting another unusual phenomenon. While ergosterol is the fungal sterol most often encountered, it is not detectable at all in the uredospores (mycelia having not been examined) of rust fungi, aquatic phycomycetes, and some but not all deuteromycetes. Thus, *Trichophyton violaceum* and *T. discoides* are reported (Blank *et al.*, 1962) to contain only brassicasterol, which is the 7-dihydro derivative of ergosterol, but this phenomenon in the deuteromycetes is species dependent. In six other *Trichophyton* species, ergosterol is the major sterol and brassicasterol is present either in trace quantities or not at all. Similarly, fungisterol (the 5,22-tetrahydro derivative of ergosterol) is the major sterol of conidial spores of a species, *Linderina pennispora*, in the Mucorales order of the phycomycetes, and no ergosterol is present (Weete and Laseter, 1974).

Fungi were originally thought to be characterized by the presence of 24-methyl sterols in the absence of sterols with one less or one more C atom at position 24, e.g., by the presence of ergosterol and the absence of cholesterol or clionasterol. However, a decade or so ago, cholesterol was found to be present as the only sterol of the deuteromycete *Penicillium funiculosum* (Chen and Haskins, 1963), and in the intervening years it has been detected among others in *Aspergillus flavus* (Vacheron and Michel, 1968) and in the spores of a smut fungus (*U. maydis*) (Weete and Laseter, 1974). Similarly, 22-dehydrocholesterol is found in *Rhizophylyctis rosea* (Bean *et al.*, 1973), and 24-ethylcholesterol and its 22-dehydro derivative were found among the sterols of several phycomycete species (Bean *et al.*, 1973), and the former's Δ^7 analog (24-ethyllathosterol) was found to be the major sterol of *Puccinia graminis* (wheat stem rust) uredospores (Weete and Laseter, 1974). Flax rust (*Melampsora lini*) uredospores are similar, having 24-ethyllathosterol and 24-ethylidenelathosterol as their major sterols (Jackson and Frear, 1968). Gas–liquid chromatographic identification of "stigmasterol" has also been reported in the sterol mixture of the ascomycete (*Pullularia pullulans*) (Merdinger *et al.*, 1968). It is evident from what has been said that neither the $\Delta^{5,7}$-diene system nor the Δ^{22} bond is necessarily characteristic of fungal sterols. This is further emphasized by the presence of 24-methylcholesterol (Bean *et al.*, 1973) and 24-methylenecholesterol (McCorkindale *et al.*, 1969) in certain phycomycetes, but the presence of ergosterol as the major sterol in all ascomycetes appears to hold the test of experiment so far. While not many basidiomycetes have been examined, ergosterol is generally the dominant sterol (Weete, 1974; Holtz and Schisler, 1972). It is accompanied frequently by the 5,6- and/or 22,23-dihydro derivatives. The bracket fungus, *Fomes applanatus* in the family Polyporaceae, is an exception in that in place of ergosterol, which cannot be found, are fungisterol and the very unusual 16,17-dehydrofungisterol (Pettit and Knight, 1962; Strigina *et al.*, 1971). The configuration of ergosterol at C-24 has been shown to be β in yeast by degradation (Tsuda *et al.*, 1960) and in *Neurospora crassa* and *Agaricus* sp. by PMR spectroscopy (Nes *et al.*, unpublished observations).

In summary, ergosterol appears to be the dominant sterol of fungi as well as of their spores with some notable exceptions. The common ascomycetes (yeasts, *Neurospora*, etc.) and homobasidiomycetes (mushrooms) are well-investigated examples of fungi in which ergosterol is the major sterol in the absence of C_{27}- or C_{29}-sterols. The basidiomycetous bracket fungus, *Fomes applanatus*, is an exception to not having ergosterol but not an exception to not having C_{27}- or C_{29}-sterols. The C_{27}-sterols are found in the spores of some heterobasidiomycetes, e.g., *U. maydis*, and in a deuteromycete (*P. funiculosum*) as well as in the three orders (Mucorales, Saprolegniales, and Leptomitales) of the class Phycomycetes. The latter two orders, the basidiomycetous rust fungi, and one species of ascomycete (which should be reexamined) are reported to possess 24-ethyl sterols. In the uredospores of the rust fungi the latter type of sterol is dominant. While the $\Delta^{5,7,22}$-triene system is most common, Δ^5-sterols and Δ^7-sterols are dominant in some species, e.g., respectively, in the deuteromycete *T. violaceum* and the conidial spores of one species (*L. pennispora*) among the Mucorales order of phycomycetes, and they occur as minor sterols in many more. Most of the work has been done on the yeasts (Class Ascomycetes), however, and generalizations about "fungi" should be taken with caution. This is especially so with respect to the configuration at C-24. Claims, for instance, that the 24-ethyl sterols are of the stigmastane rather than 24-epistigmastane series are not well founded. In the 24-methyl series the configuration at C-24 has been firmly established by degradation for ergosterol, presumably but not explicitly stated to have been derived from yeast (Tsuda *et al.*, 1960). 24-Epiergosterol has been prepared from 24α-methylcholesterol by incubation with *Tetrahymena pyriformis*, and its NMR spectrum was found to be differentiable from that of purified commercial ergosterol, also presumably from yeast (Nes *et al.*, 1975b). When the NMR spectra of ergosterol from a mushroom (genus *Agaricus*, family Basidiomycetes) and an ascomycete (genus *Neurospora*) were then compared with that of the 24-epiergosterol, the fungal sterol in both cases unequivocally possessed, and possessed only, the 24β-configuration (Nes *et al.*, unpublished observations).

Bacteria that are anaerobic cannot in principle biosynthesize sterols, since the introduction of the 3β-hydroxyl group is a mixed-function oxidase reaction requiring molecular oxygen. It is therefore not surprising that early investigations failed to find sterols (Hammerschlag, 1889; von Behring, 1930). More recently, though, the typical ascomycete and basidiomycete sequence of sterols (24-methyllathosterol, and its 7-dehydro and 7,22-bisdehydro derivatives) have been found in *Azotobacter chroococcum* (Schubert *et al.*, 1968). On the assumption that the 24-methyl group is β-oriented, the compounds are regarded as fungisterol, 22-dihydroergosterol, and ergosterol. In addition, from *Methyloccocus capsulatus* have been isolated 4,4-dimethylzymosterol and its 24-dihydro derivative (Bird *et al.*, 1971). While no mycoplasmas have been shown to biosynthesize sterols, a number of carotenoidless species require them. In the others, the sterol's role is played by the carotenoid (Smith, 1971).

The Phylum Protozoa is a diverse group of organisms which, though usually placed in the animal kingdom, includes cells in the Class Flagellata which are photosynthetic, *viz.*, the phytoflagellates, such as *Ochromonas* species. These latter microorganisms are also classed as golden algae. They (*O. malhamensis* and *O. danica*) contain poriferasterol as their principal sterol (cf. Section III,D). Among the Class Ciliata are the *Tetrahymena* species. While these organisms biosynthesize a pentacyclic triterpenoid (tetrahymanol) in place of sterols, they convert exogenous Δ^5-sterols to $\Delta^{5,7,22}$-sterols (Conner *et al.*, 1969) and 24-ethyl sterols to 24-dealkyl sterols (Nes *et al.*, 1975a). Another ciliate genus is *Paramecium*, and in the case of *P. aurelia*, as with carotenoidless mycoplasma, sterols are not biosynthesized but are required and metabolized to the 7-dehydro derivatives (Conner and Van Wagtendonk, 1955; Conner *et al.*, 1971).

IV. Minor Steroids

Many minor sterols have been encountered in plants. They are of three major types: sterols with none of the nuclear methyl groups at C-4 and C-14; those with one or more of these groups, e.g., lophenol, citrostadienol, or lanosterol; and, third, the sterols bearing a fifth ring, the 9,19-cyclo grouping, as in cycloartenol. Occasionally one also finds protosteroids or euphoids. Differences within a category depend on the number and position of double bonds, the extent of alkylation at C-24, and on occasion the presence of extra hydroxyl groups as in 22-hydroxycholesterol in *Narthecium ossifragum* (Stabursvik, 1953). Ketosterols (bearing a 3-hydroxyl group) are apparently rare, but one, carpesterol with both a 22-hydroxyl and a 6-keto group, is known (Beisler and Sato, 1971) to be present in *Solanum xanthocarpum*. The 22-hydroxyl group may be associated with the biosynthesis of sapogenins (Beisler and Sato, 1971). 3-Ketosteroids, 3-methoxysteroids, sterol esters, and oxides have also been isolated from plants. Among the 3-ketosteroids is the one corresponding to sitosterol but with a Δ^4-bond (Lavie and Kaye, 1963). Sterols with shortened side chains (C_{26}-sterols, e.g., 24,24-dimethyl-chola-5,22-dien-3β-ol, are present in algae, such as the red alga *Rhodymenia palmata*) (Idler and Wiseman, 1971; Ferezou *et al.*, 1974), where, however, they do not become labeled from acetate or mevalonate, which do label the major sterols (desmosterol, cholesterol, 24-methylenecholesterol, fucosterol, and brassicasterol) (Ferezou *et al.*, 1974).

The minor 3-hydroxysterols are primarily of interest as indicators of biosynthetic mechanisms and sequences. Where pertinent they will be mentioned in subsequent sections of this chapter, and to some extent they have been mentioned in the preceding section. The reader is referred to other recent surveys (Bean, 1973; Goad and Goodwin, 1972) for a correlation of structure and occurrence. It is not surprising that some intermediates have significant steady-state concentrations in some plant tissue at some time in the life cycle and that this can vary from tissue to tissue and from time to time. More interesting are the cases in which a normally minor sterol becomes a dominant sterol, as does 24-methylenecholesterol in some pollens or 24-ethylidenecholesterol in brown algae, or in cases in which there is a clear developmental relationship. Far too little work has been done on this subject to make interpretation meaningful.

V. Biosynthesis of Tetracyclic Structure

A. Mevalonate to Squalene Oxide

Although the biosynthesis of steroids in plants and animals differs in detail, primarily with regard to the side chain, the essence of the process as a whole is the same, and our knowledge of the fundamentals has come from work in both types of organism. The interrelation of the experiments in the two organismic types has been one of the major contributions to our belief in the unity of nature. Squalene is the central and ubiquitous inter-mediate around which much of the work has revolved. It was first isolated at the turn of the century from an animal (Tsujimoto, 1918; Chapman, 1971). Following the realization that it could be (Robinson, 1934), and actually was (Woodward and Bloch, 1953; Tchen and Bloch, 1955, 1957), an animal intermediate to sterols it was sought for and found in plants (Capstack *et al.,* 1962). Mevalonic acid (MVA) was first isolated from yeast (Wolf *et al.,* 1956, 1957; Wright *et al.,* 1956) and it was first shown to have biological significance in a bacterium, *Lactobacillus acidophilus* (Skeggs *et al.,* 1956). Subsequently it was shown to be the precursor of sterols in animals (Tavormina *et al.,* 1956), but this was shortly followed by the demonstration that it also is the precursor in both yeast (Lynen *et al.,* 1958) and angiosperms (Baisted *et al.,* 1962; Nicholas, 1962), and later in a variety of other organisms (algae, etc.). Yeast was also the tool by which Lynen (Lynen *et al.,* 1959) was able to do his Nobel Prize-winning work on the conversion of MVA to the Δ^3- and Δ^2-isopentenyl pyrophosphates (Δ^3-IPP and Δ^2-IPP), from which he discerned the mechanism of condensation by which sterols as well as all polyisopentenoids are made. Furthermore, it was the early isola-tions of geraniol from the Turkish geranium plant (Jacobsen, 1871) and farnesol from the seeds of *Hibiscus abelmoschus* (Kerschbaum, 1902) and from rose oil (Soden and Treff, 1904) together with Wallach's classic isoprene theory of biosynthesis of plant terpenes that led to the discovery of the early steps in steroid biosynthesis. The resultant of these and many other investigations is summarized with stereochemistry in Fig. 7. It will be seen that a pair of C_5 units is formed from MVA, *viz.,* Δ^3-isopentenyl pyrophos-phate (Δ^3-IPP), which then proceeds to the Δ^2-isomer (Δ^2-IPP). The allylic C-1 of the latter next attacks the pi-electron system terminating in C-4 of the former. The product, geranyl pyrophosphate (GPP) is an isopentenylog of the initial Δ^2-IPP and proceeds to attack Δ^3-IPP in the same fashion as did Δ^2-IPP. The product of this reaction is farnesyl pyrophosphate (FPP). FPP is also an isopentenylog of Δ^2-IPP and can again proceed to attack Δ^3-IPP. This occurs in carotenoid biosynthesis, *trans*-rubber biosynthesis, etc., but chain elongation is terminated at the I_3 stage in steroid biosynthesis.

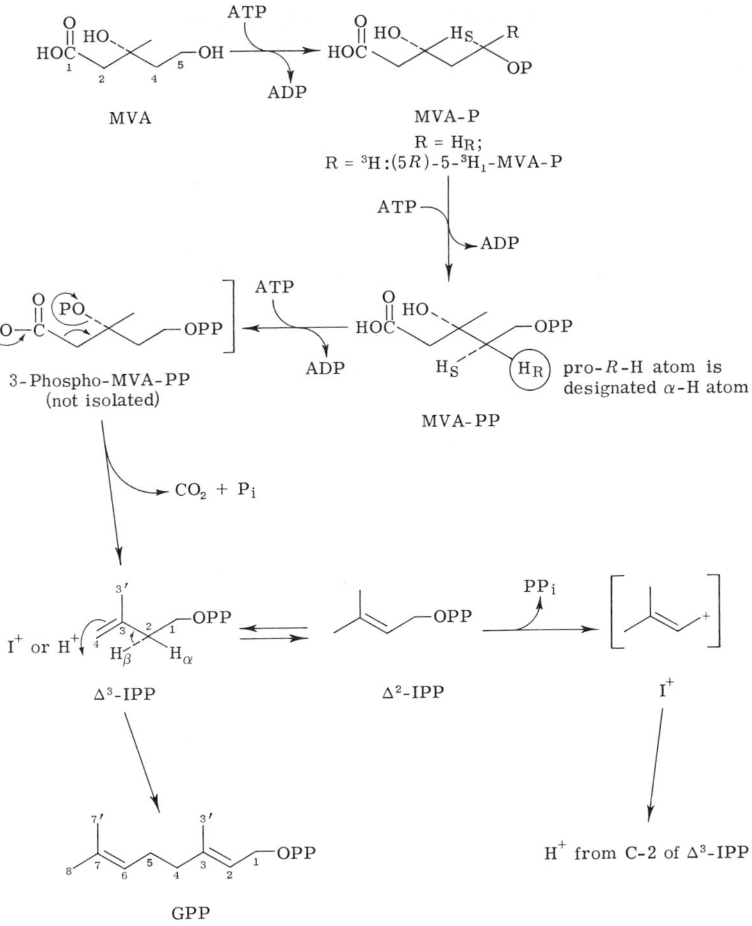

FIG. 7. Origin of C_5 unit and its condensation. MVA, mevalonic acid; IPP, isopentenyl pyrophosphate; GPP, geranyl pyrophosphate.

The factors governing this have been studied in pumpkin seeds (Nishino et al., 1972); from this study it was deduced that it is neither the number of double bonds nor the precise number of carbon atoms, but rather the number of C_5 units as a whole, that is enzymically sensed in termination of the polymerization.

The phosphorylation of MVA with ATP has been shown by Tchen (1958) in animal tissue. In view of the other overlap with plant tissue, this is normally assumed to operate phytochemically. However, kinases do exist at other stages of polymerization, since free geraniol has been shown to proceed to squalene via its phosphorylated derivative in peas (van Aller and Nes,

1968). Despite the existence of other kinases, there is an essential theoretical reason why the Δ^2-isopentenyl unit must be phosphorylated. In order to attack the Δ^3 bond of the Δ^3-isopentenyl unit, the C—O bond of the Δ^2 isomer must undergo cleavage. This is energetically "downhill" only if the alcoholic hydroxyl group is converted to the ester of a strong acid which allows stabilization of the leaving anion after cleavage is effected. If MVA is phosphorylated, in view of the isomerization equilibrium demonstrated in yeast (Agranoff *et al.*, 1960) between the Δ^3- and Δ^2-isopentenyl pyrophosphates, the Δ^2 isomer is automatically in an energetic position to attack the Δ^3 isomer. The Δ^3-isopentenyl unit is similarly arranged, so that when it becomes the oxygenated end of the dimer (GPP) it can attack the Δ^3 unit in exactly the same way as did the Δ^2 unit. The result is the trimeric farnesyl pyrophosphate (FPP). It has been suggested (van Aller and Nes, 1968) that the presence of a kinase (enzyme catalyzing phosphorylation) for geraniol represents an insurance against loss of this essential intermediate through hydrolysis. It can only proceed to the trimeric stage without being phosphorylated by undergoing isomerization to the Δ^7 isomer with a terminal methylene group and being attacked at C-8 by Δ^2-isopentenyl pyrophosphate (Fig. 8). If the resulting farnesol were pyrophosphorylated, the result would be the same as though the dimeric pyrophosphate (GPP) attacked C-4 of Δ^3-IPP except that there would be different origins for the terminal C_5 units in the two cases.

Actually, isomeric isopentenoids of the sort described for geraniol and its Δ^7-isomer are well described in plants; this means that one cannot *a priori* eliminate the sequence through the Δ^7-geraniol or its pyrophosphate. The matter could be examined, for instance, by labeling patterns in squalene or

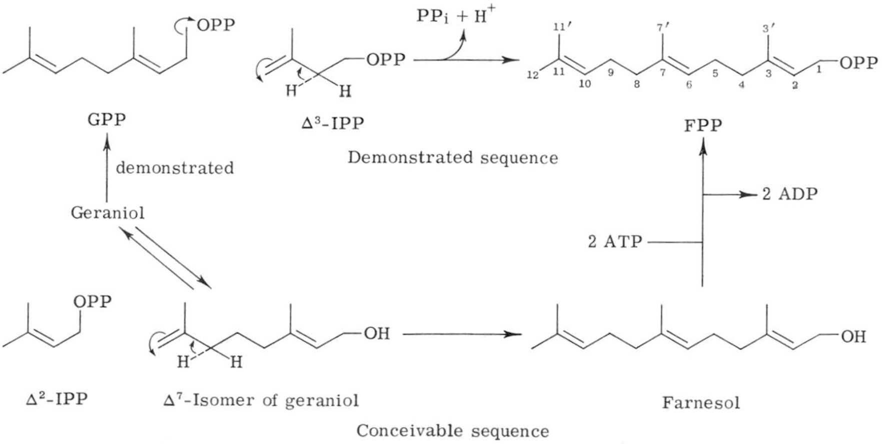

FIG. 8. Alternative routes to farnesyl pyrophosphate (FPP). IPP, isopentenyl pyrophosphate.

sterols from administered $[^{14}C]\Delta^3$-IPP. This has not been done, and so we tentatively assume the only sequence is MVA-PP to Δ^3-IPP to Δ^2-IPP to GPP, which attacks another molecule of Δ^3-IPP to give FPP. Mevalonate and phosphomevalonate kinases have been demonstrated to be present in yeast (Lynen *et al.*, 1959), in angiosperms, e.g., pumpkin (Loomis and Battaile, 1963), peas (Pollard *et al.*, 1966), rubber plant (Skilleter *et al.*, 1966), and in gymnosperms e.g., *Pinus radiata* (Beytia *et al.*, 1969). The utilization of MVA-PP (Thomas and Stobart, 1970; Oshima-Oba and Uritani, 1969; Pollard *et al.*, 1966), the isomerization of the isopentenyl pyrophosphates (Ogura *et al.*, 1971), and the synthesis of geranyl and farnesyl pyrophosphates (Pollard *et al.*, 1966) have all been demonstrated in tracheophytes.

The presence of farnesol in the milieu as the pyrophosphate is also important for mechanistic and energetic reasons. Two farnesyl units are reductively coupled with elimination of the oxygen function to give squalene (Lynen *et al.*, 1958). As in the polymerization, the formation of the C—C bond in the coupling reaction would not proceed "downhill" unless there is loss of a stable anion. While the exact mechanism of this process has not been elucidated, it is believed to occur in at least two steps. The first is the actual coupling that occurs with reductive elimination of one pyrophosphate anion to give presqualene pyrophosphate (Rilling and Epstein, 1969). This molecule, believed to possess a 3-membered ring, is subsequently rearranged to give squalene with loss of the second pyrophosphate anion. Although the cyclic structure of presqualene pyrophosphate (Fig. 9) has been documented (Altman *et al.*, 1971; Coates and Robinson, 1971; Rilling *et al.*,

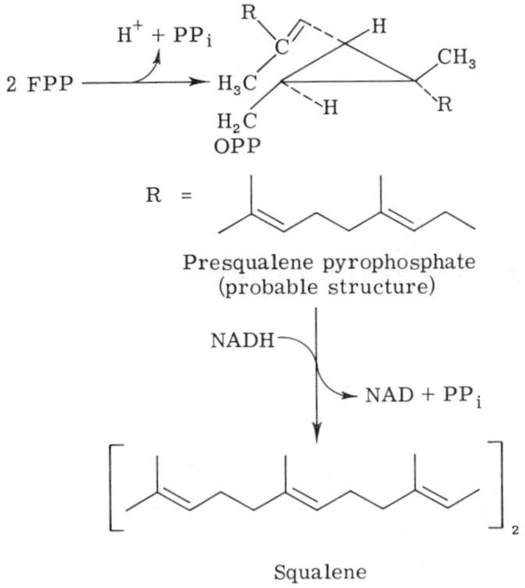

Presqualene pyrophosphate
(probable structure)

Squalene

FIG. 9.   Dimerization of farnesyl pyrophosphate (FPP).

1971), as well as its stereochemistry (Popjak *et al.*, 1973), there remains some controversy (e.g., Popjak, 1970; Wasner and Lynen, 1970), about the structure and mechanism. Despite this, there can be little doubt that there is indeed an intermediate between farnesyl pyrophosphate (FPP) and squalene (Muscio *et al.*, 1974).

The direct head-to-head union of two molecules of FPP is rather difficult to conceive mechanistically. Popjak and Cornforth (1960) and Cornforth *et al.*, (1966b) suggested that there might be a prior rearrangement of one molecule of FPP to the tertiary isomer, nerolidyl pyrophosphate (NPP), which then would condense with an unrearranged molecule of FPP. The advantage of such an intermediate is that it has a reactive pi-electronic system on C-1 that can donate bonding electrons to the electrophilic C-1 of FPP when the latter loses pyrophosphate anion. Several mechanisms can readily be imagined. All of them depend upon pyrophosphate anion from FPP functioning as an electron sink with the formation of a C-1 to C-1-σ bond arising from the pi bond between C-1 and C-2 of NPP. What is not easy to predict is the detail of how the proton is lost. It seems unlikely for it to be removed concomitantly with C—C bond formation, since the electron flow on C-1 would become confused. More likely there might be a charged transition state or neutral intermediate. Of these, a neutral intermediate produced by bond formation with the enzyme is particularly attractive. Unfortunately, while the biosynthesis of NPP has been reported in rat liver, which also forms squalene, nonenzymic divalent cation (Mn^{2+} particularly) catalysis of its formation from FPP has also been reported.

Whether such catalysis is really the source of the experimental formation of the isomer remains to be determined with certainty, but a far more serious indictment of its intermediate role is the finding that in a squalene synthesizing system (a) farnesyl and nerolidyl pyrophosphates are not interconvertible, (b) radioactivity from $[1-^3H_2]$nerolidyl pyrophosphate is not converted to squalene, and (c) the presence of unlabeled nerolidyl pyrophosphate does not alter the relative loss of hydrogen atoms from farnesyl pyrophosphate during the latter's conversion to squalene (Sofer and Rilling, 1969). Yet, there remain the very attractive, almost compelling, mechanistic reasons for invoking the tertiary structure, and a report actually exists of its depressing incorporation of FPP into squalene (Krishna *et al.*, 1966). Perhaps what is actually happening is the formation of an enzyme-bound form of NPP. One can easily imagine several ways in which this could occur: e.g., by a nucleophilic group from the enzyme feeding into C-3 of FPP as the pyrophosphate anion leaves or prior formation of an ester between FPP and the enzyme with intramolecular rearrangement and formation of an active enzyme-bound NPP which does not readily equilibrate with free NPP. Obviously more work is necessary to define this important problem, which is reminiscent of similar questions concerning the intermediacy of mevaldic acid. The reduction of presqualenyl pyrophosphate (PSPP) to squalene is believed to occur in a single step. From work on the overall condensation and reduction of 2 moles of FPP to squalene, it has been possible to show that an H atom on C-4 of reduced pyridine nucleotide (NADPH) is incorporated into squalene in one or both of the two central carbon atoms (Childs and Bloch, 1962; Popjak et al., 1962). Squalene derived from $[2\text{-}^{14}C]$MVA in the pea has the same labeling pattern (Capstack et al., 1965) as it does in animals. It has been obtained in large quantity from unlabeled MVA in the same organism, and was found to be identical with animal squalene in its physical properties (Capstack et al., 1962). Moreover, the labeled pea squalene led to labeled cholesterol in rat liver.

The various steps from the isopentenyl pyrophosphates that are not formally asymmetric all proceed in the investigated cases in a stereospecific manner (Popjak, 1970); i.e., the molecules react only in the form of a given asymmetric conformation. While this was first most elegantly examined in animals, the same stereospecificity arises in the plants that have been investigated (Goad and Goodwin, 1972). If we view MVA and all intermediates as far as farnesol in the staggered conformation, such that the oxygen function is to the right (Figs. 7 and 8), and assign the α-configuration to the front and the β-configuration to the rear, the convention will be consistent with that used in this chapter for the sterol side chain. Using this system we find from animal experiment that, as expected for a concerted process (no intermediates), the carboxyl and hydroxyl groups of MVA-PP are on opposite sides (trans-oriented) of the molecule at the time of reaction (Cornforth et al., 1966a,b).

From the known (Eberle and Arigoni, 1960) absolute configuration of MVA in which the methyl group is α-oriented (on the front side) and the β-oriented hydroxyl group extends to the rear, the carboxyl group must be rotated to the front in the actual conformer reacting. The β atom at C-4 of MVA (which is 4-pro-S) is the one eliminated in both the isomerization and polymerization as shown in Fig. 8 (Cornforth et al., 1966a). The condensation of the two C_5 units occurs with the pi system of the Δ^3 isomer striking C-1 of the Δ^2 isomer from the former's back face, i.e., C-1 of the Δ^2 isomer is behind C-4 of the Δ^3 isomer when the molecules are viewed with the carbon systems in the plane of the paper and both the two C-1 groups are to the right. The β-H atom (2-pro-R) on C-2 is then eliminated, and elimination occurs from the same side of the molecule (the rear face) that is attacked at C-4. To account for this overall cis reaction, Cornforth et al. (1966a) postulated the addition of a group, presumably from the enzyme, to the front side of C-3, forming a temporary intermediate. The stereochemistry at C-1 of the attacking allylic pyrophosphate (Δ^2-IPP, GPP, etc.) has also been elucidated (Cornforth et al., 1966b). At each condensation the configuration is inverted. This is interpreted to mean that an S-2 type of concerted reaction occurs, the pyrophosphoroxy group being removed simultaneously with the formation of the carbon–carbon bond. Thus, condensation leading, say, to geranyl pyrophosphate, occurs in two stages: formation of the C—C bond with concomitant elimination of PP_i and addition of a nucleophile, e.g., X^- from enzyme to C-3 of the Δ^3-IPP, followed in time by elimination of a proton from C-2.

The work done in plant systems has not been carried as far as in animals, but it is known that in four species of angiosperm (Goodwin and Williams, 1966; R. J. H. Williams *et al.*, 1967b; Rees *et al.*, 1966, 1968b), a brown alga (Goad and Goodwin, 1965, 1969), a phycomycete (Goodwin and Williams, 1965), and an ascomycete (Stone and Hemming, 1968), the β-H atom at C-4 of MVA (equivalent to the β-H atom of C-2 of Δ^3-IPP) is the one eliminated, as it is in animals. This was deduced from the fact that (4R)-4-tritio-MVA with a 4α-^{3}H atom leads to retention of six tritium atoms. During the biosynthesis of animal squalene (the coupling of two farnesyl units), one of the farnesyl units receives the 4-pro-S-H atom of NADPH on the β-side of its C-1 without inversion, thereby losing the β-H atom and retaining the α-H atom, and the C-1 of the other farnesyl unit undergoes inversion with the α-H atom becoming β-oriented and vice versa. Evidence for similar stereochemistry in plants has also been brought forward (R. J. H. Williams *et al.*, 1967a; Goad *et al.*, 1969). Thus, when (5R)-5-tritio-MVA with an α-oriented tritium atom was used, six tritium atoms were incorporated into squalene; and when the similarly labeled racemate was used, eleven tritium atoms were incorporated. Attempts to examine the stereospecificity of the fate of the H atoms at C-2 of MVA in plant systems has, however, led to difficulties. As discussed in greater detail elsewhere (Goad and Goodwin, 1972), it may result, among other things, from differing rates of the Δ^3-Δ^2 isomerization.

B. The Lanosterol–Cycloartenol Bifurcation

The discovery (Schulze, 1872) of lanosterol in the wool of sheep followed by its purification (Windaus and Tschesche, 1930) and structural elucidation (cf. Fieser and Fieser, 1959) was the key to the discovery (Woodward and Bloch, 1953) that it is the first tetracycle in the sequence of events to animal cholesterol. It was also found in yeast (Ruzicka *et al.*, 1946), where it was known as "cryptosterol" (Wieland *et al.*, 1937). After the work in animal tissue it was obtained radioactive from yeast incubation with [^{14}C]acetate, and upon reincubation in yeast it yielded labeled ergosterol (Schwenk and Alexander, 1958). These facts led to the essentially universal assumption of its being the obligatory intermediate to steroids in all organisms. Added weight to this idea was afforded by the demonstration that labeled lanosterol yields labeled isofucosterol in a gymnosperm (Raab *et al.*, 1968). However, with modern methods of analysis and an increased interest in plant products, investigators have looked for and failed to find lanosterol in algae or tracheophytes except in the case of some *Euphorbia* species and Paul's Scarlet rose. Instead, cycloartenol was frequently encountered (Tables X and XI).

The significance of this was first called attention to by Benveniste *et al.* (1965, 1966a,b) when they found cycloartenol in tobacco plants. Cycloartenol had first been isolated from *Artocarpus integrifolia* by Barton (1951), who determined its structure. It was then found in *Euphorbia balsomifera latex* (Chapon and David, 1952) and *Strychnos nux-vomica* (Bentley *et al.*, 1953). Recently, a quantitative survey was made (Jeong *et al.*, 1972) verifying its common occurrence. Since it leads by acid-catalysis to lanosterol (Bentley *et al.*, 1953), the suggestion was made (Benveniste *et al.*, 1965, 1966b) that it acts in place of lanosterol in tobacco as the first polycycle following squalene. Its biosynthesis from labeled precursors was achieved (Benveniste *et al.*, 1966b; Goad and Goodwin, 1966), and upon reincubation in tobacco it led to labeled 4,4,14-tridemethyl sterols (Hewlins *et al.*, 1969). Subsequently the "lanosterol" of coffee beans, corn, and *Dioscorea* were shown actually

Table X
OCCURRENCE OF LANOSTEROL IN PLANTS

Plant	Reference
Yeast	Kodicek (1959),
	Ruzicka *et al.* (1945, 1946),
	Schwenk and Alexander (1958),
	Schwenk *et al.* (1955)
Inonotus obliquus	Kuznetsova (1962),
	Loviagina and Shivrina (1962),
	Lucwiczak and Wrzeciono (1961)
Poria obliquua	Kier (1961)
Phycomyces blakesleeanus	Goulsten *et al.* (1967),
	Mercer and Johnson (1969)
Emericellopsis salmosynnemata	Kawaguchi and Okuda (1970)
Physarum polycephalum	Lenfant *et al.* (1970)
Corynebacterium sp.	Schubert and Schumann (1967)
Euphorbia sp.	Gonzalez (1964),
	Gonzalez and Mora (1952),
	Gonzalez and Toste (1952),
	Gonzalez *et al.* (1958)
	Ponsinet and Ourisson (1968a)
Paul's Scarlet rose	Williams and Goodwin (1965)
Aspergillus fumigatus	Goulsten *et al.* (1967)
Azotobacter chroococcum	Schubert *et al.* (1968)

Table XI
OCCURRENCE OF CYCLOARTENOL IN PLANTS

Plant	References
Artocarpus integrifolia	Barton (1951)
Strychnos nux-vomica	Bentley *et al.* (1953)
Solanum tuberosum	Schreiber and Osske (1962), vonArdenne *et al.* (1965)
Nicotiana tabacum	Benveniste *et al.* (1964, 1966a,b)
Pisum sativum	Goad and Goodwin (1966), Kemp *et al.* (1968)
Birch wood	Bergman *et al.* (1965)
Larix decidua leaves	Goad and Goodwin (1967)
Grapefruit peel	Williams *et al.* (1965)
Hura crepitans latex	Ponsinet and Ourisson (1965)
Spanish moss	Djerassi and McCrindle (1962)
Fucus spiralis	Goad and Goodwin (1969)
Coffee beans and oil	Alcaide *et al.* (1971), Nagasampagi *et al.* (1971)
Agave toumeyana	Erhardt *et al.* (1967)
Dioscorea composita	Erhardt *et al.* (1967)
Bramble	Erhardt *et al.* (1967)
Endive	Erhardt *et al.* (1967)
Carrot	Erhardt *et al.* (1967)
Zea mays	Goad and Goodwin (1966), Kemp *et al.* (1968)
Ochromonas malhamensis	Gershengorn *et al.* (1968)
Rhodophyta sp.	Alcaide *et al.* (1968a), Ferezou *et al.* (1974)
Chlorophyceae sp.	Gibbons *et al.* (1968)
Phaseolus volgaris leaves	Rees *et al.* (1968a)
Musa sapientum	Knapp and Nicholas (1971)
Euphorbia sp.	Chapon and David (1952), Ponsinet and Ourisson (1968a)
Euglena gracilis	Anding *et al.* (1971)

to be cycloartenol, and lanosterol was positively identified in fungi other than yeasts (Goulston and Mercer, 1969). Judged by work with cell-free systems the formation of cycloartenol occurs in the absence of lanosterol in the alga *Ochromonas malhamensis* (Rees *et al.*, 1969), the gymnosperm *Pinus pinea* (Malhotra and Nes, 1972), and the angiosperm *Phaseolus vulgaris* (Rees *et al.*, 1968a). Tissue cultures of *Nicotiana tabacum, Agave toumeyana,* and other plants also biosynthesize cycloartenol in the absence of lanosterol (Ehrhardt *et al.*, 1967; Eppenberger *et al.*, 1969), and the same phenomenon has been demonstrated *in vivo* with *Zea mays* (Gibbons *et al.*, 1971). The converse is true in fungi (Mercer and Johnson, 1969). Furthermore, neither yeast (Anding *et al.*, 1974) nor mammals (Gibbons *et al.*, 1971) will convert cycloartenol to 4,4,14-trisdemethyl sterols, but cycloartenol is converted to these compounds in both algae (Hall *et al.*, 1967; Lenton *et al.*, 1971) and tracheophytes (Gibbons *et al.*, 1971; Hewlins *et al.*, 1969; Alcaide *et al.*, 1968b; Devys *et al.*, 1968).

It thus became apparent (Gibbons *et al.*, 1971) that the cyclization of squalene oxide constitutes a bifurcation in the sterol pathway which depends not on the plant–animal division, but rather on the presence or the absence of photosynthesis. Since algae were also found to form cycloartenol, this eliminated a higher plant–lower plant dichotomy, and it now appears that nonphotosynthetic systems (animals and fungi having been investigated) utilize the lanosterol pathway, and that photosynthetic plants (algae, ferns, gymnosperms, and angiosperms having been investigated) utilize the cyclo-artenol route (Fig. 10). The obligatory character of the use of lanosterol in nonphotosynthetic systems has been shown from the fact, as already men-tioned, that both rat liver (Gibbons *et al.*, 1971) and yeast (Anding *et al.*, 1974) fail to convert cycloartenol to 4,4,14-trisdemethyl sterols under condi-tions in which lanosterol undergoes the process. Clearly in these organisms there is a lack of an isomerase for the opening of the 9,19-cyclo grouping. The only metabolite of cycloartenol found in liver was the 22,23-dihydro derivative. On the other hand, lanosterol or its 24-methylene derivative is

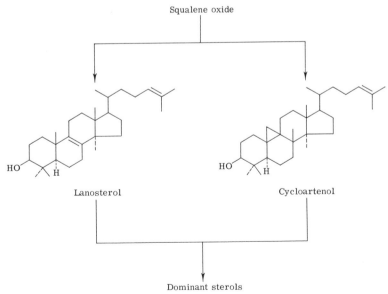

FIG. 10.   Lanosterol–cycloartenol bifurcation.

readily converted to the functional sterols by a variety of photosynthetic plants (Raab *et al.*, 1968; Russell *et al.*, 1967; Baisted *et al.*, 1968; Hall *et al.*, 1969). This then raises the question of sequence, to be discussed in a later section, but at this juncture it is worth noting that *Euphorbia lathyris* latex converts cycloartenol to lanosterol (Ponsinet and Ourisson, 1968b), presumably explaining why lanosterol has been isolated from some *Euphorbia* species and cycloartenol from others. The isolation of the isomerase from a bramble, *Rubus fruticosis*, has been reported (Heintz *et al.*, 1972), and this and other information has helped to sort out the sequence problem. Cycloartenol has also been isolated from euglenoids both in the light and dark phases of growth (Anding *et al.*, 1971) indicating that this organism is a photosynthetic plant that can operate nonphotosynthetically rather than being a nonphotosynthetic plant that can operate photosynthetically. Similarly, nonphotosynthetic tissue (endosperm) of a gymnosperm uses the cycloartenol route (Malhotra and Nes, 1972).

The bifurcation is consequently a familial phenomenon correlated with a functional aspect (the function of sterols), but the function and the pathway do not appear to be related in a cause and effect manner. Following cyclization the two pathways merge at some point. The disassociation of the bifurcation from the structure of the functional sterols is further evidenced by a lack of correlation of the two pathways with alkylation and reduction of the Δ^{24} bond (Russell *et al.*, 1967). At the present time, while the cyclization is assumed to represent only a bifurcation, it could conceivably be a trifurcation in which the $\Delta^{9(11)}$ analog (parkesterol) of lanosterol is formed. Parkeol and its 24-methylene derivative are present, for instance, in shea butter (Itoh *et al.*, 1975), and indosterol, the $\Delta^{9(11)}$ analog of stigmasterol, occurs in *Seseli indicum* (Gupta and Gupta, 1974). Whether the $\Delta^{9(11)}$ compounds are derived by cyclization or by isomerization (of cycloartenol) which seems more likely and whether or not they are directly on the pathway to dominant sterols remains to be elucidated. Similarly, the involvement of the Δ^7 analog of lanosterol is conceivable.

The true substrate for the cyclization is squalene 2,3-epoxide. After its demonstration as the intermediate in animals (van Tamelen *et al.*, 1966; Corey *et al.*, 1966; Willett *et al.*, 1967), it was shown to lead to lanosterol in yeast (Barton *et al.*, 1968) and *Phycomyces blakesleeanus* (Mercer and Johnson, 1969), to cycloartenol in *Ochromonas malhamensis* (Rees *et al.*, 1969), *Phaseolus vulgaris* (Rees *et al.*, 1968a), and *Nicotianum tabacum* (Heintz and Benveniste, 1970), and to the protosteroid fusidic acid in *Fusidium coccineum* Godtfredsen *et al.*, 1968). The term "protosterol" was coined by Corey *et al.*, (1968) to describe a substance with the stereochemistry and other structural features of squalene oxide metabolites with the trans-syn-trans-anti-trans configuration. The natural occurrence of protosterols, such as fusidic acid, and the experimental formation of one from a modified squalene oxide in the presence of the squalene oxide-lanosterol cyclase (Corey and Yamamoto, 1970), together with theoretical considerations (Eschenmoser *et al.*, 1955) have led to the assumption that sterols are formed by a nonstop (concerted) cyclization proceeding first to a charged intermediate with a structure of this type, *viz.*, the protosteroid cation. The supposition is given further weight by the failure to isolate any partially cyclized intermediates when purified enzymes are used. While extensive work has not been done with the cyclase in the plant kingdom, the use of modified substrates with the mammalian enzyme has led to a number of details of theoretical interest (Corey *et al.*, 1968, 1971; van Tamelen *et al.*, 1970, 1971), which are presumably also applicable to fungi, etc. Among the more interesting points is the role the angular methyl group (C-19 in the steroid, C-6 in squalene) plays in the cyclization. In its presence only the A/B-trans system is obtained, but in its absence not only is 19-norlanosterol obtained, but its 5β-*cis* isomer also is formed. The methyl group is apparently quite important in allowing the enzyme to direct the asymmetric folding of the molecule. On the other hand, 15-demethylsqualene oxide led only to 18-norlanosterol, and 10-demethylsqualene oxide led to lanosterol lacking the 14α-methyl group. When C-10 and C-15 were both missing from the oxide, an unrearranged protosterol bearing a side-chain hydroxyl group was formed. This is believed to indicate that steric compressions are involved in driving rearrangement from the protosterol structure to the sterol system.

Labeling and other experiments have also shown C-2 of MVA to be the 4α-methyl group of the cyclized substance (Stone *et al.*, 1969; Ghisalberti *et al.*, 1969), and at least in animals the 4α-methyl group is lost before the 4β-methyl group (Gaylor, 1974). The C-2 of MVA appears in the chain of squalene (as opposed to the branched methyl groups), and the isomerization of Δ^3-isopentenyl pyrophosphate occurs stereospecifically from a given conformer (Baisted and Nes, 1963). Similarly, the epoxidation of the Δ^2 bond of squalene occurs with maintenance of the original trans stereochemistry. The absolute configuration (S) of the oxide is known (Barton *et al.*, (1974b). When viewed in the conformer leading to sterols with incipient ring A at the left, the oxygen is in front of the plane of the paper and becomes the 3β-OH group.

These various considerations lead to the following views of the two modes of cyclization leading to sterols. In both cases (lanosterol and cycloartenol) squalene oxide is protonated on the oxygen atom, and the now electrophilic C-4 (using steroid numbering), which is placed on top (using the usual view of the nucleus) of the $\Delta^{5(10)}$ bond, condenses with C-5. This throws the H atom on C-5 to the rear, and, since C-10 must be attacked from the opposite or rear side by C-9, C-19 is thrown to the front, establishing both the absolute configurations and the A/B-trans arrangement. In proceeding to the euphoid cation (and other triterpenoid states), this sequence of overlapping continues, finally giving the all-trans-anti arrangement. The cyclizing conformer is a regular spiral with each loop below the preceding one, and the double bond closer to C-3 attacks the next one from above. Therefore, the C–C bond is formed from the back side of the first double bond and the front side of the other one. The conformer approximates an all-chair system. In the steroid-forming conformer, C-10 (still using the steroid numbering) attacks C-9 from above, but from the latter's back side (α) rather than as in the euphoid case from the front side (β). The cyclizing conformer approximates the chair–boat state for rings A and B, respectively, forming a *syn*-B/C juncture, and incipient rings C and D are forced strongly to the rear of the line that would pass through the euphoid spiral. Atoms forming rings C and D in the steroid cases form a spiral that must have the reversed stereochemistry from that in the euphoid spiral, because when C-9 is attacked from its α, or back, side C-8 must be attacked by C-14 from the opposite, or front, side (β) in order to maintain the *trans*-reaction dictated by the pi-lobes of a double bond. Consequently, the H atom at C-9 is thrown to the front, the methyl group on C-8 is thrown to the rear, and the methyl group on C-14 is thrown to the front. Similarly, C-13 now must accept C-17 with the latter on top, since C-14 was attacked from the rear. The result is a 13α-H atom and an anti-trans-anti arrangement of rings B, C, and D. The first atom in the side chain (C-20) would be a pseudoequatorial part of the spiral, and closure of the C-13,17-bond with C-17 above C-13 must force the 17-H atom into the β position. This results in the completed protosteroid cation with a positive charge at C-20.

The protosteroid cation proceeds to lanosterol by elimination of the 9β-H atom as a proton, which forces a series of 1,2-trans migrations (8α-CH$_3$ to C-14, 14β-CH$_3$ to C-13, 17β-H to C-20) in order to feed electrons to the positive charge at C-20. Nuclear positions 13, 14, and 17 are inverted by the trans process. Since the stereochemistry of the Δ^8 bond approximates that of a trans juncture of the rings, the three dimensional characteristics of an all-trans-anti tetracycle are now established. The product (lanosterol) is epimeric to euphol. In proceeding to cycloartenol, a proton must be eliminated from C-19 instead of C-9 with the 9β-H atom migrating to C-8 and C-19 attacking C-9. Evidence for this has been obtained from retention of the label from 4-^{3}H-MVA in cycloartenol, but the stereochemistry is not right for C-19 to attack C-9. The process would not occur in a trans fashion, and the 9β-H atom is in the way. In view of this, it seems likely that the enzyme donates electrons to the α face of C-9 inducing the 1,2 migrations and that this is then followed by elimination of a proton from C-19, with the latter attacking the β side of C-9 and elimination of the enzyme proceeding on the α face. This double-inversion mechanism would account for retention of configuration in cycloartenol. If the protosteroid–enzyme complex were partially stable or if the elimination of the 19-H atom could be inhibited, proof for the process could be obtained. One would expect, for instance, that 6-demethyl squalene (lacking the steroidal C-19) would not go beyond the stage of the enzyme complex if a deprotonating agent is located two bond lengths away from the steroidal C-10 so that it reacts only with a 19-H atom. If deprotonation is not that specific, introduction of some other group might block the loss of the enzyme. The point is important, because no direct evidence yet exists for how the 9,19-cyclo grouping is introduced, and its formation, contrasted to introduction of the Δ^8 bond, is the only difference in the photosynthetic and nonphotosynthetic cyclizations. Consideration of bond angles, bond strains, and bulk interactions leads to the inevitable conclusion that the 3-membered ring is much more energetic than the Δ^8 bond. This is given experimental verification by the conversion of cycloartenol to lanosterol and its Δ^7 and $\Delta^{9(11)}$ analogs by acid catalysis (Bentley et al., 1953; Itoh et al., 1975). The route to cycloartenol is energetically less favored than the one through lanosterol, which is in turn less favorable theoretically than the one to euphol. How and why nature has chosen and maintained the least-favored route in photosynthetic systems is quite mysterious.

Evidence adduced in several ways indicates that the lanosterol–cycloartenol bifurcation does not influence whether or not C-24 is alkylated. Thus, lanosterol usually leads to 24-methyl sterols in yeast and to 24-demethyl sterols in animals. Cycloartenol and lanosterol both undergo alkylation in a cell-free system from peas (Russell et al., 1967). 24-Methylenecycloartanol has frequently been isolated from photosynthetic plants and 24-methylene sterols from lanosterol-using yeast. The presence of 9,19-cyclo-14α-methylcholestanol (pollinastanol) in pollen, etc. (Devys and Barbier, 1967; Bekaert et al., 1974) shows that plants can reduce instead of alkylate the side chain of a 9,19-cyclosterol, and the very presence of cholesterol in animals shows that the side chain of the sterol lacking a 9,19-cyclo group can also be reduced instead of alkylated. Finally, cycloartenol appears to be reduced in animal tissue (Gibbons et al., 1971). The simple sequence in photosynthetic plants of cycloartenol to lanosterol to alkylated sterols (sitosterol, etc.) does not appear to exist normally (except perhaps in Euphorbia and related species), nor do the differential sequences of cycloartenol to alkylated sterols and lanosterol to nonalkylated sterols (cholesterol, etc.) appear to operate. The small amount of cholesterol in most plants has inhibited careful examination of its origin, but cycloartanol and 31-norcycloartanol have been identified in a red alga (*Rhodymenia palmata*) in which labeled acetate leads to labeled desmosterol and cholesterol (Ferezou *et al.*, 1974). There is, therefore, every reason to believe at the moment that in photosynthetic plants both 24-alkylated and nonalkylated sterols arise through the same cyclized metabolite of squalene oxide, but the point is sufficiently important to warrant further documentation, which it is hoped will be forthcoming.

While there can be no doubt about the final configurations in the nucleus of the sterol molecule in view both of theory and experiment, until recently the configuration at C-20 has remained anomalous in terms of its mechanistic origin. Since the terminal double bond ($\Delta^{17(20)}$ in steroidal numbering) of squalene oxide is trans oriented and since C-13 attacks it from below (rear), C-20 should be attacked from above (front). Indeed, the protosteroid cation bears a properly oriented 17β-H atom to do this. However, since the trans configuration of the $\Delta^{17(20)}$ bond places C-22 and the rest of the side chain to the left, instead of to the right as we usually write it, migration of the 17β-H atom to C-20 would produce a 20β-H atom. Based on a long series of degradations and interrelationships, the configuration of animal cholesterol is known (Fieser and Fieser, 1959) to be the opposite one, i.e., a 20α-H atom, and PMR studies (Nes *et al.*, 1977) have shown that the same configuration (20α-H) exists in sterols derived from algae, fungi, and vascular plants. Carbon-20 must undergo an inversion by being attacked from the front side by the enzyme, OH^-, etc., at the protosteroid stage with subsequent 180° rotation about the C-17,20 bond prior to both migration of the H atom from C-17 to C-20 and elimination of the substituent (enzyme, etc.) at C-20. That migration does occur follows from labeling data from MVA in the animal case. Furthermore, the 20-hydroxy derivative (dammarenediol) of the euphoid cation has been isolated from Dipterocarpaceae resins (e.g., Fischer and Seiler, 1961). The configuration (20α-OH) is in agreement with the expectation of attack from the rear with C-22 to the left. Is it possible that a 20β-substituted derivative exists even transiently as an intermediate to sterols? If so, it should not be the 20β-hydroxyprotosterol itself, since the latter would not readily undergo alkyloxygen cleavage at C-20 to set in motion the rearrangements. It would have to be phosphorylated to give a good leaving anion. Since neither an intermediate nor an ATP requirement is found in the cyclization, inversion presumably occurs through the transient addition of some nucleophilic group from the enzyme. The configurational question also raises a conformational one. In sterols with a 20α-H atom the preferred conformation about the 17(20) bond is the one with C-22 to the right ("right-handed"), but the intermediate with the enzyme attached at C-20 will have the left-handed and eclipsed conformation. Energy minimization then accounts for the rotation from the left- to right-handed conformer. This rotation also places the enzyme in back, allowing the front-oriented

H atom on C-17 to displace the enzyme in a trans reaction (Nes *et al.*, 1977).

In the conversion of lanosterol or cycloartenol to functional sterols, changes in both the nucleus and the side chain must occur. The latter is considered first, because events in the nucleus for reasons unknown are related to metabolism in the side chain.

VI. Metabolism of the Side Chain

A. The Reduction-Alkylation Bifurcation

The formation of a tetracycle leaves eight of the ten C atoms of the terminal two isopentenoid residues of squalene oxide in an acyclic condition with one double bond remaining (Δ^{24}). It is this double bond that dominates future events, although this has only recently been appreciated. Robinson (1955) was the first person to think seriously about the origin of the different sterol side chains. At the time he considered the problem, squalene was unknown in plants, and the mevalonate pathway was also unknown. However, an acetate origin for steroids was deemed likely and much work had been accomplished on the conversion of acetate units not only to fatty acids but to nonisopentenoidal polycycles. It had become clear from both theory and experiment that the polymerization of C_2 units occurred by enolate condensations (C-2 attacking C-1), which meant if a higher acid, e.g., propionate, were involved, then a branched chain must result. Only C-1 and C-2 of the acid could be in the linear chain. It occurred to Robinson that the typical C_1 and C_2 branches at C-24 of the plant sterols could arise by inclusion of propionate and butyrate, respectively, in an acetate polymerization. The C_3 acid would lead to a C_1 branch, and the C_4 acid would yield a C_2 branch. While this would not account for why one does not find a longer homologous series, say a C_6 branch from a C_8 acid, this is not a serious drawback, and in fact the 24-C_3 branch (present in 29-methylisofucosterol of the scallop *Placopecten magellanicus*) has recently been discovered (Idler *et al.*, 1971). Schwenk decided to test Robinson's hypothesis experimentally by incubating labeled propionate with a yeast system that actively biosynthesizes the 24-C_1 sterol, ergosterol. Ergosterol did not, however, become labeled. (Alexander *et al.*, 1958). Moreover, at about the same time, squalene was isolated from yeast and from a tracheophyte and found to possess no extra alkyl group. Thus, the C-24 alkyl groups must be introduced not in the course of the polymerization, but at some stage after formation of squalene. Since Schwenk found lanosterol proceeded to ergosterol and since in the same period lanosterol was found to proceed to cholesterol in animals, both the alkylation and the reduction must commonly occur after cyclization. This is corroborated by the failure of any one to find a reduced squalene in fungi, algae, or higher plants, although 2-dihydrosqualene as well as 2,22-tetrahydrosqualene do occur in the halophilic bacterium *Halobacterium cutirabum* (Kramer *et al.*, 1972).

Schwenk next tried labeled formate as a precursor in yeast and this time achieved incorporation of the label into the sterol. Since inhibition of the tetrahydrofolate reductase system inhibited incorporation of label from formate (Alexander and Schwenk, 1958), reduction of formate must occur prior to condensation with the sterol. This led to the incubation of yeast with methyl-labeled methionine, and it was very efficiently incorporated into ergosterol (Alexander *et al.*, 1958). Degradation proved the label to reside only in the 24-methyl group (Alexander *et al.*, 1958).

Schwenk's work on the problem unfortunately came to an end at this point, but Parks (1958) found that S-adenosylmethionine (SAM) is the actual C_1 donor. The fact that this is an electrophilic sulfonium ion and that the first tetracycle in the biosynthetic sequence bears a nucleophilic set of π electrons in the Δ^{24} bond led Nes and his co-workers (Castle *et al.*, 1963) to conclude that condensation of SAM with C-24 of a Δ^{24}-sterol occurs to give a C-25 cation which by H migration and elimination of a proton from C-28 would yield a 24-methylene sterol (Fig. 11). Condensation of a sterol containing a double bond with an electrophile to give a product with a double bond has the requisites of a polymerization, and the dimeric stage (24-C_2) at least might be realizable. With concomitant or subsequent reduction, this would account then for the common plant sterols, e.g., 24-methyl- and 24-ethyl-cholesterol, and would allow for an even higher homologous series by further condensations, H migrations, and proton-elimination from the incoming C_1 group. It also accounted for the existence of the then known 24-methylene- and 24-ethylidene cholesterols, and introduction of a Δ^{22} bond in some other manner would account for the side chains of sterols, such as ergosterol and stigmasterol. Although other mechanisms have been considered (Lederer, 1964, 1969), the latter overall view (Fig. 11) of the process as an electrophilic attack on the Δ^{24} bond not only has proved to be basically correct, but has been greatly extended and refined in the past decade.

The principal experimental reasons for believing that the alkylation is a sequential series of electrophilic attacks on the Δ^{24} bond of a tetracycle are as follows. Not only is the 24-C_1 group derived from SAM (Parks, 1958; Katsuki and Bloch, 1967; Moore and Gaylor, 1969), but both carbon atoms of the 24-C_2 group are known to be derived from methionine (Bader *et al.*, 1964; Villanueva *et al.*, 1964; Castle *et al.*, 1967). The methyl group of methionine does not enter the isopentenoid pathway prior to squalene and become part of the "backbone" of the molecule, since β-amyrin, which is

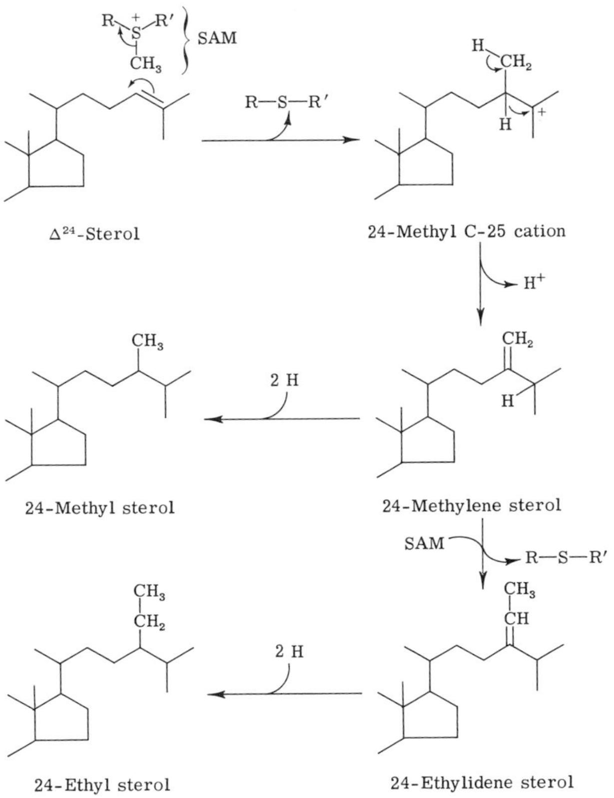

FIG. 11. Basic mechanism of alkylation.

derived from squalene, does not incorporate label from methionine under conditions in which β-sitosterol does incorporate label in the presence of active β-amyrin biosynthesis (Castle *et al.*, 1963, 1967). Furthermore, as already mentioned, no alkyl squalene has been discovered. In a cell-free system from peas, substrates bearing a Δ^{24} bond yield 24-methylene derivatives, but the 24-dihydro substrates remain unchanged (Russell *et al.*, 1967). This proves the necessity of the Δ^{24} bond. The H atom at C-24 (of lanosterol or cycloartenol) actually migrates to C-25 in both yeast (Akhtar *et al.*, 1967) and a gymnosperm (Raab *et al.*, 1968), and evidence exists for it in brown algae (Goad *et al.*, 1966). The H migration is in accord with the predicted mechanism with the formation or intermediacy of a $\Delta^{24(28)}$-sterol. $\Delta^{24(28)}$-Sterols exist in plants that contain mostly sterols without this double bond in agreement with its acting in an intermediary status, and sterols in most organisms incorporate the number of H atoms from the methyl group

(Table XII) of methionine, which is predicted from a route through a $\Delta^{24(28)}$-sterol. However, alternatives arise that have been most adroitly examined by Goad and Goodwin (1972). The alternative routes, discussed in subsequent paragraphs, are variations ensuing from the main theme in which a chemical species (SAM) acting as if it were a methyl carbonium ion attacks a double bond. Neither the ethyl group from ethionine nor the carbon atoms from acetate appear in the alkyl group at C-24 when incubated with peas (Castle *et al.*, 1963). The yeast enzyme catalyzing the C_1 transfer from SAM has been purified (Moore and Gaylor, 1969) and holds promise of being a tool for further mechanistic studies, but enzymes for side-chain alkylation have not yet been isolated from other plants. The basic pathway elucidated with sterols has also been found to operate in the production of branched-chain fatty acids.

Since the Δ^{24}-bond has also been shown to yield the unalkylated, reduced side chain (Stokes *et al.*, 1958), we are led to the existence of a bifurcation in the sterol pathway that depends in its simplest form on whether the Δ^{24} bond is alkylated or reduced (Fig. 12). The central role is played by the C-25 cation. It is achieved either by attack of H^+ or of CH_3^+ on C-24, the former leading (by attack of H^- from NADH to C-25) to reduction and the latter (by elimination of a proton or conceivably, but not documented, by attack of H^-) to alkylation. If a proton is eliminated from C-28, a second alkylation can then ensue, and so forth. Similarity of the mechanisms of reduction and alkylation finds additional support in that they are both inhibited by triparanol (Malhotra and Nes, 1971).

Attack of a nucleophile on C-24 instead of C-25 follows chemical expectation. Stabilization of the C-25 cation (from the *gem*-dimethyl group by hyperconjugation) should be greater than for C-24, and steric hindrance should be less for attack on C-24. Similarly, attack of an electrophile on C-28 of the 24-methylene intermediate should yield a more stable cation (positive charge on C-24) than attack on C-24 (positive charge on C-28), and steric hindrance should be less by attack on C-28. Thus, the mechanism also accounts for the direction of attack in both the first and the second C_1 transfers in the dominant sterols of plants. However, such classical considerations of the stability of carbonium ions do not account for all the known facts. For instance, the deprotonation at C-28 to give the 24-methylene and 24-ethylidene derivatives must be governed by the enzyme, presumably by the positioning of a deprotonating agent, because alternatives not only exist but are known to occur. An example is the occurrence of $\Delta^{25(27)}$-sterols in the green alga *Codium fragile* (Rubinstein and Goad, 1974a), which, at least in other species (*Trebouxia*) of another order (Chlorococcales), arise directly during the course of the C_1 transfer (Goad *et al.*, 1972; Wojchiechowski *et al.*, 1973).

Table XII

PLANTS USING $\Delta^{24(28)}$ INTERMEDIATES BASED ON INCORPORATION OF DEUTERIUM FROM C^2H_3-METHIONINE

Plant	Sterol	No. of ^{2}H Atoms	Reference
Fungi			
Neurospora crassa	Ergosterol	2	Jaurequiberry et al. (1965)
Gliocladium roseum	Ergosterol	2	Lenfant et al. (1969b)
Polyporus sulphureus	Eburicoic acid	2	Villanueva et al. (1967)
Daedalea quercina	Pachymic acid	2	Lederer (1969)
Oospora virescens	Ergosterol	2	Vareune et al. (1971)
Lichen mycobiont			
Xanthoria parietina	Ergosterol	2	Lenton et al. (1973b)
	Lichesterol	2	Lenton et al. (1973b)
Golden algae			
Ochromonas malhamensis	Brassicasterol	2	Smith et al. (1967)
	Poriferasterol	4	Goad et al. (1974)
O. sociablis	Poriferasterol	4	Goad et al. (1974)
O. danica	Poriferasterol	4	Goad et al. (1974)
	Clionasterol	4	Lederer (1969)
Phaeodactylum tricornutum	24-Epibrassicasterol	2	Rubinstein and Goad (1974b)
Tracheophytes			
Hordeum vulgare	Stigmasterol	4	Goad et al. (1974)
	Sitosterol	4	
	Campesterol	2	

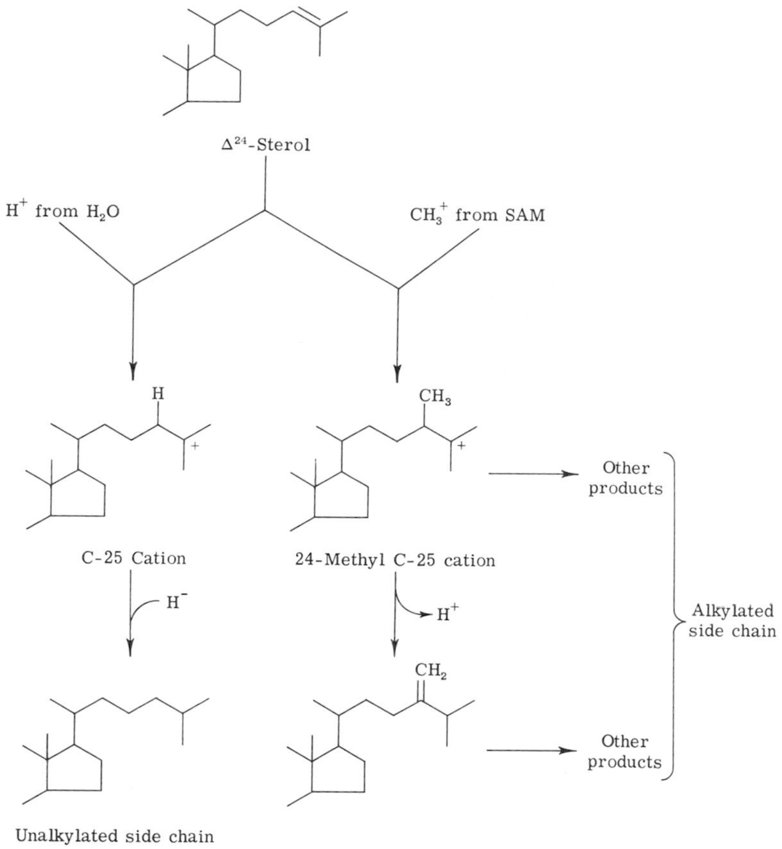

Δ^{24}-Sterol

H⁺ from H₂O

CH₃⁺ from SAM

H

CH₃

Other products

C-25 Cation

24-Methyl C-25 cation

Alkylated side chain

– H⁻

H⁺

CH₂

Unalkylated side chain

Other products

FIG. 12. Alkylation–reduction bifurcation.

Similarly, several compounds have now been found in which addition of a methyl group has occurred to a carbon atom other than C-24. They include gorgosterol (Hale *et al.*, 1970; Ling *et al.*, 1970), isolated from coelenterates belonging to the *Gorgonia* genus, which is the 22,23-methylene-23,24-dimethyl derivative of cholesterol. The 23-demethyl derivative of gorgosterol is also known (Schmitz and Pattabhiraman, 1970). All three of these compounds must have arisen from a precursor with a Δ^{22} bond which operated in addition to the Δ^{24} bond as the pi-electron source in the C_1 transfer from SAM. This illustrates that the enzyme can position the methyl group of SAM opposite to a given place on the sterol, i.e., both Δ^{22}- and Δ^{24}-alkylases exist and can be subdivided into classes depending on positioning of the deprotonating agent. A reasonable route to gorgosterol would be attack of CH_3^+ (from SAM) on C-23 of, for instance, brassicasterol with loss of a proton at C-23 reestablishing the Δ^{22} bond. A second attack on C-22 with loss of a proton from the attacking methyl group would yield the observed structure (Fig. 13). The 23-demethylgorgosterol presumably arises in the same way except that the initial attack on C-23 is eliminated. A further example is cycloneolitsin, which is the 3-methyl ether of 24-methylcyclolaudenol; i.e., it contains a 24,24-dimethyl group and has been isolated from *Neolitsea dealbata* (Ritchie *et al.*, 1969) (Fig. 14). In this case the enzyme has directed the last methyl group either to the position of least stability, if a $\Delta^{24(28)}$ intermediate is involved, or has chosen one of two approximately equally stable positions, if a $\Delta^{24(25)}$ intermediate is involved.

In those cases where the C-25 cation is formed by attack of CH_3^+ on the Δ^{24} bond, several alternatives exist for stabilization (Figs. 14–17). The one that is perhaps most expected, if the process were concerted, is elimination

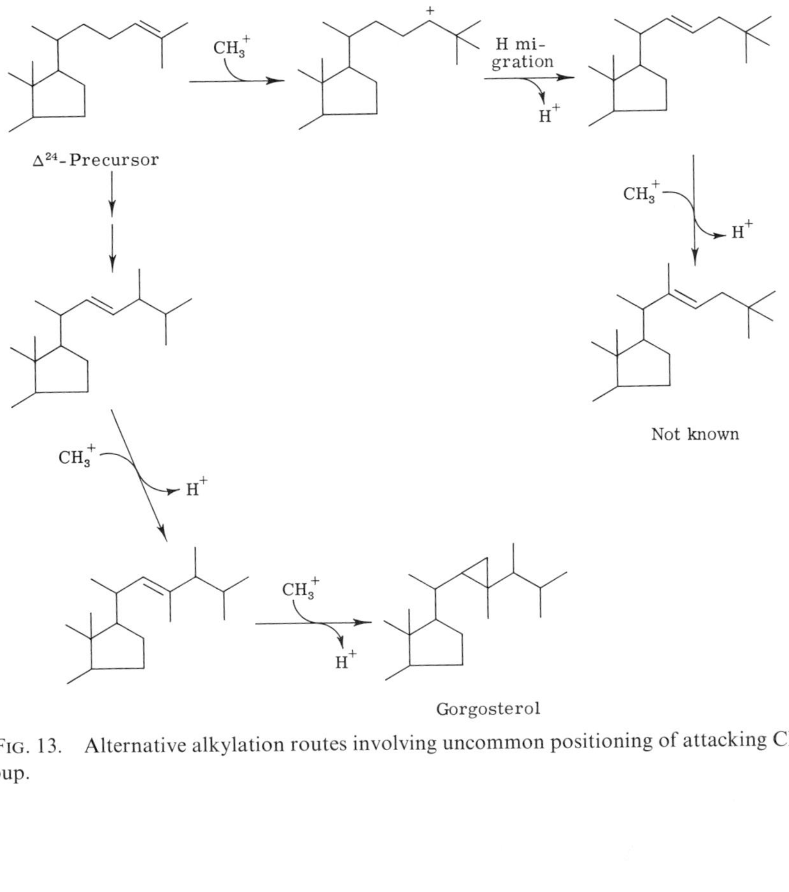

FIG. 13.   Alternative alkylation routes involving uncommon positioning of attacking CH_3^+ group.

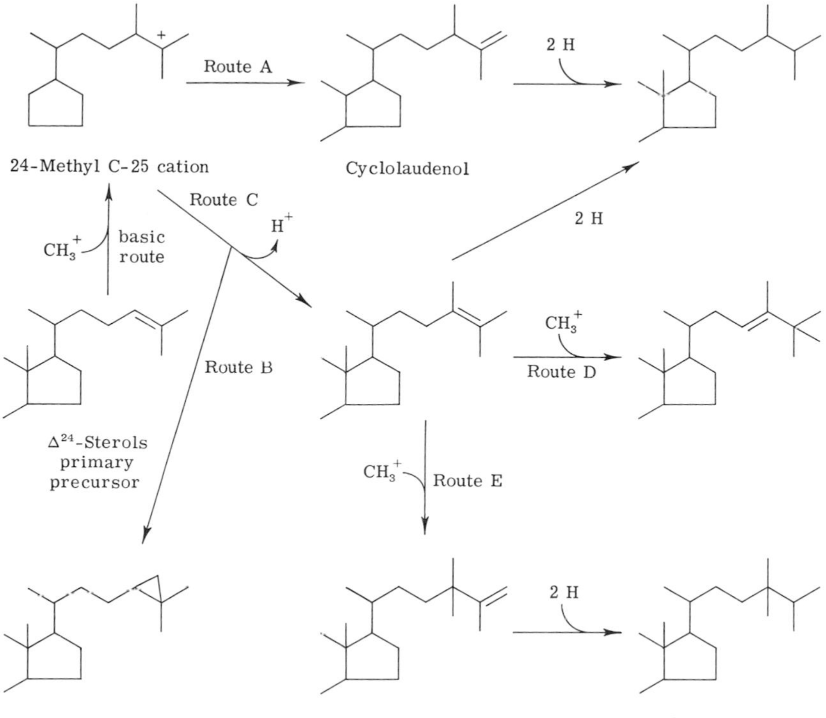

FIG. 14. Alternative alkylation routes starting from C_1 attack on the Δ^{24} bond without H migration.

of a proton from one of the *gem*-dimethyl groups after the first C_1 transfer. This indeed happens in the formation of cyclolaudenol (Ghisalberti *et al.*, 1969). When experimentally derived in *Polypodium vulgare* from labeled MVA, it retains an H atom at C-24 from C-4 of the MVA. This means it could not have been derived through a $\Delta^{24(28)}$ intermediate. Similarly, in *Clerodendrum campbelli* the 4-H atom of MVA is retained at C-24 in 25(27)-dehydroporiferasterol, and the 25-methylene group (C-27) must be derived from C-3′ of MVA, since it was shown not to have label from 2-^{14}C-MVA (Bolger *et al.*, 1970). In the case of 25(27)-dehydroporiferasterol the 24-H atom would have been expected to migrate to C-25 during the first C-1 transfer to give the $\Delta^{24(28)}$ intermediate necessary for the second alkylation.

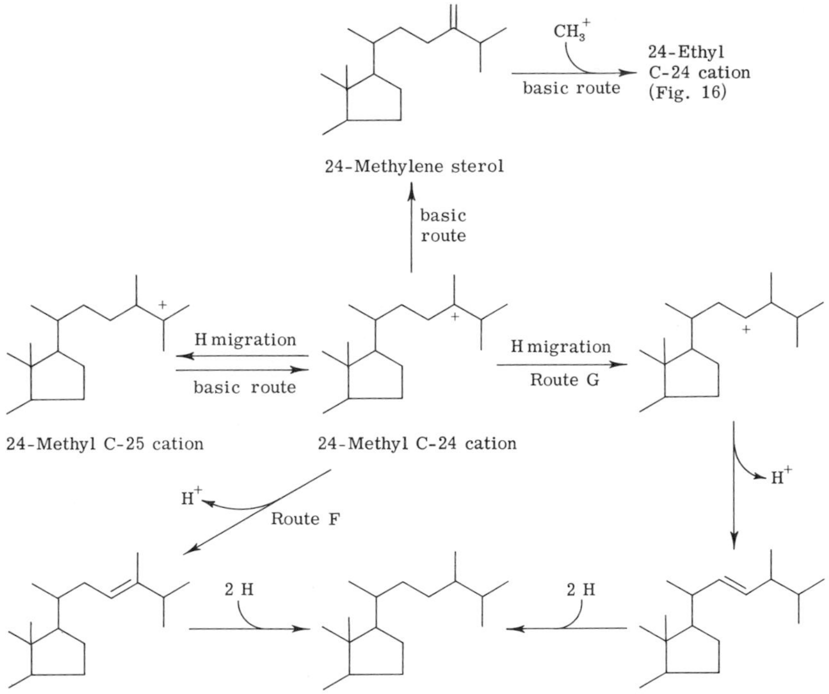

FIG. 15.   Alternative alkylation routes starting from C_1 attack on the Δ^{24} bond with H migration.

Then, upon attack with the second $CH_3{}^+$ group, a C-24-cation must have proceeded to the C-25 cation by H migration from C-25 back to C-24. Evidence for this process has also come from labeling experiments with methionine in which the methyl group contains deuterium (C^2H_3) (Tables XII and XIII). If a $\Delta^{24(28)}$ intermediate is formed and then reduced, a 24-methyl sterol should contain two ^2H atoms, and a 24-ethyl sterol four. This technique was first introduced in Lederer's laboratory (Jaurequiberry et al., 1965), and from the early and succeeding work it is clear that the foregoing expectation is actually the case for fungi, golden algae, and at least one tracheophyte (Table XII). However, for slime molds and green algae, three and five deuterium atoms, respectively, for the 24-C_1 and 24-C_2 cases, are incorporated. This is consistent with the intermediacy of a $\Delta^{25(27)}$-sterol that is subsequently reduced, but it is equally consistent with other routes, especially (a) loss of a proton from C-24 to give a $\Delta^{24(25)}$ intermediate (Tomita et al., 1970), (b) loss of a proton from C-23 with an H migration from C-24 to C-25 (in

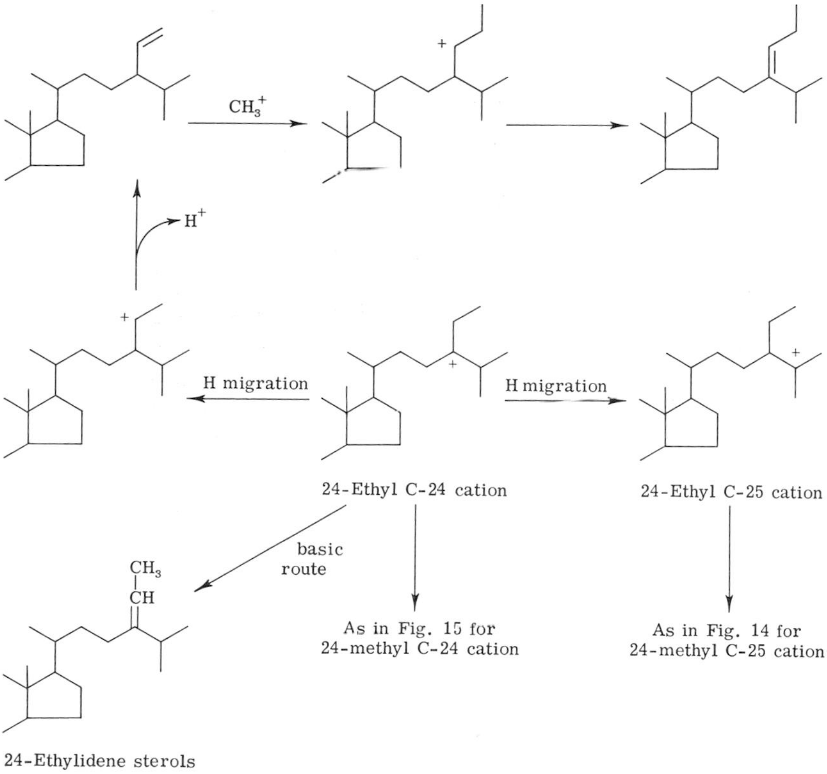

24-Ethylidene sterols

FIG. 16. Alternative alkylation pathways starting from second C_1 transfer to 24-methylene sterol.

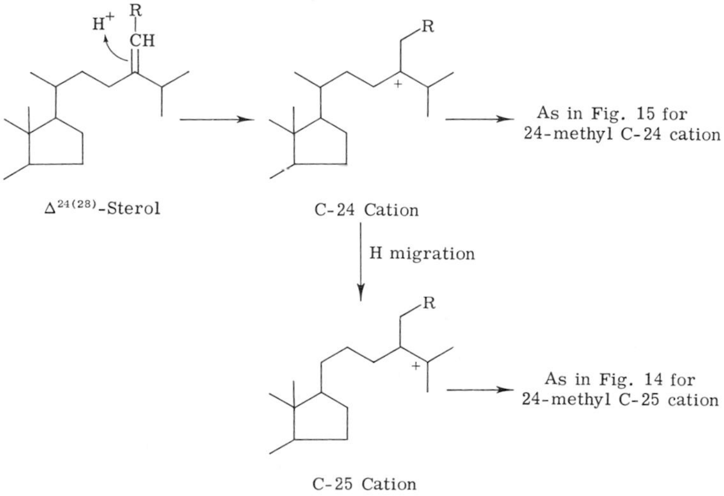

FIG. 17. Subsidiary alkylation route involving double-bond migration.

Table XIII

PLANTS FAILING TO USE $\Delta^{24(28)}$ INTERMEDIATES BASED ON INCORPORATION OF DEUTERIUM FROM C^2H_3-METHIONINE

Plant	Sterol	No. of ^2H Atoms	References
Slime molds			
Physarum polycephalum	Stigmastanol	5	Lederer (1969)
Dictostelium discoideum	5-Dihydrostigmasterol	5	Lenfant et al. (1969a)
Green algae			
Chlorella ellipsoidea	Poriferasterol	5	Tomita et al. (1971)
	22-Dihydrobrassicasterol	3	Tomita et al. (1971)
C. vulgaris	Chondrillasterol	5	Tomita et al. (1970)
	22-Dihydrochondrillasterol	5	Tomita et al. (1970)
	Fungisterol	3	Tomita et al. (1970)
C. emersonii	Chondrillasterol	5	Adler and Patterson (personal communication)
	Fungisterol	3	Adler and Patterson (personal communication)
C. fusca	Chondrillasterol	5	Adler and Patterson (personal communication)
	22-Dihydrochondrillasterol	5	Adler and Patterson (personal communication)
	Fungisterol	3	Adler and Patterson (personal communication)
C. glucotropha	Chondrillasterol	5	Adler and Patterson (personal communication)
	22-Dihydrochondrillasterol	5	Adler and Patterson (personal communication)
	Fungisterol	3	Adler and Patterson (personal communication)
C. pringsheimii	Poriferasterol	5	Adler and Patterson (personal communication)
	Brassicasterol	3	Adler and Patterson (personal communication)
	22-Dihydrobrassicasterol	5	Adler and Patterson (personal communication)
C. saccharophila	Poriferasterol	5	Adler and Patterson (personal communication)
	22-Dihydrobrassicasterol	3	Adler and Patterson (personal communication)
C. ellipsoidea	Poriferasterol	5	Adler and Patterson (personal communication)
	22-Dihydrobrassicasterol	3	Adler and Patterson (personal communication)
C. sorokiniana	Ergosterol	3	Adler and Patterson (personal communication)
Scenedesmus obliquus	Chondrillasterol	5	Goad et al. (1974)
	22-Dihydrochondrillasterol	5	Goad et al. (1974)
	Fungisterol	3	Goad et al. (1974)
Trebouxia sp. 213/3	Poriferasterol	5	Goad et al. (1972)
	Clionasterol	5	Goad et al. (1972)
	22-Dihydrobrassicasterol	3	Goad et al. (1972)

the first alkylation but unnecessary in the second) to give a Δ^{23} intermediate (Boid *et al.*, 1974), and (c) loss of a proton from C-22 to give a Δ^{22} intermediate with appropriate H migrations from C-23 to C-24, etc. (Lenfant *et al.*, 1969a; Ellouz and Lenfant, 1970). It has not yet been possible to discriminate with certainty among these alternatives, although in two species of green algae belonging to the orders Siphonales and Chlorococcales the available evidence from labeling and occurrence strongly indicates the route through the $\Delta^{25(27)}$-sterols (Goad *et al.*, 1972; Rubinstein and Goad, 1974a) is operating. The existence of a double bond in the side chain of a plant sterol is consistent with, but not proof that it plays, an intermediary role.

Since Δ^{22}-sterols are common, a route through them has merit. Unfortunately, evidence exists for the Δ^{22} bond being introduced directly by dehydrogenation. In the ciliated protozoan *Tetrahymena pyriformis* it definitely can be (Conner *et al.*, 1969), and it is also apparently true for yeast (Akhtar *et al.*, 1968, 1969a) and the tracheophyte *Digitalis lanata* (Bennett and Heftmann, 1969). Furthermore, a $\Delta^{22,25(27)}$-sterol occurs in *Clerodendrum campbelli* suggesting in itself that one of the two double bonds arises by dehydrogenation. However, in the slime mold, *Dictyostelium discoideum*, evidence both for and against direct 22-dehydrogenation exists (Ellouz and Lenfant, 1969a,b, 1970). This may indicate that introduction of the Δ^{22} bond can occur by dehydrogenation as well as by the migration route concomitantly with alkylation. If both routes really do operate in the same organism, the problem is still more complicated than it is already, and until additional evidence is available caution is necessary. Multiple routes are discussed further in Section VII.

Evidence for intermediacy of the $\Delta^{24(28)}$-sterols has come from various experiments in addition to those already discussed. In particular, a gymnosperm (*Pinus pinea*) will convert 24-methylenecholesterol to 24-methylcholesterol, and 24-ethylidenecholesterol (isofucosterol) is isolable (van Aller *et al.*, 1968, 1969). Isofucosterol or related sterols, e.g., citrostadienol and 24-ethylidenelophenol, have also been isolated from other plants. In all cases except brown algae the configuration is trans. This had led Goad and Goodwin (1972) to suggest that a possible reason why fucosterol is not reduced in brown algae is that it has the "wrong" configuration, but this would not explain why isofucosterol is not reduced in green algae of the order Ulvales, where it is the dominant sterol (Table VI) nor the report that fucosterol is reduced in another green alga, *Chlorella ellipsoidea*, to give clionasterol (Patterson and Karlander, 1967). Perhaps a better explanation is the lack of a reductase in the two cases or control of the position of equilibrium of the oxidation–reduction reaction on the side of oxidation. While the configuration about the $\Delta^{24(28)}$ bond is known to influence the rate of dehydrogenation at C-22 and C-23 due to steric phenomena (Nes *et al.*, 1971), it is not immediately obvious how it could have other effects. Another empirical possibility is directing the orientation of the asymmetric configuration at C-24, but neither theory nor data on occurrence seems to warrant such an assumption. The significance of the existence of cis and trans configurations must remain obscure for the time being. The presence in plants of small amounts of sterols with the *trans*-ethylidene group is more common than was earlier appreciated, which suggests either a physiological role or that the reduction is slower than alkylation. Several observations of an accumulation of radioactivity from $[2-^{14}C]MVA$ in the ethylidene fraction are consistent with the latter interpretation. Reasons for believing that the elimination of the proton from C-28 may be rate-limiting in the production of 24-ethylidene sterols have also been presented (Goad *et al.*, 1972). While the $\Delta^{24(28)}$-sterols have not been shown to undergo double-bond migration, this remains a possible alternative (Fig. 17) in the total biosynthetic scheme.

The reduction of the various double bonds in the side chain has not been the subject of much direct investigation in the plant kingdom, but the mechanism for the reduction of the Δ^{24} bond in animals (Duchamp *et al.*, 1971; Greig *et al.*, 1971) is probably a good model. A proton ultimately from water attacks the least highly substituted C atom, and a hydride ion from NADH attacks the other C atom in a cis manner, presumably with the intermediacy of a substrate–enzyme complex in which the enzyme attacks C-25 on the opposite site from the attack of the proton. In the final structure, the 25-H atom is in back when viewed with C-26 up and in front and C-27 down and in front. The direction of addition (H^+ to C-24) is in agreement with classical theory, but, as in the case of positioning of SAM and deprotonating agents, the reductase could conceivably position a protonating agent and NADH in the reverse order; for the Δ^{22} bond there is no obvious choice, since both C atoms are equally substituted.

B. DEALKYLATION

Dealkylation at C-24 occurs and has been the subject of extensive study in invertebrate animals, especially insects. The subject has recently been reviewed (Thompson *et al.*, 1973). The demonstrated process is introduction of a $\Delta^{24(28)}$ bond followed by loss of the substituent and formation of a dealkylated $\Delta^{24(25)}$-sterol, which is then reduced, e.g., sitosterol via fucosterol and demosterol to cholesterol. The 24(28)-oxide is believed to be an intermediate (Morisaki *et al.*, 1972). In most cases cholesterol is the end product, but in the Mexican bean beetle Δ^5-24α-ethyl sterols are converted to cho-

lestanol and lathosterol (Svoboda *et al.*, 1975). With the exception of the
oxide, the steps are the reverse of plant alkylation by the "basic route."
Dealkylation of 24-ethyl sterols (but not of 24-methyl sterols) also occurs in
the protozoan *Tetrahymena pyriformis* (Mallory and Conner, 1971; Nes *et
al.*, 1971, 1975a). Neither $\Delta^{24(28)}$-nor $\Delta^{24(25)}$-sterols are intermediates, however, in the protozoan case. This indicates more than one route for the
removal of the alkyl to be operating. Reversal of the "basic route" for
alkylation would conceivably follow the course shown in Fig. 18. The essence
of it is that the sulfur atom of homocysteine or a similar nucleophile donates
electrons to a methyl group that is on a carbon atom adjacent to a double
bond that receives a proton. The known intermediates in insects are in
accord with the process, but more work is necessary to establish it. The
reversal mechanism proposed here has the merit of also explaining the
existence of the so-called "C_{26}-sterols" (Fig. 19). These compounds, also
known as 24-norsterols, have the same side chain as cholesterol except that
one of the CH_2 groups in the body of the side chain is missing. They were
first isolated from marine invertebrates (Idler *et al.*, 1970), but they occur
also in red algae, where, however, they do not appear to be biosynthesized
(Ferezou *et al.*, 1974). Their origin can be explained by donation of electrons
to C-26 (or C-27) of a $\Delta^{24(28)}$-sterol with protonation at C-28 and electron
redistribution to give a $\Delta^{24(25)}$-24-methyl-25-demethylsterol, which proceeds
by double-bond migration to a Δ^{23}-sterol. The latter is now electronically in
condition to undergo a second demethylation at the end of the chain, yielding
a $\Delta^{24(25)}$-methyl-26,27-bisnorsterol which, by reduction with or without
double-bond migration, affords the cholesterol side chain lacking a CH_2

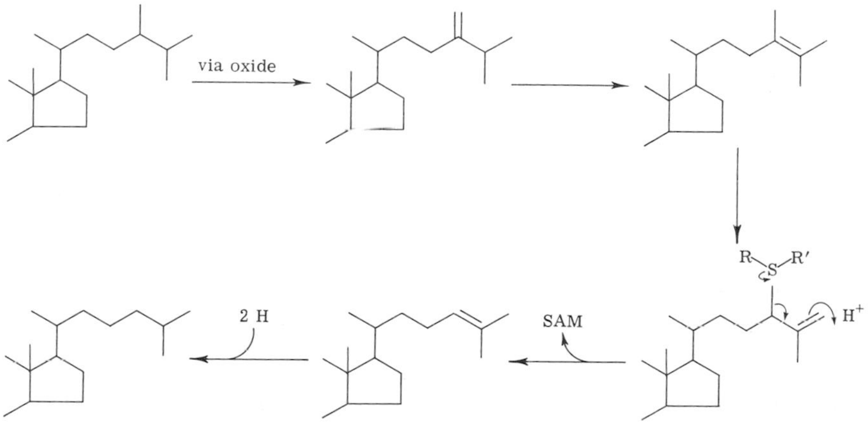

FIG. 18.   Reversal of dealkylation.

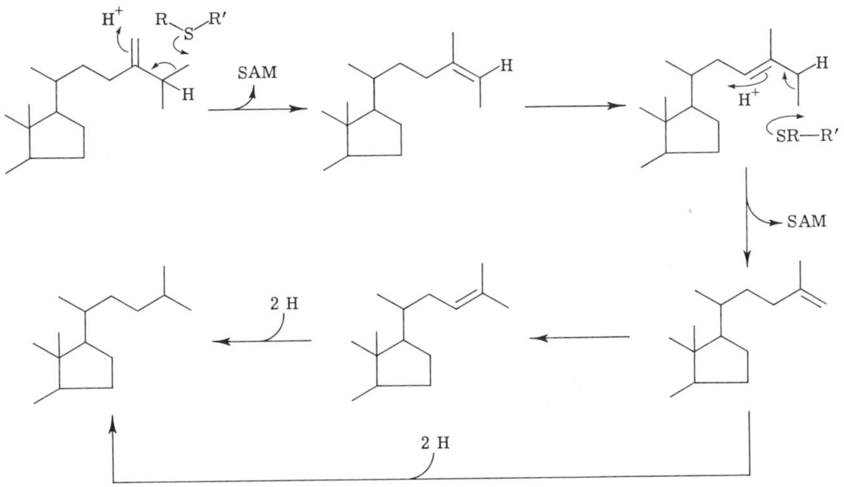

Fig. 19.   Hypothetical dealkylation pathway to C_{26} sterols.

group. The summation of the process is that both of the original *gem*-dimethyl groups have been removed and replaced by C-28 and C-25. Since the original C_8 side chain has added one CH_3 group (C-28) and lost two (C-26 and C-27), a C_7 side chain results.

VII. The Biosynthetic Sequence after Cyclization

The sequence of biosynthetic events following cyclization has not been entirely resolved, but from the occurrence of various sterols that could reasonably be intermediates, from the use of inhibitors, from the sterol composition of mutants, and from the use of various sterols as substrates, the following view emerges.

Metabolism of the Δ^{24} bond seems to occur primarily as the first step, although it does not appear to be obligatory at this stage. The principal reasons for believing this are that 24-methylenecycloartanol is formed in cell-free systems (Russell *et al.*, 1967; Malhotra and Nes, 1972) and has been found in a number of plants. Cycloartanol has also been found, i.e., both C_1 transfer and reduction are known unequivocally to occur immediately after cyclization. On the other hand, the C_1-transferase from a photosynthetic plant is not specific for cycloartenol, accepting both lanosterol and desmosterol (Russell *et al.*, 1967); this means that metabolism of the Δ^{24} bond probably has a preferred, but not absolute, place at the beginning of the sequence. Similar conclusions can be drawn for the animal kingdom. 24-Dihydrolanosterol is known to occur and has been converted to cholesterol.

At the same time desmosterol occurs in some tissues and also is convertible to cholesterol. None of the enzymes in liver biosynthesis can have absolute specificity for the presence or the absence of the Δ^{24} bond, since in the presence of a reductase inhibitor, triparanol, desmosterol accumulates despite the fact that dihydrolanosterol, as mentioned, will proceed through the pathway. Early metabolism of the Δ^{24} bond in yeast also is known to occur since $4\alpha,14\alpha$-dimethyl-24-methylenecholest-8-enol has been isolated (Trocha *et al.*, 1974), but zymosterol also occurs, showing that all transformations except reactions in ring B can occur without altering the Δ^{24} bond.

Removal of the three nuclear methyl groups has been well examined both in plants (Goad and Goodwin, 1972) and animals (Gaylor, 1974). The 14α-methyl group is believed to be removed first in animals followed in turn by removal of the 4α- and 4β-methyl groups. As discussed subsequently the plant sequence is different. Removal of each methyl group involves mixed-function oxidases. At C-4 sequential conversion of the methyl groups through the primary alcohol to the carboxylic acid leads, after oxidation to the 3-ketone (now a β-keto acid), to decarboxylation. The ketone is then reduced back to the 3-alcohol (Fig. 20). Complete oxidation and removal of one methyl group occurs prior to operations on another. The removal of the 4α-methyl group (known to be derived from C-2 of MVA) leads to an enolate anion lacking asymmetry at C-4. Upon ketonization, the more stable, equatorial 4α-methyl group results, i.e., the axial 4β-methyl group of the 4,4-dimethyl sterol becomes the 4α-methyl group after demethylation.

While a β-keto acid has not been identified in the removal of the 14α-methyl group, C-14 is apparently involved in some way, since a 14-H atom disappears in plants, and in both plants (Chan *et al.*, 1974; Chan and Patterson, 1973; Dickson and Patterson, 1972) and animals (Lutsky and Schroepfer, 1968; Akhtar *et al.*, 1969b; Lutsky *et al.*, 1971; Hsiung *et al.*, 1975) a $\Delta^{7,14}$- or $\Delta^{8,14}$-diene is a known intermediate. It is not clear whether the Δ^8 bond migrates to the Δ^7 position necessarily before or after formation of the Δ^{14} bond, but it is known to be capable of doing so in the absence of the Δ^{14} bond, in which case the equilibrium favors the Δ^7-sterol. On the other hand, the $\Delta^{7,14}$-diene isomerizes to the $\Delta^{8,14}$-diene, and the reverse reaction does not occur. The $\Delta^{8,14}$-diene is reduced by NADH (H^+ going to C-15 and H^- to C-14) at least in animals.

The remaining steps in nuclear transformations are 5-dehydrogenation and Δ^7- or Δ^8-reduction. In the animal kingdom the sequence $\Delta^7 \rightarrow \Delta^{5,7} \rightarrow \Delta^5$ has been very well studied at the enzymologic level (Dempsey, 1965) and is probably the sequence in plants, since $\Delta^{5,7}$-sterols exist in both algae and tracheophytes as well as in fungi. However, the recently well described presence of sterols with an unconjugated $\Delta^{5,8(9)}$-diene system in fungi and

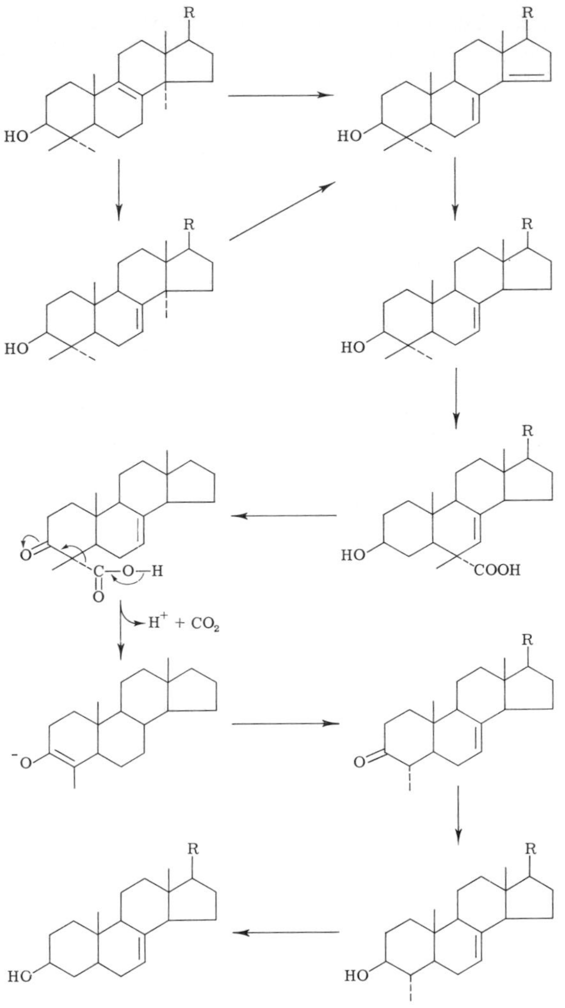

FIG. 20.   A sequence for the removal of nuclear methyl groups.

algae casts at least some doubt on an obligatory route through Δ^7-sterols. Empirically the sequence $\Delta^{8,14} \rightarrow \Delta^8 \rightarrow \Delta^{5,8} \rightarrow \Delta^{5,7} \rightarrow \Delta^5$ could operate. The question revolves around whether or not the dehydrogenation is necessarily allylic either mechanistically or in terms of enzyme specificity. The empirical route $\Delta^{5,8} \rightarrow \Delta^5$ also exists, and the final stereochemistry at the B/C ring junction is *trans* as would be reasonable for direct H^+/H^- addition to the Δ^8 bond. In the reduction of the Δ^7 bond, NADPH is the reductant

(Kandutsch, 1962; Dempsey *et al.*, 1964) with H^+ going to C-7 and H^- to C-7α (Wilton *et al.*, 1968), and all steps beyond cyclization are microsomal.

In the cycloartenol route at some stage in biosynthesis the 9,19-cyclo group is opened with an isomerase to give a Δ^8-sterol. This isomerization constitutes a "crossover reaction" (Nes, 1971) between the two otherwise independent routes. That it can occur as the first step after cyclization is strongly indicated by the existence of both lanosterol and cycloartenol in *Euphorbia* species. Similarly 31-norlanosterol occurs in *Funtumia* and *Solanum* species indicating that opening of the ring can occur not later than the second step. However, the existence of 31-norcycloartenol, cyclo-eucalenol, and 31-norcyclolaudenol, indicate that opening of the ring also occurs later. Studies (Heintz and Benveniste, 1974) of the substrate specificity of the isomerase from a higher plant (*Rubus fruticosis*) add clarifying quantitation. Cycloartenol and its 24-methylene derivative are both isomerized but much more slowly than 4-methyl and 4,4-demethyl substrates. The one tried with the highest reaction rate was cycloeucalenol (24-methylene-4α,14α-dimethylcycloartanol. As will be seen in what follows, this is but one example of the interdigitation of events in the side chain with those taking place in the nucleus. A simple view of one series of operations proceeding to completion before the other starts unfortunately does not happen.

Unlike the first C_1-transfer, the second addition of a C-atom (to give the ethyl or ethylidene group) seems always to be delayed until after the opening of the 9,19-cyclo group. This follows from the failure to observe the existence of 24-C_2-sterols bearing the 3-membered ring as well as from the failure of isomerase-lacking cell-free systems from higher plants to convert MVA beyond the 24-methylenecycloartanol stage (Russell *et al.*, 1967; Malhotra and Nes, 1972). However, sterols with a 24-C_2 group, e.g., 24-ethylidenelophenol, are known in which the 3-membered ring has been opened but incomplete removal of the nuclear methyl groups and incomplete double-bond transformations have occurred. Having once passed through the stages of alkylation and removal of the methyl groups, the sequence finally appears to involve alterations in the double-bond character of ring B. Similarly, the introduction of the Δ^{22} bond by dehydrogenation is tentatively believed to be among the last steps. There can be very little doubt that within the framework of what has been outlined a number of sequences actually occur. As pointed out by Goad and Goodwin (1972), the sequence depends in part on the details of the mechanism of alkylation, notably on whether or not a $\Delta^{24(28)}$ intermediate is reduced. This is independent of the structure of the final product. Thus, ergosterol is produced in algae, e.g., *Chlorella sorokiniana*, but also arises in fungi. In the former case strong evidence exists for cyclolaudenol's being an intermediate (Chan *et al.*, 1974) whereas in the latter it is not; instead, yeast uses the route passing through a 24-methylene

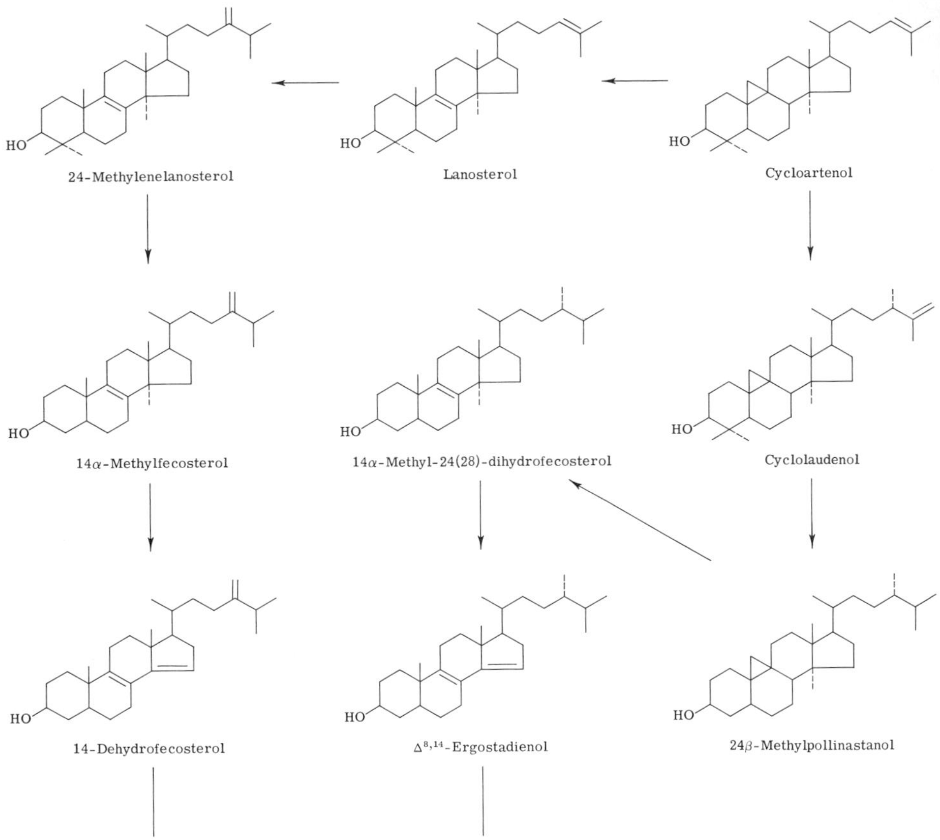

24-Methylenelanosterol   Lanosterol   Cycloartenol

14α-Methylfecosterol   14α-Methyl-24(28)-dihydrofecosterol   Cyclolaudenol

14-Dehydrofecosterol   Δ^{8,14}-Ergostadienol   24β-Methylpollinastanol

FIG. 21.   Caption on following page.

intermediate that is reduced. The algal pathway proposed (Chan *et al.*, 1974) involves early reduction of the 25-methylene group, since 24-methylpolli-nastanol is present. In yeast, reduction of the 24-methylene group apparently occurs later, since fecosterol and its 14α-methyl derivative (Trocha *et al.*, 1974) as well as episterol and ergosta-5,7,24(28)-trienol are found (Barton *et al.*, 1974a).

The recent recognition of the presence of both ergosterol (Yokoyama and White, 1968; Nes *et al.*, 1975b) and 22-dihydrobrassicasterol (Nes *et al.*, 1976) in higher plants together with the well-known presence of cyclolaudenol and brassicasterol leads to the possibility that the 24β-methyl sterols of tracheophytes arise by the same essential route as in algae. In particular, cyclolaudenol could lead to ergosterol (Fig. 21), which by successive reduc-tions would give brassicasterol and then 22-dihydrobrassicasterol. This is

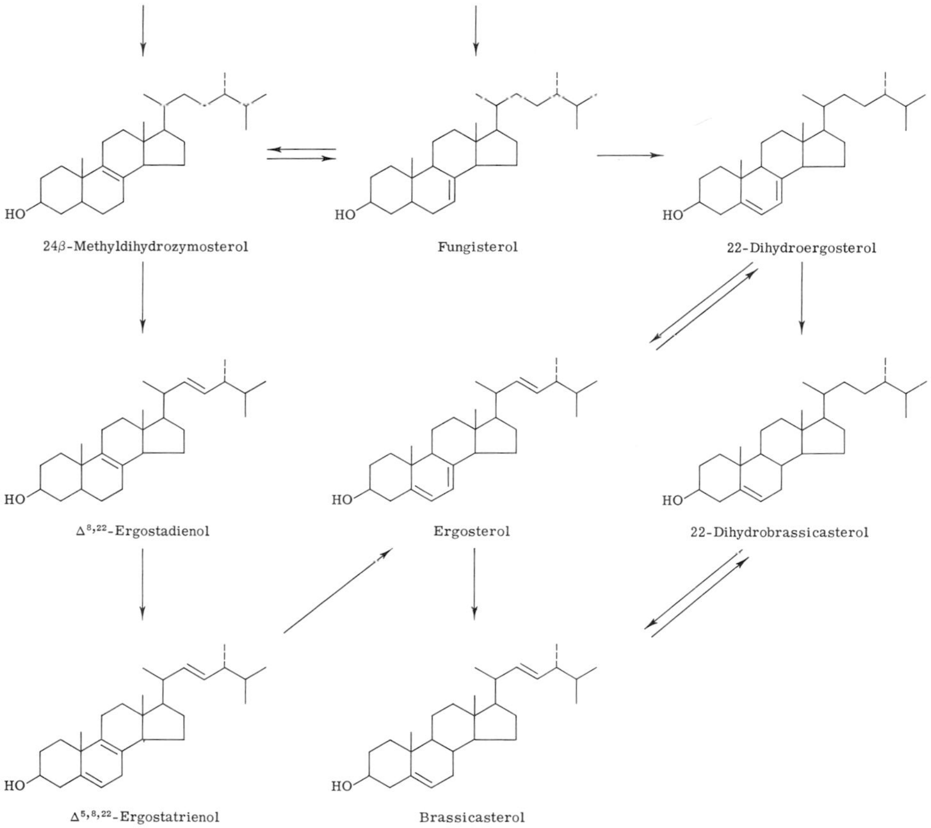

FIG. 21. Example of alternative routes to 24 β-methyl sterols.

given further weight by the following observations. While seeds of the cruciferae, especially the genus *Brassica*, contain brassicasterol, they contain campesterol but no 22-dihydrobrassicasterol (24β-methylcholesterol). Conversely, leaves contain 22-dihydrobrassicasterol and campesterol but no brassicasterol (Nes *et al.*, 1976), and during development of the seed to mature plants the brassicasterol level falls essentially to zero (Knights, 1968; Ingram *et al.*, 1968). This is consistent with brassicasterol's being the precursor to the dihydrobrassicasterol. It therefore becomes possible to write a general pathway to 24β-methyl sterols, as shown in Fig. 21, with two parallel sequences (beginning from lanosterol and cycloartenol) converging at ergosterol, which can then proceed to brassicasterol and 22-dihydrobrassicasterol. Actually, the convergence is tantamount to a crossover between the two parallel sequences, and other crossovers are possible. Some are shown in

Fig. 21. Other sequences from lanosterol have been discussed by Fryberg
et al. (1972) based on their own studies and the substrate specificity of the
yeast C_1-transferase examined by Moore and Gaylor (1970). The main
differences from the sequence found in Fig. 21 lie in the exact placing of
alkylation and of reduction of the $\Delta^{24(28)}$ bond. The evidence indicates that
several sequences may actually operate. However, this does not contravene
the basic dichotomy to be seen in Fig. 21 between the $\Delta^{24(28)}$ and $\Delta^{25(27)}$
routes.

The 24α-methyl component of higher plants probably arises through
a 24-methylene derivative, for the following reasons. 24α-Methylcholes-
terol (campesterol) is present at about twice the concentration of its C-24
epimer in the various plants for which data are available (Nes et al., 1976),
except, as mentioned, in Brassica seeds, where only campesterol is present.
Since 24-methylenecholesterol is known to be reduced to a 24-methylcholes-
terol in peas (van Aller et al., 1969), and since in Hordeum vulgare the 24-
methyl sterol incorporates only two deuterium atoms from deuteriated
methionine (Goad et al., 1974), in both cases it is reasonable to suppose that
the data derive from the major 24-methyl component, campesterol. If this
is true then the totality of the evidence speaks for two routes to 24-methyl
sterols in the same plant, one leading through cyclolaudenol to the 24β-
methyl component (Fig. 21) and one through 24-methylenecycloartanol to
the 24α-methyl component (Fig. 22). In the latter case, several of the sterols,
e.g., cycloeucalenol, obtusifoliol, and 24-methylenelophenol, which are postulated as intermediates, are known to occur in higher plants. The 24α-methyl
route here suggested (Fig. 22) differs from the route to 24β-methyl sterols
(Fig. 21) in the detail of the deprotonation at the time of the C_1 transfer, the
order of removal of the three nuclear methyl groups, and the place in the
sequence at which the 9,19-cyclo group is opened and the Δ^{22} bond introduced. The extent to which these differences will ultimately prove valid
either as a generality or in detail remains for further work.

As already discussed, the second C_1 transfer occurs theoretically with
concomitant introduction of, for instance, a Δ^{22}, $\Delta^{24(28)}$, or $\Delta^{24(27)}$ bond,
and evidence exists for all three, the first in slime molds, the second for
24α-ethyl sterols in tracheophytes, and the third for 24β-ethyl sterols in
tracheophytes. The mechanism operating in algae is not entirely clear except
that it does not proceed with formation of a $\Delta^{24(28)}$-sterol. Since, however,
upon inhibition of Chlorella species (Chan and Patterson, 1973; Dickson
and Patterson, 1972, 1973; Chan et al., 1974), the organisms accumulate
24-methylenecycloartanol, cycloeucalenol, obtusifoliol, 4α-methyl-24α-ethyl-
$\Delta^{8,14}$-cholestadienol, and 24β-ethyl-Δ^8-cholestenol, and since no Δ^{22}-sterols
are observed earlier in the pathway than that corresponding to 24α-ethyl-
$\Delta^{5,7,22}$-cholestatrienol, it is a reasonable assumption to make that the Δ^{22}

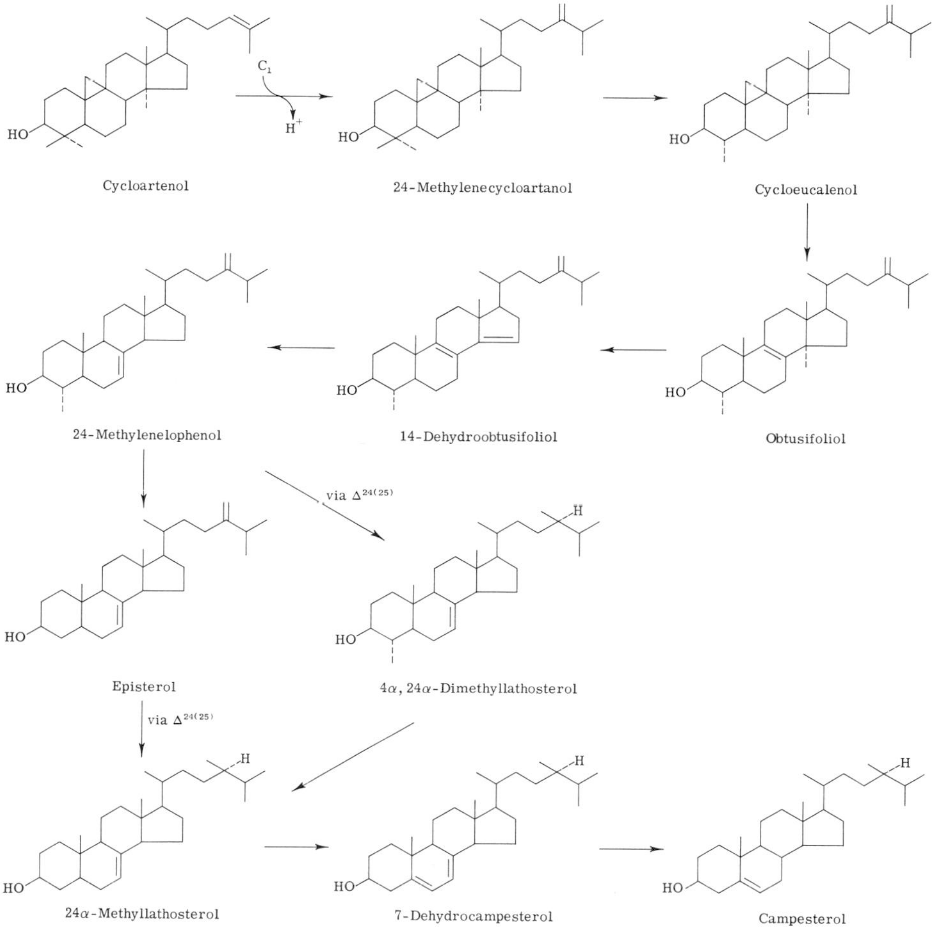

Cycloartenol

24-Methylenecycloartanol

Cycloeucalenol

24-Methylenelophenol

14-Dehydroobtusifoliol

Obtusifoliol

Episterol

$4\alpha, 24\alpha$-Dimethyllathosterol

via $\Delta^{24(25)}$

24α-Methyllathosterol

7-Dehydrocampesterol

Campesterol

via $\Delta^{24(25)}$

FIG. 22. Probable route to 24 α-methyl sterols.

bond is introduced by dehydrogenation and therefore that the second C_1 transfer yields a $\Delta^{25(27)}$-sterol, as it does in the first C_1 transfer. This then gives us a reasonable pathway from cycloartenol to 24β-ethyl sterols as shown in Fig. 23, in which 14-dehydroobtusifoliol (or perhaps obtusifoliol) is the substrate for the second C_1 transfer. The resulting $\Delta^{25(27)}$-sterol then proceeds to 24β-ethyllathosterol (Δ^7-chondrillastenol), which by appropriate dehydrogenations and reductions yields chondrillasterol, poriferasterol, and clionasterol.

The sequence leading to 24α-ethyl sterols can now be reasonably well-understood in terms of the evidence for the other pathways together with

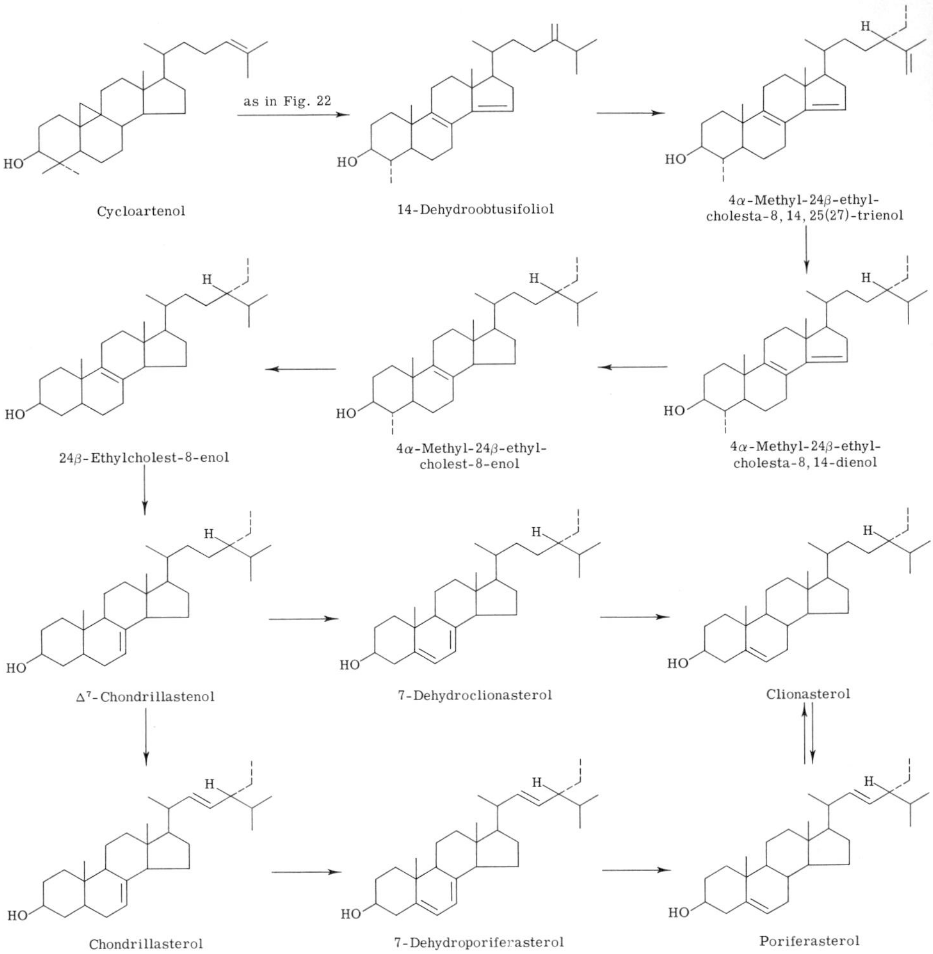

FIG. 23.   Probable route to 24 β-ethyl sterols.

evidence previously discussed for occurrence and metabolism in tracheo-phytes. Obtusifoliol (derived through cycloeucalenol and 24-methylenecy-cloartanol) or its 14-dehydro derivative must act as the substrate for the second C_1 transfer as in the route to 24β-ethyl sterols except that a *trans*-ethylidene derivative is produced instead of a $\Delta^{25(27)}$-sterol. The se-quence would then proceed to Δ^7-avenasterol or via a $\Delta^{5,7}$ derivative to isofucosterol with stereospecific reduction to 24-ethyllathosterol or sitosterol, which dehydrogenate to give spinasterol and stigmasterol, respectively. Some minor alternatives could operate, especially with regard to sequencing of the final dehydrogenations and reductions, as shown in Fig. 24. The crucial

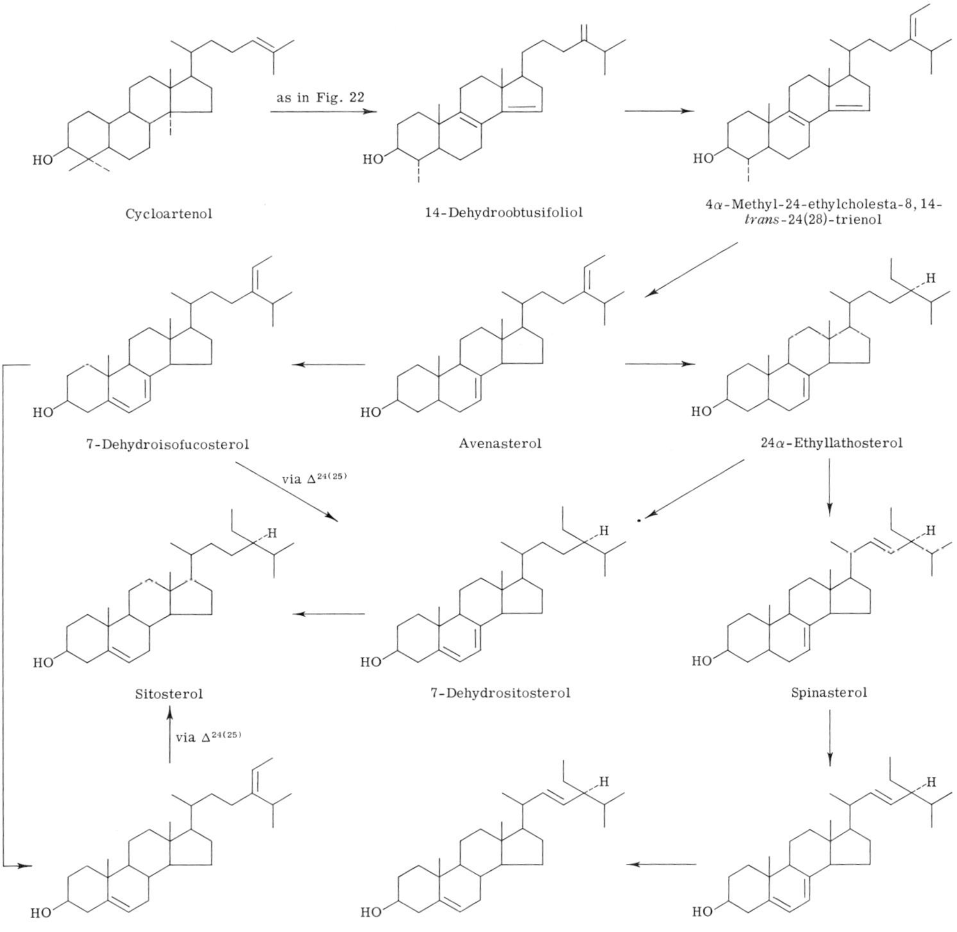

FIG. 24. Probable route to 24 α-ethyl sterols.

choice as to whether a 24α- or 24β-ethyl sterol is produced would therefore appear to lie in discrimination between C-27 and C-28 as a site for deprotonation at the time of the C_1 transfer.

VIII. The Function of Sterols

Sterols have several functions in plants. The major one appears to be, as it is in animals, an architectural role in membranes. The evidence for this has been reviewed in detail elsewhere (Nes, 1974b). Sterols are biosynthesized or an exogenous source is required by all organisms with some important exceptions. These include the protozoan *Tetrahymena pyriformis*, where the sterol's role is played by a pentacyclic triterpenoid, tetrahymanol, and some mycoplasmas, where a carotenoidal alcohol replaces the sterol. The fungal genera *Phytophtora* and *Pythium* are unusual in that the mycelium is believed not to contain sterol and no other substance is (yet?) known to replace it.

Yeast especially has been the subject of substantial investigation. It was discovered by Andreasen and Stier (1953, 1954) that in the absence of oxygen no growth occurs unless sterol and oleic acid are added. This is now understandable in terms of the mixed-function oxidase reaction of squalene to produce squalene oxide and of stearic acid to produce oleic acid. Squalene accumulates as expected. Energy for growth in the supplemented medium is derived by glucolysis, and mitochondria are not seen by electron microscopy (Linnane *et al.*, 1962). However, in the absence of sterol (but in the presence of oleic acid) the cytoplasmic and nuclear membranes also disappear and death ensues (Morpurgo *et al.*, 1964). Mutant strains of yeast that lack the ability to biosynthesize sterols have also been obtained (Karst and Lacroute, 1973, 1974; Gollub *et al.*, 1974; Resnick and Mortimer, 1966), but all require sterol (ergosterol having been used) when grown aerobically. Moreover, the amount of sterol in aerobically grown normal yeast can be manipulated by supplements of fatty acid and ergosterol.

From Arrhenius plots of the mitochondrial ATPase activity of the different cultures, it was shown that the activity of this membrane-bound enzyme is dependent on the sterol content (Cobon and Haslam, 1973). Analogous studies by Thompson and Parks (1974a) have shown that the mitochondrial enzymes cytochrome oxidase and S-adenosylmethionine:Δ^{24}-sterol methyltransferase are affected by the amount and kind of sterol present. From a study of sterol-requiring mutants (Karst and Lacroute, 1973) as well as from a study of growth patterns of anaerobic yeast in the presence of different sterols (Proudlock *et al.*, 1968), it has been concluded that the structural requirements are not absolute for the ergosterol molecule itself. Similarly, the sterol composition in normal yeast can be altered with thiamine, leading to accumulation of lanosterol and two other (unidentified) sterols without major changes in growth patterns (Nagai and Katsuki, 1974), and nystatin-resistant mutants are known which biosynthesize sterols other than ergosterol (Barton *et al.*, 1974a; Trocha *et al.*, 1974). Some of these lack the C_1-transferase, some the Δ^8-isomerase, some the Δ^5-dehydrogenase, some the Δ^{22}-dehydrogenase, and some the enzymes responsible for removal of the 14α-methyl group. Under anaerobic conditions even cholestanol and lanosterol are reported to support growth (Proudlock *et al.*, 1968). The latter is consistent with accumulations of lanosterol in some of the mutants

(Trocha *et al.*, 1974) and agrees with general predictions based on structure–activity considerations of the necessity for planarity (Nes, 1974b). However, the failure to correlate growth with the presence of the Δ^{22}-24-methyl and $\Delta^{5,7}$ systems is anomalous, since ascomycetes (and basidomycetes) generally biosynthesize ergosterol itself as the dominant sterol. A conceivable explanation may lie in different structural requirements of the various membranes, for which some evidence does exist. Thus, Thompson and Parks (1974b) found that fermentative growth was unaffected by sterol composition but a definite decrease in both optimal and permissive growth temperatures of respiring cultures occurred when ergosterol was replaced by $\Delta^{8(9),22}$-ergostadienol, and a similar effect on the C_1-transferase occurred. Furthermore, although ergosterol has been identified in the outer membrane of *Neurospora crassa* mitochondria (Hallermayer and Newpert, 1974), so far only sterols believed to be 24(28)-dehydroergosterol and zymosterol have been found in *Saccharomyces cerevisiae* protoplast membranes (Longley *et al.*, 1968). The outer mitochondrial membrane, incidentally, of *N. crassa* is 59% lipid (and 41% protein), composed principally of phospholipid and ergosterol in a molar ratio of 3:1; and the *S. cerevisiae* protoplast is 45% lipid, 49% protein, the remaining material being RNA and carbohydrate. About one-eighth of the lipid is sterol. However, despite the difference in sterol structures actually isolated from these membranes, yeast clearly can grow aerobically with functional mitochondrial and other membranes in the absence of the sterol it biosynthesizes in the wild state.

A second undoubted function for sterols, which has been discussed in depth by Heftmann (1971, 1974), is as precursors to other steroids, e.g., sapogenins, alkaloids, cardiac glycosides, and hormones, but whether the pathway to these various compounds proceeds normally from the dominant sterols themselves or from an earlier precursor remains unclear. Finally, an intriguing role for sterols has been suggested by Smith (1971)—that of carbohydrate carriers—and he was able to present some evidence for it in mycoplasmas. Sterol-requiring mycoplasmas clearly utilize their sterol in the plasma membrane, but Smith's evidence suggests that glucose is transported across the membrane as a cholesterol glucoside. Steryl glucosides are actually not uncommon among higher plants as well (Lepage, 1964; Bush and Grunwald, 1972; Meance and Duperon, 1973), where their biosynthesis has been studied extensively, e.g., by Bush and Grunwald (1974), whose work will also constitute a key to the literature.

Much less work has been done on the function of sterols in photosynthetic plants, but in those cases that have been studied sterol is found to be at least principally particulate in agreement with a membranous role. The amounts of sterols in all organisms also fall within the same range, varying from about 0.001% to 0.1% of wet weight. Why there should be as much variation as there is remains to be elucidated. However, in yeast, again best studied, the range among several hundred different species and strains comprising 20 genera varied from 0.1 to 10.0% of dry weight (Dulaney *et al.*, 1954); when converted to wet weight, this is essentially the same as just mentioned for the variation among all organisms. In addition, as Dulaney *et al.* (1954) and many others have shown, the amount of sterol varies with the composition of the culture medium, especially in terms of the kind and amount of sugar. While some of the high levels may represent storage, it may also be that variations in the phospholipid composition will be found to correlate with variations in the sterol content.

IX. Phylogenetic and Evolutionary Implications

The sterol pathway appears to have developed more or less at the same time as did life itself. This follows from the existence of the early steps in the pathway in anaerobic bacteria, which lead in the well-examined cases to a polyprenol used as a carbohydrate carrier in cell wall synthesis and from the presence in blue-green algae of sterols themselves (cf. Section III,D), which must be biosynthesized *in situ*, since the organism containing the sterols was grown in a chemically defined medium. Both bacteria and blue-green algae are regarded from microfossil studies to be 3×10^9 years old. For a key to the literature, the reader should consult Nes (1971, 1974b). Although it has been thought that evolution could have occurred in a more or less linear fashion, with bifurcations or branches here and there to give a "tree of life," recent evidence from a variety of sources indicates that the process is probably more complicated than that. There could, for instance, have been multiple lines from the very beginning, as indeed the archeological evidence for the coexistence of bacteria and blue-green algae suggests. It is not possible for us to make phylogenetic correlations using the sterols and their relatives as tools without colliding with these very basic concepts of how organisms arose, interact with their environment, and change. While our knowledge of the subject is still far from complete, several correlations appear to be emerging that may ultimately be useful in solving the riddle of the origin of living systems and the relationships among them.

If we assume from its existence in most higher plants and animals that a completed sterol pathway proceeds to Δ^5-sterols (cholesterol, etc.) with or without a substituent at C-24 or a Δ^{22} bond, then it becomes possible to assess the existence of biosynthetic blocks. These are known to occur in wild organisms earlier than the formation of squalene, at the epoxidation of squalene, at various stages of the metabolism of the side chain, and at the steps concerned with the double-bond character of ring B (Tables XIV

Table XIV
ABSOLUTE BIOSYNTHETIC BLOCKS[a]

Step blocked	Alternative pathway or sterol	Organismic examples
Earlier than squalene	a. Exogenous sterols b. Carotenols	a. Some mycoplasmas; insects and perhaps all Arthropoda b. Some mycoplasmas
Squalene to squalene oxide	a. Tetrahymanol pathway b. Exogenous sterol	a. Tetrahymena species b. Terrestrial annelids and Paramecium aurelia
Earlier than squalene oxide cyclization	Unknown	Anaerobic bacteria and perhaps other bacteria and the vegetative phase of Phytophthora and Pythium fungi
Δ^{24}-Alkylation	24-Dealkylsterols	All animals and most red algae
Δ^{24}-Reduction	Δ^{24}-Sterols or 24-alkyl or alkenyl sterols	Partially or wholly in some red algae and perhaps in some higher plants especially in some stages of evolutionary and ontogenetic development
$\Delta^{24(28)}$-Reduction	$\Delta^{24(28)}$-Sterol	Fucus species and most other brown algae; Ulvales; perhaps some pollens
$\Delta^{25(27)}$-Reduction	$\Delta^{25(27)}$-Sterol	Codium fragile (a green alga)
Δ^{22}-Introduction	22-Dihydrosterol	Varied but frequent for 24z-ethylsterols in early ontogenesis of higher plants
Δ^{22}-Reduction	22-Dehydrosterol	Ascomycetes and Basidomycetes and common for 24β-methyl sterols in early ontogenesis of Cruciferae
Δ^{7}-Reduction of $\Delta^{5,7}$-sterols	$\Delta^{5,7}$-Sterols	Ascmycetes, Basidomycetes, some algae, e.g., Chlorella sorokiniana, and partially in some other plants, e.g., the blue-green alga Phormidium luridum and the tracheophyte Lycopodium complanatum
Δ^{5}-Introduction	Δ^{7}-Sterols	Cucurbitales, some green algae, and partially in some higher plants, e.g., Dryopteris noveboracensis

[a] Full pathways assumed are to cholesterol, 24-alkylcholesterol, or the latter's Δ^{22}-derivatives.

and XV). In addition, some of these blocks seem to occur ontogenetically either partially or wholly. Let us examine the ontogenetic phenomenon first.

In germinating peas the cyclization of squalene oxide is directed almost entirely toward β-amyrin; only later, more or less coincidently with the development of leaves, does the formation of sterols take place at a significant rate, and squalene accumulates during the early phase of development (Nes et al., 1967). A similar situation exists in pine seeds both with the endosperm and embryo (McKean and Nes, unpublished observations). Squalene also accumulates in both of the latter cases upon administration of MVA, but, unlike the pea, in the pine the squalene is not shunted toward a pentacyclic molecule prior to the development of activity in the cycloartenol cyclase. The accumulation of squalene in all three systems can be regarded as evidence for the regulatory nature of its epoxidation. However, this does not immediately explain the differential in the activities of the cyclases in the pea, and at least empirically there appears to be an ontogenetic block leading to sterols. Perhaps a clearer ontogenetic block occurs in the Cruciferae, especially among plants of the genus Brassica. With development from seeds to mature plants the brassicasterol levels falls (Ingram et al., 1968) and 24β-methylcholesterol appears (Mulheirn, 1973; Nes et al., 1976). The seeds, therefore, appear to have a block at the reduction of the Δ^{22} bond. A similar but less well-described phenomenon appears to arise with respect to the introduction of the Δ^{22} bond in the 24α-ethyl sterol pathway. In particular, stigmasterol is found in some cases only after maturation of the plant.

Absolute blocks at all stages of development have been more thoroughly documented, but no incisive correlations are obvious. Thus, brown algae usually fail to reduce the $\Delta^{24(28)}$ bond, but so do green algae of the order Ulvales (Table VI). Similarly, most green algae appear to reduce the $\Delta^{25(27)}$ bond, but Codium fragile does not (Table VI), and ascomycetes and basidomycetes have a block at the second C_1-transfer to the side chain, but other fungi do not (cf. Section III,G). Some Chlorella species have a block at the reduction of the Δ^7 bond, but again others of the same genus do not (Tables VI–VIII). The absence of Δ^5 introduction into the dominant sterols of the Cucurbitaceae and in the tea family is also clearly defined.

A phylogenetic relationship is elusive, but some speculations are to be found at the end of this section. The mystery is further deepened by the presence in the family Cucurbitaceae of an especially fascinating alternative pathway. Either at the squalene oxide cyclization stage or very shortly thereafter, species of this group allow a rearrangement to occur to give a Δ^5-sterol with a migrated C-19 (the cucurbitacins). It is the migration of C-19 from C-10 to C-9 which mechanistically allows the formation of the Δ^5 bond. This is tantalizingly suggestive of an "attempt" to correct for the absence of the Δ^5-dehydrogenase by the introduction of the modified pathway

Table XV

PATHWAYS IN DIFFERENT ORGANISMS

Pathway	Organism
Lanosterol	Fungi, animals, and presumably all nonphotosynthetic organisms
Cycloartenol	Algae; higher plants; apparently all photosynthetic organisms including nonchloroplastic tissue; euglenoids in both light and dark phases
24-Alkylation Δ^{24}-Reduction	All plants except most of the red algae; absent in all animals Common and dominant in animals and many red algae; common but not dominant in plants; absent in Ascomycetes and Basidomycetes
$\Delta^{24(28)}$-Reduction	Common and dominant in Tracheophyta, leading to 24α-alkyl sterols, and in Ascomycetes, and presumably other fungi, leading to 24β-alkyl sterols
$\Delta^{25(27)}$-Reduction	Apparently the algal and tracheophyte route to 24β-alkyl sterols
Δ^{22}-Introduction as last step	Apparently operates in Tracheophytas for 24α-ethyl sterols but not for 24α-methyl sterols or 24β-alkyl sterols
Δ^{22}-Introduction prior to Δ^{7}-reduction	May constitute the route to 24β-alkyl sterols in all organisms biosynthesizing them

(Nes, 1974b). The block following Δ^7-sterols in the Cucurbitaceae appears at the moment to extend to all members of the family, but, as mentioned with the genus *Chlorella*, there are no apprent rules by which we can *a priori* associate a given block with a given taxonomic grouping. Such is also the case for the red algae. In this Division (or Phylum) most species studied lack the 24-alkylase, but not all do (Ferezou *et al.*, 1974).

The anaerobic bacteria, mycoplasmas, terrestrial annelids (at least *Lumbricus terrestris*), all arthropoda examined and two well studied protozoan genera (*Tetrahymena* and *Paramecium*) have in common a block earlier than the cyclization of squalene oxide. The literature has been reviewed earlier (Nes, 1974b). Some use an alternative pathway to give other types of isopentenoid. Others require exogenous sterol. In some cases (notably most bacteria and the vegetative phase of certain fungi) an alternative to the sterol pathway remains obscure. The only relationships between these diverse organisms is that they are all nonphotosynthetic. By contrast, all photosynthetic organisms examined biosynthesize sterols *de novo*.

The replacement of one pathway for another, seen in some of the mycoplasmas and protozoa, occurs more dramatically with respect to the lanosterol–cycloartenol bifurcation. All examined nonphotosynthetic organisms (mycoplasmas, protozoa, fungi, and animals) are blocked at the cyclization of squalene oxide to cycloartenol. Those that biosynthesize sterols, e.g., fungi and vertebrate animals, utilize the lanosterol pathway. Conversely, it appears that all photosynthetic organisms are blocked at the cyclization of squalene oxide to lanosterol, and all examined use the cycloartenol pathway instead (Fig. 10). This is known from the data on occurrence (Tables X and XI), from the appearance of cycloartenol in inhibited algae (Chan and Patterson, 1973; Chan *et al.*, 1974), and from other facts discussed in Section V,B. The lanosterol–cycloartenol bifurcation thus appears to divide biological systems fundamentally into those with and those without the capacity to assimilate energy from light. The bifurcation can then be used to examine other phylogenetic aspects. Two are worthy of note. The euglenoids can exist in both a light and a dark phase. Are they then nonphotosynthetic organisms able to operate photosynthetically, or is the converse true? Or do they use one pathway in one phase and the other in the other phase? The answer is that in both phases cycloartenol (Anding *et al.*, 1971) gives sterols (Brandt *et al.*, 1970) showing that there is no association with the presence or the absence of photosynthesis at the functional level, but rather only at the phylogenetic level. Second, there is some evidence to suggest that higher plants might have evolved from symbionts of algae (perhaps blue-green algae) and fungi, suggesting in turn a dual pathway to sterols in higher plants, viz., the cycloartenol route in chloroplasts and the lanosterol route in other tissue. Such, however, is not the case. As with the euglenoids, nonphotosynthetic tissue (white endosperm of *Pinus pinea*) uses only the cycloartenol route (Malhotra and Nes, 1972). If symbiosis did occur, only one of the two routes must have survived. It is interesting to emphasize before we pass to another subject that, as previously alluded to, the lanosterol–cycloartenol bifurcation does not influence the structure of the final functional sterol, since lanosterol leads to both ergosterol and cholesterol (in fungi and animals, respectively) and cycloartenol leads to the same compounds by inference from their occurrence in tracheophytes as well as in algae, since pollinastanol (4,4-demethyl-cycloartanol) leads experimentally to cholesterol in tobacco leaves and is found in ferns and higher plants (Barbier, 1974), since cycloartanol is present in the red alga *Rhodymenia palmata*, in which cholesterol comprises 20% of the sterol (Ferezou *et al.*, 1974), and since the C_1-transferase of peas will accept either lanosterol or cycloartenol as a substrate (Russell *et al.*, 1967). The lack of relationship to the functional sterol makes the bifurcation that much more interesting as a phylogenetic marker, because the genes responsible for the choice should have no ecological pressures on them to change. Presumably, selection by environmental factors could only operate at the functional level. The implication of this would seem to be that photosynthetic and nonphotosynthetic organisms either had separate origins or diverged from each other at a very early stage.

The divergence of plants from animals also finds expression in the sterol pathway at a bifurcation, *viz.*, the reduction–alkylation bifurcation. Organisms with a clearly defined nervous system all lack the process of alkylation at C-24 in the cases well-examined which have been reviewed elsewhere (Nes, 1974b). The Phylum Porifera (sponges) are somewhat anomalous, since they contain 24-alkyl sterols. However, biosynthesis has not been demonstrated, and the sterols may be ingested; or perhaps sponges are not animals, but rather plants. Sponges actually do not have a clearly defined nervous system, and this correlates with the presence of 24-alkyl sterols. Protozoa, on the other hand, which also lack a nervous system, dealkylate 24-ethyl sterols (Nes *et al.*, 1975a) but not 24-methyl sterols (Nes *et al.*, 1975b; Mallory and Conner, 1971). Insects with a fully developed nervous system dealkylate both kinds of sterol (Thompson *et al.*, 1973). The reason for these differences is far from obvious. True plants, however, differ clearly from true animals in that alkylation can (but does not necessarily) take place; i.e., while cholesterol is frequently a minor component in plants and on rare occasions the only component, the major component is commonly a 24-alkyl sterol.

The great evolutionary jump from algae to more complicated plants culminating in the Tracheophyta is characterized in most cases examined by an inversion of the configuration at C-24 in the dominant sterol. Algae, with the exception of the 24-epibrassicasterol-containing diatoms and the isofucosterol-containing green algae, appear to have 24β-alkyl sterols, while Tracheophytes, with the exception of *Clerodendrum*, have a 24α-alkyl sterol (usually sitosterol) as the dominant one. This appears to be correlated with the mechanism of alkylation. The evidence suggests a shift from the $\Delta^{25(27)}$ route leading to 24β-alkyl sterols to dominance of the $\Delta^{24(28)}$ route yielding 24α-alkyl sterols. The variety of pathways which exist, however, in plants makes a simple correlation very difficult, but here again the symbiont hypothesis finds little support. All the existing evidence is against the presence of the fungal route to 24β-methyl sterols in tracheophytes even though in both types of organism there can be found the same compound (ergosterol). In fungi ergosterol arises by reduction (presumably H^- to C-24) of a $\Delta^{24(28)}$ intermediate, whereas in tracheophytes the evidence strongly indicates that the configuration is set at the time of the C_1 transfer (giving cyclolaudenol). Moreover, reduction of $\Delta^{24(28)}$-sterols in tracheophytes appears to lead to the configuration at C-24 that is opposite to that produced by the same reaction in fungi. These important problems need further detailed investigation. Among the many unknown facts is the configuration at C-24 in blue-green algae together with any knowledge of the pathway, details of configuration, and mechanism in fungi other than ascomycetes and basidomycetes, and unequivocal proof of the origin of 24-methyl sterols in a sufficient variety of algae and higher plants to allow precise phylogenetic interpretation. At the experimental level, we still lack a method to separate small quantities of the C-24 epimers, and until a way to do this is found progress in this field will be impeded.

Finally, if, as at the beginning of this section, we assume Δ^5-sterols, such as cholesterol, to represent completion of the pathway, the extent to which biosynthetic intermediates accumulate can be taken as a measure of the extent of evolution of the pathway and therefore presumably of the organism itself. Two types of evolution can be discerned *a priori*. One has to do with quantitative regulation of the rates of the various reactions in the sequence. The other is concerned with absolute blocks, probably but not necessarily reflecting the absence of the gene for the appropriate enzyme. In the first instance we would expect and generally find regulation, so that essentially only the end product has a significant concentration. For instance, only a few sterols, e.g., cholesterol and its 24-methyl and 24-ethyl derivatives, which are not in a product–precursor relationship, are found above trace levels in the average higher plant. The same phenomenon is frequently found in algae and fungi. However, in some plants Δ^7-sterols, $\Delta^{5,7}$-sterols, or $\Delta^{24(28)}$-sterols have appreciable concentrations. It would therefore appear that regulatory phenomena are not as advanced in these organisms as in those where such intermediates are absent. Examples are the less advanced tracheophyte *Lycopodium complanatum* (Nes *et al.*, 1975b) and the (blue-green) alga *Phormidium luridum* (de Souza and Nes, 1968) in which $\Delta^{5,7}$-sterols are present in substantial amounts, and the fern, *Dryopteris noveboracensis*, which contains Δ^7- along with Δ^5-sterols (Nes *et al.*, unpublished observations). At the other end of the pathway, *Strychnos nux-vomica* contains unusually large amounts of cycloartenol.

Absolute blocks are more difficult to assess but also more interesting. We could, for instance, assign ergosterol-containing fungi to a level of pathway evolution coinciding with development of the Δ^5-dehydrogenase, but not as far as the development of the Δ^7-reductase. This assumes that all precursor organisms lack Δ^5-sterols, but two alternative conclusions are available. They are (a) that the Δ^7-reductase was lost and (b) that there is no simple line of ascent up the evolutionary ladder. We know very little about fungal evolution, and so the question about ergosterol in, say, yeast is very difficult to consider, but tracheophytes, being more complicated, have enjoyed more detailed study. There is little doubt that the sequence ferns, gymnosperms, and angiosperms, representatives of which all contain Δ^5-sterols (Nes *et al.*, 1976), constitute an increasing order of evolution. Whether it is in direct ascent or not is another question, but the flowering plants containing only Δ^7-sterols may eventually offer an answer. They must have lost or never had the Δ^5-dehydrogenase and (presumably) Δ^7-reductase. If it develops that the latter is true, it would indicate that these plants are incompletely evolved relative to the sterol pathway and, more important, that their evolutionary line was separate from that of the majority of plants that contain the Δ^5-sterols. Conversely, if genetic deletion occurred, then it would become possible to use the deletion as a tracer to assess lineage as well as to estimate the time of deletion.

References

Aaronson, S., and Baker, H. (1961). *J. Protozool.* **8**, 274.
Agranoff, B. W., Eggerer, H., Henning, U., and Lynen, F. (1960). *J. Biol. Chem.* **235**, 326.
Ahmadjian, V. (1965). *Annu. Rev. Microbiol.* **19**, 1.
Ahmadjian, V. (1966). *Symbiosis* **1**, 35.
Akhtar, M., Hunt, P. F., and Parvez, M. A. (1967). *Biochem. J.* **103**, 616.
Akhtar, M., Parvez, M. A., and Hunt, P. F. (1968). *Biochem. J.* **106**, 623.
Akhtar, M., Parvez, M. A., and Hunt, P. F. (1969a). *Biochem. J.* **113**, 727.
Akhtar, M., Watkinson, I. A., Rahimtula, A. D., Wilton, D. C., and Munday, K. A. (1969b). *Chem. Commun.* p. 1406.
Alcaide, A., Devys, M., and Barbier, M. (1968a). *Phytochemistry* **7**, 329.
Alcaide, A., Devys, M., Bottin, J., Fetizon, M., Barbier, M., and Lederer, E. (1968b). *Phytochemistry* **7**, 1773.
Alcaide, A., Barbier, M., Potier, P., Magueur, A. M., and Teste, J. (1969). *Phytochemistry* **8**, 2301.
Alcaide, A., Devys, M., Barbier, M., Kaufman, H. P., and Sen Gupta, A. K. (1971). *Phytochemistry* **10**, 209.

Alexander, G. J., and Schwenk, E. (1958). *J. Biol. Chem.* **232**, 611.

Alexander, G. J., Gold, A. M., and Schwenk, E. (1958). *J. Biol. Chem.* **232**, 599.

Altman, L. J., Kowerski, R. C., and Rilling, H. C. (1971). *J. Am. Chem. Soc.* **93**, 1782.

Anderson, R. J., Shriner, R. L., and Burr, G. O. (1926). *J. Am. Chem. Soc.* **48**, 2987.

Anding, C., Brandt, R. D., and Ourisson, G. (1971). *Eur. J. Biochem.* **24**, 259.

Anding, C., Parks, L. W., and Ourisson, G. (1974). *Eur. J. Biochem.* **43**, 459.

Andreasen, A. A., and Stier, T. J. B. (1953). *J. Cell. Comp. Physiol.* **41**, 23.

Andreasen, A. A., and Stier, T. J. B. (1954). *J. Cell. Comp. Physiol.* **43**, 271.

Bader, S., Guglielmetti, L., and Arigoni, D. (1964). *Proc. Chem. Soc., London* p. 16.

Baisted, D. J., and Nes, W. R. (1963). *J. Biol. Chem.* **238**, 1947.

Baisted, D. J., Capstack, E., and Nes, W. R. (1962). *Biochemistry* **1**, 537.

Baisted, D. J., Gardner, R. L., and McReynolds, L. A. (1968). *Phytochemistry* **7**, 945.

Barbier, M. (1970). *Prog. Phytochem.* **2**, 1.

Barbier, M. (1974). *J. Am. Oil Chem. Soc.* **51**, 527A.

Barbier, M., Hugel, M. F., and Lederer, E. (1960). *Bull. Soc. Chim. Biol.* **42**, 91.

Barton, D. H. R. (1951). *J. Chem. Soc.* p. 1444.

Barton, D. H. R., Gosden, A. F., Mellows, G., and Widdowson, D. A. (1968). *Chem. Commun.* p. 1067.

Barton, D. H. R., Corrie, J. E. T., Widdowson, D. A., Bard, M., and Woods, R. A. (1974a). *Chem. Commun.* p. 30.

Barton, D. H. R., Jarman, T. R., Watson, K. G., Widdowson, D. A., Boar, R. B., and Damps, K. (1974b). *Chem. Commun.* p. 861.

Bates, R. B., Brewer, A. D., Knights, B. R., and Rowe, J. W. (1968). *Tetrahedron Lett.* p. 6163.

Bean, G. A. (1973). *Adv. Lipid Res.* **2**, 193.

Bean, G. A., Patterson, G. W., and Motta, J. J. (1973). *Comp. Biochem. Physiol. B* **43**, 935.

Beastall, G. H., Rees, H. H., and Goodwin, T. W. (1971). *Tetrahedron Lett.* 4935.

Beisler, J. A., and Sato, Y. (1971). *J. Org. Chem.* **36**, 3946.

Bekaert, A., Devys, M., and Barbier, M. (1974). *Tetrahedron Lett.* p. 1671.

Bennett, R. D., and Heftmann, E. (1969). *Steroids* **14**, 403.

Bentley, H. R., Henry, J. A., Irvine, D. S., and Spring, F. S. (1953). *J. Chem. Soc.* p. 3673.

Benveniste, P., Hirth, L., and Ourisson, G. (1964). *C.R. Acad. Sci.* **259**, 2284.

Benveniste, P., Hirth, L., and Ourisson, G. (1965). *Bull. Soc. Fr. Physiol. Veg.* **11**, 252.

Benveniste, P., Hirth, L., and Ourisson, G. (1966a). *Phytochemistry* **5**, 31.

Benveniste, P., Hirth, L., and Ourisson, G. (1966b). *Phytochemistry* **5**, 45.

Bergman, J., Lindgren, B. O., and Svahn, C. M. (1965). *Acta Chem. Scand.* **19**, 1661.

Bergmann, W., and Feeney, R. J. (1950). *J. Org. Chem.* **15**, 812.

Bergmann, W., and McTique, F. H. (1948). *J. Org. Chem.* **13**, 738.

Beytia, E., Valenzuela, P., and Cori, O. (1969). *Arch. Biochem. Biophys.* **129**, 346.

Bills, C. E. (1954). *In* "The Vitamins" (W. N. Sebrell, Jr. and R. S. Harris, eds.), Vol. 2, p. 149. Academic Press, New York.

Bird, C. W., Lynch, J. M., Pirt, F J., Reid, W. W., Brooks, C. J. W., and Middleditch, B. S. (1971). *Nature (London)* **230**, 473.

Blank, F., Shorland, F. E., and Just, G. (1962). *J. Invest. Dermatol.* **39**, 91.

Boid, R., Rees, H. H., and Goodwin, T. W. (1974). *Biochem. Soc. Trans.* **2**, 1066.

Bolger, L. M., Rees, H. H., Ghisalberti, E. L., Goad, L. J., and Goodwin, T. W. (1970). *Biochem. J.* **118**, 197.

Brandt, R. D., Pryce, R. J., Anding, C., and Ourisson, G. (1970). *Eur. J. Biochem.* **17**, 344.

Brooks, C. J. W., and Middleditch, B. S. (1973). *In* "Modern Methods of Steroid Analysis" (E. Heftmann, ed.), p. 140. Academic Press, New York.

Bush, P. B., and Grunwald, C. (1972). *Plant Physiol.* **50**, 69.

Bush, P. B., and Grunwald, C. (1974). *Plant Physiol.* **53**, 131.

Cahn, R. S., Ingold, C. K., and Prelog, V. (1956). *Experientia* **12**, 81.

Cahn, R. S., Ingold, C. K., and Prelog, V. (1966). *Angew. Chem., Int. Ed. Engl.* **5**, 385.

Capstack, E., Baisted, D. J., Newschwander, W. W., Blondin, G. A., Rosin, N. L., and Nes, W. R. (1962). *Biochemistry* **1**, 1178.

Capstack, E., Rosin, N. L., Blondin, G. A., and Nes, W. R. (1965). *J. Biol. Chem.* **240**, 3258.

Carter, P. W., Heilbron, I. M., and Lythgoe, B. (1939). *Proc. R. Soc., Ser. B* **128**, 82.

Castle, M., Blondin, G. A., and Nes, W. R. (1963). *J. Am. Chem. Soc.* **85**, 3306.

Castle, M., Blondin, G. A., and Nes, W. R. (1967). *J. Biol. Chem.* **242**, 5796.

Chan, J. T., and Patterson, G. W. (1973). *Plant Physiol.* **52**, 246.

Chan, J. T., Patterson, G. W., Dutky, S. R., and Cohen, C. F. (1974). *Plant Physiol.* **53**, 244.

Chapman, A. C. (1971). *J. Chem. Soc.*, **111**, 56.

Chapon, S., and David, S. (1952). *Bull. Chim. Soc. Fr.* p. 456.

Chen, Y. S., and Haskins, R. H. (1963). *Can. J. Chem.* **41**, 1647.

Childs, C. R., and Bloch, K. (1962). *J. Biol. Chem.* **237**, 62.

Coates, R. M., and Robinson, W. H. (1971). *J. Am. Chem. Soc.* **93**, 1785.

Cobon, G. S., and Haslam, J. M. (1973). *Biochem. Biophys. Res. Commun.* **52**, 320.

Conner, R. L., and Van Wagtendonk, W. J. (1955). *J. Gen. Microbiol.* **12**, 31.

Conner, R. L., Mallory, F. B., Landrey, J. R., and Iyengar, C. W. L. (1969). *J. Biol. Chem.* **244**, 2325.

Conner, R. L., Landrey, J. R., Kaneshiro, E. S., and Van Wagtendonk, W. J. (1971). *Biochim. Biophys. Acta* **239**, 312.

Corey, E. J., Russey, W. E., and Ortiz de Montellano, P. R. (1966). *J. Am. Chem. Soc.* **88**, 4750.

Corey, E. J., and Yamamoto, H. (1970). *Tetrahedron Lett.* p. 2385.

Corey, E. J., Ortiz de Montellano, P. R., and Yamamoto, H. (1968). *J. Am. Chem. Soc.* **90**, 6254.

Corey, E. J., Kreif, A., and Yamamoto, H. (1971). *J. Am. Chem. Soc.* **93**, 1493.

Cornforth, J. W., Cornforth, R. H., Popjak, G., and Yengoyan, L. (1966a). *J. Biol. Chem.* **241**, 3970.

Cornforth, J. W., Cornforth, R. H., Donninger, C., and Popjak, G. (1966b). *Proc. R. Soc., Ser. B* **163**, 492.

Dempsey, M. E. (1965). *J. Biol. Chem.* **240**, 4176.

Dempsey, M. E., Seaton, J. D., Schroepfer, G. J., and Trockman, R. W. (1964). *J. Biol. Chem.* **239**, 1381.

de Souza, N. J., and Nes, W. R. (1968). *Science* **162**, 363.

de Souza, N. J., and Nes, W. R. (1969). *J. Lipid Res.* **10**, 240.

Devys, M., and Barbier, M. (1967). *Bull. Soc. Chim. Biol.* **49**, 865.

Devys, M., Alcaide, A., Barbier, M., and Lederer, E. (1968). *Phytochemistry* **7**, 613.

Dickson, L. G., and Patterson, G. W. (1972). *Lipids* **7**, 635.

Dickson, L. G., and Patterson, G. W. (1973). *Lipids* **8**, 443.

Djerassi, C., and McCrindle, R. (1962). *J. Chem. Soc.* p. 4034.

Duchamp, D. J., Chidester, C. G., Wickramasinghe, J. A. F., Caspi, E., and Yagen, B. (1971). *J. Am. Chem. Soc.* **93**, 6283.

Dulaney, E. L., Stapley, E. O., and Simpf, K. (1954). *Appl. Microbiol.* **2**, 371.

Eberle, M., and Arigoni, D. (1960). *Helv. Chim. Acta* **43**, 1508.

Ellingboe, J., Nystrom, E., and Sjovall, J. (1970). *J. Lipid Res.* **11**, 266.

Elliott, C. G., Hendrie, M. R., Knights, B. A., and Parker, W. (1964). *Nature (London)* **203**, 427.

Ellouz, R., and Lenfant, M. (1969a). *Tetrahedron Lett.* p. 609.

Ellouz, R., and Lenfant, M. (1969b). *Tetrahedron Lett.* p. 2655.

Ellouz, R., and Lenfant, M. (1970). *Tetrahedron Lett.* p. 3967.

Eppenberger, U., Hirth, L., and Ourisson, G. (1969). *Eur. J. Biochem.* **8**, 180.

Erhardt, J. D., Hirth, L., and Ourisson, G. (1967). *Phytochemistry* **6**, 815.

Eschenmoser, A., Ruzicka, L., Jeger, O., and Arigoni, D. (1955). *Helv. Chim. Acta* **38**, 1890.

Ferezou, J. P., Devys, M., Allais, J. P., and Barbier, M. (1974). *Phytochemistry* **13**, 593.

Fieser, L. F., and Fieser, M. (1949). "Natural Products Related to Phenanthrene." Reinhold, New York.

Fieser, L. F., and Fieser, M. (1959). "Steroids." Reinhold, New York.

Fieser, L. F., Fieser, M., and Charavarti, R. N. (1949). *J. Am. Chem. Soc.* **71**, 2226.

Fischer, F. G., and Seiler, N. (1961). *Justus Liebigs Ann. Chem.* **644**, 146.

Frost, D. J., and Ward, J. P. (1968). *Tetrahedron Lett.* p. 3779.

Fryberg, M., Oehlschlager, A. C., and Unrau, A. M. (1972). *Biochem. Biophys. Res. Commun.* **48**, 593.

Gaylor, J. L. (1974). *In* "Biochemistry of Lipids" (T. W. Goodwin, ed.), MTP International Review of Science, Biochemistry, Series One, Vol. 4, pp. 1–38. Butterworth, London.

Gershengorn, M. C., Smith, A. R. H., Goulsten, G., Goad, L. J., Goodwin, T. W., and Haines, T. H. (1968). *Biochemistry* **7**, 1698.

Ghisalberti, E. L., de Souza, N. J., Rees, H. H., Goad, L. J., and Goodwin, T. W. (1969). *Chem. Commun.* p. 1403.

Gibbons, G. F., Goad, L. J., and Goodwin, T. W. (1967). *Phytochemistry* **6**, 677.

Gibbons, G. F., Goad, L. J., and Goodwin, T. W. (1968). *Phytochemistry* **7**, 983.

Gibbons, G. F., Goad, L. J., Goodwin, T. W., and Nes, W. R. (1971). *J. Biol. Chem.* **246**, 3967.

Goad, L. J., and Goodwin, T. W. (1965). *Biochem. J.* **96**, 79P.

Goad, L. J., and Goodwin, T. W. (1966). *Biochem. J.* **99**, 735.

Goad, L. J., and Goodwin, T. W. (1967). *Eur. J. Biochem.* **1**, 357.

Goad, L. J., and Goodwin, T. W. (1969). *Eur. J. Biochem.* **7**, 502.

Goad, L. J., and Goodwin, T. W. (1972). *Prog. Phytochem.* **3**, 113.

Goad, L. J., Hammam, A. S. A., Dennis, A., and Goodwin, T. W. (1966). *Nature (London)* **210**, 1322.

Goad, L. J., Gibbons, G. F., Bolger, L. M., Rees, H. H., and Goodwin, T. W. (1969). *Biochem. J.* **114**, 885.

Goad, L. J., Knapp, F. F., Lenton, J. R., and Goodwin, T. W. (1972). *Biochem. J.* **129**, 12.

Goad, L. J., Lenton, J. R., Knapp, F. F., and Goodwin, T. W. (1974). *Lipids* **9**, 582.

Gollub, E. G., Trocha, P., Liu, P. K., and Sprinson, D. B. (1974). *Biochem. Biophys. Res. Commun.* **56**, 471.

Gonzalez, A. G. (1964). *Chem. Abstr.* **60**, 5585C.

Gonzalez, A. G., and Mora, M. C. G. (1952). *An. R. Soc. Esp. Fis. Quim., Ser. B* **48**, 475.

Gonzalez, A. G., and Toste, A. H. (1952). *An. R. Soc. Esp. Fis. Quim., Ser. B* **48**, 487.

Gonzalez, A. G., Breton, J. L., and Padron, A. G. (1958). *An. R. Soc. Esp. Fis. Quim., Ser. B* **54**, 595.

Goodwin, T. W., and Williams, R. J. H. (1965). *Biochem. J.* **94**, 5C.

Goodwin, T. W., and Williams, R. J. H. (1966). *Proc. R. Soc., Ser. B* **163**, 515.

Godtfredsen, W. O., Lorck, H., van Tamelen, E. E., Willett, J. D., and Clayton, R. B. (1968). *J. Am. Chem. Soc.* **90**, 208.

Goulsten, G., and Mercer, E. I. (1969). *Phytochemistry* **8**, 1945.

Goulsten, G., Goad, L. J., and Goodwin, T. W. (1967). *Biochem. J.* **102**, 15C.

Greig, J. B., Varma, K. R., and Caspi, E. (1971). *J. Am. Chem. Soc.* **93**, 760.

Gupta, G. S., and Gupta, N. L. (1974). *Tetrahedron Lett.* p. 1221.

Hale, R. L., Leclerq, L., Tursch, B., Djerassi, C., Gross, R. A., Weinheimer, A. J., Gupta, K., and Scheuer, P. J. (1970). *J. Am. Chem. Soc.* **92**, 2179.

Hall, J., Smith, A. R. H., Goad, L. J., and Goodwin, T. W. (1967). *Biochem. J.* **102**, 15.

Hall, J., Smith, A. R. H., Goad, L. J., and Goodwin, T. W. (1969). *Biochem. J.* **112**, 129.

Hallermayer, G., and Newpert, W. (1974). *Hoppe-Seyler's Z. Physiol. Chem.* **355**, 279.

Hammerschlag, A. (1889). *Monatsh. Chem.* **10**, 9.
Hart, M. C., and Heyl, F. W. (1932). *J. Biol. Chem.* **95**, 311.
Heftmann, E. (1968). *Lloydia* **31**, 293.
Heftmann, E. (1971). *Lipids* **6**, 128.
Heftmann, E. (1974). *Lipids* **9**, 626.
Heftmann, E., Wright, B. E., and Liddel, G. (1960). *Arch. Biochem. Biophys.* **91**, 266.
Heilbron, I. M. (1942). *J. Chem. Soc.* p. 79.
Heilbron, I. M., Phiphers, R. F., and Wright, H. R. (1934). *J. Chem. Soc.* p. 1572.
Heintz, R., and Benveniste, P. (1970). *Phytochemistry* **9**, 1944.
Heintz, R., and Benveniste, P. (1974). *J. Biol. Chem.* **249**, 4267.
Heintz, R., Benveniste, P., and Bimpson, T. (1972). *Biochem. Biophys. Res. Commun.* **46**, 766.
Hewlins, M. J. E., Erhardt, J. D., Hirth, L., and Ourisson, G. (1969). *Eur. J. Biochem.* **8**, 184.
Hillman, J. R., Knights, B. A., and McKail, R. (1975). *Lipids* **10**, 542.
Holtz, R. B., and Schisler, L. C. (1972). *Lipids* **7**, 251.
Hsiung, H. M., Spike, T. E., and Schroepfer, G. J. (1975). *Lipids* **10**, 623.
Hugel, M. F., Vetter, W., Audier, H., Barbier, M., and Lederer, E. (1964). *Phytochemistry* **3**, 7.
Idler, D. R., and Wiseman, P. (1971). *Comp. Biochem. Physiol. A* **38**, 581.
Idler, D. R., Saito, A., and Wiseman, P. (1968). *Steroids* **11**, 465.
Idler, D. R., Wiseman, P. M., and Safe, L. M. (1970). *Steroids* **16**, 451.
Idler, D. R., Safe, L. M., and MacDonald, E. F. (1971). *Steroids* **18**, 545.
Ikekawa, N., Tsuda, K., and Morisaki, N. (1966). *Chem. Ind. (London)* p. 1179.
Ikekawa, N., Morisaki, N., and Tsuda, K. (1968). *Steroids* **12**, 41.
Ingram, D. S., Knights, B. A., McEvoy, I. J., and McKay, P. (1968). *Phytochemistry* **7**, 1241.
Itoh, T., Tamura, T., and Matsumoto, T. (1973). *J. Am. Oil Chem. Soc.* **50**, 122.
Itoh, T., Tamura, T., and Matsumoto, T. (1974). *Lipids* **9**, 173.
Itoh, T., Tamura, T., and Matsumoto, T. (1975). *Lipids* **10**, 454.
Ives, D. A. J., and O'Neill, A. N. (1958). *Can. J. Chem.* **36**, 434.
Jackson, L. L., and Frear, D. S. (1968). *Phytochemistry* **7**, 654.
Jacobsen, O. (1871). *Justus Liebigs Ann. Chem.* **157**, 232.
Jaurequiberry, G., Law, J. H., McCloskey, J. A., and Lederer, E. (1965). *Biochemistry* **4**, 347.
Jeong, T. M., Itoh, T., Tamura, T., and Matsumoto, T. (1975). *Lipids* **10**, 634.
Johnson, D. F., Bennett, R. D., and Heftmann, E. (1963). *Science* **140**, 198.
Johnson, D. F., Bennett, R. D., and Heftmann, E. (1966). *Phytochemistry* **5**, 231.
Kandutsch, A. A. (1962). *J. Biol. Chem.* **237**, 358.
Karst, F., and Lacroute, F. (1973). *Biochim. Biophys. Acta* **52**, 741.
Karst, F., and Lacroute, F. (1974). *Biochim. Biophys. Acta* **59**, 370.
Katsuki, H., and Bloch, K. (1967). *J. Biol. Chem.* **242**, 222.
Kawaguchi, A., and Okuda, S. (1970). *J. Chem. Soc. D* p. 1012.
Kemp, R. J., and Mercer, E. I. (1968). *Biochem. J.* **110**, 111.
Kemp, R. J., Hammam, A. S. A., Goad, L. J., and Goodwin, T. W. (1968). *Phytochemistry* **7**, 747.
Kerschbaum, M. (1902). described in a patent of Haarmann and Reimer, *Chem. Zentralblatt* **I**, 975 (1904).
Kier, L. B. (1961). *J. Pharm. Sci.* **50**, 471.
Kircher, H. (1970). *Phytochemistry* **9**, 1879.
Knapp, F. F., and Nicholas, H. J. (1971). *Phytochemistry* **10**, 85.
Knights, B. A. (1968). *Phytochemistry* **7**, 1707.
Knights, B. A. (1970a). *Phytochemistry* **9**, 701.
Knights, B. A. (1970b). *Phytochemistry* **9**, 903.
Knights, B. A. (1972). *Phytochemistry* **11**, 1177.

Knights, B. A. (1973). *In* "Modern Methods of Steroid Analysis" (E. Heftmann, ed.), p. 103. Academic Press, New York.

Knights, B. A., and Berrie, A. M. M. (1971). *Phytochemistry* **10**, 131.

Knights, B. A., and Laurie, W. (1967). *Phytochemistry* **6**, 407.

Kodicek, E. (1959). *In* "Biosynthesis of Terpenes and Sterols" (G.E.W. Wolstenholme and M. O'Connor, eds.), p. 173. Churchill, London.

Kramer, J. K. G., Kushwaha, S. C., and Kates, M. (1972). *Biochim. Biophys. Acta* **270**, 103.

Krishna, G., Whitlock, H. W., Feldruegge, D. H., and Porter, J. W. (1966). *Arch. Biochem. Biophys.* **114**, 200.

Kuznetsova, G. A. (1962). *J. Gen. Chem. USSR* **32**, 4014.

Lavie, D., and Kaye, I. A. (1963). *J. Chem. Soc.* p. 5001.

Lederer, E. (1964). *Biochem. J.* **93**, 449.

Lederer, E. (1969). *Quart Rev., Chem. Soc.* **23**, 453.

Lenfant, M., Ellouz, R., Das, B. C., Zissman, E., and Lederer, E. (1969a). *Eur. J. Biochem.* **7**, 159.

Lenfant, M., Farrugia, G., and Lederer, E. (1969b). *C. R. Acad. Sci.* **268**, 1986.

Lenfant, M., Lecompte, M. F., and Farrugia, G. (1970). *Phytochemistry* **9**, 2529.

Lenton, J. R., Hall, J., Smith, A. R. H., Ghisalberti, E. L., Rees, H. H., Goad, L. J., and Goodwin, T. W. (1971). *Arch. Biochem. Biophys* **143**, 664.

Lenton, J. R., Goad, L. J., and Goodwin, T. W. (1973a). *Phytochemistry* **12**, 1135.

Lenton, J. R., Goad, L. J., and Goodwin, T. W. (1973b). *Phytochemistry* **12**, 2249.

Lepage, M. (1964). *J. Lipid Res.* **5**, 587.

Levin, E. Y., and Bloch, K. (1964). *Nature (London)* **202**, 4927.

Ling, N. C., Hale, R. L., and Djerassi, C. (1970). *J. Am. Chem. Soc.* **92**, 5281.

Linnane, A. W., Vitols, E., and Nowland, P. G. (1962). *J. Cell Biol.* **13**, 343.

Longley, R. P., Rose, A. H., and Knights, B. A. (1968). *Biochem. J.* **108**, 401.

Loomis, W. D., and Battaile, J. (1963). *Biochim. Biophys. Acta* **67**, 54.

Loviagina, E. V., and Shivrina, A. (1962). *Biochemistry (USSR)* **27**, 673.

Lucwiczak, R. S., and Wrzeciono, U. (1961). *Chem. Abstr.* **55**, 9789g.

Lutsky, B. N., and Schroepfer, G. J. (1968). *Biochem. Biophys. Res. Commun.* **33**, 492.

Lutsky, B. N., Martin, J. A., and Schroepfer, G. J. (1971). *J. Biol. Chem.* **246**, 6737.

Lynen, F., Eggerer, H., Henning, U., and Kessel, I. (1958). *Angew. Chem.* **70**, 738.

Lynen, F., Agranoff, B. W., Eggerer, H., Henning, U., and Moeslein, E. M. (1959). *Angew. Chem.* **71**, 657.

McCorkindale, N. J., Hutchinson, S. A., Pursey, B. A., Scott, W. T., and Wheeler, R. (1969). *Phytochemistry* **8**, 861.

Malhotra, H. C., and Nes, W. R. (1971). *J. Biol. Chem.* **246**, 4934.

Malhotra, H. C., and Nes, W. R. (1972). *J. Biol. Chem.* **247**, 6243.

Mallory, F. B., and Conner, R. L. (1971). *Lipids* **6**, 149.

Marsili, A., and Morelli, I. (1968). *Phytochemistry* **7**, 1705.

Marsili, A., and Morelli, I. (1970). *Phytochemistry* **9**, 651.

Méance, J., and Dupéron, R. (1973). *C. R. Acad. Sci., Ser. D* **277**, 849.

Mercer, E. I., and Johnson, M. W. (1969). *Phytochemistry* **8**, 2329.

Mercer, E. I. London, R. A., Kent, I. S. A., and Taylor, A. J. (1974). *Phytochemistry* **13**, 845.

Merdinger, E., Kohn, P., and McClain, R. C. (1968). *Can. J. Microbiol.* **15**, 1021.

Middleditch, B. S., and Knights, B. A. (1972). *Phytochemistry* **11**, 1183.

Miller, J. D. A. (1962). *In* "Physiology and Biochemistry of Algae" (R. A. Lewis, ed.), p. 327. Academic Press, New York.

Minale, L., and Sodano, G. (1974). *J. Chem. Soc., Perkin Trans.* **1**, p. 1888.

Moore, J. T., and Gaylor, J. L. (1969). *J. Biol. Chem.* **244**, 6334.

Moore, J. T., and Gaylor, J. L. (1970). *J. Biol. Chem.* **245**, 4684.

Morisaki, M., Ohtaka, H., Okubayashi, M., and Ikekawa, N. (1972). *Chem. Commun.* p. 1275.

Morpurgo, G., Serlupi-Crescenzi, G., Tecce, G., Valente, F., and Venettacci, D. (1964). *Nature (London)* **201**, 897.

Mulheirn, L. J. (1973). *Tetrahedron Lett.* p. 3175.

Mulheirn, L. J. (1974). *J. Am. Oil Chem. Soc.* **51**, 530A.

Muscio, F., Carlson, J. P., Kuehl, L., and Rilling, H. C. (1974). *J. Biol. Chem.* **249**, 3746.

Nagasampagi, B. A., Rowe, J. W., Simpson, R., and Goad, L. J. (1971). *Phytochemistry* **10**, 1101.

Nagai, J., and Katsuki, H. (1974). *Biochem. Biophys. Res. Commun.* **60**, 555.

Nes, W. R. (1971). *Lipids* **6**, 219.

Nes, W. R. (1974a). *J. Am. Oil Chem. Soc.* **51**, 517A.

Nes, W. R. (1974b). *Lipids* **9**, 596.

Nes, W. R., Baisted, D. J., Capstack, E., Newschwander, W. W., and Russell, P. T. (1967). *In* "Biochemistry of the Chloroplast" (T. W. Goodwin, ed.), Vol. 2, p. 273. Academic Press, New York.

Nes, W. R., Malya, P. A. G., Mallory, F. B., Ferguson, K. A., Landrey, J. R., and Conner, R. L. (1971). *J. Biol. Chem.* **246**, 561.

Nes, W. R., Alcaide, A., Mallory, F. B., Landrey, J. R., and Conner, R. L. (1975a). *Lipids* **10**, 140.

Nes, W. R., Krevitz, K., Behzadan, S., Patterson, G. W., Landrey, J. R., and Conner, R. L. (1975b). *Biochem. Biophys. Res. Commun.* **66**, 1462.

Nes, W. R., Krevitz, K., and Behzadan, S. (1976). *Lipids* **11**, 118.

Nes, W. R., Varkey, T. E., and Krevitz, K. (1977). *J. Am. Chem. Soc.* **99**, 260.

Nicholas, H. J. (1962). *J. Biol. Chem.* **237**, 1481.

Nishino, T., Ogura, K., and Seto, S. (1972). *J. Am. Chem. Soc.* **94**, 6849.

Ogura, K., Nishino, T., Koyama, T., and Seto, S. (1971). *Phytochemistry* **10**, 779.

Orcutt, D. M., and Patterson, G. W. (1975). *Comp. Biochem. Physiol. B* **50**, 579.

Orcutt, D. M., and Richardson, B. (1970). *Steroids* **16**, 429.

Oshima-Oba, K., and Uritani, I. (1969). *Plant Cell Physiol.* **10**, 827.

Parks, L. W. (1958). *J. Am. Chem. Soc.* **80**, 2023.

Patterson, G. W. (1968). *Comp. Biochem. Physiol.* **24**, 501.

Patterson, G. W. (1969). *Comp. Biochem. Physiol.* **31**, 391.

Patterson, G. W. (1971a). *Anal. Chem.* **43**, 1165.

Patterson, G. W. (1971b). *Lipids* **6**, 120.

Patterson, G. W. (1972). *Phytochemistry* **11**, 3841.

Patterson, G. W. (1974). *Comp. Biochem. Physiol. B* **47**, 453.

Patterson, G. W., and Karlander, E. P. (1967). *Plant Physiol.* **42**, 1651.

Patterson, G. W., and Krauss, R. W. (1965). *Plant Cell Physiol.* **6**, 211.

Patterson, G. W., Thompson, M. J., and Dutky, S. R. (1974). *Phytochemistry* **13**, 191.

Pettit, G. R., and Knight, J. C. (1962). *J. Org. Chem.* **27**, 2696.

Pollard, C. J., Bonner, J., Haagen-Smit, A. J., and Nimmo, C. C. (1966). *Plant Physiol.* **41**, 66.

Ponsinet, G., and Ourisson, G. (1965). *Phytochemistry* **4**, 813.

Ponsinet, G., and Ourisson, G. (1968a). *Phytochemistry* **7**, 89.

Ponsinet, G., and Ourisson, G. (1968b). *Phytochemistry* **7**, 757.

Popjak, G. (1970). *In* "Natural Substances Formed Biologically from Mevalonic Acid" (T. W. Goodwin, ed.), pp. 17–33. Academic Press, New York.

Popjak, G., and Cornforth, J. W. (1960). *Adv. Enzymol. Relat. Subj. Biochem.* **22**, 281.

Popjak, G., Cornforth, J. W., Cornforth, R. H., Ryhage, R., and Goodman, D. W. S. (1962). *J. Biol. Chem.* **237**, 56.

Popjak, G., Edmond, J., and Wong, S. M. (1973). *J. Am. Chem. Soc.* **95**, 2713.

Proudlock, J. W., Wheeldon, L. W., Jollow, D. J., and Linnane, A. W. (1968). *Biochim. Biophys. Acta* **152**, 434.

Raab, K. H., de Souza, N. J., and Nes, W. R. (1968). *Biochim. Biophys. Acta* **152**, 742.

Rees, H. H., Mercer, E. I., and Goodwin, T. W. (1966). *Biochem. J.* **99**, 726.

Rees, H. H., Goad, L. J., and Goodwin, T. W. (1968a). *Tetrahedron Lett.* p. 723.

Rees, H. H., Goad, L. J., and Goodwin, T. W. (1968b). *Biochem. J.* **107**, 417.

Rees, H. H., Goad, L. J., and Goodwin, T. W. (1969). *Biochim. Biophys. Acta* **176**, 892.

Reitz, R. C., and Hamilton, J. G. (1968). *Comp. Biochem. Physiol.* **25**, 401.

Resnick, M. A., and Mortimer, R. K. (1966). *J. Bacteriol.* **92**, 597.

Rilling, H. C., and Epstein, W. W. (1969). *J. Am. Chem. Soc.* **91**, 1041.

Rilling, H. C., Poulter, C. D., Epstein, W. W., and Larsen, B. (1971). *J. Am. Chem. Soc.* **93**, 1783.

Ritchie, E., Senior, R. G., and Taylor W. C. (1969). *Aust. J. Chem.* **22**, 2371.

Robinson, R. (1934). *Chem. Ind. (London)* **53**, 1062.

Robinson, R. (1955). "Structural Relations of Natural Products, pp. 19–20. Oxford Univ. Press (Clarendon), London and New York.

Rubinstein, I., and Goad, L. J. (1974a). *Phytochemistry* **13**, 481.

Rubinstein, I., and Goad, L. J. (1974b). *Phytochemistry* **13**, 485.

Rubinstein, I., Goad, L. J., Clague, A. D. H., and Mulheirn, L. J. (1976). *Phytochemistry* **15**, 195.

Russell, P. T., van Aller, R. T., and Nes, W. R. (1967). *J. Biol. Chem.* **242**, 5802.

Ruzicka, L., Denss, R., and Jeger, O. (1945). *Helv. Chim. Acta* **28**, 759.

Ruzicka, L., Denss, R., and Jeger, O. (1946). *Helv. Chim. Acta* **29**, 204.

Safe, L. M., Wong, C. J., and Chandler, R. F. (1974). *J. Pharm. Sci.* **63**, 464.

Saito, A., and Idler, D. R. (1966). *Can. J. Biochem.* **44**, 1195.

Schmitz, F. J., and Pattabhiraman, T. (1970). *J. Am. Chem. Soc.* **92**, 6073.

Schreiber K., and Osske, G. (1962). *Kulturpflanze* **10**, 372.

Schubert, K., and Schumann, W. (1967). *Acta Biol. Med. Ger.* **18**, 439.

Schubert, K., Rose, G., Wachtel, H., Horhold, C., and Ikekawa, N. (1968). *Eur. J. Biochem.* **5**, 246.

Schulze, E. (1872). *Ber. Dtsch. Chem. Ges.* **5**, 1075.

Schwenk, E., and Alexander, G. J. (1958). *Arch. Biochem. Biophys.* **76**, 65.

Schwenk, E., Alexander, G. J., Fish, C. A., and Stoudt, T. H. (1955). *Fed. Proc., Fed. Am. Soc. Exp. Biol.* **14**, 752.

Skeggs, H. R., Wright, L. D., Cresson, E. L., MacRae, G. D. E., Hoffman, C. H., Wolf, D. E., and Folkers, K. (1956). *J. Bacteriol* **72**, 519.

Skilleter, D. N., Williamson, I. P., and Reckwick, R. G. O. (1966). *Biochem. J.* **98**, 27P.

Smith, A. R. H., Goad, L. J., Goodwin, T. W., and Lederer, E. (1967). *Biochem. J.* **104**, 56C.

Smith, P. F. (1971). "The Biology of Mycoplasmas," Academic Press, New York.

Soden, H., and Treff, W. (1904). *Chem. Ber.* **37**, 1094.

Sofer, S. S., and Rilling, H. C. (1969). *J. Lipid Res.* **10**, 183.

Stabursvik, A. (1953). *Acta Chem. Scand.* **7**, 1220.

Stern, A. I., Schiff, J. A., and Klein, H. P. (1960). *J. Protozool.* **7**, 52.

Stokes, W. M., Hickey, F. C., and Fish, W. A. (1958). *J. Biol. Chem.* **232**, 347.

Stone, K. J., and Hemming, F. N. (1968). *Biochem. J.* **109**, 877.

Stone, K. J., Roeske, W. R., Clayton, R. B., and van Tamelen, E. E. (1969). *Chem. Commun.* p. 530.

Strigina, L. I., Elkin, Y. N., and Elyakov, G. B. (1971). *Phytochemistry* **10**, 2361.

Sucrow, W., and Girgensohn, B. (1970). *Chem. Ber.* **103**, 750.

Sucrow, W., and Reimerdes, A. (1968). *Z. Naturforsch. B* **23**, 42.

Sucrow, W., Schubert, B., Richter, W., and Slopianka, M. (1971). *Chem. Ber.* **104**, 3689.
Svoboda, J. A., Thompson, M. J., Robbins, W. E., and Elden, T. C. (1975). *Lipids* **10**, 524.
Takeda, K., Kubota, T., and Matsui, Y. (1958). *Chem. Pharm. Bull.* **6**, 437.
Tavormina, P. A., Gibbs, M. H., and Huff, J. W. (1956). *J. Am. Chem. Soc.* **78**, 4498.
Tchen, T. T. (1958). *J. Biol. Chem.* **233**, 1100.
Tchen, T. T., and Bloch, K. (1955). *J. Biol. Chem.* **226**, 931.
Tchen, T. T., and Bloch, K. (1957). *J. Biol. Chem.* **226**, 931.
Teshima, S.-I., Kahazama, A., and Ando, T. (1974). *Comp. Biochem. Physiol. B* **47**, 507.
Thomas, D. R., and Stobart, A. K. (1970). *Phytochemistry* **9**, 1443.
Thompson, E. D., and Parks, L. W. (1974a). *Biochem. Biophys. Res. Commun.* **57**, 1207.
Thompson, E. D., and Parks, L. W. (1974b). *J. Bacteriol.* **120**, 779.
Thompson, M. J., Robbins, W. E., and Baker, G. L. (1963). *Steroids* **2**, 505.
Thompson, M. J., Dutky, S. R., Patterson, G. W., and Gooden, E. L. (1972). *Phytochemistry* **11**, 1781.
Thompson, M. J., Kaplanis, J. N., Robbins, W. E., and Svoboda, J. A. (1973). *Adv. Lipid Res.* **2**, 219.
Tomita, Y., Uomori, A., and Minato, H. (1970). *Phytochemistry* **9**, 555.
Tomita, Y., Uomori, A., and Sakurai, E. (1971). *Phytochemistry* **10**, 573.
Tornabene, T. G., Kates, M., and Volcani, B. E. (1974). *Lipids* **9**, 279.
Trocha, P., Jasne, S. J., and Sprinson, D. B. (1974). *Biochem. Biophys. Res. Commun.* **59**, 666.
Tsuda, K., and Sakai, K. (1960). *Chem. Pharm. Bull.* **8**, 554.
Tsuda, K., Akagi, S., and Kishida, Y. (1957). *Science* **126**, 927.
Tsuda, K., Akagi, S., and Kishida, Y. (1958a). *Chem. Pharm. Bull.* **6**, 101.
Tsuda, K., Akagi, S., Kishida, Y., Hayatsu, R., and Sakai, K. (1958b). *Chem. Pharm. Bull.* **6**, 724.
Tsuda, K., Hayatsu, R., Kishida, Y., and Akagi, S. (1958c). *J. Am. Chem. Soc.* **80**, 921.
Tsuda, T., Kishida, Y., and Hayatsu, R. (1960). *J. Am. Chem. Soc.* **82**, 3396.
Tsujimoto, M. (1918). *Chem. Zentralblatt* **I**, 638, 1048.
Vacheron, M. J., and Michel, G. (1968). *Phytochemistry* **7**, 1645.
van Aller, R. T., and Nes, W. R. (1968). *Phytochemistry* **7**, 85.
van Aller, R. T., Chikamatsu, H., de Souza, N. J., John, J. P., and Nes, W. R. (1968). *Biochem. Biophys. Res. Commun.* **31**, 842.
van Aller, R. T., Chikamatsu, H., de Souza, N. J., John, J. P., and Nes. W. R. (1969). *J. Biol. Chem.* **244**, 6645.
van Tamelen, E. E., Willett, J. D., Clayton, R. B., and Lord, K. E. (1966). *J. Am. Chem. Soc.* **88**, 4752.
van Tamelen, E. E., Hanzlik, R. P., Clayton, R. B., and Burlingame, A. L. (1970). *J. Am. Chem. Soc.* **92**, 2137.
van Tamelen, E. E., Smaal, J. A., and Clayton, R. B. (1971). *J. Am. Chem. Soc.* **93**, 5279.
Vareune, J., Polonsky, J., Cagnoli-Bellavista, N., and Ceccherelli, P. (1971). *Biochimie* **53**, 261.
Villanueva, V. R., Barbier, M., and Lederer, E. (1964). *Bull. Soc. Chim. Fr.* p. 1423.
Villanueva, V. R., Barbier, M., and Lederer, E. (1967). *Bull. Soc. Chim. Biol.* **49**, 389.
vonArdenne, M., Osske, G., Schreiber, K., Steinfelder, K., and Tummler, R. (1965). *Kulturpflanze* **13**, 101.
von Behring, H. (1930). *Hoppe-Seyler's Z. Physiol. Chem.* **192**, 112.
Wasner, H., and Lynen, F. (1970). *FEBS Lett.* **12**, 54.
Weete, J. D. (1973). *Phytochemistry* **12**, 1843.
Weete, J. D. (1974). "Fungal Lipid Biochemistry." Plenum, New York.
Weete, J. D., and Laseter, J. L. (1974). *Lipids* **9**, 575.
Wieland, H., Pasedach, H., and Ballanf, A. (1937). *Justus Liebigs Ann. Chem.* **529**, 68.

Willett, J. D., Sharpless, K. B., Lord, K. E., van Tamelen, E. E., and Clayton, R. B. (1967). *J. Biol. Chem.* **242**, 4182.

Williams, B. L., and Goodwin, T. W. (1965). *Phytochemistry* **4**, 81.

Williams, B. L., Goodwin, T. W., and Ryley, J. F. (1966). *J. Protozool.* **13**, 227.

Williams, B. L., Goad, L. J., and Goodwin, T. W. (1967). *Phytochemistry* **6**, 1137.

Williams, B. L., Goad, L. J., and Mercer, E. I. (1965). *Biochem. J.* **96**, 31P.

Williams, R. J. H., Britton, G., Charlton, J. M., and Goodwin, T. W. (1967a). *Biochem. J.* **104**, 767.

Williams, R. J. H., Britton, G., and Goodwin, T. W. (1967b). *Biochem. J.* **105**, 99.

Willstätter, R., and Page, H. J. (1914). *Justus Liebigs Ann. Chem.* **404**, 237.

Wilton, D. C., Munday, K. A., Skinner, S. J. M., and Akhtar, M. (1968). *Biochem. J.* **106**, 803.

Windaus, A., and Hauth, A. (1906). *Chem. Ber.* **39**, 4378.

Windaus, A., and Tschesche, R. (1930), *Hoppe-Seyler's Z. Physiol. Chem.* **190**, 51.

Wing, R. M., Okamura, W. H., Pirio, M. R., Sine, S. M., and Norman, A. W. (1974). *Science* **186**, 939.

Wojchiechowski, Z. A., Goad, L. J., and Goodwin, T. W. (1973). *Biochem. J.* **136**, 405.

Wolf, D. E., Hoffman, C. H., Aldrich, P. E., Skeggs, H. R., Wright, L. D., and Folkers, K. (1956). *J. Am. Chem. Soc.* **78**, 4499.

Wolf, D. E., Hoffman, C. H., Aldrich, P. E., Skeggs, H. R., Wright, L. D., and Folkers, K. (1957). *J. Am. Chem. Soc.* **79**, 1486.

Woodward, R. B., and Bloch, K. (1953). *J. Am. Chem. Soc.* **75**, 2023.

Wright, D. E., Cresson, E. L., Skeggs, H. R., MacRae, G. D. E., Hoffman, C. H., Wolf, D. E., and Folkers, K. (1956). *J. Am. Chem. Soc.* **98**, 5273.

Yokoyama, H., and White, M. J. (1968). *Phytochemistry* **7**, 493.

Author Index

Numbers in italics refer to the pages on which the complete references are listed.

Subject Index

A

Acetylcholine receptor, 24
α_1-Acid glycoprotein, 86
Acylglycerides in fungi, 185, 186, 188, 189
Adrenal steroid hormones, 68
Albumin, 84
Algae, sterols in, 255–262
Androgen(s), 69, 89
  effect on CNS, 120
  minimal brain dysfunction in, children, 130
Androstane, 26
4-Androstene-3,17-dione, 67
Antibody technique, double, for steroids, 65
Aryl hydrocarbon hydroxylase, 77
Ascomycetes
  fatty acids in, 167, 169–175, 199, 200
  sterols in, 169, 176, 177, 201
Ascosterol, 239
Avenasterol, 239
  biosynthesis of, 305

B

Bacillus megaterium, 29
Bacteria, sterols in, 265
Basidiomycetes
  fatty acids in, 177–183, 199, 200
    of spores from, 180–182
  sphingolipids in, 191
  sterols in, 183, 201
Behavior, effect of steroids on, 128
Bilayer models of biomembranes, 3–11
Biomembranes
  bilayer hypothesis, 3–11
  cooperativity of components, 36–41
  fluid-mosaic model, 21–28
  iceberg model, 11–21
  interactions among membrane lipids, 34–36
  long-range order in, 1–51
  models of organization, 3–28
  plate model, 41–50
  protein crystal model, 11–21
Birth defects, 114, 115
Brain dysfunction, *see* Hyperkinesis
Brassicasterol, 238, 292
  biosynthesis of, 301
  PMR spectra, 245
Bryophyta, sterols in, 255

C

Campestanol, 238
Campesterol, 238
  biosynthesis of, 303
  PMR spectra, 244
Cancer, *see also* Tumors, Carcinogens
  breast, 88, 89, 102, 105, 106
  effect of reserpine on, 105
  prostate, 106
  safety testing of steroids, 96–103
Carcinogens
  chloro derivatives as, 102, 103
  cholesterol oxidation products, 100–103
  estrogen as, 102
  immune defense mechanism, 99, 100
Carpesterol, 239
Cell surface, 44, *see also* Biomembranes
Cell wall, lipids in, 202
Celsianol, 239
Central nervous system, effects of steroids on, 119–141
Cerebrosides, biosynthesis of, 216, 217
Cerebrospinal fluid, steroids and, 81, 82
Chlorophyll, 35
Cholestanol
  PMR spectra, 247
  structure of, 237
β-Cholestanol as carcinogen, 101
Cholesterol, 23, 26, 238
  autoxidation of, 80
  in biomembranes, 9
  crystal deposition *in vivo*, 92
  in membranes, 91
  oxidation of, 80, 81
    nonenzymic, 80, 81
    radiation-induced, 81
  PMR spectra of, 243, 244
  structure of, 237
  synthesis of, 90, 91
  transport, 91
Cholesterol 24-hydroxylase, 77
Cholesterol α-oxide as carcinogen, 100, 101
Δ^7-Chondrillastenol, biosynthesis of, 304
Chondrillasterol, 238, 292
  biosynthesis of, 304
Chylomicrons, 91
Chytridiomycetes, fatty acids in, 162, 199, 200

CONTENTS OF PREVIOUS VOLUMES

357